THE TAYLOR SERIES

dover publications inc. new york

THE TAYLOR SERIES

an introduction to the theory of functions of a complex variable

by P. Dienes

This new Dover edition, first published in 1957, is an unabridged and unaltered republication of the 1st edition with errata incorporated into the text. It is published through special arrangement with Oxford University Press.

Library of Congress Catalog Card Number: 57-14598

Manufactured in the United States of America

Dover Publications, Inc.

180 Varick Street

New York 14, N. Y.

PREFACE

THERE are three different approaches to the theory of functions of a complex variable, due to Cauchy, Weierstrass, and Riemann respectively. Riemann's method, based on an appropriate generalization of the complex plane (Argand's diagram) and leading to the beautiful but arduous problem of uniformization, does not seem suitable for an introduction to the theory. Therefore the way of approach adopted in this book is a combination of the first two.

Cauchy starts with functions of a complex variable which are uniform and differentiable (monogenic, synectic) in a domain, establishes his famous formulae for their integrals, and proves that in a sufficiently small circle about any point of the domain such a function can be represented as the sum of a Taylor series.

Weierstrass starts with functions defined by a Taylor series and its analytic continuations, as the simplest kind of functions after polynomials, and in the examination of their properties he makes as much use as possible of their Taylor expansions.

Cauchy's method only defines a part, a so-called uniform branch, of a complete analytic function so that it must be supplemented at a later stage by the idea of analytic continuation. Ultimately the two methods lead to the same class of functions.

The post-Weierstrassian development of complex function theory is still dominated by the ideas and results of Poincaré, Picard, Hadamard, Mittag-Leffler, and Borel. The bulk of Poincaré's work lies in Riemann's direction, so that his share in the development of function theory will not be manifest in this introduction. (See Osgood, 1923, in Bibliography.)

Picard's famous theorem on essential points leading through Borel's 'elementary' proof to Landau's and Schottky's already classical results has become in Montel's hands the starting-point of a new method. This book contains but the bare elements of this powerful new instrument. (See Montel's beautiful book, 1927.)

Hadamard's penetrating researches on the singularities of analytic functions, Mittag-Leffler's expansions in the star-domain, and Borel's systematic handling of divergent series are mainly responsible for a large class of more recent researches in close connexion with the Taylor series. The second half of this book is an attempt at the coordination of these results, and is preceded by a chapter on biuniform mapping of domains by analytic functions, a comparatively new method widely used nowadays in this kind of work (see e.g. Lindelöf, 1915, Julia, 1930). As examples of two different kinds of recent results, Ostrowski's theorems on overconvergence and Hardy and Littlewood's work on the mechanism of arithmetic means may be mentioned.

An analytic function is defined by a Taylor series $\Sigma a_n(z-z_0)^n$ and by its formal continuations obtained successively by the transformation of the series into $\Sigma b_n(z-z_1)^n$, where z_1 is any point within the circle of convergence of the first series. The circle of convergence of the second series may extend beyond that of the first. Continuing in this way, we define the complete analytic function by an infinite network of Taylor series. It follows that an analytic function is completely determined by the sequence of coefficients a_n and by the formal properties of Taylor series. To detect the properties of the function from those of the coefficients is the central problem of the Taylor series and that of this book.

For this problem we have to establish as many special and general relations as possible between the mechanism of representation which is in our case a chain of Taylor series and the function determined by this mechanism. To conquer the function, the infinite chain of Taylor series must be replaced by a single formula whenever this is possible. Since the original Taylor series is divergent outside its circle of convergence, the most direct line of attack is to find a suitable generalization of the sum of an infinite series which, when applied to a divergent Taylor series, will lead, under specified conditions, to the value of the analytic function outside the circle of convergence.

Therefore chapter XII on divergent series is an attempt to give a systematic account of the general results obtained so far on generalized limits and sums. Here and there some new, unpublished results, due to L. S. Bosanquet and to the author, fill some obvious gaps in the general theory. This survey of the outstanding problems of divergence may possibly lead to research on the subject.

The first part of this book, chapters I–VII, gives the elements of the usual Cauchy-Weierstrass theory of functions of a complex variable, with due regard to the ideas and results needed in the sequel.

Chapter I deals with the properties of functions of real variables which are essential for a thorough understanding of complex function theory, and which are as a rule hardly touched upon in works on Calculus. Short of Lebesgue integration and Riemann's theory of trigonometrical series, which are used in the last two chapters, the book is self-contained in the sense that only the elements of ordinary Calculus are supposed to be known.

At the end of chapter II on complex algebras the reader will find a sketch of hypercomplex algebras meant to induce generalizations of function theory to those fields. (See e.g. Dienes, 1930.) The results of Articles 21–2a are not used in the sequel.

Since in this book infinite series are methodically and extensively used from the beginning, a thorough grasp of their mechanism is a first necessity for the understanding of the argumentation. Chapters III and IV provide the material and some help for this purpose.

Chapter V on complex differentiation contains the first group of fundamental theorems on analytic functions, namely those which can be established without Cauchy's theory of complex integration.

Chapter VI on Jordan's theorem and on the connectivity of domains is an introduction to complex integration. On a first reading, Jordan's theorem for polygons together with the intuitively rather obvious results on connectivity may form a good enough preparation for the next chapter. Jordan's theorem is, however, unavoidable in proving that mathematics does not involve geometry, Euclidean or otherwise.

A detailed study of special functions is beyond the scope of this work. The second half of Whittaker and Watson's *Modern*

Analysis is an excellent introduction to special functions, and monographs like Watson's *Bessel Functions* and Titchmarsh's *Zeta-function of Riemann* (Cambridge tracts, 1930) will supply the reader with the necessary detail.

In the first half of the book the exercises at the end of chapters are either straightforward illustrations of important results or further developments of the theory, in which case the proof is always indicated. In the second half, the examples are incorporated in the text. The best companion book to this work is Pólya and Szegö's excellent *Aufgaben und Lehrsätze*, 1925.

I am specially indebted to Professors G. H. Hardy (Cambridge) and A. R. Richardson (Swansea) for their encouragement and insistence on my writing this book. I was also very fortunate in finding some colleagues whose interest and help in my attempt at producing an up-to-date account of some problems in connexion with the Taylor series made my task ever so much easier. I owe R. Wilson (Swansea) many helpful remarks on the first five chapters, D. E. Littlewood (Swansea) some on chapter VI, R. G. Cooke (Birkbeck College, London) on chapter X, B. E. Lawrence (Goldsmith College, London) on chapter VII, and above all L. S. Bosanquet (University College, London) on nearly every page.

I can hardly overestimate the value of Dr. Bosanquet's help. He went through all the heavy proofs of fundamental results, clearing up the intricate reasonings involved. I also owe him some original contributions to the theory of divergent series. Moreover, Dr. Bosanquet most kindly helped me in revising the proof-sheets. I acknowledge with great pleasure my indebtedness and gratitude to him.

Finally my thanks are due to the Clarendon Press who met all my requirements with complete thoroughness.

P. D.

BIRKBECK COLLEGE, LONDON.
June 1931.

CONTENTS

CHAPTER I

Real Variables

CHAPTER II

Complex Algebra

CHAPTER III

Infinite Series

CHAPTER IV

Elementary Functions

CHAPTER V

Complex Differentiation

CHAPTER VI

Geometrical Language

CHAPTER VII

Complex Integration

CHAPTER VIII

Biuniform Mapping. Picard's Theorem

CHAPTER IX

Representation of Analytic Functions

CHAPTER X

Singularities of Analytic Functions

CHAPTER XI

Overconvergence and Gap Theorems

CHAPTER XII

Divergent Series

CHAPTER XIII

The Taylor Series on its Circle of Convergence

CHAPTER XIV

Divergence and Singularities

THE TAYLOR SERIES

CHAPTER I

REAL VARIABLES

1. *The idea of real numbers.* Integers and fractions describe the result of direct comparison of magnitudes. Hence their name rational numbers, i.e. ratio numbers. Our belief in the continuity of physical events leads to the logical analysis of the idea of continuity. According to this belief a changing magnitude like the length of a heated rod, the velocity of a particle, &c., is supposed to pass through every possible magnitude between the initial and the final one. Since the precise measurement of a magnitude is naturally expressed by a decimal fraction, the logical equivalent of 'all possible magnitudes' is 'all possible decimal forms'.

We notice, however, that not all decimal forms can be transformed into vulgar fractions. In fact, the decimal form of the vulgar fraction a/b is necessarily either a terminated or a recurring decimal form (after a certain decimal place), the recurring group containing less than b figures. And, on the other hand, the decimal form $A = 0{\cdot}123\ldots91011\ldots$, where we write down the integers one after the other (10 occupying two, 100 occupying three places, &c.), is an infinite decimal form that does not consist of the repetition of a group of digits after any decimal place. Thus A cannot be transformed into a vulgar fraction; A is a new symbol. On the other hand, A may represent a length just as well as any recurring decimal fraction like $0{\cdot}333\ldots$. Consequently, if we want symbols for 'all possible lengths', we have to add to our system of rational numbers the 'irrational' numbers, i.e. the infinite non-recurring decimal forms. The united class of rational and irrational numbers is the class of *real* numbers.

Equality, addition and multiplication of real numbers are defined as follows: We say that the positive real number $a = a_0 \cdot a_1 a_2 \ldots$ *precedes* $b = b_0 \cdot b_1 b_2 \ldots$ if (1) $a_0 < b_0$, or

$$(2) \quad a_0 = b_0,\ a_1 = b_1,\ \ldots,\ a_{n-1} = b_{n-1},\ \text{but}\ a_n < b_n.$$

The reverse holds for negative real numbers, and every negative number precedes every positive one.

We say that b is *between* a and c if either a precedes b and b precedes c or c precedes b and b precedes a. There is no number between $a_0 \cdot a_1 a_2 \dots a_{n-1} a_n 000\dots$ and $a_0 \cdot a_1 a_2 \dots (a_n - 1) 999\dots$. Definition of equality: $a = b$ *if there is no number between* a *and* b.

Two equal numbers have identical symbols except terminated decimals which have two distinct symbols, as above.

2. *Manipulation of real numbers.* The definitions of elementary operations are based on the following lemma.

Lemma 1. *To every bounded monotone sequence of real numbers there corresponds a determinate real number said to be associated with the sequence.*

If a set of numbers is contained in a finite interval, i.e. between two numbers, we say that the set is *bounded.* A never-decreasing or a never-increasing sequence is said to be *monotone.*

Proof for increasing sequences. Consider the sequence

$$(1)\qquad \begin{aligned} a_1 &= a_{10} \cdot a_{11} a_{12} \dots, \\ a_2 &= a_{20} \cdot a_{21} a_{22} \dots, \\ &\dots \\ a_n &= a_{n0} \cdot a_{n1} a_{n2} \dots, \\ &\dots \end{aligned}$$

By hypothesis, $a_n \leqslant a_{n+1}$ and there is a B such that, for every n, $a_n < B$. Consequently the sequence of integral parts $a_{10}, a_{20}, \dots$ is also increasing and bounded, i.e. there is a greatest integer a_0' among them, and, say for $n > n_0$, we have $a_{n0} = a_0'$. We take this greatest integral part a_0' for the integral part of a real number A, so that $A = a_0' \cdot \dots$. We determine the first decimal figure of A by considering the part of the sequence (1) after the suffix n_0 (in which the integral parts are the same, viz. a_0'). Since the sequence is increasing, the first decimal figures $a_{n_0,1}, a_{n_0+1,1}, \dots$ form an increasing sequence of integers all less than 10. Thus there is a maximum integer a_1', such that, for $n > n_1$, all the decimal forms of (1) have the same integral part and the same first decimal figure. Restricting ourselves to this part of the sequence we determine in a similar way the maximum second decimal figure and assign it to A, and so forth. The number A so determined is called the number associated with the sequence.

If after a suffix n, $a_{n+i} = a_n$ for every i, we say that a_n is the number associated with the sequence.

Similarly for decreasing sequences.

The addition of infinite decimal forms, recurring or not, cannot be started, as in elementary arithmetic, from the right-hand side, for there is no end on this side. However, if $a = a_0 \cdot a_1 a_2 \ldots$ and $b = b_0 \cdot b_1 b_2 \ldots$ are two positive real numbers, we can add the two terminated decimals $(a)_n = a_0 \cdot a_1 \ldots a_n$ and $(b)_n = b_0 \cdot b_1 \ldots b_n$, called the n-th sections of a and b respectively. The sequence $(a)_n + (b)_n$ is an increasing sequence of real rational numbers and

$$(a)_n + (b)_n < a_0 + b_0 + 2.$$

Hence, by Lemma 1, there is a determinate real number associated with this sequence. We call this number the *sum* of a and b and denote it by $a + b$.

The difference $b - a$ of two positive numbers a and b, $b > a$, is defined as the solution of the equation

$$x + a = b. \tag{2}$$

We prove the existence and uniqueness of the solution as follows. There is an N such that $(b)_n > a$ for $n > N$. If this condition is satisfied, $x + (a)_m = (b)_n$ has a unique solution $x_{m,\, n}$ which is positive and decreases when m increases; and the sequence $x_{m,\, n}$ $(m = 1, 2, \ldots)$ defines a unique solution x_n of $x + a = (b_n)$. This solution in turn increases with n, and thus the number associated with the sequence

$$x_{n+i}, \quad i = 1, 2, 3 \ldots$$

is the unique solution, $b - a$, of (2). If $b < a$, we put

$$b - a = -(a - b).$$

To define addition of a positive and a negative number we put $a + (-b) = a - b$. Similarly we put $-a + (-b) = -(a + b)$. Thus subtraction becomes a particular case of addition. We notice that $a - (a)_n < 1/10^{n+1}$.

The product $a . b$, of two positive numbers is similarly defined by the process which we might call *partial multiplication*, since $(a)_n \cdot (b)_n$ is an increasing and bounded sequence.

For negative numbers we put

$$a \,.\, (-b) = (-a) \,.\, b = -(ab), \; (-a)(-b) = ab.$$

The reciprocal of a positive number $a > 0$ is defined as the solution of

$$(3) \qquad ax = 1.$$

As $a > 0$, there is an n such that $(a)_n > 0$ and the equations $(a)_{n+i} \cdot x = 1$ determine a decreasing sequence x_{n+i} of positive (rational) decimal forms. The number associated with this sequence is a solution of (3) and also of $xa = 1$ and is said to be the reciprocal of a; in symbols $1/a$ or a^{-1}. If a is negative, we put $1/a = -(1/-a)$. The quotient of a by b is, by definition, $a/b = a \,.\, b^{-1} = b^{-1} \,.\, a$, so that division is a special case of multiplication.

As partial sums and products are operations on rational numbers, they obey all the manipulative laws of rational numbers, so that the same is readily proved for sums and products of real numbers. E.g. it follows from

$$(a)_n + (b)_n = (b)_n + (a)_n$$

and $(a)_n(b)_n = (b)_n(a)_n$ that $a + b = b + a$ and $ab = ba$.

Table I contains all the essential laws of manipulation with real numbers.

TABLE I

(*E*) *Equality*:

(E_1) Identical symbols are equal, i.e. $A = A$.

(E_2) Equality is symmetrical, i.e. if $A = B$, then $B = A$.

(E_3) Equality is transitive, i.e. if $A = B$ and $B = C$, then $A = C$.

(*A*) *Addition*:

(A_1) Addition is uniform with respect to equality, i.e.

$$A + B = A' + B'$$

if $A = A'$ and $B = B'$.

(A_2) Addition is commutative, i.e. $A + B = B + A$.

(A_3) Addition is associative, i.e. $(A + B) + C = A + (B + C)$.

(A_4) There is a symbol Z such that, for every A, $A + Z = A$ We denote the symbol Z by 0 (zero).

(A_5) Addition obeys the law of implication, i.e. if

$$A + B = A' + C$$

and $A = A'$, then $B = C$.

(*M*) *Multiplication*:

(M_1) Multiplication is uniform with respect to equality, i. e. $AB = A'B'$ if $A = A'$, $B = B'$.

(M_2) Multiplication is commutative, i. e. $AB = BA$.

(M_3) Multiplication is associative, i. e. $(AB)C = A(BC)$.

(M_4) There is a symbol E such that for every A, $EA = AE = A$. We denote E by 1.

(M_5) Multiplication obeys the law of implication, i. e. if $AB = A'C$ and $A = A'$, then $B = C$.

(M_6) Multiplication is distributive with respect to addition, i. e. $A(B+C) = AB+AC$.

(M_7) Multiplication obeys the product law for 0, i. e.

$$A\,0 = 0A = 0$$

and if $AB = 0$ then either A or $B = 0$ (or both).

3. *The root in the algebra of real numbers.* The sequence of successive integers, i. e. counting, is the ultimate source of mathematical ideas. For instance, the addition of 4 to 5 means counting up to 4 and continuing by 5 consecutive steps. Multiplication of integers is a special case of addition when all the terms are the same. Similarly a power is a special case of a product. Subtraction and division are the *inverse* operations of addition and multiplication respectively, i. e. one of the numbers a and b determining the sum $a+b$ or product ab being given, we have to determine the second number. The solution of the equation $a^b = c$, in which c and either a or b are given leads to two different operations, since the interchange of a and b affects the result. The determination of x by the equation

$$x^k = a \tag{1}$$

is called the extraction of the *k-th root* of a. The solution x of the equation

$$b^x = a \tag{2}$$

is called *the logarithm of a to the base b.*

Thus the scheme of the seven operations of algebra is as follows.

Counting → addition → multiplication → power
addition ↓ subtraction
multiplication ↓ division
power ↙ root, ↘ log.

Consider first equation (1) when k is a positive integer. As $(-x)^{2n} = x^{2n} > 0$, *there is no solution if* $a < 0$ *and* k *is even.* If $a < 0$ and $k = 2n+1$, we have $(-x)^{2n+1} = -x^{2n+1}$, i. e. we have to solve $x^k = -a > 0$ and then $-x$ will be the solution of (1).

Thus, if k is odd, (1) determines a single number x_1, denoted by $\sqrt[k]{a}$. But, if l is even, the symbol $\sqrt[kl]{a^l}$ denotes two values, viz. the two solutions x_1 and $-x_1$ of the equation $x^{kl} = a^l$. In fact, from $x_1{}^k = a$ and $(-x_1)^k = -a$, we have $x_1{}^{lk} = a^l$ and $(-x_1)^{lk} = a^l$.

Moreover, if $a < 0$ and k is even, there is no (real) number corresponding to the symbol $\sqrt[k]{a}$, but, if l is even, there are two numbers denoted by $\sqrt[kl]{a^l}$, viz. the two solutions of $x^{kl} = a^l > 0$. If $a < 0$, k is even and l is odd, there is no number corresponding to either of the two symbols $\sqrt[k]{a}$ and $\sqrt[kl]{a^l}$. Finally, if $a > 0$ and k is even, $\sqrt[k]{a}$ and $\sqrt[kl]{a^l}$ both denote two numbers.

Therefore, an equality involving roots, e. g.

$$\sqrt[k]{a} = \sqrt[kl]{a^l},$$

has the following meaning. If one side denotes r different numbers $x_1, x_2, \ldots, x_r$ and the other side s different numbers, $s \geqslant r$, say, then *every* x_i *is equal to some* y_k. In particular, when we put $x = \sqrt[k]{a}$, we mean that we consider the case where $\sqrt[k]{a}$ has one or two values and, in the latter case, x denotes *either* of these two values.

We now proceed to establish the main properties of roots.

(a) $\sqrt[k]{a^\alpha} = \sqrt[kl]{a^{\alpha l}}$, where α is any integer.

Proof. Putting $x_1 = \sqrt[k]{a^\alpha}$, we have $x_1{}^k = a^\alpha$, i. e. $x_1{}^{kl} = a^{\alpha l}$. This shows that x_1 is also a solution of $x^{kl} = a^{\alpha l}$ and is therefore equal to a value of the right-hand side.

(b) $$\sqrt[k]{a^\alpha} = (\sqrt[k]{a})^\alpha.$$

Proof. Putting $x_2 = \sqrt[k]{a}$, we have $x_2{}^k = a$, i. e.

$$x_2{}^{k\alpha} = (x_2{}^\alpha)^k = a^\alpha,$$

and thus $x_2{}^\alpha$ is also a value of the left-hand side.

(c) $$\sqrt[k]{a}\ \sqrt[k]{b} = \sqrt[k]{ab}.$$

Proof. Putting $x_1 = \sqrt[k]{a}$, $x_2 = \sqrt[k]{b}$, we have

$$x_1^k\, x_2^k = (x_1\, x_2)^k = ab$$

and thus $x_1\, x_2$ is a value of the right-hand side.

(d) $$\sqrt[l]{\sqrt[k]{a}} = \sqrt[lk]{a}.$$

Proof. Putting $x_2 = \sqrt[lk]{a}$ we have $x_2{}^{lk} = (x_2{}^l)^k = a$, and thus $x_2{}^l$ is a value of $\sqrt[k]{a}$. Therefore x_2 itself is a value of $\sqrt[l]{\sqrt[k]{a}}$.

4. *Logarithms of positive numbers to the base* 10. In order to define the logarithms of positive numbers we must introduce irrational and negative indices. Let $\alpha = \alpha_0 \cdot \alpha_1 \alpha_2 .. \alpha_r \ldots$ be an irrational number and a a positive number. The bounded monotone sequence $a^{\alpha_0}, a^{\alpha_0 \cdot \alpha_1}, a^{\alpha_0 \cdot \alpha_1 \alpha_2}, \ldots, a^{\alpha_0 \cdot \alpha_1 \alpha_2 \ldots \alpha_r} \ldots$ of positive real numbers (they are all between 0 and $a^{\alpha_0 + 1}$) defines, by Lemma I, a decimal fraction, A, associated with the sequence. We define irrational indices by putting $a^\alpha = A$ and negative indices by putting $a^{-\alpha} = 1/a^\alpha$. Finally we put $a^o = a^\alpha . a^{-\alpha} = 1$.

It is easy to verify that irrational and negative indices, together with the zero index, satisfy the three laws of indices: $a^\alpha . a^\beta = a^{\alpha+\beta}$, $a^\alpha b^\alpha = (ab)^\alpha$, $(a^\alpha)^\beta = a^{\alpha\beta}$, which justifies the definition.

Take now the equation

(1) $$10^x = a \qquad (a > 0).$$

The number a is either between two consecutive numbers of the sequence $\ldots, 10^{-n}, \ldots, 10^{-1}, 10^0, 10^1, \ldots, 10^n, \ldots$ or is equal to one of them. Suppose that $10^{\alpha_0} \leqq a < 10^{\alpha_0+1}$. Take α_0 for the integral part of a decimal fraction α and consider the ten numbers, $10^{\alpha_0 \cdot 0}, 10^{\alpha_0 \cdot 1}, \ldots, 10^{\alpha_0 \cdot 9}$, and suppose that

$$10^{\alpha_0 \cdot \alpha_1} \leqq a < 10^{\alpha_0 \cdot \alpha_1 + 1/10}.$$

Take α_1 for the first decimal figure of α and continue the process. By construction the number $\alpha = \alpha_0 \cdot \alpha_1\, \alpha_2 \ldots$ determined in this way* satisfies equation (1), for the meaning of the symbol 10^α is just the decimal associated with the sequence $10^{\alpha_0 \cdot \alpha_1 \alpha_2 \cdots \alpha_n}$, $(n = 1, 2, \ldots)$. We call α the logarithm of a to the base 10.

The properties of the logarithm, i.e. $\log (a/b) = \log a - \log b$,

* With the convention, in case α_0 is negative, that

$$\alpha_0 \cdot \alpha_1\, \alpha_2 \ldots = \alpha_0 + \cdot\, \alpha_1\, \alpha_2 \ldots.$$

$\log (ab) = \log a + \log b$, $\log (a^\alpha) = \alpha \log a$, *for every real value of* α and for positive a and b, are easily deduced from its definition as an index.

Polynomials $P(x) = a_0 + a_1 x + \ldots a_n x^n$, their ratios called rational functions, radicals like $[P(x)/Q(x)]^{p/q}$, exponential functions 10^x, $10^{P(x)/Q(x)}$, logarithmic functions $\log x$, $\log P(x)$, &c., and their finite combinations form *the class of elementary functions of a real variable.*

Some of these functions, such as rational functions, are *uniform* (one valued, monovalued), some are *multiform* (e.g. $\sqrt{x}$ is two-valued). The function x of the independent variable y determined by the equation $y = f(x)$ is the *inverse* function of $f(x)$: $\sqrt[k]{x}$ is the inverse function of x^k; $\log x$ is the inverse function of 10^x.

5. *The idea of infinitely many (transfinite cardinals).* The idea of 'infinitely many' is the most fundamental of all mathematical notions. It is essentially a negative idea. When we say that the series of integers is infinite, we mean that, any one of them being given, there is another integer greater than the given one: *no greatest can be given.* When we say that there are infinitely many fractions, we mean that labelling them by means of the integers as first, second, &c. we cannot exhaust them by a finite number of integers.

One method of so labelling them is to group together fractions p/q for which $p+q$ is a given integer, e.g. the fractions for which $p+q = n$ are all included in $1/(n-1)$, $2/(n-2)$, ..., $(n-2)/2$. Taking $n = 3$, we find only $1/2$, for $n = 4$, only $1/3$; for $n = 5$, $1/4$, $2/3$, $3/2$, &c. Thus the sequence

(1) $1/2$; $1/3$; $1/4$, $2/3$, $3/2$; $1/5$; $1/6$, $2/5$, $3/4$, $4/3$, $5/2$; $1/7 \ldots$

contains all the fractions in a certain order.

Counting objects means, in general, labelling them by integers in a similar way, i.e. establishing a one-one correspondence between the objects to be counted and a section of the integers. This idea of one-one correspondence extends to infinite sets.

For instance, (1) shows that there are just as many fractions as integers. Similarly the correspondence in which n corresponds to $2n$, shows that there are as many even numbers as there are integers. But, so far this means only that both sets contain infinitely many numbers. Let us try, however, to label all the real numbers, or more precisely all the decimal forms, whose integral part is 0, irrespective of equality, so that 0·1 is considered as different from 0·0999.... It is easy to show that we cannot succeed. In fact, suppose that the sequence

$$\cdot a_{11}a_{12}\ldots,\ \cdot a_{21}a_{22}\ldots,\ \ldots,\ \cdot a_{n1}a_{n2}\ldots,\ \ldots$$

exhausts all the decimal forms between 0 and 1. The decimal form whose first decimal figure is $a_{11}+1\,(=0$ if $a_{11}=9)$, whose second is $a_{22}+1$, &c., differs from the first decimal form of the sequence, for their first figures are different, differs from the second, for its second figure differs from a_{22}, &c. Thus $\cdot(a_{11}+1)(a_{22}+1)\ldots$, with the convention of writing 0 when $a_{ii}+1=10$, is not included in the proposed sequence:

I. *No sequence of decimal forms exhausts the whole class of decimal forms.* (Cantor 1873.)

Hence the 'infinitely many' of decimal forms is distinguished from the 'infinitely many' of integers by the test of one-one correspondence. Generalizing in this way the idea of cardinal number ('how many'), we may say that the cardinal number, (called also *power*), of decimal forms is not the same as the cardinal number of integers. Therefore the information contained in (1), i. e. that the cardinal number of the fractions is the same as that of the integers, acquires a clear sense, since we know now that 'infinitely many' can have different meanings in different cases. If the cardinal number of a set is that of the integers, we say that the set is *enumerable* (countable), i. e. *it can be written out in the form of a sequence.* We note that as a rule also a finite set of numbers is included in the class of enumerable sets. All the real numbers between a and b, $a<b$, are said to form an interval (a, b) or a continuum. We denote by c the cardinal number of any set that can be put into one-one correspondence with the interval (0, 1).

The chief properties of transfinite cardinal numbers are as follows. If S_1 and S_2 are two distinct sets, i. e. have no common number, we denote by S_1+S_2 the united set. If both S_1 and S_2 are enumerable, each can be written out in the form of a sequence ($x_1, x_2, \ldots$ and $y_1, y_2, \ldots$), and so $S_1 + S_2$ can be written out in the sequence $x_1, y_1, x_2, y_2, \ldots$. If S_1 and S_2 have common numbers, the result holds *a fortiori*. *The sum of two enumerable sets is an enumerable set.* This property extends to an enumerable infinity of enumerable sets:

II. *An enumerable infinity of enumerable sets is itself enumerable.* (Cantor 1875.)

Proof. Write the sets in the form of a table:

$$\begin{array}{ll} S_1: & x_{11}, x_{12}, x_{13}, \ldots \\ S_2: & x_{21}, x_{22}, x_{23}, \ldots \\ & \ldots \qquad \ldots \\ S_n: & x_{n1}, x_{n2}, x_{n3}, \ldots \\ & \ldots \qquad \ldots \end{array}$$

The so-called diagonal process, i. e. writing first the numbers x_{ik} of the table for which $i+k = 2$, then $i+k = 3$, &c. leads to a unique sequence containing every number of the given table; which proves the proposition.

We know that both integers and fractions are enumerable. Thus rational numbers are enumerable. Passing to decimal forms, there are decimal forms like 1·1 and 1·0999... corresponding to *equal* rational numbers. But an irrational number has only one decimal form. Therefore if irrational numbers were enumerable, the complete set of decimal forms would consist of three enumerable sets, viz. irrational numbers, rational numbers, and the duplicates of some rational numbers, which contradicts I. On the other hand the fraction $(x-a)/(b-a) = y$ establishes a one-one correspondence between the intervals (a, b) and $(0, 1)$. Similarly $x/|\sqrt{x^2+1}|$ establishes one-one correspondence between the complete set of real numbers and the interval $(0, 1)$. Hence

III. *The cardinal number of all the real numbers and also that of irrational numbers is c.* (Cantor 1875.)

We remark without proving it that there is no one-one correspondence between all the functions of a real variable and all the numbers of an interval, so that there are cardinal numbers 'greater' than c, but we do not know whether there is a non-enumerable subset of the continuum whose cardinal number is less than c (problem of the continuum).

6. *Transfinite ordinals.*

If we consider the numbers of the two sequences $(n-1)/n$ and $1+(n-1)/n$ together in their natural order of magnitude, we have no ordinals to denote the 'rank' of the numbers of the second sequence. In fact 0 is the first, $1/2$ is the second, &c., $(n-1)/n$ is the nth number of the combined set, and 1 comes just after having exhausted all the finite ordinals, and $1+1/2$ comes after this, &c. Therefore we introduce symbols indicating such orders. We shall say that the number 1 of the united set is in order of magnitude the $(\omega+1)$th number of the set, $1+1/2$ is the $(\omega+2)$th &c. If we have three or more, or even an enumerable sequence of sequences, we might use the symbols $\omega+\omega+1=2\omega+1$, $2\omega+2$, &c. $3\omega+k, \ldots, \omega\omega+1=\omega^2+1$, &c. For instance, the numbers $(n-1)/n$, $1+(n-1)/n$, $2+(n-1)/n, \ldots$ in their natural order of magnitude form a transfinite sequence of numbers of ω^2 type. An ordinary sequence is, in this terminology, a sequence of ω type.

In this book we shall consider only transfinite sequences formed by an enumerable sequence of ordinary sequences. By 5. II, we can of course write such a transfinite sequence in the form of an ordinary sequence (of ω type), but in many questions the order of the numbers in the sequence will be of importance. It will be so in the case of simple and double infinite series. The only result we need about general transfinite sequences is the following theorem, which shows how difficult it is to pass beyond the class of enumerable transfinite sequences.

I. *A monotone transfinite sequence of different real numbers is enumerable*, i.e. *it can be written in the form of an ordinary sequence.* (Dienes 1923.)

Proof. Suppose that a transfinite sequence $a_1, a_2, \ldots, a_{\omega+1}, a_{\omega+2}, \ldots$ is increasing, i.e. $a_i < a_{i+1}$ and that the sequence is bounded: all the numbers of the sequence are $< B$. In this case $|a_n - a_m| < B - a_1 = \delta$ and as the sequence is increasing,

$$a_p - a_m > a_{m+1} - a_m$$

if $p > m+1$. Hence

$$\delta > a_{p+1} - a_m = (a_{p+1} - a_p) + (a_p - a_m) > (a_{p+1} - a_p) + (a_{m+1} - a_m),$$

so that there is at most one number a_m for which $a_{m+1} - a_m \geqslant \delta/2$. Similarly there are at most two numbers of the sequence such that $a_{m+1}-a_m \geqslant \delta/3$, and so on. In this way we write out the numbers of the transfinite sequence in an ordinary sequence.

If the transfinite sequence is not bounded, our preceding result shows that those of its members between two integers are enumerable and thus, by 5. II, the whole sequence is enumerable. A similar proof holds for decreasing transfinite sequences.

For instance, *a set of non-overlapping intervals is enumerable,* since otherwise, by adding the lengths of intervals completely included in $(-1, 1)$, $(-2, 2)$, ... respectively, we should obtain a non-enumerable sequence of increasing numbers. This result (Cantor 1875) is in fact equivalent to I.

7. *Limiting numbers.* All the numbers between a and b $(b > a)$ are said to form the interval (a, b). It is *closed* if the two extremities are included, *open* if neither of them is included. An *inner* point of (a, b) is a number of the open interval (a, b). We say that a number x is *isolated* or separated from another number a if there is an interval $(x-d, x+d')$, $d>0$, $d'>0$ such that a is not an inner point of this interval. The number (or point) x is isolated from a set of numbers S if there is an interval $(x-d, x+d')$, not containing numbers of S, (except x if x is a number of S). For instance, 0 is not isolated from the numbers of the form $1/n$ since, for every d, there is in $(-d, d)$ a fraction of the form $1/n$. In fact, if the first non-zero decimal figure of d is the k-th, $1/10^{k+1} < d$. A number not isolated from the given set is said to be a *limiting number* of the set.

On the other hand, every number other than 0 is isolated from the set $(1/n)$. In fact, this is obvious for numbers outside $(0, 1)$, and a number of $(0, 1)$ is either a number of S, $1/n$, say, and then is isolated from the other numbers of S by $(1/(n+1), 1/(n-1))$, or is between two consecutive numbers of S, i.e. in an interval not containing any number of S. *The set* $(1/n)$ *has a unique limiting number*, 0.

The set F of all the fractions in $(0, 1)$ is so dense that no number a of this interval is isolated from F. To prove this we have to show that the interval $(a-d, a+d)$ contains a fraction for an arbitrarily given d, however small. But if the first non-vanishing decimal figure of d is the n-th, we see from $a-(a)_n < 1/10^n$ and $d \geqslant (d)_n \geqslant 1/10^n$ that

$$(a)_n > a - 1/10^n \geqslant a-d,$$

i.e., as $(a)_n \leqq a$, we see that the fraction $(a)_n$ is in $(a-d, a+d)$. Thus no numbers of F are isolated from the other numbers of F, and neither are the irrational numbers in (0, 1), i.e. *all the numbers of* (0, 1) *are limiting numbers of* F.

Similarly for the set R of all the real numbers in (0, 1). In fact, if the first non-vanishing decimal figure of d is the n-th, $a+1/10^{n+1}$ is in $(a-d, a+d)$. On the other hand every number a is isolated from the set of integers because, if a is not an integer, it lies between two consecutive integers separating it from the integers, and if a is one of the integers, it lies between $a-1$ and $a+1$, i.e. the interval $(a-1, a+1)$ separates it from the other integers. *The set of integers has no limiting number.*

This gives rise to the problem of determining the class of sets having a limiting number. The fundamental result is due to Bolzano.

I. *An infinite set of real numbers contained in a finite interval has a limiting number in that interval.*

(Bolzano 1851, Weierstrass in his lectures.)

We split up the proof into two useful theorems.

II. *The number associated with a monotone bounded sequence is the only limiting number of that sequence.*

We have to prove that the number in question is not isolated from the sequence and that every other number is. If (x_n) is the sequence and x is the number associated with it, $x > x_n$, by construction, and there is an N such that the first m decimal figures of x_n for $n > N$ are the same as those of x, i.e. $x - x_n < 1/10^m$. Thus, if $d \geqslant 1/10^m$ (i.e. if we take for m the place-index of the first non-vanishing decimal figure of the arbitrarily given d), x_n is in $(x-d, x+d)$, which proves the first part of the statement. For the second part we have only to notice (1) that if $a < x_1$, or if $a > x$, a is obviously isolated from the numbers of the sequence x_n, (2) that if $a < x$, then also $a < x_n$ for a conveniently chosen n. This is obvious since there is a first decimal figure (or the integral part), the n-th say, in which a and x differ, and, by hypothesis, $(a)_n < (x)_n$, while, on the other hand, there is an x_n such that its first n decimal figures (integral part included) are the same as in x, so that $a < x_n$. It follows from the second remark that a is either one of the numbers x_n, which is separated from the rest by (x_{n-1}, x_{n+1}), or else a lies between two consecutive x_n.

The same proof applies to decreasing bounded sequences.

III. *An infinite set of real numbers contains a monotone sequence.*

Proof. As an infinite set contains by hypothesis an infinite sequence of different numbers, it is sufficient to establish the result for infinite sequences. We first consider a special case. *If the sequence $y_1, y_2, \ldots$ has no greatest term, it contains an increasing infinite sequence.* In fact in this case there are infinitely many terms after any of them, y_n say, greater than the term y_n. Thus, starting with y_1, we pass to the nearest term $y_{n_1} > y_1$, and then from y_{n_1} to the nearest term $y_{n_2} > y_{n_1}$, &c. without being stopped. Similarly *if the sequence has no least term, it contains a decreasing infinite sequence.*

Denote now the group of numbers $x_n, x_{n+1}, \ldots, x_m$ of the original sequence by ${}_n(x_i)_m$. Either there is an n such that the sequence ${}_n(x_i)_\infty$ has no greatest or no least number, in which case ${}_n(x_i)_\infty$, and thus also the complete sequence ${}_1(x_i)_\infty$ contains a monotone sequence, or else all the sequences ${}_n(x_i)_\infty$ have both a greatest and a least number for every n. In the latter case the greatest numbers of ${}_n(x_i)_\infty$, for $n = 1, 2, \ldots$, form a decreasing sequence (and the least numbers form an increasing sequence). Further, this sequence contains infinitely many different numbers, since the greatest term x_m of ${}_n(x_i)_\infty$ will not figure in ${}_{m+k}(x_i)_\infty$.

Since, by II, a monotone sequence has a (unique) limiting number, Bolzano's theorem is proved by III.

If a set is not bounded above, i.e if the set contains numbers greater than any integer, we say that $+\infty$ is a limiting number of the set. Similarly, if a set is not bounded below, $-\infty$ is said to be a limiting number of the set. With this convention we can state Bolzano's theorem in the general form.

IV. *An infinite set of real numbers has a limiting number* (finite or conventional).

We add the remark that a finite number of numbers x_i has no limiting number, for there is a least difference d of $|x_i - x_k|$ and there are no numbers x_i in $(a-d, a+d)$ except perhaps a itself.

To sum up, *no finite set of real numbers has a limiting number, and every infinite set of real numbers either has a limit-*

ing number or else it is unbounded (and has one or two conventional limiting numbers).

V. *If every number of a set S of real numbers is isolated, S is enumerable.*

Proof. Isolate a number of S by an interval I_1. Isolate another number of S by an interval I_2, not overlapping I_1, and so on. Adding the lengths of our isolating intervals we obtain a sequence (in general transfinite) of increasing different numbers whose number is, by 6. I, enumerable. This means that after an enumerable number of steps the set will have been emptied.

8. *Limits.* We define a limit as follows: *The limit of a set is its unique limiting number (conventional limiting numbers taken into account).* Thus, if a set has more than one limiting number, we say that it has no limit (but several limiting numbers). For instance, the set $1/n$ has 0 for its limit; in symbols:

$$\lim_{n=\infty} (1/n) = 0,$$

where $n = \infty$ indicates that n assumes successively all the integral values $1, 2, \ldots$. The sequence $1, 1/2, 3, 1/4, 5, \ldots$ has no limit since it has two limiting numbers, viz. 0 and $+\infty$. If, in a sequence x_n, the same number x is repeated infinitely many times, so that every section $_n(x_i)_\infty$ $(n = 1, 2, \ldots)$ has numbers in $(x-d, x+d)$, e.g. x, we consider x as one of the limiting numbers of the sequence. Otherwise there is no difference between the definition of the limit for sets and sequences. In fact

I. *If a set has a limit x, say, the set can be written out in the form of a sequence.* To prove this statement we have only to remark that outside $(x-1/n, x+1/n)$ there is only a finite number of numbers (otherwise, by Bolzano's theorem 7 I, the set would have a limiting number outside this interval and thus would have more than one limiting number). Thus enumerating first the numbers of the sequence outside $(x-1, x+1)$, we continue by adding to the list the numbers of the set inside $(x-1, x+1)$ and outside $(x-1/2, x+1/2)$, and so forth.

Thus, in dealing with limits we may restrict ourselves to

sequences. When the sequence x_n has the limit x, it is convenient sometimes to say that x tends or converges to x. In symbols $x_n \to x$. In this case we say also that x_n is a convergent (or regular) sequence. If $x_n \to 0$, x_n is said to be a 0-sequence.

II. *If* $x_n > 0$ *and* $x_n \to 0$, *and if* $|y_n| < x_n$, *then also* $y_n \to 0$. In fact, as there is only a finite number of x_n outside $(-d, d)$, the same holds for y_n. We denote 0-sequences by ϵ_n, η_n, ζ_n, &c.

III. *The sum, difference or product of a finite number of 0-sequences is a 0-sequence.* We write out the proof for two sequences. In fact, by hypothesis, there is only a finite number of ϵ_n and η_n outside $(-\epsilon/2, \epsilon/2)$, i.e. only a finite number of numbers $\epsilon_n + \eta_n$ outside $(-\epsilon, \epsilon)$. As for the product, from a sufficiently large n on, $|\eta_n| < 1$, so that $|\epsilon_n \eta_n| < |\epsilon_n|$, which proves the result.

IV. *If* c *is any number,* $c\epsilon_n$ *is a 0-sequence. And if* $|c_n| \leqslant c$, $c_n \epsilon_n$ *is also a 0-sequence.* In fact, outside $(-\epsilon/c, \epsilon/c)$ there is only a finite number of ϵ_n, hence outside $(-\epsilon, \epsilon)$ there is only a finite number of $c\epsilon_n$ or $c_n \epsilon_n$.

The meaning of $\lim x_n = +\infty$ is that the set of numbers x_n has no finite limiting number, is bounded below and unbounded above. Similarly, $\lim x_n = -\infty$ means that x_n has no finite limiting number, is bounded above and unbounded below.

The fundamental property of *convergent sequences* is expressed by the following theorem.

V. *If* $x_n \to x$, *then* $x_n = x + \epsilon_n$, *where* ϵ_n *is a 0-sequence. Conversely, if* ϵ_n *is a 0-sequence,* $x + \epsilon_n \to x$.

Proof. If $x_n \to x$ and η is an arbitrary small positive number, there is an N such that all the numbers x_n, $n > N$, are in $(x-\eta, x+\eta)$, for there is only a finite number of x_n outside this interval. Hence, for $n > N$, $|x - x_n| \leqslant \eta$. Applying this remark to $\eta = 1/2, 1/3, \ldots$ we see, by II, that $x - x_n$ is a 0-sequence. Conversely, if $\epsilon_n \to 0$, there is only a finite number of $x + \epsilon_n$ outside $(x - \epsilon, x + \epsilon)$ for any arbitrary ϵ, which proves the second part.

The following property of convergent sequences is of frequent use.

VI. *If* $x_n \to x$, $y_n \to y$, *then* $x_n \pm y_n \to x \pm y$, $x_n y_n \to xy$, $x_n/y_n \to x/y$, *provided in the last instance* $y_n \neq 0$ *and* $y \neq 0$.

Proof. By V, $x_n = x + \epsilon_n$, $y_n = y + \eta_n$, i.e.

$$x_n + y_n = x + y + \epsilon_n + \eta_n.$$

Similarly $x_n y_n = xy + \epsilon_n y + \epsilon_n x + \epsilon_n \eta_n$. Thus III and IV prove the first equations of the theorem. To prove the fourth result we have to remark that as $y \neq 0$, there is an ϵ such that $0 < \epsilon < |y|$. There is only a finite number of y_n outside the interval $(y - \epsilon, y + \epsilon)$ and, as none of them is 0, there is a least $|y_n| = a$, say. Hence for every n, $|1/y_n| \geqslant 1/a$, and since $(y + \epsilon_n)/y_n = 1$, we have $1/y_n = 1/y - \epsilon_n/yy_n$, where $1/|y_n y| \leqslant 1/|ay|$, and so, by IV, $1/y_n = 1/y + \eta_n$. Now

$$x_n/y_n = (x + \epsilon_n)(1/y + \eta_n) = x/y + x\eta_n + \epsilon_n/y + \epsilon_n \eta_n,$$

which proves the result in question (by IV and III).

There are no general rules for the determination of the limit of a set. All we can do is to establish the existence and determine the value of the limit in particular cases, and to reduce unknown cases to known ones. Theorem VI furnishes the most useful artifices for this purpose.

9. *Bounds and extreme limiting numbers.* In the case of a convergent sequence x_n tending to x, we know that any of the intervals $(x - 1/n, x + 1/n)$ contains an infinity of numbers x_n and only a finite number of these numbers are not covered by this interval. The expression 'any of the intervals $(x - 1/n, x + 1/n)$' or, what amounts to the same, 'any of the intervals $(x - \epsilon_n, x + \epsilon_n)$' is shortened into 'the neighbourhood (or vicinity) of x'. Thus we might say that an infinity of the numbers x_n lies in the neighbourhood of x. In this case, knowing the limit, we can locate the bulk of the set.

In the general case we locate the set S by two pairs of bounds. The first pair is the *upper and lower bound* of S and is defined as follows. If S is not bounded above (below), we say that $+\infty$ $(-\infty)$ is its upper (lower) bound. If all the numbers of S are less than A, we proceed in the following way. Suppose first that all the numbers of S are positive. There is only a finite number of different integers figuring as integral parts of the numbers of S. Take the greatest of them, x_0 say. Consider now the numbers of S with the integral part x_0. There is a greatest first decimal figure x_1, say, assumed by these numbers. Consider now the numbers of S whose decimal forms begin with $x_0 \cdot x_1$. There is a greatest second decimal figure, x_2, say, assumed by these numbers, and so forth. The number $U = x_0 \cdot x_1 x_2 \ldots$ thus determined by the set S is its upper bound. Similarly for the lower bound L. If S contains both positive and negative numbers, in the determination of U we restrict ourselves to the positive numbers and define L as being the upper bound of the numbers of S with reversed signs. If S contains only negative numbers $-x_n$, the U of x_n is the L of $-x_n$, and vice-versa.

We might also say that the *lower and upper bounds of a set S are the two extremities of the shortest interval containing S.*

If a set consists of a single number a, we have $L = U = a$, and conversely, if $L = U$, the set consists of a single number $a = U = L$.

U (as well as L) may be a number of S, in which case it is its greatest (least) number. For example, for $1/n$, $U = 1$ (a number of the set) and $L = 0$ (not a number of the set). For $(n-1)/n$, $U = 1$ (not a number of the set), and $L = 0$ (a number of the set). For the fractions a/b, $(0<a<b)$, $U = 1$, and $L = 0$, neither of them being a number of the set.

I. *If U (L) is not a number of the set S, it is a limiting number of S.*

Proof. If there are no numbers of the set in $(U-d, U)$ the set is contained in $(L, U-d)$, i.e. its upper bound is not U but a number $\leqslant U-d$.

We notice, however, that if U (L) is a number of the set, U (L) may be either an isolated number or a limiting number of the set.

If we know the U and L of a set S, we know the shortest interval containing S, but in many problems the really important point is the position of limiting numbers. We call the set S' of all the limiting numbers of S the *derived set* of S. The lower and upper bounds L' and U' of this derived set S' form the second pair of bounds characterizing the set S. They have the important property of being limiting numbers of S, i.e. numbers of S'. If all the limiting numbers of S are numbers of S, we say that S is *closed*. To establish that U' and L' are numbers of S', we prove a more general theorem.

II. *The derived set S' of any set S is closed.*

Proof. If x' is a limiting number of S', there are numbers x_n' of S' in any neighbourhood of x'. As, for every n, there are numbers of S in any neighbourhood of x_n', there are numbers of S in any neighbourhood of x', i.e. x' is not isolated from S and is, therefore, a limiting number of it, which proves the theorem.

The two bounds L' and U' of S' are therefore the least and the greatest limiting numbers of S. In symbols

$$L' = \lim\inf S = \underline{\lim}\, S, \quad U' = \lim\sup S = \overline{\lim}\, S.$$

We say conventionally that the greatest limiting number U' is $+\infty$ when S is not bounded above ($+\infty$ is a limiting number of S). $U' = -\infty$ means that the greatest, i. e. the only limiting number of S, is the conventional limit $-\infty$. $L' = -\infty$ means that S is not bounded below ($-\infty$ is a limiting number of S), $L' = +\infty$ means that the least and the only limiting number of S is $+\infty$.

10. *Closed sets.* We are going to discuss shortly the properties of the most important class of sets, viz. those of closed sets. They contain by definition all their limiting numbers or contain only a finite number of numbers. The set $1/n$ is not closed, for its only limiting number 0 does not belong to the set; but by adding 0 to it we close the set. Since to close the set of rational numbers requires the addition of all the irrational numbers, it follows that the operation of closing a set may radically alter its structure. (Art. 7.)

The simplest example of a closed set is an interval, with its extremities included (closed interval). Consider now a sequence of closed intervals (a_1, b_1), $(a_2, b_2)\ldots$, (a_n, b_n), ..., each encasing the next, i.e. (a_n, b_n) is a portion of (a_{n-1}, b_{n-1}). This means that the left-hand extremities $a_1, a_2, \ldots, a_n, \ldots$ form an increasing (never decreasing) sequence necessarily tending to a limit a and $b_1, b_2, \ldots, b_n, \ldots$ a decreasing (never increasing) sequence tending to a limit b. If c is any number of the closed interval (a, b), the inequalities $a_n \leqslant a \leqslant c \leqslant b \leqslant b_n$ show that c is contained in all the intervals, in fact the whole interval (a, b) is a portion of all the intervals (a_n, b_n). In particular if $a = b$,

i. e. if the lengths $b_n - a_n \to 0$, the intervals (a_n, b_n) have a single number $a = b$ in common. Thus we have

I. *The closed intervals* (a_n, b_n), $n = 1, 2, \ldots$, *such that* (a_n, b_n) *is contained in* (a_{n-1}, b_{n-1}), *have a common interval or, if* $\lim (b_n - a_n) = 0$, *they have a single common point.*

If from the set $1/n$ we take away first 1, then 1 and 1/2, &c., we obtain sets, each contained in the preceding ones, and yet there is no number common to all the sets. If we close the set by adding 0 to it, and require that all the subsequent sub-sets be also closed, we cannot take away 0, and thus 0 will be a common number of the closed sub-sets. We are going to prove that this is true for any sequence of closed sets each containing the next. To denote the fact that every number of S_2 is a number of S_1 we shall use the symbol $S_2 \leqslant S_1$; moreover, if S_1 has a number not contained in S_2, we write $S_2 < S_1$.

II. *A sequence of closed and not empty sets of numbers* $S_1, S_2, \ldots, S_n, \ldots, S_n < S_{n-1}$, *has at least one common number and the set of the common numbers is closed.*

Proof. If none of the sets S_n is bounded, $+\infty$ or $-\infty$ is a common (conventional) number of all of them. If one of them, S_m, is bounded, $S_{m+1}, S_{m+2}, \ldots$ are all bounded and for the common numbers we may restrict ourselves to that sequence, and so to bounded sets. Divide the interval (a, b) containing S_1 into equal sub-intervals $(a, a_1), (a_1, a_2), \ldots, (a_k, b)$. If the interval (a_i, a_{i+1}) has no number belonging to *every* S_n, there is, by I, an S_{n_i} having no number in (a_i, a_{i+1}), and this is then true of the sets $S_{n_i+1}, \ldots$ also. If the same is true for all the $k+1$ intervals and, if n is the greatest of the suffixes $(n_1, n_2, \ldots, n_{k+1})$, we see that none of the sub-intervals has numbers of S_n, i. e. $S_n, S_{n+1}, \ldots$ must be empty, which is contrary to our hypothesis. Thus *at least one of the sub-intervals* (a_i, a_{i+1}) *contains a number belonging to every* S_n. Sub-dividing these sub-intervals and applying the same reasoning we can construct a sequence of intervals (b_n, c_n), $c_n - b_n \to 0$, such that $I_n < I_{n+1}$. By I, they have a single common number x. This number x is a common number of all the S_n. In fact, if a number does not belong to a closed set S, there are no numbers of S in its neighbourhood, i. e. there is an interval $(x-d, x+d)$ not containing numbers of S. Thus, if x were not a common number of all S_n, there would be an S_n having no numbers in $(x-d, x+d)$. But, by construction, there are common numbers of all the S_n in every neighbourhood of x. This proves the first part of the theorem, viz., that the set σ of common numbers is not empty.

To show that σ is closed we have only to remark that if $x_1, x_2, \ldots$ are numbers of σ tending to x, then, by hypothesis, all the numbers $x_1\ x_2, \ldots$ are numbers of all the S_n and, these being closed, x also belongs to all the S_n.

These two important theorems extend to sets of points (x, y) of a plane, and to sets of points $(x_1, x_2, \ldots x_n)$ of an n-dimensional manifold. We formulate definitions and results for plane sets.

The square $[A, B]$, $A = (a, a')$, $B = (b, b')$, consists of all the points (x, y) satisfying the inequalities

$$a<x<b,\ a'<y<b'.$$

If also equality be admitted, the points are said to form a closed square. The circle of radius r, centre (a, a'), consists of all the points (x, y) satisfying the inequality

$$(x-a)^2+(y-a')^2<r^2.$$

If also equality be admitted, the points are said to form a closed circle.

In an n-dimensional manifold the square is replaced by the *cell* $[A, B]$, $A = (a_1, \ldots, a_n)$, $B = (b_1, \ldots, b_n)$, $a_i<b_i$, which consists of the points satisfying the inequalities

$$a_i<x_i<b_i,\ \ i = 1, \ldots, n.$$

The centre of $[A, B]$ is $\left(\frac{a+b}{2}, \frac{a'+b'}{2}\right)$. The four points

$$A_1 = \left(a, \frac{a'+b'}{2}\right) \qquad A_2 = \left(\frac{a+b}{2}, a'\right),$$

$$A_3 = \left(\frac{a+b}{2}, b'\right), \qquad A_4 = \left(b, \frac{a'+b'}{2}\right)$$

bisect the sides and together with the centre decompose $[A, B]$ into four equal squares. This mathematical process of decomposing a square will be referred to as the division of a square into four equal squares by parallels to the axes.

A point (a, a') is said to be isolated from the points of a given set S if there is a square (or a circle) centre (a, a') containing no point of S. If (a, a') is not isolated from S, we say that (a, a') is a *limiting point* of S. If S contains all its limiting points, S is said to be *closed*; if every point of S is a limiting point of S, we say that S is *everywhere dense*. For example, all the points (x, y) with rational co-ordinates x, y form a set which is everywhere dense but not closed. If S is everywhere dense and closed, S is said to be *perfect*. A set is *bounded* if it is contained in a sufficiently large square.

III. *If the sequence of closed parallel squares (concentric circles) q_n is such that q_n is contained in q_{n-1}, there is a square (circle), perhaps reduced to a single point, contained in every q_n.*

Proof. Since the sides of q_n are parallel to those of q_{n-1}, the four corners of the squares tend to definite points, for their co-ordinates form monotone sequences. Thus, there is a limiting square (perhaps reduced to a point) contained in all the squares q_n.

For concentric circles, the limit of the radii determines the circle contained in every circle of the sequence.

To extend II to plane sets, we divide the square q_1 containing the first set S_1 into four equal squares, common sides being considered as belonging to both. If neither of the four squares contained points of S_n, S_n would be empty. Thus, *one of the four squares contains a point belonging to every S_n*. By subdividing this square we establish as before theorem II. We formulate our results in the following theorem.

IV. *A sequence of non-empty closed sets $S_1, S_2, \ldots S_n, \ldots$ of points of a plane (or of an n-dimensional manifold) with $S_n < S_{n-1}$ have at least one common point and the set of common points is closed.*

A classical example is furnished by the successive derivatives of a set. We have seen that the derived set S' of any set S is closed. Thus also the derived set S'' of S' is closed (or empty, of course). The sequence of successive derivatives $S', S'', \ldots$ form the example required. Their common set is called the derivative of the order $\omega+1$. By II, it is a closed set $S^{\omega+1}$, and thus we can start the derivation anew.

Does this process end? As the derivative of $1/n$ consists of the single number 0, its second derivative is empty, and so are all the successive derivatives. On the other hand, the derivative of the closed interval (0, 1) is this interval, the derivative is identical with the set. The set is *perfect*. In this case all the derivatives are identical.

V. *If S is any set of real numbers, it has a derivative of an enumerable order which is either empty or perfect.*

Proof. We have seen already that if a number (or point) x does not belong to a closed set S, there is a complete interval or cell $(x-d, x+d)$ not belonging to S. Hence, if $S'' < S'$, i.e. if there is at least one number x in S' left out in passing to S'', there is a complete interval of length $2d$ [or cell of volume $(2d)^n$] not belonging to S''. Similarly in passing from S'' to S''' either S'' equals S''', i.e. S'' is perfect (or empty), or there is a new interval or cell outside S''' and so forth. Adding these intervals or cells we obtain an increasing transfinite sequence of different numbers whose number is, by 6. I, necessarily enumerable, i.e. after an enumerable infinity of steps we must have $S^i = S^{i-1}$, i.e. S^{i-1} is either empty or perfect. This proves the theorem.

Since in passing from a set S to its derivative S', we retain all its limiting numbers, the numbers left out are isolated numbers of S and thus their number is necessarily enumerable. Thus, in reaching the empty or perfect set, we have left out an enumerable number of enumerable sets, i.e.

VI. *A closed set is either enumerable or the sum of a perfect set and an enumerable set.*

The fact that if a number x does not belong to a closed set S, then there is a complete interval $(x-d, x+d)$ not belonging to S, shows also that the numbers not belonging to S form complete open intervals, i.e.

VII. *Every closed set is formed by suppressing in the complete continuum a finite or enumerable number of open intervals (cells).*

The number of these intervals is necessarily finite or enumerable, since there is only an enumerable number of non-overlapping intervals.

11. *Distance of sets. Borel's lemma.* We say that the distance

$d(S, \bar{S})$ between two sets S and $\bar{S}$ is the lower bound of distances $|x-\bar{x}|$, where x is any point of S and $\bar{x}$ is any point of $\bar{S}$. For example, if they have a common point, their distance is 0. The distance, however, may be 0 without the sets having a common point, e.g. the distance between the sets $-1/n$ and $1/n$. We are going to show that if S and $\bar{S}$ are two bounded *closed* sets, they either have a common point or their distance is greater than 0.

I. *If the distance of two bounded closed sets S and $\bar{S}$ is d, there is a point in S and a point in $\bar{S}$ such that their distance is exactly d.*

Proof. Since by definition d is the lower bound of differences $|x-\bar{x}|$, either there is a pair x_0, $\bar{x}_0$ such that $|x_0-\bar{x}_0| = d$ (in which case the statement is verified) or else there are pairs $x_n, \bar{x}_n$ such that $\lim |x_n-\bar{x}_n| = d$. The numbers x_n do not necessarily tend to a limit, but being bounded they have a limiting number x approached by a subsequence x_{n_1} say (where n_1 assumes a certain infinite sequence of integral values). Similarly, the sequence x_{n_1} contains a subsequence $\bar{x}_{n_2}$ tending to a limit $\bar{x}$. Obviously, $|x-\bar{x}| = d$. Since the x_n are points of the closed set S, their limit also belongs to S. Similarly $\bar{x}$ belongs to $\bar{S}$. This proves the statement.

When one of the two sets is not closed, we can close it by adding to it its limiting points, i.e. by replacing S by $S+S'$. It is readily proved that

II. $$d(S, S_1) = d(S+S', S_1+S'_1).$$

Proof. Adding points to S or S_1, or to both, cannot increase their distance, i.e. $d(S, S_1) \geqslant d(S+S', S_1+S_1')$. On the other hand, as $S+S'$ and S_1+S_1' are closed, there is a point A of $S+S'$ and a point B of S_1+S_1' such that $d(S+S', S_1+S_1') = d(A, B)$, and there are points of S and S_1 as near to A and B respectively as we like, i.e. $d(S, S_1) \leqslant d(A, B)$. Thus II is established.

The upper bound of distances between the points of a set S is said to be the *diameter* of S. It is 0 only if the set consists of a single number or if the set is empty.

The most important properties of closed sets are condensed in a result due to Borel, of great importance in every part of function theory.

Imagine that we cover every point of a bounded closed set S by an interval (the 'covered' point being an inner point of the covering interval). The number of intervals is in general infinite, enumerable or not. Borel's lemma states that a *finite number of these intervals* conveniently chosen covers the whole set S.

To understand the import of the statement we notice that the result does not in general hold for non-closed sets. Cover, for example, the n-th fraction a_n of the sequence

(1) $1/2,\ 1/3,\ 2/3,\ 1/4,\ 3/4,\ 1/5,\ 2/5,\ 3/5,\ 4/5,\ 1/6, \ldots,$
containing all fractions in $(0, 1)$, by $(a_n - \epsilon/2^n,\ a_n + \epsilon/2^n)$ where ϵ is an arbitrarily given small positive number $< 1/2$. The total length of intervals (mostly overlapping) is

$$2\epsilon(1/2 + 1/2^2 + \ldots) = 2\epsilon,$$

i.e. as small as we please. On the other hand, the total length of a finite number of the intervals is $< 2\epsilon < 1$, i.e. if we retain only a finite number of our intervals, complete intervals, necessarily containing fractions, will be left uncovered. Thus Borel's result does not apply in this case. The set of fractions is, of course, not closed, since all the integers and irrational numbers are limiting numbers of it. We notice a great difference between finite and infinite sets of covering intervals. Roughly speaking, an infinity of intervals with a very small total length may be dense everywhere, i.e. scattered all along $(0, 1)$ so that no complete interval is left uncovered.

To make easier the complete understanding of the lemma, we are going to establish it first for the case when S is a closed interval (a, b). Suppose now that I is an infinite set of intervals, such that every number of (a, b) is covered by an interval of I. In particular the first point a is covered by I_a. If a_1 is the right-hand extremity of I_a, I_a and I_{a_1} cover the part (a, a_2), say, of (a, b), (a_2 being the right-hand extremity of I_{a_1}). Similarly I_a, I_{a_1}, I_{a_2} form a chain of overlapping intervals reaching (covering) all the points (a, a_3) of (a, b). Thus there is a part of (a, b) that can be reached by a finite chain of overlapping intervals.

Suppose now that, contrary to Borel's statement, there are points in (a, b) that cannot be reached by a finite chain. The lower bound c of these points is the first point not reached. In fact, if c were reached, c would be an inner point of an interval I belonging to a finite chain, and the same interval I would also cover points $>c$, i. e. c would not be the lower bound of points not reached. On the other hand, the left-hand extremity of the interval I_c is, by hypothesis, reached by a finite chain $I_a, I_{a_1}, \ldots, I_{a_k}$. Therefore the finite chain $I_a, I_{a_1}, \ldots, I_{a_k}, I_c$ reaches c. Consequently there is no first point that is not reached, which proves the result for a finite closed interval.

More generally, if S is a closed set in (a, b), the points of (a, b) not belonging to S form a set I' of open intervals. The two sets of intervals I and I' cover the whole interval (a, b), and thus, according to our previous result, there is a finite number of them covering (a, b). Suppressing the intervals completely outside S, we obtain Borel's general lemma:

III. *Borel's lemma. If a bounded closed set S is covered by a set of intervals I, there is a finite number of these intervals covering S.* (E. Borel 1895.)

The proof readily extends to sets of points of more than one dimension when intervals are replaced by the corresponding neighbourhoods.

When the numbers of a set S can be covered by intervals with an arbitrarily small total length, we say that the (linear) measure of S is 0. As we have seen, the set of all the fractions is of zero measure.

In many problems we avoid a good deal of complication by restricting ourselves to intervals or corresponding complete neighbourhoods, like squares, cells. In fact, the boundary points of a set S require in most problems independent and sometimes delicate considerations. Hence the need of a rigorous terminology, especially in the case of sets of more than one dimension. We are going to formulate our conventions for two dimensional-plane sets, but, *mutatis mutandis*, they apply also to linear and three or more dimensional sets.

An inner point A of a given set S is characterized by the fact that S contains an open square (all the points of a square, sides not counted), centre A. It follows from this definition that a curve in a plane, for example a parabola, has no inner point, for the set of its points contains no complete square. On the other hand the x axis, considered as a *linear* set and not as a part of the plane, contains inner points since it contains complete *intervals*. Similarly the surface of a sphere considered as a set of points of the three dimensional manifold (x, y, z), has no inner point. *The definition of inner point implies a reference to a fundamental manifold.* The latter is explicitly mentioned only when it is not obvious. The set of fractions has no inner point with respect to the complete set of real numbers because there are irrational numbers in every interval.

A boundary point B of S is characterized (defined) by the fact that in every square, centre B, however small, there are points of S as well as points not belonging to S. For example, if S is an open or closed circle, every point of its circumference is a boundary point. Thus a boundary point may or may not belong to the set.

An outer point C of S is characterized by the fact that there is a square centre C containing no point of S.

To bridge over the gap between the abstract notion of sets of points and the geometrical notion of region, we introduce the idea of *open set*. S is said to be an open set if it contains only inner points. For example, the inner points of a circle or the inner points of two circles outside one another form open sets. If we add to an open set S its boundary points, i. e. if we close the set, we obtain a closed set called a *region*. A region differs from a general closed set by the fact that it necessarily contains inner points and therefore approaches our visual picture of a portion of the plane, whereas a closed set, like an interval of the x axis considered as a plane set, may contain no inner point.

A region may consist of disconnected portions of the plane; for example, the region formed by several or even infinitely many circles outside one another. To obtain a 'connected' part of the plane we have to give a mathematical definition of *connectivity*.

Two inner points a and b of a set S are said to be *connected*, if there is a finite sequence of open circles (or squares) lying entirely in S, such that consecutive circles overlap one another (a chain of open circles of S), and such that a is in the first circle and b is in the last.

If all the inner points of S are connected with one another we say that S is *connex*. A connex open set is said to be a *domain*. For example, the points between two concentric circles (the points on the two circles excluded) form a domain. In our terminology a domain is always open, i.e. has only inner points.

12. *Oscillation, continuity.* The notion of a limit and allied notions are the main instruments in studying functions. We want, first of all, a measure for the change of a function in an interval. If the function $f(x)$ has a maximum value M and a minimum value m in the interval (a, b), we say that $M-m = O$ is the oscillation of $f(x)$ in (a, b). However, the values of a function may not contain a maximum or a minimum among them. Consider, for example, the function $f(x) = x/2$ from 0 to a (a excluded), and $f(a) = A$, where $0 < A < a/2$. This function has no maximum value in $(0, a)$, for $a/2$ is not a value of the function. Consequently, we have to define its oscillation in $(0, a)$ as the upper bound of the differences $|f(x_1)-f(x_2)|$, which is, in this particular case, $a/2$.

We define, therefore, *the oscillation of a function* $f(x)$ as *the upper bound of* $|f(x_1)-f(x_2)|$ *in the interval in question.* This upper bound may be finite or infinite, but it is always positive, and in the case of a constant function, i.e. one which assumes the same value throughout the interval, and only in that case, the oscillation is 0. The oscillation in a part of an interval cannot be greater than the oscillation in the whole interval.

Consider the function $\sin(1/x)$. Its value for $1/x = \pi/2 + 2k\pi$, i.e. $x = 1/(\pi/2 + 2k\pi)$, is 1 and for $1/x = 3\pi/2 + 2k\pi$, i.e. $x = 1/(3\pi/2 + 2k\pi)$, is -1, for all integral values of k. Taking $k = 1, 2, \ldots, n, \ldots$ the values

$$x_1 = 1/(\pi/2 + 2\pi),\ x_2 = 1/(\pi/2 + 4\pi), \ldots, \quad x_n = 1/(\pi/2 + 2n\pi), \ldots$$

tend to 0. But the values $x'_k = 1/(3\pi/2 + 2k\pi)$ also tend to 0. Consequently there are values of x as near to 0 as we like for which $\sin(1/x) = 1$, and other values of x as near to 0 as we like for which $\sin(1/x) = -1$. Hence, in any interval containing the origin the upper bound of $|f(x_2)-f(x_1)|$ is at least 2. Since it cannot surpass 2, we see that *in any interval including the origin the oscillation of sin* $(1/x)$ *is* 2. We notice that at the points $x_k' = 1/(\alpha + 2k\pi)$ the function $\sin(1/x)$ assumes the value $\sin \alpha$, so that in any interval including the origin $\sin(1/x)$ assumes the whole range of values between -1 and $+1$.

In any interval including c the oscillation of the function given in fig. 1 is greater than k. Taking smaller and smaller intervals containing c the oscillation decreases but never sinks below k. The limit of the oscillations when the intervals tend to the point c is exactly k, and this limit characterizes the *discontinuity* (jump, saltus) of the function at c.

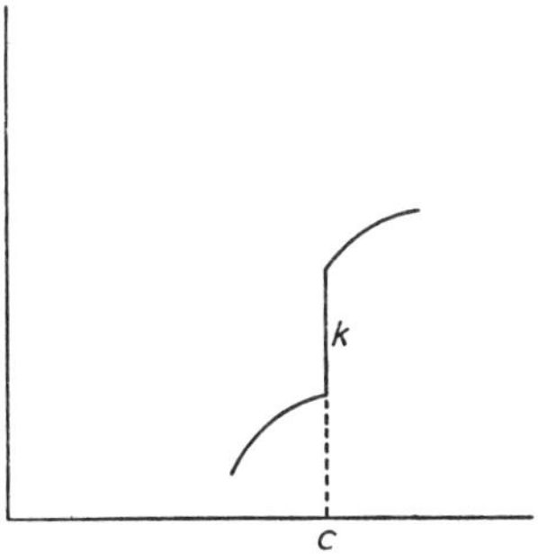

FIG. 1.

Consider the function $\phi(x)$ equal to 1 if x is rational and to 0 if x is irrational. Since in any interval there are rational as well as irrational points, the maximum of $|\phi(x_2) - \phi(x_1)|$ in every interval is 1 and its minimum is 0. *The function is discontinuous at every point.* Denote by $\theta_c(\delta_n, f)$ the oscillation of the function $f(x)$ in the interval $(c - \delta_n, c + \delta_n)$. We shall say that *a function is continuous at a point* c *if* the sequence $\theta(\delta_n, f)$ tends to 0 with δ_n. For example, x^k, where k is a positive integer, is continuous at every point a; in fact putting $x_2 = x_1 + \xi$,

$$(x_1 + \xi)^k - x_1^k = kx_1^{k-1}\xi + \frac{k(k-1)}{1 \cdot 2} x_1^{k-2}\xi^2 + \ldots + \xi^k.$$

But in the interval $(a - \delta_n, a + \delta_n)$ we have $|\xi| < 2\delta_n$ and thus

$$\theta_a(\delta_n) \leqslant k|x_1|^{k-1} 2\delta_n + \frac{k(k-1)}{1 \cdot 2} |x_1|^{k-2} 4\delta_n^2 + \ldots + 2^k\delta_n^k.$$

Since the expressions

$$k|x_1|^{k-1} 2\delta_n, \ \frac{k(k-1)}{1 \cdot 2} |x_1|^{k-2} 4\delta_n^2, \ \ldots, \ 2^k\delta_n^k$$

are 0-sequences if δ_n is one, their sum is a 0-sequence, i. e.

$$\lim_{n=\infty} \theta_a(\delta_n) = 0,$$

which proves the statement.

It follows that a polynomial $a_0+a_1x+\ldots+a_nx^n$ is continuous for every finite value of x. If a function is continuous at every point of the interval (a, b) we say that it is continuous in (a, b).

Geometrical intuition seems to show that if $f(x)$ is continuous at c, it must also be continuous near c, or at least on one side of c. We are going to show by an example that this is not so.

Consider the function $g(x)$ vanishing for every irrational x and equal to $1/q$ for $x=p/q$ (p and q being supposed to have no common factor).

Take the point p/q. The value of the function at that point is $1/q$. But as near to any fraction as we please there are irrational numbers for which the function vanishes. Hence, for some x_1, x_2 in any interval containing the point p/q, we have

$$|g(x_2)-g(x_1)|\geqslant 1/q.$$

Taking smaller and smaller intervals containing p/q the oscillation remains $\geqslant 1/q$. *The function considered is discontinuous at every rational point.*

Consider now an irrational point x. At the irrational values near x the function vanishes, but as near to x as we please there are fractional values of x for which the function is different from 0, i.e. $\theta_x(\delta_n)>0$. We are going to prove, however, that $\lim\limits_{n=\infty}\theta_x(\delta_n)=0$. Since the function is the same between any two integers, we suppose that x is between 0 and 1.

Marking the points $1/2$; $1/3$, $2/3$; $1/4$, $3/4$; $1/5$, $2/5$, $3/5$, $4/5$; we divide $(0, 1)$ into subintervals. At every fractional value of x *inside* these subintervals, $g(x)<1/5$. In the same way, marking all the points p/q with $q\leqslant n$, we see that inside these subintervals $g(x)<1/n$. But the irrational point x is an inner point of a subinterval for every n. Hence there is a δ_n-neighbourhood of x such that $g(x)<1/n$ in $(x-\delta_n, x+\delta_n)$; and, in $(x-\delta_n, x+\delta_n)$, $|g(x_2)-g(x_1)|<1/n$, which proves that the upper bound of $|g(x_2)-g(x_1)|$ tends to 0 with δ_n, i.e. $g(x)$ is continuous at x.

13. *Functional limit.* A function may have different properties on the left and on the right of a point. For instance, the function $f(x)$ equal to $x/2$ in $(0, 1)$, the point 1 excluded, and equal

to $x/2+1$ in $(1, +\infty)$ (1 included), is continuous on the right of 1, i.e. at the point 1 of any interval $(1, b)$, where $b>1$, *if we disregard the function outside that interval.* On the other hand, the function is discontinuous *on the left* of 1, i.e. is discontinuous at the point 1 of any interval $(a, 1)$, where $0<a<1$, even if we disregard the function outside that interval. For at 1 the value of the function is $3/2$ so that the oscillation in $(a, 1)$ is $3/2-a/2$, i.e. in $(1-\epsilon, 1)$ is $3/2-(1/2-\epsilon/2) = 1+\epsilon/2$, the lower limit of which is 1, not 0.

If the value of $f(x)$ at 1 is different both from $1/2$ and from $3/2$, $f(x)$ is discontinuous both on the left and on the right of 1. The characteristic property of this discontinuity is that, if we attribute to $f(x)$ the value of $1/2$ or $3/2$ at 1, it becomes continuous on the left or on the right. The discontinuity of $\sin 1/x$ at the origin is much more complicated because the function in approaching the origin on the left and on the right passes through every value between -1 and $+1$. To distinguish between these cases we say that when x approaches 1 on the left, $f(x)$ approaches $1/2$, and when x approaches 1 on the right, $f(x)$ approaches $3/2$, whereas $\sin(1/x)$ has no limit when x approaches the origin. More precisely, taking $x_n<a$ and $\lim_{n=\infty} x_n = a$, the limiting numbers of the sequence $f(x_n)$ are called *left-hand limiting values* of *$f(x)$ at a.* Taking all possible sequences $x_n<a$ tending to a, the united set of all limiting values forms the limiting set L_a^- of $f(x)$ on the left of a. Similarly we obtain L_a^+ on the right-hand side of a. We notice that the value *at a* does not figure in the definition of the sets L_a^- and L_a^+. In the case of $\sin(1/x)$, L_0^- and L_0^+ consist of all the real numbers between -1 and $+1$. If $L_a^-(f)$ consists of a single number l (in certain cases $+\infty$ or $-\infty$) we say that $f(x)$ tends to l when x tends to $a-0$ (that is to a on the left); in symbols:

$$\lim_{x\to a-0} f(x) = l = f(a-0).$$

Similarly for the right-hand side: if $L_a^+(f)$ consists of a single number l', we write

$$\lim_{x\to a+0} f(x) = l' = f(x+0).$$

If $l = l'$, we say that $f(x)$ tends to l when x tends to a:

$$\lim_{x \to a} f(x) = l.$$

In general, the upper and lower bounds, M_a^-, m_a^- of L_a^- are called the upper and lower limits of indetermination on the left. The four numbers, M_a^-, m_a^-, M_a^+, m_a^+, characterize the fluctuation of the function in the neighbourhood of a. If $f(x)$ is continuous at a, all these four numbers are equal to $f(a)$. Conversely, if all these four numbers are equal to $f(a)$, the function is continuous at the point. If the oscillation of $f(x)$ in the closed interval $(x-d, x)$ tends to 0 with d, we say that $f(x)$ is continuous on the left of x. If the oscillation of $f(x)$ in $(x, x+d)$ tends to 0 with d, we say that $f(x)$ is continuous on the right of x.

We remark that a limit, in general, implies a sequence, whereas a functional limit refers to a single function. Moreover, the limit of a sequence is determined by a countable set, whereas a functional limit implies all the values of the function in the interval, i. e., a continuum of values.

I. *If $f(x)$ is continuous on the left of a, $\lim_{x \to a-0} f(x) = f(a)$. If $f(x)$ is continuous on the right of a, $\lim_{x \to a+0} f(x) = f(a)$. If $f(x)$ is continuous at a, $\lim_{x \to a} f(x) = f(a)$.*

Proof. We prove only the first statement. By hypothesis, for arbitrarily small given ϵ, there is a d such that $|f(x) - f(a)| < \epsilon$ for $a-d<x<a$. Now if $x \to a$, we have $x_n = a - d_n$, and for sufficiently large n, $d_n < d$, i. e. $|f(x) - f(a)| < \epsilon$. Therefore all the limiting values of the sequence $f(x_n)$ are between $f(a) - \epsilon$ and $f(a) + \epsilon$; ϵ being arbitrary, the only limiting number is $f(a)$. Q. E. D.

Limit relations are also denoted by the following symbols:

$$f(x) \sim g(x) \quad \text{as} \quad x \to a$$

'$f(x)$ comparable with $g(x)$ as x tends to a' means that

$$\lim_{x \to a} \frac{f(x)}{g(x)} = 1.$$

This notation is used, in particular, when the two functions tend to 0 or to infinity, provided there is no ambiguity as to the variable tending to a.

Another less precise notation, due to Landau, is used when we do not need or possess exact information about the limit.

$$f(x) = O[g(x)] \quad \text{as} \quad x \to a$$

means that

$$\overline{\lim_{x \to a}} \left| \frac{f(x)}{g(x)} \right|$$

is finite ($< \infty$). If $f(x)$ and $g(x)$ tend to ∞ as x tends to a, this relation means that, colloquially speaking, the two infinities are equally strong. Similarly

$$f(x) = o[g(x)] \quad \text{as} \quad x \to a$$

means that

$$\lim_{x \to a} \frac{f(x)}{g(x)} = 0.$$

If $f(x)$ and $g(x)$ tend to infinity, this relation means that the infinity of $g(x)$ is stronger than that of $f(x)$. Landau's notations are used mainly in the case where $a = +\infty$ and $\lim_{x \to \infty} g(x) = +\infty$.

14. *Continuous functions.* We are going to give a short account of the principal properties of continuous functions.

I. *If $f(x)$ is continuous in the closed interval (a, b) and if we denote by M the upper bound of all its values assumed in (a, b), there is a point c in (a, b) such that $f(c) = M$, i.e. the upper bound is one of the values of the function. Similarly for the lower bound. M may be $+\infty$.*

Proof. Dividing (a, b) into n closed subintervals $i_1, i_2, \ldots, i_n$ of equal length, there is obviously a subinterval in which the upper bound of $f(x)$ is M. Subdividing, e.g. halving, that subinterval and reasoning as before we see that there are subintervals I_n, each encasing the next, and such that (a) the length of I_n tends to 0 when $n \to \infty$, (b) in every I_n the upper bound of $f(x)$ is M.

It follows from (a), by 10. I, that the intervals I_n have one, and only one, common point c, say. Moreover, by the definition of oscillation, every value of $f(x)$ in I_n is $\leqslant M \leqslant f(c) + O_c(I_n)$. But as $f(x)$ is continuous at c, $O_c(I_n) \to 0$ when $n \to \infty$, which proves that $M = f(c)$. Q. E. D.

If every individual value of $f(x)$ in (a, b) is finite, it follows, by I, that

II. *If a function $f(x)$ is continuous in the closed interval (a, b), and if every value of $f(x)$ in (a, b) is finite, $f(x)$ is bounded in (a, b).*

The example $1/x$ shows that the function may be continuous at every *inner* point of an interval, e.g. $1/x$ in $(0, 1)$ without being bounded in the interval, i.e. *theorems* I *and* II *do not, in general, hold for open intervals.*

The most obvious property of continuous functions from the geometrical point of view is described by the following theorem:

III. *If $f(x)$ is continuous in the closed interval (a, b) and C is any number between $f(a)$ and $f(b)$, there is a point c in (a, b) at which $f(c) = C$.*

Proof. We are going to prove first the particular case in which the sign of $f(a)$ differs from that of $f(b)$ and $C = 0$. Suppose, for instance, that $f(a)$ is negative and $f(b)$ is positive. If x_1 is the middle point between a and b, then either $f(x_1) = 0$ and the theorem is established, or $f(x_1) \neq 0$. In the latter case if $f(x_1) > 0$, the first interval, and if $f(x_1) < 0$, the second interval, is such that the sign of $f(x)$ is different at the two extremities. Halving the interval possessing the property in question, and repeating the reasoning, we obtain a sequence of intervals I_n, each encasing the next, so that (a) they have one and only one common point c, say, (b) the sign of $f(x)$ is different at the two extremities of I_n. Since, by hypothesis, $f(x)$ is continuous at c, we have $|f(x_2) - f(x_1)| < \epsilon$ for $c - d < x < c + d$. Taking n so large that the length of I_n is less than d, we have $|f(x_2) - f(x_1)| < \epsilon$ in I_n, and, since $f(x)$ assumes positive as well as negative values in I_n, $|f(x)| < \epsilon$. In particular, $|f(c)| < \epsilon$ and ϵ is arbitrary. Hence $f(c) = 0$. To prove the general statement we have only to apply this particular result to $f(x) - C$, which has different signs at a and b, and thus there is a c such that $f(c) - C = 0$. Q.E.D.

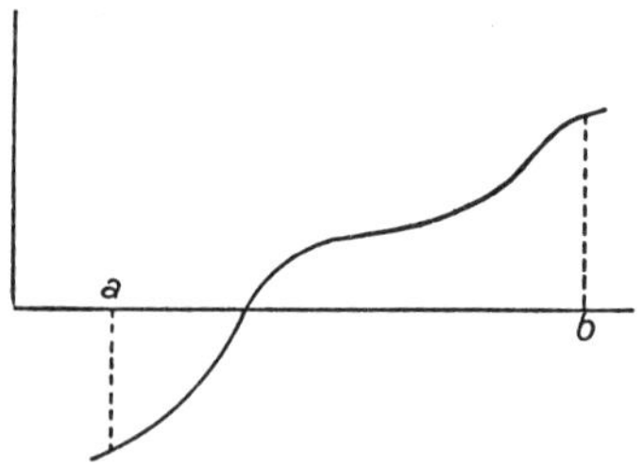

FIG. 2.

The last property of continuous functions might be considered as a (new) definition of continuity. But in this case, functions like $y = \sin(1/x)$ would be continuous at the origin. In fact, as we have seen, in every neighbourhood of $x = 0$, y assumes *every* value between -1 and $+1$. Therefore, in particular, given two different values $f(-a)$ and $f(b)$, $a > 0$, $b > 0$, y assumes in $(-a, b)$ every intermediate value between $f(-a)$ and $f(b)$.

Lebesgue (1928, p. 90) has given an example showing that the function may be discontinuous in the usual sense at every point of $(0, 1)$, say, and still assumes every intermediate value between two given values $f(a)$ and $f(b)$.

The notion of continuity readily extends to functions of several independent variables. We formulate the results for functions of two variables. Consider a function $f(x, y)$, defined in a set of points P which is everywhere dense. P, as a rule, is a domain or region. The upper bound of all the differences $|f(x, y) - f(x', y')|$ where (x, y) and (x', y') are any two points of a set S in P is said to be the oscillation of $f(x, y)$ in S. Consider now a point (a, b), and squares (or circles) $q_n < q_{n-1}$, centre at (a, b), with their sides tending to 0 as $n \to \infty$. The oscillation of $f(x, y)$ at the points of P in the successive squares forms a never increasing sequence of positive numbers. The limit of this sequence is said to be the oscillation of $f(x, y)$ at the point (a, b). The function $f(x, y)$ is said to be continuous at (a, b) if its oscillation at (a, b) is zero. If $f(x, y)$ is continuous at every point of the set S, we say that $f(x, y)$ is continuous in S.

IV. *If $f(x, y)$ is continuous in a perfect and bounded set P, there is a point in P at which $f(x, y)$ assumes the upper bound M of all its values in P, i.e. the upper bound is one of the values of the function. Similar result holds for the lower bound. The upper bound M may be $+\infty$.*

Proof. Since, by hypothesis, P is bounded, it is contained in a square q. Divide q into four equal closed squares by parallels to the sides (see Art. 10). In at least one of the four closed squares so obtained the upper bound of $f(x, y)$ is certainly M. Dividing one of the squares in which the upper bound of $f(x, y)$ is M, and continuing the process, we obtain a sequence of squares q_n, each encasing the next, and thus, by 10. I, they dwindle to a point (a, b). Since there are points of P as near to (a, b) as we like, and since P is closed, (a, b) is a point of P.

On the other hand, by the definition of oscillation, every value of $f(x, y)$ at the points of P in q_k is $\leqslant f(a, b) + O(f, q_k)$. Hence, also, the upper bound M of these values is $\leqslant f(a, b) + O(f, q_k)$. Since $f(x, y)$ is continuous at (a, b), $O(f, q_k) \to 0$, which proves that $M \leqslant f(a, b)$. But, by the definition of the upper bound, $f(a, b) \leqslant M$, which proves the theorem.

V. *If $f(x, y)$ is continuous in a perfect bounded set P and if every value of $f(x, y)$ in P is finite, then $f(x, y)$ is bounded in P.*

Proof. By IV, the upper bound is a value of $f(x, y)$. Hence, by hypothesis, it is a finite number.

VI. *If $f(x, y)$ is continuous in a perfect set P containing (a, b), and if $f(a, b) > 0$, there is a sufficiently small square q centre (a, b) such that $f(x, y) > 0$ at every point of P in q.*

Proof. If there were no such square, the continuous function $f(x, y)$ would vanish at a point of every square centre (a, b), i.e. at points tending to (a, b). Since $f(x, y)$ is continuous at (a, b), it would follow that $f(a, b) = 0$.

As an application of VI, we are going to prove

VII. *The points of a square or those of a circle form a domain.*

Proof. We give the proof for the circle. We have to show that all the points (x, y) satisfying the inequality

$$(1) \qquad (x-a)^2 + (y-b)^2 < r^2$$

are inner points, and that any two such inner points are connected with one another. If (x', y') satisfies (1), then, by VI, the same inequality is satisfied in a square, centre (x', y'), since the left-hand side is a continuous function of x and y. On the other hand, if two points, (x', y') and (x'', y'') satisfy (1), there is a number $r' < r$, such that r'^2 is greater than either value of the left-hand side for (x', y') and (x'', y''), and so the circle of radius r' covers both points.

We remark finally that, denoting a point by its co-ordinates $[x, y, \ldots]$, the distance $d(S, [x, y, \ldots])$ is a continuous function of $x, y, \ldots$, since

$$d(S, [x+h, y+k, \ldots]) \leqslant d(S, [x, y, \ldots]) + d([x+h, y+k, \ldots], [x, y, \ldots])$$

and

$$d(S, [x, y, \ldots]) \leqslant d(S, [x+h, y+k, \ldots]) + d([x+h, y+k, \ldots], [x, y, \ldots])$$

15. *Functions of bounded variation.* Consider the function $y = x \sin \frac{1}{x}$. For $x = 0$ this formula is meaningless, but if $x_n \to 0$, $\left| x_n \sin \frac{1}{x_n} \right| < |x_n|$, and so $y(x_n) \to 0$. Thus, if we complete the definition of y by putting $y(0) = 0$, the function so defined is continuous for every real value of x, including $x = 0$. On the other hand, the factor $\sin \frac{1}{x}$ vanishes at $x = \frac{1}{k\pi}$ $(k = \pm 1, \pm 2, \ldots)$, i.e. $y(x)$ vanishes infinitely many times in every interval $(-\delta, +\delta)$ and also in $(0, \delta)$. The graph of this function shows that the tangent to the curve has no final position when x approaches 0. This kind of singularity seems less simple than a mere saltus, or jump of the function from one value to another (e. g. we usually imagine the density of matter as being 0 in the immediate vicinity of a body and jumping to a finite value when we reach the body). In order to define a class of functions none of which possesses a singularity like that possessed by $x \sin \frac{1}{x}$ at the origin, we must characterize in a mathematical way the type of singularity to be excluded.

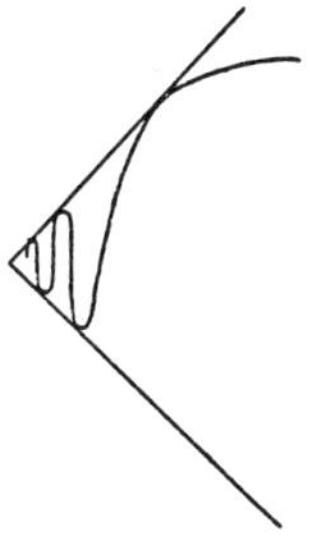

FIG. 3.

Divide the interval (a, b) into subintervals by the points $x_0 = a, x_1, \ldots, x_{n-1}, x_n = b$ and consider the sum

$$v(x_1, x_2, \ldots, x_n) = \sum_{i=0}^{n-1} |f(x_{i+1}) - f(x_i)|.$$

If for all possible subdivisions of (a, b), the corresponding positive numbers v have a finite upper bound $V(a, b)$, we say that the function $f(x)$ is of *bounded variation* in (a, b) and $V(a, b)$ is called its *total variation* in (a, b). If this upper bound is $+\infty$, the function is said to be of unbounded variation. At the points $x = \frac{1}{\pi k + \frac{1}{2}\pi}$, $(k = 1, 2, \ldots)$, $\left| \sin \frac{1}{x} \right| = 1$, i.e. $\left| x \sin \frac{1}{x} \right| > \frac{1}{\pi(k+1)}$, and at the points $x = \frac{1}{k\pi}$, $\sin \frac{1}{x} = 0$. Thus the variation of $x \sin \frac{1}{x}$ for the subdivision

$$\left[0, \frac{1}{n\pi}, \frac{1}{(n-1)\pi+\frac{1}{2}\pi}, \ldots, \frac{1}{2\pi}, \frac{1}{\pi+\frac{1}{2}\pi}, \frac{1}{\pi}\right]$$

of the interval $\left(0, \frac{1}{\pi}\right)$ is greater than $\frac{2}{\pi}\sum_{k=2}^{n-1}\frac{1}{k}$. But, for sufficiently large values of n, that sum surpasses any given number M. In fact, $\frac{1}{3}+\frac{1}{4}>\frac{1}{4}+\frac{1}{4}=\frac{2}{4}$; $\frac{1}{5}+\frac{1}{6}+\frac{1}{7}+\frac{1}{8}>\frac{4}{8}=\frac{1}{2}$, and so on, and, by adding a sufficiently large number of halves, we get as large a number as we please. *The function* $x \sin\frac{1}{x}$, *though continuous at* $x=0$, *is of unbounded variation in the neighbourhood of that point.*

If $f(x)$ *is increasing in* (a, b), *i.e. if* $f(x)>f(y)$, *for* $x>y$, *the function* $f(x)$ *is of bounded variation in* (a, b), because for every subdivision of (a, b), $v(x_1, x_2, \ldots x_n)=f(b)-f(a)$.

Similarly, if $f(x)$ is decreasing in (a, b),

$$v(x_1, x_2 \ldots, x_n)=f(a)-f(b).$$

We use the word *monotone* for either 'constantly increasing' or 'constantly decreasing'.

I. *The only kind of discontinuity a monotone function may have is a simple saltus.*

Proof. Suppose that $f(x)$ is constantly increasing in (a, b), and consider the sequence $x_n \to x$, where $x_{n+1}>x_n$, and the sequence of the corresponding values $f(x_n)$. As $f(x_{n+1}) \geqslant f(x_n)$ and $f(x_n) \leqslant f(x)$, the sequence $f(x_n)$ is constantly increasing and bounded. Consequently it has a limit A, say. Taking another sequence $y_m \to x$, the sequence $f(y_m)$ tends to a limit B, say. We state that $A=B$. In fact, as y_m tends to x and x_n tends to x, there is a $y_m>x_n$, and similarly there is an n' such that $x_{n'}>y_m$. It follows that $f(y_m)>f(x_n)$, i. e. $B \geqslant A$ and also $f(x_{n'}) \geqslant f(y_m)$, i. e. $A \geqslant B$. Which proves that, for every sequence x_n tending to x on the left of x, the sequence $f(x_n)$ has one and the same limit usually denoted by $f(x-0)$. Since the same reasoning applies to the right-hand side of x, we see that the limit $f(x+0)$ also exists. If these two numbers are different, the function has a simple saltus at x. If they are equal the function is continuous at x. The same proof applies to constantly decreasing functions. Thus the statement is proved.

16. We proceed now to establish the main properties of functions of bounded variation. Obviously, if a function is of bounded variation in (a, b), it is of bounded variation in any subinterval of (a, b).

Denote by p the sum of the positive differences in

$$\sum[f(x_{i+1})-f(x_i)],$$

and by $-n$ the sum of the negative differences. Then

$$v(x_1,\ldots, x_n) = p+n.$$

On the other hand, $p-n = \sum [f(x_{i+1})-f(x_i)] = f(b)-f(a)$.

Hence, $v = 2p+f(a)-f(b)$, or $v = 2n+f(b)-f(a)$. It follows that the upper bounds P, N of p and n are finite, provided that of v is finite, and

$$V(a, b) = 2P(a, b)+f(a)-f(b),\ V(a, b) = 2N(a, b)+f(b)-f(a).$$

P and N are called *positive and negative total variations* respectively. Applying this result to the subinterval (a, x), we have

$$V(a, x) = 2P(a, x)+f(a)-f(x),\ V(a, x) = 2N(a, x)+f(x)-f(a).$$

Hence

$$f(x) = f(a)+P(a, x)-N(a, x).$$

But $f(a)+P(a, x)$ and $N(a, x)$ are constantly increasing functions of x. Thus

I. *Every function of bounded variation is the difference between two constantly increasing functions.*

It follows from the properties of monotone functions, 15. I, that

II. *The only kind of discontinuity that a function of bounded variation may possess is a simple saltus*, i.e. *the two limiting values $f(x-0)$ and $f(x+0)$ exist at every point.*

The geometrical representation might suggest that in that case the number of points of discontinuity in (a, b) must be finite. This is not so. Consider the function $g(x)$ equal to 0 in

$(0, \frac{1}{2})$, to $\frac{1}{2}$ in $(\frac{1}{2}, \frac{2}{3})$, to $\dfrac{n-1}{n}$ in $\left(\dfrac{n-1}{n}, \dfrac{n}{n+1}\right)$; and let $g(1) = 1$.

When x varies from 0 to 1, $g(x)$ is constantly increasing (more precisely constantly non-decreasing) and jumps from one value to another at infinitely many points. Define $g(x)$ in $(1, 2)$ by the following conditions: $g(x) = 3$ in $(1{\cdot}5, 2)$; $g(x) = 2\frac{1}{2}$ in $(1\frac{1}{3}, 1\frac{1}{2})$; and in general, $g(x) = 2+\frac{1}{n}$ in $\left(1+\frac{1}{n+1}, 1+\frac{1}{n}\right)$. $g(x)$ is constantly increasing in $(1, 2)$. In the neighbourhood of $x = 1$, the function has infinitely many jumps on both sides and the two limits $g(1+0) = 2$ and $g(1-0) = 1$ are different. At 1 the function $g(x)$ jumps from 1 to 2.

On the other hand,

III. *The set of points x, at which a function of bounded variation is discontinuous, is enumerable.*

Proof. Write $f(x) = f_1(x) - f_2(x)$ where f_1 and f_2 are constantly increasing functions in (a, b); $f(x)$ can be discontinuous at x only if either f_1 or f_2, or both, are discontinuous at x. We have thus to prove that the number of jumps of a constantly increasing function is enumerable.

Consider the jumps j of a constantly increasing function $f(x)$ at the points of discontinuity x. Obviously, $j \leqslant f(b)-f(a)$, and the number of jumps equal to $f(b)-f(a)$ is either 0 or 1. More generally, the number of jumps $j_i > \dfrac{f(b)-f(a)}{n}$ is less than n. Denote by x_1 the point (if any) at which

$$\tfrac{1}{2}(f(b)-f(a)) < j_i \leqslant f(b)-f(a);$$

by x_2, x_3 the points, if any, at which

$$\tfrac{1}{4}(f(b)-f(a)) < j_i \leqslant \tfrac{1}{2}(f(b)-f(a)), \text{ \&c.}$$

In this way every point of discontinuity has a place in the sequence of points $x_1, x_2, x_3, \ldots$, which shows that the set of the points of discontinuity is enumerable. This proves the theorem.

Now add all the saltuses $j_i < \dfrac{f(x)-f(a)}{n}$ in (a, x) (in number less than n) and denote this sum by $J_n(x)$. Since for every n, $J_n(x) < f(x)-f(a)$ and for a fixed x, $J_n(x)$ constantly increases with n, the sequence J_n, $(n = 1, 2, \ldots)$, tends to a limit which we denote by $J(x)$ (*jump function*).

The difference $f(x)-J(x) = g(x)$ is continuous at every point of (a, b) because the jump of $J(x)$ when x passes through a point of discontinuity of $f(x)$ equals and thus destroys the jump of $f(x)$. We notice that in an interval in which $f(x)$ is continuous, $J(x)$ is constant. It is a stair-like function.

EXERCISES I

1. a, b, c, d are rational numbers, x is irrational. Find the condition that $(ax+b)/(cx+d)$ be rational.

2. a, b, c, d are rational numbers, c and d positive and not perfect squares. Show that $a\sqrt{c}+b\sqrt{d}$ is either 0 or irrational.

3. Find the bounds and extreme limiting numbers of

$(-1)^{n+1}(1+1/n)$. $\quad (\underline{B}=-1{\cdot}5,\ \overline{B}=2,\ L=-1,\ U=1)$.

4. Find the bounds and extreme limiting numbers of

$(-1)^n n/(2n+1)$, $(-1)^n(n+1)/(2n+1)$,
$n+(-1)^n/(2n+1)$, $2n+1+(-1)^n n$.

5. Show that the sequence $\sin(n\pi/6)$ consists of the repetition of the seven numbers $0, \pm 1/2, \pm\sqrt{3}/2, \pm 1$;

$(1+1/n)\sin(n\pi/6)$ has the same seven limiting numbers but only 0 is attained;

$(1+1/2n)\cos(n\pi/3)$ has four limiting numbers $\pm 1/2$, ± 1 and none of them is attained.

6. The sequence $a_{n+1}=+\sqrt{k+a_n}$, $k>0$, $a>0$, is monotone and converges to the positive root of $x^2=x+k$.

7. $a_{n+1}=k/(1+a_n)$, $k>0, a_1>0$, converges to the positive root of $x^2+x=k$ and $b_{n+1}=k/b_n-1$ converges to its negative root.

8. *Bernoulli's inequality*:

$$(1+x)^n>1+nx \text{ if } n\geqslant 2 \text{ and } 1+x>0.$$

Proof. For $n=2$, $(1+x)^2=1+2x+x^2>1+2x$. Suppose it is true for $n=k$. Then

$$(1+x)^{k+1}>(1+kx)(1+x)=1+(k+1)x+kx^2>1+(k+1)x.$$

When $x>0$, $(1+x)^n$ is greater, of course, than any term or group of terms in its binomial expansion.

9. If $a>0$, then $\sqrt[n]{a}\to 1$. If $a>1$, put $\sqrt[n]{a}=1+x_n$. Then by Bernoulli's inequality, $a=(1+x_n)^n>1+nx_n>nx_n$, i. e. $x_n<a/n$. If $0<a<1$, i. e. $1/a>1$ we have $\sqrt[n]{1/a}\to 1$. Apply 8. VI.

10. Prove that if $x_n \to 0$, then $a^{x_n} \to 1$, $(\,|\,x_k\,| < 1/n$ for sufficiently large k).

11. If $a > 0$ and $x_n \to x$, $a^{x_n} \to a^x$. From $a^{x_n} - a^x = a^x(a^{x_n - x} - 1)$ by Ex. 10.

12. If $x_n \to 0$ and α is any positive real number, $(x_n)^\alpha \to 0$. For sufficiently large n, $x_n < \epsilon^{1/\alpha}$.

13. If $x_n \to 0$, $+\sqrt[k]{1+x_n} \to 1$. From

$$a^k - b^k = (a-b)(a^{k-1} + a^{k-2}b + \dots + ab^{k-2} + b^{k-1})$$

where we put $a = +\sqrt[k]{1+x_n}$, $b = 1$, $x_n' = \sqrt[k]{1+x_n} - 1$, we obtain $x_n' = x_n / [(\sqrt[k]{1+x_n})^{k-1} + (\sqrt[k]{1+x_n})^{k-2} + \dots + 1]$, i.e. $|\,x_n'\,| < |\,x_n\,|$.

14. If $x_n \to 0$, $y_n = \log(1+x_n) \to 0$. If $b > 1$ is the base of the logarithm and $\epsilon > 0$ is given, we put $b^\epsilon - 1 = \epsilon_1$, $1 - b^{-\epsilon} = \epsilon_2$ and denote by ϵ' the smaller of the two (necessarily > 0). Choose N so large that for $n > N$, $|\,x_n\,| < \epsilon'$. Then $-\epsilon_2 < x_n < \epsilon_1$, i. e.

$$b^{-\epsilon} < 1 + x_n < b^\epsilon \text{ for } n > N. \text{ Hence } |\,y_n\,| < \epsilon.$$

15. If $x_n \to 1$ and ρ is any real number, $x_n^\rho \to 1$. By Ex. 14, $\rho_n = \rho \log x_n \to 0$. Hence, by Ex. 10, $x_n^\rho = b^{\rho_n} \to 1$.

16. If $x_n \to x$ and ρ is any real number, $x_n^\rho \to x^\rho$. In fact $x_n^\rho - x^\rho = x^\rho[(x_n/x)^\rho - 1]$ and as $x_n / x \to 1$, Ex. 15 proves 16.

Ex. 11 and 16 are very important limit relations. We write them in the form

$$\text{(A)} \qquad \lim a^{x_n} = a^{\lim x_n}, \ (a > 0).$$

$$\text{(B)} \qquad \lim x_n{}^\rho = [\lim x_n]^\rho.$$

17. If $x_n > 0$ and $x_n \to x > 0$, $\log x_n \to \log x$. Apply Ex. 14 to $\log x_n - \log x = \log(x_n / x)$.

18. $x_n \to +\infty$. The sequence has a minimum term.

19. A convergent sequence has either a minimum term or a maximum term or both.

20. If $x_n > 0$, $x_n \to x > 0$, then x_n has a positive (> 0) lower bound B. There is only a finite number of $x_n < x/2$ (if any). The least of them or $x/2$ is a lower bound for the sequence.

21. If $x_{n+1} > x_n - \epsilon_n$ were $\epsilon_n \to 0$, then all the numbers between the two extreme limiting numbers of x_n are limiting numbers of x_n.

Proof. For every $\epsilon = (U-L)/m$ there is a term x_{n_1} in $(L, L+\epsilon)$ and another x_{n_2}, $n_2 > n_1$, in $(U-\epsilon, U)$ so that after an n such that $\epsilon_n < \epsilon$ the sequence $x_{n_1}, x_{n_1+1}, \dots x_{n_2}$ cannot reach U from L by $< m-1$ jumps of length $< \epsilon$.

22. $a_n \to 0$, $a_n > 0$, $s_n = a_1 + a_2 + \dots + a_n \to \infty$; $[s_n]$ denotes the integral part of s_n. Every number of (0, 1) is a limiting number of the sequence $s_n - [s_n]$.

23. If $x_n \to x$, also $x'_n = (x_0 + x_1 + \dots + x_n)/(n+1) \to x$.

(a) $x = 0$. There is an m such that for $n > m$, $|x_n| < \epsilon$ i.e.

$$|x'_n| \leqslant |x_0 + \dots + x_m|/(n+1) + \epsilon(n-m)/(n+1).$$

As the first term tends to 0 and the second to ϵ when $n \to \infty$, all the limiting numbers of x' are in $(-\epsilon, \epsilon)$. The number being arbitrary the diameter of the derived set is exactly 0, i.e. it contains at most one number 0, and by Bolzano's theorem it does contain one.

(b) $x \neq 0$. $[(x_0 - x) + (x_1 - x) + \dots + (x_n - x)]/(n+1) = x'_n - x \to 0$.

24. $x_n > 0$ and $x_n \to x > 0$. Then $x'_n = \sqrt[n]{x_1 x_2 \dots x_n} \to x$. Put $y_n = \log x_n \to \log x = y$ and apply Ex. 15.

25. $x^n \to 0$ when $-1 < x < 1$. For positive x we put

$$x = \frac{1}{1 + \dfrac{1-x}{x}}$$

and thus, by Ex. 8, $x^n = 1/(1+y)^n < 1/(1+ny) < 1/ny \to 0$. For negative x we have $x^n = (-1)^n |x|^n$.

26. $a_n = r^n/n! \to 0$ for any real r. For $n > |r|$, we have

$$\frac{a_{2n}}{a_n} = \frac{r}{n+1} \, \frac{r}{n+2} \cdots \frac{r}{2n}$$

and thus $|a_{2n}| < |r| |a_n|/2n < a_n/2$.

If $m > r$, we have thus

$$|a_{2m}| < |a_m|/2, \ |a_{4m}| < |a_{2m}|/2 < |a_m|/2^2, \ \dots, \ |a_{2^k m}| < |a_m|/2^k \to 0.$$

If we add that $|a_n|$ steadily decreases after m, the result is proved.

27. $\sqrt[n]{n} \to 1$. Putting $n = (1 + x_n)^n$ we see that $n > n(n-1)x_n^2/2$, i.e. $x_n^2 < 2/(n-1) \to 0$.

This is our first example where both base and index vary and their tendency is opposite, viz., the base tends to increase the quantity to infinity and the n-th root (index $1/n$) tends to reduce the radical to 1. We notice that the index is in this case more powerful than the base. In the preceding example the numerator tends to increase the quantity to infinity and the denominator tends successfully, to reduce it to 0.

28. $na^n \to 0$ for $|a|<1$. Put

$$|a| = 1/(1+r)\,;\ |a^n| = 1/(1+r)^n < 1/\tbinom{n}{2} r^2$$

and $(na^n) < 1.2/(n-1)r^2$. Similarly $n^\alpha a^n \to 0$, α real. Proof is needed only for $\alpha>0$. Putting $|a|^{1/\alpha} = a_1 < 1$ we know that $na_1{}^n \to 0$, i.e. also $(na_1{}^n)^\alpha \to 0$.

29. $\operatorname{Log} n / n^\sigma \to 0$ for $\sigma>0$ whatever the base $b>1$ of the logarithm is. $b^\sigma>1$, i.e. $n/(b^\sigma)^n \to 0$ and thus for $n>m$, say, $n/(b^\sigma)^n < \epsilon / b^\sigma$ and $\log n / n^\sigma < (g+1)/(b^g)^\sigma = b^\sigma(g+1)/(b^\sigma)^{g+1}$ where g is the integral part of $\log n$. Hence for $n>b^m$, also $g+1>m$ and thus $\log n / n^\sigma < b^\sigma . \epsilon / b^\sigma$, i.e. $\log n / n^\sigma < \epsilon$ for $n > b^m$.

30. For positive real α and β, $\log^\alpha n / n^\beta \to 0$. Proof.

$$\log n / n^{\beta/\alpha} \to 0.$$

31. *The number e.* When n increases, every term of

$$x_n = (1+1/n)^n = 1 + n\frac{1}{n} + \frac{n(n-1)}{1\,.\,2}\frac{1}{n^2} + \dots + \frac{n(n-1)\dots(n-p+1)}{p\,!}\frac{1}{n^p} + \dots + \frac{1}{n^n}$$

$$= 1 + 1 + \frac{1}{2}\Bigl(1-\frac{1}{n}\Bigr) + \dots + \frac{1}{p\,!}\Bigl(1-\frac{1}{n}\Bigr)\Bigl(1-\frac{2}{n}\Bigr)\dots\Bigl(1-\frac{p-1}{n}\Bigr) + \dots$$

increases and also the number of terms. Thus x_n is a steadily increasing sequence. On the other hand the $(p+1)^{\text{th}}$ term is $< 1/p\,! < 1/2^{p-1}$, i.e.

$$x_n < 1+1+1/2+1/2^2+\dots+1/2^n = 1 + \frac{1-(1/2)^{n+1}}{1-1/2}$$
$$= 1+2-(1/2)^n < 3.$$

Thus x_n tends to a limit lying between 2 and 3. Its limit is called e and its first decimals are $e = 2{\cdot}718281828459045\ \dots$

32. If $x_n \to 0$, $(1+x_n)^{1/x_n} \to e$.

(a) $x_n > 0$. If $1/x_n$ is between the integers n and $n+1$, we have $(1+1/(n+1))^n < (1+x_n)^{1/x_n} < (1+1/n)^{n+1}$ and both sides tend to e as $[1+1/(n+1)]^n = [1+1/(n+1)]^{-1}.[1+1/(n+1)]^{n+1}$,

$$(1+1/n)^{n+1} = (1+1/n)(1+1/n)^n.$$

(b) $x_n < 0$. From a certain suffix m on, $x_n > -1$, and then we put $1+x_n = 1/(1+y_n)$ such that $y_n > 0$ for $n>m$ and $y_n \to 0$. Thus $(1+x_n)^{1/x_n} = (1+y_n)^{(1+y_n)/y_n} = (1+y_n)(1+y_n)^{1/y_n}$ which reduces the case to (*a*).

33. If $\epsilon_n \to 0$, $(1+x\epsilon_n)^{1/\epsilon_n} \to e^x$; $x\epsilon_n = \eta_n \to 0$ and thus

$$(1+\eta_n)^{x/\eta_n} = [(1+\eta_n)^{1/\eta_n}]^x \to e^x.$$

In particular $(1+x/n)^n \to e^x$.

34. $\sqrt[n]{n!}/n \to 1/e$. By Ex. 24,

$$\sqrt[n]{\left(\frac{2}{1}\right)^1\left(\frac{3}{2}\right)^2\cdots\left(\frac{n+1}{n}\right)^n} = \sqrt[n]{\frac{(n+1)^n}{n!}} = \frac{n+1}{\sqrt[n]{n!}} \to e.$$

35. The only functions of a real variable x which are bounded in an interval $(0, d)$ and satisfy the equation

$$(1) \qquad f(x+y) = f(x) + f(y)$$

are ax where a is any real constant.

Proof. A property like (1) establishes a kind of solidarity between the properties of $f(x)$ at distant intervals. As $f(2x) = 2f(x)$ and in particular $f(0) = 0$ we have $f(-x) = -f(x)$. Now if $|f(x)| < A$ in the interval $(0, a)$, then $|f(x)| < 2A$ in the interval $(0, 2a)$, i. e., the function is bounded in every finite interval. Therefore we can suppose that $(0, d)$ contains $(0, 1)$. Denote by $[x]$ the whole portion of x. It follows from (1) that $f(x) = f(x-[x]) + [x]f(1)$. As $|f(x-[x])|$ is bounded and $\lim\limits_{|x|\to\infty} [x]/x \to 1$, we have

$$\lim_{x\to\infty}[f(x)/x] = f(1).$$

In particular $\lim\limits_{n=\infty} [f(nx)/nx] = f(1)$. But $f(x)/x = f(nx)/nx$ and thus, for every x, $f(x)/x = \lim\limits_{n=\infty} [f(nx)/nx] = f(1)$, which proves the statement.

Extend the theorem to functions of several real variables.

36. The only real functions of a real variable x bounded in $(0, d)$, not constantly 0, and satisfying the equation $f(x+y) = f(x)f(y)$ are the functions c^x where c is a positive constant.

Proof. As $f(x)$ is not constantly 0, we may suppose that $f(d) \neq 0$. As $f(2x) = [f(x)]^2$, $f(x) \geqslant 0$. From $f(d) = f(x)f(d-x)$ and $f(d-x) < A$, it follows that $f(x) > f(d)/A$, i.e., the lower bound of $f(x)$ in $(0, d)$ is positive and not 0. Consequently if we put $\log_b f(x) = g(x)$, (b any positive number), $g(x)$ is bounded in $(0, d)$ and on the other hand it satisfies (1). Hence, by the result of Ex. 35, $\log f(x) = ax$, i. e. $f(x) = b^{ax} = c^x$.

37. Let the numbers of the interval (0, 1) be expressed as finite or infinite decimals $x = \cdot a_1 a_2 \ldots a_n \ldots$ and put

$$f(x) = (a_1/10)^2 + (a_2/100)^2 + \ldots.$$

The function $f(x)$ is monotone. Prove that it is discontinuous for every value of x represented by a finite decimal. (Hobson.)

38. Examine the discontinuity of the function $f(x)$ which equals $\cdot 0a_1 0a_2 \ldots 0a_n \ldots$ when $x = \cdot a_1 a_2 a_3 \ldots$.

39. Prove that the sum, difference or product of two functions of bounded variation is also of bounded variation.

40. Let $M(a, b)$ be the upper bound of all the values of the real $f(x)$ in the interval (a, b). Taking smaller and smaller intervals $(x-h, x+h)$ the limit $M(x)$ of $M(x-h, x+h)$ when h tends to 0 is called the maximum of $f(x)$ at x (Baire). For a bounded function $f(x)$ the maximal function $M(x)$ is perfectly determinate at every point. Same for the minimal function $m(x)$. Show that if $g(x)$ is continuous, $g(x)+M(x)$ and $g(x)+m(x)$ are the maximal and minimal functions of $f(x)+g(x)$.

41. Let (x) denote the positive or negative excess of x over the nearest integer and when x exceeds an integer by $1/2$, let $(x)=0$. Determine the points of discontinuity of the function and examine the nature of the singularity.

42. Let $[x]$ denote the integral part of x. Examine this function.

CHAPTER II

COMPLEX ALGEBRA

17. *Complex Algebra.* We have seen that real algebra is not complete with respect to the third direct operation, power, i. e. the two inverse operations of power, root and logarithm, have a meaning only for a restricted class of real numbers. For instance, there is no real number whose square is negative, i. e., the equation $x^2+a^2=0$ has no solution in real algebra. Similarly negative numbers have no logarithm. Geometrical and physical applications would suggest the introduction of threefold numbers like vectors consisting of three real numbers. Mathematical problems; in particular the solution of algebraic equations like

$$(1) \qquad x^2+1 = 0,$$

suggest as a first step the introduction of a single new symbol i satisfying (1). This leads to the construction of twofold numbers called complex numbers, $a+bi$, where the two 'components' a and b are real numbers and i is a new symbol with the property

$$(2) \qquad ii = -1.$$

Equality $a+bi = c+di$ is defined as meaning two real equalities $a = c$ and $b = d$. Addition and subtraction are defined as the addition and subtraction of the corresponding components.

$$(3) \qquad a+bi \pm (c+di) = (a\pm c)+(b\pm d)i.$$

Multiplication is defined by the requirement that it should be distributive with respect to addition, and that i should satisfy (2):

$$(a+bi)\,(c+di) = ac+bic+adi+bidi = ac-bd+(bc+ad)i,$$

$$(4) \qquad (a+bi)\,(c+di) = ac-bd+(ad+bc)i.$$

It is readily proved that the twofold number system so constructed satisfies all the conditions of Table I (p. 4).

I. *The algebra of complex numbers is regular.*

In $a+bi$, $a = Rl.(a+bi)$ is said to be the *real part*,

$$b = Im.(a+bi)$$

the *imaginary part* of $a+bi$.

If we consider only complex numbers whose imaginary parts are 0, (3) and (4) show that

$$a+0i+c+0i = a+c+0i, (a+0i)(c+0i) = ac+0i,$$

i.e. addition and multiplication lead to numbers of the same type, the operations themselves reducing to ordinary addition and multiplication of a and c. Thus the numbers $a+0i$ form a distinct sub-algebra identical, as far as mathematical operations go, with real algebra (writing $+0i$ after every number is only a modification of the symbol). Thus real algebra is contained in the complex algebra and the latter is an extension of the former.

We call the positive number $|\sqrt{a^2+b^2}| = |a+bi|$ the absolute value or modulus of $a+bi$.

II. *The equation* $|a+bi| = 0$ *is equivalent to the two equations* $a = 0$ *and* $b = 0$, for $a^2+b^2 = 0$ implies $a = 0$ and $b = 0$.

$a-bi$ is said to be the conjugate of $a+bi$. We see that

(5) $$|a-bi| = |a+bi|.$$

(6) $$(a+bi)(a-bi) = a^2+b^2 = |a+bi|^2.$$

The binomial formula extends to complex binomials with positive integral index.

Taking a and b as the abscissa and ordinate of a point in a plane we see that to every complex number corresponds a point of the plane and vice-versa. The plane whose points (x, y) are denoted by the corresponding complex number $z = x+yi$ is referred to as the *complex plane* (Argand's diagram) and $x+iy$ is the complex name or affix of the corresponding point. If we represent $z = x+iy$ by an arrow (vector) from the origin to the point $x+iy$, addition of complex numbers reduces to the addition of the two vectors by the parallelogram rule (see figure 4).

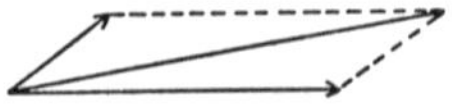

FIG. 4.

Similarly for subtraction: $z_1 - z_2$ is represented by the arrow from z_2 to z_1.

We notice that $i^3 = i^2 . i = -i$, $i^4 = i^2 . i^2 = 1$ so that in general

(7) $$i^{4n} = 1, \quad i^{4n+1} = i, \quad i^{4n+2} = -1, \quad i^{4n+3} = -i.$$

These formulae reduce any power z^n to the form $a + bi$. For instance

$$z^2 = (x+iy)(x+iy) = x^2 - y^2 + 2xyi,$$
$$z^3 = (x^2 - y^2 + 2xyi)(x+iy) = x^3 - 3xy^2 + (3x^2y - y^3)i, \text{ \&c.}$$

If $a = a_1 + a_2 i$, $b = b_1 + b_2 i$, where a_1, a_2, b_1, b_2 are real numbers, and b_1 and b_2 are not both 0, the division of a by b is, by definition, the solution of the equation

(8) $$bz = a.$$

As $|b| \neq 0$, i.e. $b \neq 0 + 0i$, if $\bar{b}$ denotes the conjugate of b (i.e. $\bar{b} = b_1 - b_2 i$), $z = a\bar{b}/|b|^2$ is a solution of (8), and there is only one solution, for if z and z' are two solutions of (8), we have $b(z - z') = 0$, and, by the product law, since $b \neq 0$, $z = z'$. Hence

(9) $$a/b = (a_1 + a_2 i)(b_1 - b_2 i)/(b_1{}^2 + b_2{}^2)$$
$$= (a_1 b_1 + a_2 b_2)/(b_1{}^2 + b_2{}^2) + i(a_2 b_1 - a_1 b_2)/(b_1{}^2 + b_2{}^2).$$

III. *In complex algebra division is always possible (except by* 0) *and leads to a determinate number.*

IV. *If z' denotes the conjugate number, we have*

$$(z_1 + z_2)' = z_1' + z_2', \quad (z_1 z_2)' = z_1' z_2', \quad (z_1/z_2)' = z_1'/z_2',$$

i.e. the *four elementary operations and the process of passing to the conjugate are interchangeable.*

We leave the proof, which is quite straightforward, to the reader.

We may represent complex numbers also on the surface of a sphere standing on the complex plane at the origin. The point of the sphere at the origin is called the south pole, its opposite point is the north pole. The straight line joining any point z of the plane to the north pole pierces the surface of the sphere at a single point z'. Thus every complex number corresponds to a determinate position on the sphere and vice-versa. Circles about the origin are circles (latitudes) on the sphere. Straight lines passing through the origin are great circles (longitudes) on the sphere passing through the poles. The part of the complex plane outside a very large circle centre at the origin, i. e. $|z| > R$ corresponds to the inside of a small circle about the north pole. Thus we might say that the north pole corresponds to $z = \infty$.

18. *Limit in the complex field.* The idea of limit for real numbers was based on the idea of isolation of a number from a given set. The definition of limit for complex numbers requires the definition of isolation on the complex plane. All the numbers $z = x + iy$ satisfying the inequalities $a_1 < x < b_1$, $a_2 < y < b_2$ are said to form an open rectangle whose opposite vertices are $a = a_1 + a_2 i$ and $b = b_1 + b_2 i$. We shall denote the set of the inner points of this rectangle by the symbol $[a, b]$, where it is explicitly supposed that $a_1 < b_1$ and $a_2 < b_2$.

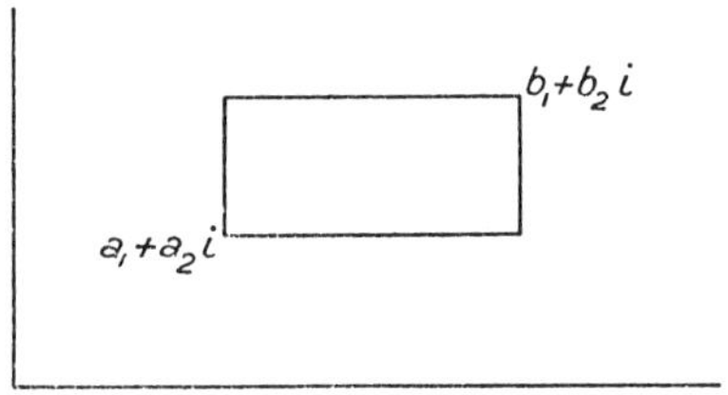

FIG. 5.

We say that the number $c = c_1 + ic_2$ (*by number, in the sequel, we shall always mean complex number*, which, of course, may perhaps be a real one) is isolated from the numbers of a given set S if there is a rectangle containing c and containing no number of S, except c itself if c belongs to S. *If a number is not isolated from S, we say that this number is a limiting number of S.* This means that, however small $h > 0$ and $k > 0$ may be, there are numbers of S other than c in the rectangle $[c - h - ki, c + h + ki]$ in other words, there are numbers $x_n + y_n i$ of S such that $x_n \to c_1$ and $y_n \to c_2$.

If the absolute values of the numbers of S are not bounded, i. e. if S has numbers outside any rectangle however large, we say that infinity (∞) is a limiting number of S. We do not distinguish between $+\infty$ and $-\infty$, since now there are infinitely many directions along which our numbers may tend to infinity. *If S has only one limiting number, we call it the limit of S.* For example, $\lim (1/n + i/n) = 0$; $\lim (n + ni) = \infty$, for there is no finite limiting number.

Bolzano's fundamental theorem on limiting numbers readily extends to sets of complex numbers.

I. *If all the numbers of an infinite set S are in an open or closed rectangle* $[a, b]$, *S has a limiting number in the closed rectangle* $[a, b]$.

Proof. By definition, if $z = x+iy$ is any number of S, we have $a_1<x<b_1$, $a_2<y<b_2$. Hence, applying Bolzano's original theorem to the real parts of the numbers of S, we see that there are real parts x_n such that x_n tends to a limit, x, say. The corresponding imaginary parts y_n may not tend to a definite limit but, applying Bolzano's theorem to them, we see that there are suffixes n' such that $y_{n'}$ tends to a definite limit, y, say. Hence $x_{n'}+y_{n'}i \to x+iy$, which shows that $x+iy$ is a limiting number of S, and, as all the numbers $x_{n'}+y_{n'}i$ lie in $[a, b]$, their limit lies either in $[a, b]$ or on one of its sides. Q.e.d.

Since for unbounded sets we consider ∞ as a (conventional) limiting number, we have

II. *Every infinite set of complex numbers has a limiting number.* On the other hand

III. *A finite set of complex numbers has no limiting number.* In fact, if $a_k = a_k'+ia_k''$, $(k = 1, 2, \ldots, m)$ are the different numbers of the finite set S, denote by h the smallest of the numbers $|a_k'-a_j'|$, $|a_k''-a_j''|$ that do not vanish, $(k, j = 1, 2, \ldots m$ but $k \neq j)$, then, a being any number, S has no number in the square

$$[a-h-ih,\ a+h+ih],$$

except a itself if a belongs to S.

IV. *If a set has a limit, $z = x+iy$, say, the set can be written in the form of a sequence.* In fact, by I, outside the square $Q_n = [z-1/n-i/n,\ z+1/n+i/n]$ the set S has only a finite number of numbers (otherwise S would have a limiting number outside this square). Thus, enumerating first the numbers of S outside Q_1, and adding to the list the numbers outside Q_2 but inside Q_1 (if any), and continuing in this way, we enumerate all the numbers of S, except perhaps $x+iy$ itself. If $x+iy$ belongs to S, we may take it as the first number of our sequence.

We call the upper bound of the differences $|z_i-z_k|$, where z_i and z_k are any numbers of a given set S, the diameter of S. If the diameter is 0, S contains only one number or none.

The properties of 0-sequences readily extend to sequences of complex numbers.

V. *If* $z_n \to 0$ *and* $|z'_n| < |z_n|$, *then also* $z'_n \to 0$. *The sum or product of a finite number of* 0-*sequences is a* 0-*sequence;* $c\epsilon_n \to 0$ *where* c *is any complex number and* ϵ_n *any* 0-*sequence.*

Consequently the fundamental rules for the evaluation of limits, 8. VI, extend also to complex numbers.

VI. *If* $z_n \to z$ *and* $z'_n \to z'$, *then* $z_n + z'_n \to z + z'$, $z_n z'_n \to zz'$, $z_n/z'_n \to z/z'$, *provided in the last instance* $z'_n \neq 0$ and $z' \neq 0$. The proof of the first two propositions is the exact repetition of that given for 8. VI. For the last limit equation, we have to remark that, taking the positive $\epsilon < |z'|/2$, z' is outside the square $[-\epsilon - i\epsilon, \epsilon + i\epsilon]$, i. e. there is only a finite number of z'_n in this square, and, as none of them is 0, there is a positive number a such that, for every n, $|z'_n| > a$ or $|1/z'_n| < 1/a$. Since $(z' + \epsilon_n)/z'_n = 1$, we have $1/z'_n = 1/z' - \epsilon_n/z'_n z'$, and so $1/z'_n = 1/z' + \eta_n$. Hence we finish as in 8. VI.

There are no general rules for determining the limit of a sequence. Theorem VI is used to reduce unknown cases to a finite combination of known ones. But its application is limited. It is therefore important in many cases to establish at least the existence of the limit, i. e. to prove that the sequence in question has a unique limiting number.

VII. *The necessary and sufficient condition that a sequence* z_n *shall tend to a definite limit is that to every positive* ϵ *there shall correspond a suffix* n *such that, for every positive* p,

$$|z_{n+p} - z_n| < \epsilon. \qquad \text{(Cauchy.)}$$

Proof. The condition is *necessary*. In fact, if $z_n \to z_0$, there is only a finite number of z_n outside the circle $|z - z_0| = \epsilon/2$, i. e. after a sufficiently large suffix N, for $m > N$, $n > N$ we have $|z_m - z_n| < \epsilon$. The condition is *sufficient*. In fact, by hypothesis, all the terms z_{n+p} are in the square $[z_n - \epsilon - i\epsilon, z_n + \epsilon + i\epsilon]$ Thus all the limiting numbers of the sequence z_n also lie in the same square (for there is only a finite number of numbers outside). The diameter of the derived set is $\leqslant 3\epsilon$. Since ϵ is arbitrary and the diameter of a set is a fixed non-negative quantity, the diameter of the derived set is exactly 0. But the set is not empty, consequently it contains just one number, i.e. z_n has a definite limit.

19. *Fundamental theorem of algebra.*

I. *Fundamental theorem of algebra: an algebraic equation,* $P(x) = a_0 + a_1 x + \ldots + a_n x^n = 0$, *has a root.*

(a) If the coefficients are real and n is odd, the equation has a real root. In fact,

$$\frac{a_0 + \ldots + a_n x^n}{x^n} = \frac{a_0}{x^n} + \ldots + a_n$$

tends to a_n when $|x|$ tends to infinity. But if we change x into $-x$ the sign of x^n changes. Since the sign of the ratio, for a sufficiently large x, is invariably that of a_n, the sign of

$$a_0 + \ldots + a_n(-x)^n,$$

for sufficiently large $|x|$ differs from that of $a_0 + \ldots + a_n x^n$. Hence, a polynomial being a continuous function, it vanishes for an intermediate value, which proves our first statement.

(b) The equation $x^n = a + ib$ has a root. For $n = 2$,

$$(\zeta + i\eta)^2 = a + ib$$

is satisfied by

$$\zeta = \sqrt{\frac{a + \sqrt{a^2 + b^2}}{2}}, \quad \eta = \epsilon\sqrt{\frac{-a + \sqrt{a^2 + b^2}}{2}},$$

where ϵ is $+1$ if b is positive, and -1 if b is negative. If n is even, the extraction of the n-th root is equivalent to a succession of square and odd roots. Thus we have still to establish the theorem for n odd. But the coefficients of the equation in ζ

$$(1) \qquad i(a - ib)(\zeta + i)^n - i(a + ib)(\zeta - i)^n = 0$$

are all real (since the left-hand side does not change when we replace i by $-i$). Hence, by (a), it has a real root τ.

In virtue of (1) the expression $\dfrac{a + ib}{(\tau + i)^n}$ is also real, for

$$\frac{a + ib}{(\tau + i)^n} = \frac{a - ib}{(\tau - i)^n}.$$

Denote by η_0 its real n-th root; then $x = \tau\eta_0 + i\eta_0$ satisfies the equation $x^n = a + ib$.

(c) If $|a_i| \leqslant A$, $(i = 0, 1, \ldots, n)$, p is any positive number, and $R = 1 + \dfrac{A + p}{|a_n|}$, then, for $|x| \geqslant R$, we have $|P(x)| > p$.

In fact, for $|x| \geqslant R$,

$$|a_n x^n| = \frac{A+p}{R-1}|x|^n,$$

$$|a_{n-1}x^{n-1}+\ldots+a_0| \leqslant A(|x|^{n-1}+\ldots+|x|+1)$$
$$= A\frac{|x|^n-1}{|x|-1} < \frac{A|x|^n}{R-1}$$

and thus

$$|P(x)| > \frac{A+p}{R-1}|x|^n - \frac{A|x|^n}{R-1} = \frac{p|x|^n}{R-1} \geqslant \frac{pR^n}{R-1} > p.$$

Incidentally we see that $1+\dfrac{A}{|a_n|}$ is an upper bound for the roots.

(d) As $|P(x)|$ is a continuous function of the variables ξ and η, it assumes its minimum value at least once, at $\alpha = \xi_0 + i\eta_0$, say, in the circle $|\xi+i\eta| \leqslant R$. We are going to prove that, if $P(\alpha) \neq 0$, there is another point $\alpha+h$ in $|\xi+i\eta| < R$ such that

$$|P(\alpha+h)| < |P(\alpha)|,$$

in contradiction of the fact that $|P(\alpha)|$ is the smallest possible value of $|P(x)|$. Thus our hypothesis that $|P(\alpha)| \neq 0$ is impossible, i.e. $P(\alpha) = 0$; and α is a root of the equation $P(x) = 0$.

Taking $p > |a_0|$, the minimum value of $P(x)$ is assumed at an inner point of the corresponding circle of radius R, for $|a_0|$ is the value of $|P(x)|$ at $x = 0$, and, by (c), at every point outside or on the boundary of R, $|P(x)| > p > |a_0|$. Putting $R - |\alpha| = \rho$ and writing $P(x)$ in ascending powers of $x-\alpha$, we have, since

$$x^k = (x-\alpha+\alpha)^k = (x-\alpha)^k + C_1^k(x-\alpha)^{k-1}\alpha + \ldots + \alpha^k,$$
$$P(x) = P(\alpha) + b_1(\alpha)(x-\alpha) + b_2(\alpha)(x-\alpha)^2 + \ldots + a_n(x-\alpha)^n.$$

According to our hypothesis, $P(\alpha) \neq 0$, $a_n \neq 0$. Some of the coefficients b may vanish. Let $b_m(\alpha)$ be the first non-vanishing coefficient. Thus

$$P(x) = P(\alpha) + b_m(x-\alpha)^m + \ldots + b_{n-1}(x-\alpha)^{n-1} + a_n(x-\alpha)^n.$$

Putting $x-\alpha = h$, we have

$$P(\alpha+h) = P(\alpha) + b_m h^m\left(1 + \frac{b_{m+1}}{b_m}h + \ldots + \frac{a_n}{b_m}h^{n-m}\right)$$
$$= P(\alpha) + b_m h^m(1+Q(h)).$$

Since $$\lim_{|h|\to 0} Q(h) = 0,$$

(2) $$|Q(h)| < 1$$

for a sufficiently small $|h|$, say when $|h| < \epsilon \leqslant \rho$.

Consider now the equation

(3) $$h^m = -\delta \frac{P(\alpha)}{b_m},$$

where $\delta < 1$ is chosen so that $\delta < \left| \epsilon^m \frac{b_m}{P(\alpha)} \right|$. By (b), equation (3) has a root h and, in virtue of the last inequality, $|h| < \epsilon$, so that (2) is satisfied also. Thus $\alpha + h$ is an inner point of the circle of radius R, and

$$P(\alpha+h) = P(\alpha) - \delta P(\alpha) - \delta P(\alpha) Q(h) = P(\alpha)(1-\delta) - \delta P(\alpha) Q(h),$$

i. e.

$$|P(\alpha+h)| \leqslant |P(\alpha)|(1-\delta) + \delta |P(\alpha)| |Q(h)|$$
$$< |P(\alpha)|(1-\delta) + \delta |P(\alpha)| = |P(\alpha)|,$$

which proves (d), and hence the fundamental theorem.

We remark that, ϵ being given, the various conditions imposed upon δ can all be fulfilled by choosing the smallest δ satisfying the different conditions, which are finite in number.

II. *Factorization theorem. There are n numbers $z_1, \ldots, z_n$ such that* $a_0 + a_1 z + \ldots + a_n z^n = a_n(z-z_1) \ldots (z-z_n)$.

Proof. For every α and for every polynomial $P(z)$ of degree n there is another polynomial $Q(z)$ of degree $n-1$ such that $P(z) = (z-\alpha)Q(z) + P(\alpha)$. We can in fact determine the coefficients of $Q(z)$ by identifying the coefficients of $z^k, (k = 1, 2, \ldots, n)$ on both sides. This process is called division of $P(z)$ by $z - \alpha$ and can be carried out directly in the usual way. Indeed, the division of two integers, 3493 by 651, say, is in reality the division of the polynomial $3x^3 + 4x^2 + 9x + 3$ by $6x^2 + 5x + 1$ when $x = 10$. The only difference is that, in the general case, negative remainders also are admitted. In particular, the process of finding the H.C.F. of two integers is valid, word for word, for polynomials. Thus, by a finite number of elementary operations we can determine the highest common factor of two polynomials.

Hence when α is a root, $P(z) = (z-\alpha)Q(z)$. Repeating the process for $Q(z)$ and so on, we establish the theorem.

20. *Partial fractions.* In this article capital letters will denote polynomials in z.

I. *If* $A = BQ+R$, *the* H.C.F. *of* A *and* B *is the* H.C.F. *of* B *and* R.

Proof. Every common factor of B and R obviously divides A, and thus divides A and B. On the other hand, since $R = A-BQ$, every common factor of A and B divides R and thus divides B and R. The result follows immediately.

We determine the H.C.F. of A and B in the following way. First divide A by B, i. e. write $A = BQ_1+R_1$, then divide B by R_1, i.e. write $B = R_1Q_2+R_2$, and so on. This process ends after a finite number of steps, (as in the case of numbers), and we obtain a constant remainder R_n. If $R_n = 0$, the last equation is $R_{n-2} = R_{n-1}Q_n$, which shows that the H.C.F. of R_{n-1} and R_{n-2} is R_{n-1}. Going back to the last equation but one, we see that R_{n-1} is the H.C.F. of R_{n-2} and R_{n-3}, and so on, until finally we see that R_{n-1} is the H.C.F. of A and B. If $R_n \neq 0$, A and B have no common divisor (other than a constant): A and B are then said to be *prime* to each other.

II. *If* A *and* B *are prime to each other, there are two polynomials* L *and* M *such that* $AL+BM = 1$.

Proof. The equation $R_1 = A-Q_1B$ shows that the first remainder is of the form $PA+QB$. Eliminating R_1 from the second equation, $R_2 = B-Q_2R_1$, by means of the first equation, we obtain $R_2 = -Q_2A+(1+Q_1Q_2)B$. Continuing the process, we see that the last remainder also can be written in the form $R_n = PA+QB$. Dividing by the constant R_n we obtain the theorem.

III. *If* A *and* B *are prime to each other, every fraction* P/AB *can be written in the form* $Q+A'/A+B'/B$, *where the degrees of* A' *and* B' *are smaller than those of* A *and* B *respectively.*

Proof. By II. we can write $AL+BM = 1$. Multiplying by P/AB we have $P/AB = PL/B+PM/A$. If the degree of PL or PM is higher than that of B or A respectively, we obtain by division $PL/B = P'+B'/B$ and $PM/A = P''+A'/A$, which proves the statement.

Applying this result to $\frac{P(z)}{Q(z)} = \frac{P(z)}{(z-z_1)^{m_1}(z-z_2)^{m_2}\dots(z-z_k)^{m_k}}$,

we see that

$$(1)\quad \frac{P(z)}{Q(z)} = S(z) + \frac{A_{11}}{z-z_1} + \frac{A_{12}}{(z-z_1)^2} + \dots + \frac{A_{1m_1}}{(z-z_1)^{m_1}}$$
$$+ \frac{A_{21}}{z-z_2} + \frac{A_{22}}{(z-z_2)^2} + \dots + \frac{A_{2m_2}}{(z-z_2)^{m_2}} + \text{\&c.},$$

where $S(z)$ is a polynomial and A_{ik} are constants.

Suppose now that P and Q are *real* polynomials, i.e. all their coefficients are real numbers. Some of the roots z_i (or all of them) may be complex, but *if* $Q(a+ib) = 0$, *then also* $Q(a-ib) = 0$, for if
$$Q(x+iy) = Q_1(x, y) + iQ_2(x, y),$$
then
$$Q(x-iy) = Q_1(x, y) - iQ_2(x, y),$$
and the equation $Q(a+ib) = 0$ means that $Q_1 = 0$ and $Q_2 = 0$. Dividing $Q(x+iy)$ by $(x-a+ib)(x-a-ib) = (x-a)^2+b^2$, we see that if $a+ib$ is a double root of $Q(z) = 0$ then $a-bi$ is also a double root of $Q(z) = 0$, and so on.

Consequently, if a real polynomial $Q(x) = 0$ has a complex root $a+ib$, it contains the real factor $(x-a)^2+b^2$ or its powers: $Q(x) = [(x-a)^2+b^2]^m R(x)$, where R is also a real polynomial. Thus if $x_1, \dots, x_k$ are the real roots and $a_r \pm b_r i$ the complex roots, we obtain, by III,

(2)

$$\frac{P(x)}{Q(x)} = S(x) + \frac{A_{11}}{x-x_1} + \dots + \frac{A_{1m_1}}{(x-x_1)^{m_1}} + \frac{A_{21}}{x-x_2} + \dots + \frac{A_{2m_2}}{(x-x_2)^{m_2}}$$
$$+ \dots + \frac{A_{k1}}{x-x_k} + \dots + \frac{A_{km_k}}{(x-x_k)^{m_k}} + \frac{B_{1,1}(x)}{(x-a_1)^2+b_1^2} + \frac{B_{1,3}(x)}{[(x-a_1)^2+b_1^2]^2}$$
$$+ \dots + \frac{B_{1,2n_1-1}(x)}{[(x-a_1)^2+b_1^2]^{n_1}} + \dots + \frac{B_{r,1}(x)}{(x-a_r)^2+b_r^2} + \frac{B_{r,3}(x)}{[(x-a_r)^2+b_r^2]^2}$$
$$+ \dots + \frac{B_{r,2n_r-1}(x)}{[(x-a_r)^2+b_r^2]^{n_r}},$$

where $B_{r,s}$ is a polynomial in x of degree s. This is called the decomposition of the rational function $P(z)/Q(z)$ or $P(x)/Q(x)$ into *partial fractions.*

The position of complex algebra in the theory of number systems.

21. *Vector and quaternion algebra.* Just as the examination of non-Euclidian geometries throws a new light on the Euclidian system itself, so the position of the algebra of complex numbers in more general algebras reveals important features of the complex algebra. We are going to discuss two results in this connexion, noticing, however, that the knowledge of this section is not needed for the understanding of the sequel.

The extension of the number system beyond complex numbers is suggested by the three-dimensional character of our space, in which a point is characterized by three real numbers in a certain succession. In physics time also comes in as a fourth independent variable.

Symbols of the type $a_1e_1 + \ldots + a_ne_n = \Sigma a_re_r$, where the coefficients $a_1, \ldots, a_n$, (called also coordinates or components), are real or complex numbers, are the simplest elements for the extension of the ordinary complex, or more precisely two-dimensional, algebra to several dimensions. We define equality by the equality of the corresponding coordinates, i. e. $\Sigma a_re_r = \Sigma b_re_r$ if and only if $a_r = b_r$ $(r = 1, 2 \ldots, n)$. Addition (subtraction) is defined by the addition (subtraction) of the corresponding coordinates, i. e. $\Sigma a_re_r \pm \Sigma b_re_r = \Sigma (a_r \pm b_r)e_r$.

In general, multiplication is defined formally by the equations $ae_r = e_ra$, $\Sigma a_re_r \,.\, \Sigma b_se_s = \Sigma a_rb_se_re_s$. If $e_1, \ldots, e_n$ are the only 'units' of the algebra, and if we suppose that multiplication does not lead out of the algebra, e_re_s reduces to a number of the form $a_1e_1 + \ldots + a_ne_n$, i. e. there is a *multiplication table*

$$e_re_s = \sum_k m_{rsk}e_k$$

where m_{rsk} are real or complex numbers. If the algebra is restricted to symbols with real coordinates, and if the multiplication table is real, i. e. the coefficients m_{rsk} are all real, the algebra is called a *real algebra*.

The 'units' $e_1, e_2, \ldots, e_n$ are particular elements of the algebra, (e_1 has for its first coordinate 1 and for all the others 0). We may take for 'units' any other n elements $E_i = \sum_{j=1}^{n} t_{ij}e_j$ such that the determinant $\|t_{ij}\| \neq 0$. The new multiplication table is deduced from the former one by expressing the product $E_i E_j$ in terms of E_i. The new algebra so constructed is called the *transform* of the initial algebra. The two algebras are also said to be *equivalent* under linear transformation of units, or *isomorphic*. We shall not consider isomorphic algebras as distinct.

These generalities will now be illustrated by the vector and quaternion algebras.

Vector algebra is a real algebra with three units and with the multiplication table: $e_i e_i = 0$, $e_i e_j = -e_j e_i = e_k$, $i, j, k = 1, 2, 3$. The three units are usually denoted by i, j, k; the corresponding multiplication table is

$$\begin{array}{lll} ii = 0, & ji = -k, & ki = j, \\ ij = k, & jj = 0, & kj = -i, \\ ik = -j, & jk = i, & kk = 0. \end{array}$$

Vector algebra contains also a second kind of multiplication characterized by the table: $e_i e_i = -1$, $e_i e_j = 0$, or

$$\begin{array}{lll} ii = -1, & ji = 0, & ki = 0, \\ ij = 0, & jj = -1, & kj = 0, \\ ik = 0, & jk = 0, & kk = -1. \end{array}$$

This third fundamental operation is called *scalar multiplication*, and the name multiplication is justified inasmuch as it is uniform with regard to equality and is distributive with regard to addition. We shall denote vector multiplication by the ordinary symbols: $a \times b$, $a \,.\, b$, ab, and scalar multiplication by $\vdash a, b \dashv$ or $\vdash ab \dashv$.

Vector multiplication is not associative, i. e. $(ab)c \neq a(bc)$. For example, $e_i(e_j e_j) = e_i \,.\, 0 = 0$, whereas $(e_i e_j)e_j = e_k e_j = -e_i$. Scalar multiplication is not associative, for $a \vdash bc \dashv$ is a real multiple of the vector a whereas $\vdash ab \dashv c$ is a real multiple of c.

Scalar multiplication leads out of the class of vectors to scalars (ordinary real numbers). Consequently, from the mathematical point of view, we have to complete vector algebra by defining addition of vectors to scalars. In other words, the complete elements of vector algebra are neither vectors nor scalars, but expressions of the form $ae + bi + cj + dk$, where e is the principal unit, 1. A complete multiplication table resuming the two multiplications of the vector algebra is the following:

	e,	i,	j,	k
e	e,	i,	j,	k
i	i,	$-e$,	k,	$-j$
j	j,	$-k$,	$-e$,	i
k	k,	j,	$-i$,	$-e$

i. e. the rule for multiplication is

$$(a+bi+cj+dk)(a'+b'i+c'j+d'k)$$
$$= aa'-bb'-cc'-dd'+(cd'-dc')i+(db'-bd')j+(bc'-cb')k.$$

If $a = a' = 0$, i. e. if we multiply two vectors, the scalar part of the product is the scalar product of the two vectors, and the vector part is their vector product.

This algebra is Hamilton's *quaternion algebra.* From the mathematical point of view it is considerably simpler than vector algebra. In fact, *it contains only one multiplication, and this is associative.* We can also show that *quaternions obey the product law,* (which is not so for vectors), and that $AB = AC$ implies that $B = C$ provided $A \neq 0$. Thus the commutative property of multiplication is the only one of table I (p. 4) which is not possessed by quaternions.

$q' = a-bi-cj-dk$ is called the conjugate of $q = a+bi+cj+dk$ and $N(q) = a^2+b^2+c^2+d^2 = qq' = q'q$ the *norm* of q. It is readily seen that $q^{-1} = q'/N(q)$. If $q \neq 0$, the unique solution of $qx = q_1$ is $x = q^{-1}q_1$ and that of $yq = q_1$ is $y = q_1q^{-1}$. Thus division by q is possible and unique if, and only if, $N(q) \neq 0$.

The superiority of quaternion algebra over vector algebra becomes more obvious when we consider relations between vectors. A mathematical operation like $(ai+bj+ck)(xi+yj+zk)$ or $(xi+yj+zk)^2$ leading from a vector to another vector is called a vector function. But scalar multiplication leads from a vector to a scalar. Thus we have also to consider vector-scalar and scalar-vector functions. This circumstance together with the clumsiness of both multiplications leads to great complexity, which practically rules out function theory in vector variables.

In quaternion algebra, every operation leads from a quaternion to a quaternion, for scalars are particular quaternions. Moreover its associative character makes a succession of operations possible, only the order of multiplications has to be carefully watched. Since limit, continuity, and allied notions can easily be defined in any finite or even infinite algebra by the limit, &c. of the coordinates, quaternion function theory is a quite possible generalization of our ordinary Analysis based on complex numbers. But so far it has not been much developed. The main difficulty in the construction of quaternion Analysis is that the inversion of multiplication is twofold, and that the inverse operations of power (i. e. the operations corresponding to root and logarithm) appear to be too complicated.

22. *Associative algebras with product law.* The existence of quaternion algebra leads to the following problem. Is it possible to construct a real algebra with three units possessing all the properties of table I except the commutative property of multiplication? Such an algebra would provide the simplest symbolism for the representation of directed physical magnitudes. The answer, as we are going to prove, is negative. First of all, we will establish a general property of real associative algebras.

I. *Every number of a real, associative algebra with product law is a root of a quadratic equation with real coefficients.*

Proof. Let a be a number of a real, n-dimensional associative algebra, and denote $a \, . \, a$ by a^2, $a \, . \, a \, . \, a$ by a^3, &c. Since, by hypothesis, the algebra contains n independent units, there is a real, linear relation between any $n+1$ numbers of the algebra, in particular between $1, a, a^2, \dots, a^n$: $c_0 + c_1 a + \dots + c_n a^n = 0$. Replacing a by the ordinary complex variable z, we apply the factorization theorem 19. II:

$$(1) \qquad c_0 + c_1 z + \dots + c_n z^n = f_1(z) f_2(z) \dots f_\mu(z),$$

where the factors $f_i(z)$ are real, linear or quadratic, expressions in z. Reintroducing a in the place of z and noticing that the passage from the right-hand side of the identity (1) to the left-hand side involves only additions and multiplications, we have, in virtue of the associative and distributive character of the algebra, $c_0 + c_1 a + \dots + c_n a^n = f_1(a) f_2(a) \dots f_\mu(a)$. Thus, according to the product law, one of the factors vanishes. This proves the theorem.

A simple consequence of this result is the following theorem, due to Weierstrass.

II. *If a real finite hypercomplex algebra satisfies all the conditions enumerated in table* I, *it reduces to the ordinary complex algebra.*

Proof. Since every number x of the algebra satisfies a quadratic equation $x^2+rx+s=0$ where r and s are real, we can write $x^2-(a+b)x+ab=0$, with complex a and b. In a real hypercomplex algebra $x^2-(a+b)x+ab \neq (x-a)(x-b)$ because $xb \neq bx$ (the equality holds only for real b). However, if the commutative law holds, we conclude that

$$x^2+rx+s=(x-a)(x-b).$$

Hence, by the product law, $x=a$ or $x=b$, i. e. x is an ordinary complex number.

III. *Frobenius's theorem. The only finite associative real algebras with principal unit and product law are the real, complex and quaternion algebras.*

Proof. If there is only one unit, i. e. every number is a multiple of e, the algebra is the real algebra. If there are other units, denote them by $1, e_1, \ldots, e_n$. But, by I,

$$e_i^2+2r_ie_i+s_i=0,$$

i. e. $(e_i+r_i)^2=r_i^2-s_i$ (r_i and s_i being real). Hence after the transformation of units $e_i'=e_i+r_i$, $e_i'^2$ is real. If $e_i'^2 \geqslant 0$, we can write $e_i'^2=c^2$ where c is positive or zero. Hence

$$(e_i'-c)(e_i'+c)=0,$$

and e_i' would be real. We have consequently $e_i'^2<0$. Then, by a transformation of units, we can suppose that $e_i'^2=-1$.

If $n=1$, we obtain in that way the ordinary complex numbers. If $n>1$, we are going to prove that $e_1'e_2'$ *is independent* of $1, e_1'$ and e_2', i. e. that the algebra contains at least *four* units.

In fact, if $e_1'e_2'=r_0+r_1e_1'+r_2e_2'$, we have

$$(e_1'-r_2)\left(e_2'+\frac{r_0+r_1r_2}{1+r_2^2}e_1'+\frac{r_0r_2-r_1}{1+r_2^2}\right)$$
$$=e_1'e_2'-\frac{r_0+r_1r_2}{1+r_2^2}+\frac{r_0r_2-r_1}{1+r_2^2}e_1'-r_2e_2'$$
$$-r_2\frac{r_0+r_1r_2}{1+r_2^2}e_1'-r_2\frac{r_0r_2-r_1}{1+r_2^2}=0,$$

for, replacing $e_1'e_2'$ by $r_0+r_1e_1'+r_2e_2'$, the scalar part and the coefficients of e_1' and e_2' all vanish. But by hypothesis neither of the factors is zero, which is absurd. Thus $e_1'e_2'$ cannot be written in the suggested form, i. e. it is independent of 1, e_1', e_2'.

Now, $e_1'+e_2'$ and $e_1'-e_2'$ are roots of quadratic equations, i. e.

$$(e_1'+e_2')^2 = -2+e_1'e_2'+e_2'e_1' = r_1(e_1'+e_2')+s_1$$
$$(e_1'-e_2')^2 = -2-e_1'e_2'-e_2'e_1' = r_2(e_1'-e_2')+s_2,$$

where r_1, s_1, r_2, s_2, are real. Adding, we obtain

$$(r_1+r_2)e_1'+(r_1-r_2)e_2'+s_1+s_2+4 = 0.$$

Since 1, e_1', e_2' are linearly independent, $r_1 = r_2 = 0$ and thus

$$(2) \qquad e_1'e_2'+e_2'e_1' = 2r \qquad (r \text{ real}).$$

If the algebra has four units and if $(e_1'e_2')^2 \neq -1$, we transform the units by the formulae

$$1 = 1,\ i = e_1',\ j = \frac{e_2'+re_1'}{\sqrt{1-r^2}},\ k = \frac{e_1'e_2'-r}{\sqrt{1-r^2}},$$

leading to quaternions.

We remark that this transformation is real, i. e. $1-r^2>0$. In fact,

$$(e_1'e_2')^2 = e_1'(e_2'e_1')e_2' = e_1'(2r-e_1'e_2')e_2' = 2re_1'e_2'-1,$$

i. e.
$$(e_1'e_2'-r)^2 = r^2-1.$$

If $r^2-1 \geqslant 0$, $e_1'e_2'$ would be real, which proves the remark.

More generally if t is not a quaternion (and is consequently neither real nor complex), we deduce from it the existence of a non-quaternion L such that $L^2 = -1$, and then by the reasoning leading to (2) we see that $iL+Li = c_1$, $jL+Lj = c_2$, $kL+Lk = c_3$ with c_1, c_2, c_3 real constants. Hence

$$Lk = (Li)j = (c_1-iL)j = c_1j-i(c_2-jL) = c_1j-c_2i+kL,$$

i. e. $2kL = c_3+c_2i-c_1j$. Multiplying by k on the left we obtain $-2L = c_3k+c_2j+c_1i$, which is absurd, since L is not a quaternion. Thus the theorem is established. (This simple proof is due to L. E. Dickson, 1923.)

22*a*. *Remark on infinite algebras.* Weierstrass's and Frobenius's theorems considerably restrict the number of simple algebras. We have, however, established these theorems only for algebras with a finite number of units. Take a single unit e and its powers $ee = e^2, \dots$ for as many new units, and consider the symbol

$$a = \sum_{i=0}^{\infty} a_i e^i, \qquad e^0 = 1.$$

This symbol does not involve any limit process. It is similar to an infinite decimal fraction, i.e. it is fully equivalent to a rule for the successive digits a_i.

Define addition and multiplication by putting

$$a \pm b = \sum_i a_i e^i \pm \sum_i b_i e^i = \sum_i (a_i \pm b_i) e^i,$$

$$ab = \sum_i a_i e^i \sum_j b_j e^j = \sum_k (a_1 b_{k-1} + a_2 b_{k-2} + \ldots + a_{k-1} b_1) e^k.$$

This infinite algebra satisfies all the conditions of table I. The reader will easily verify this statement so that we will establish the product law only.

For that purpose we notice that $ab = 0$ means that

(1) $$a_1 b_{i-1} + a_2 b_{i-2} + \ldots + a_{i-1} b_1 = 0,$$

which shows first of all that if one of the factors, b, say, is zero, i.e. $b_i = 0$ for every i, then $ab = 0$. On the other hand, if the product vanishes, i.e. all the expressions (1) are 0, and if one of the factors, a, say, is not zero, then $b = 0$. In fact, by hypothesis, there is a first coefficient, a_{i-1}, say, different from 0. Since $a_1 = a_2 = \ldots = a_{i-2} = 0$, equation (1) shows that $a_{i-1} b_1 = 0$. As a_{i-1} and b_1 are ordinary real or complex numbers and $a_{i-1} \neq 0$, we have $b_1 = 0$. The next equation

$$a_1 b_i + a_2 b_{i-1} + \ldots + a_{i-1} b_2 + a_i b_1 = 0$$

reduces to $a_{i-1} b_2 = 0$, i.e. to $b_2 = 0$, and so on; which proves that $b = 0$.

Division is perfectly determined, i.e. the equation $a = bx$ has a unique solution provided $b_1 \neq 0$. In fact, this equation is equivalent to the system of equations

$$\begin{aligned} a_1 &= b_1 x_1, \\ a_2 &= b_1 x_2 + b_2 x_1, \\ &\cdot \quad \cdot \quad \cdot \quad \cdot \\ a_i &= b_1 x_i + b_2 x_{i-1} + \ldots + b_i x_1, \\ &\cdot \quad \cdot \quad \cdot \quad \cdot \quad \cdot \quad \cdot \end{aligned}$$

which successively determines $x_1, x_2, \ldots, x_i, \ldots$ without ambiguity. If $b_1 = 0$ and $a_1 \neq 0$, the division of a by b is meaningless. More generally, if $b_1 = 0, \ldots, b_{i-1} = 0$, $b_i \neq 0$, the division by b has a meaning only for numbers a for which $a_1 = a_2 = \ldots = a_{i-1} = 0$, and for such numbers division is uniform. In fact the equation $a_i = b_1 x_i + \ldots + b_i x_1$ reduces to $a_i = b_i x_1$, which determines x_1, and so forth.

If we denote the solution of the equation $a = bx$ by a/b, the formal laws of addition, subtraction, multiplication, and division extend to fractions formed by these numbers with infinitely many units. This example shows that *Weierstrass's theorem does not extend to infinite algebras.*

More generally, take n units $e_1, e_2, \ldots, e_n$, and consider the forms $\sum_{i=0}^{\infty} P_i(e_1, \ldots, e_n)$, where P_0 is a real or complex number, $P_k(e_1, \ldots e_n)$ is a homogeneous polynomial of degree k in $e_1, \ldots, e_n$, with real or complex coefficients:

$$P_k = \sum_{i_1, \ldots, i_n = 1}^{n} a_{i_1, \ldots, i_n} e_1^{i_1} e_2^{i_2} \ldots e_n^{i_n}, \quad i_1 + i_2 + \ldots + i_n = k.$$

Define addition by the addition of the corresponding coefficients, so that

$$\Sigma a_{i_1, \ldots, i_n} e_1^{i_1} \ldots e_n^{i_n} + \Sigma b_{i_1, \ldots, i_n} e_1^{i_1} \ldots e_n^{i_n} = \Sigma (a_{i_1, \ldots, i_n} + b_{i_1, \ldots, i_n}) e_1^{i_1} \ldots e_n^{i_n},$$

and multiplication by the formal rule

$$\Sigma a_{i_1, \ldots, i_n} e_1^{i_1} \ldots e_n^{i_n} \Sigma b_{j_1, \ldots, j_m} e_1^{j_1} \ldots e_n^{j_m} = \Sigma a_{i_1, \ldots, i_n} b_{j_1, \ldots, j_m} e_1^{i_1} \ldots e_n^{i_n} e_1^{j_1} \ldots e_m^{j_m},$$

where $i_1 + \ldots + i_n = r$, $j_1 + \ldots + j_m = s$.

This is extended to non-homogeneous forms by the distributive law. The product of two homogeneous forms of degree r and s respectively is of degree $r + s$. In general, we do not suppose that $e_j e_i = e_i e_j$, since the commutative law does not hold.

If we define the zero-element of our algebra as a form with purely 0 coefficients, we readily see that this algebra satisfies all the conditions of table I, except the commutative law. We see in that way that *there are remarkably simple and very general algebras with infinitely many units.*

The *Tensor algebra* of relativity theory is such a *real* algebra, with two sets of fundamental units, $e_{(1)}, \ldots, e_{(n)}$ and $e^{(1)}, \ldots, e^{(n)}$, and with two kinds of multiplication.

EXERCISES II

1. Prove algebraically that if $z = x+iy$, then

$$(|x|+|y|)/\sqrt{2} < |z| < |x|+|y|.$$

2. Prove algebraically that

$$|z_1+z_2+\dots+z_n| \leqslant |z_1|+|z_2|+\dots+|z_n|.$$

3. Determine the points of the complex plane for which

(a) $0 < \mathrm{Rl}\,(iz) < 2\pi$

(b) $\mathrm{Rl}\,(z^2) = a\ (\gtreqless 0)$,

(c) $\mathrm{Im}\,(z^2) = a\ (\lesseqgtr 0)$.

4. Same for

(a) $|z^2-z| < 1$.

(b) $|z^2-4| = a > 0$.

(c) $|1/z| < d > 0$.

5. Same for

(a) $|(z-1)/(z+1)| < 1$.

(b) $|z/(z+1)| = a$.

(c) $|(z-z_1)/(z-z_2)| = 1$.

6. Same for $|z-a|+|z-b| = k$, $|z-a|+|z-b| < k$, $k>0$ (ellipse).

7. Same for $|z^2+az+b| < r^2$. For what values of r do the required points form two distinct regions? If z_1 and z_2 are the two roots, the points in question are the inner points of

$$|z-z_1|\,.\,|z-z_2| = r^2$$

and for $r < |z_1-z_2|/2$ we obtain two regions.

8. Same for $|(z-a)/(1-\bar{a}z)| \lesseqgtr 1$, where $|a| < 1$ and $\bar{a}$ is the conjugate of a. (Three separate examples.) The condition is equivalent to $|z-a|^2 \lesseqgtr |1-az|^2$, i.e. to $(1-|a|^2)(|z|^2-1) \lesseqgtr 0$, and thus for $<$ we obtain the inner points of the unit circle; for $=$ the points of the circumference and for $>$ the outer points.

9. If $|z_1| = |z_2| = |z_3| = 1$ and $z_1+z_2+z_3 = 0$, the affixes z_1, z_2, z_3, form an equilateral triangle in the unit circle.

10. $(-i)^n/n \to 0$, $(1+i\sqrt{3})^n/3^n \to 0$.

11. If $z_n \to 0$, then $|z_n| \to 0$ and conversely.

12. Prove that all the complex numbers $x+iy$ with rational coordinates x and y can be written out in a single sequence. Construct such a sequence. Determine the set of their limiting numbers.

13. Determine all the limiting numbers of the set of numbers satisfying the inequality $|z| < 1$.

14. Show that if z is a limiting number of z_n, the sequence z_n contains a subsequence tending to z.

15. If $z_n \to z$, then $z'_n = (z_1 + z_2 + \ldots + z_n)/n \to z$. Proof as in Example I. 21.

16. If $z_n \to z$, $p > 0$ and $p_1 + \ldots + p_n \to \infty$, then

$$(p_1 z_1 + p_2 z_2 + \ldots + p_n z_n)/(p_1 + p_2 + \ldots + p_n) \to z.$$

(Similar proof.)

17. $0 < a_0 < a_1 < \ldots < a_n$. Prove that all the roots of

$$P(x) = a_0 x^n + a_1 x^{n-1} + \ldots + a_n = 0$$

are outside the circle of radius 1 (*Kakeya*, 1912).

Proof.

$$(1-x)P(x) = a_n - [(a_n - a_{n-1})x + (a_{n-1} - a_{n-2})x^2 + \\ \ldots + (a_1 - a_0)x^n + a_0 x^{n+1}].$$

Hence $|(1-x)P(x)| \geqslant a_n - [(a_n - a_{n-1})|x|$

$$+ (a_{n-1} - a_{n-2})|x|^2 + \ldots + (a_1 - a_0)|x|^n + a_0|x|^{n+1}],$$

i. e. for $|x| \leqslant 1$ (but $x \neq 1$),

$$|(1-x)P(x)| > a_n - [(a_n - a_{n-1}) + \ldots + (a_1 - a_0) + a_0] = 0,$$

and also for $x = 1$, $P(1) = a_n + \ldots + a_0 > 0$. Q.e.d.

18. Show that

$$a_0 z^n + a_1 z^{n-1} + \ldots + a_n = \\ a_0 \begin{vmatrix} z + a_1/a_0 & a_2/a_1 & a_3/a_2 \ldots & a_{n-1}/a_{n-2} & a_n/a_{n-1} \\ -a_1/a_0 & z & 0 \ldots & 0 & 0 \\ 0 & -a_2/a_1 & z \ldots & 0 & 0 \\ \cdot & \cdot & \cdot & \cdot & \cdot \\ 0 & 0 & 0 \ldots & -a_{n-1}/a_{n-2} & z \end{vmatrix}$$

19. Extend the binomial theorem to complex binomials—and calculate the real and imaginary parts of $(x+iy)^n$.

20. Show that every rational function $R(z)$ of a complex variable z can be written in the form $R(z) = R_1(x, y) + iR_2(x, y)$, where R_1 and R_2 are rational functions of their arguments. (Show it first for polynomials.)

21. Show that if the coefficients of $R(z)$ are real and

$R(z) = R_1(x, y) + iR_2(x, y)$, then $R(x - iy) = R_1(x, y) - iR_2(x, y)$.

(Show it first for polynomials.)

22. Prove by the result of the preceding example that if $a+ib$ is a root of an algebraic equation with real coefficients, then $a-ib$ is another root of the same equation.

23. $P(x)$ is a real polynomial ; p is the number of changes of sign in the successive terms of $P(x)$, q the number of changes of sign in those of $P(-x)$. Prove that the equation $P(x)=0$ has at least $n-p-q$ complex roots.

24. $P(x)$ is a real polynomial ; prove that if $P(a)$ and $P(b)$ have the same sign, the number of roots of $P(x)=0$ in (a, b) is even or zero ; if $P(a)$ and $P(b)$ have opposite signs the number of roots in (a, b) is odd. Use the factorization theorem to put $P(x)$ in the form $P(x) = Q(x)(x-x_1) \ldots (x-x_r)$, where $x_1, \ldots, x_r$ are the real roots.

25. $P(x)$ is a real polynomial of an odd degree. Prove that $P(x)=0$ has a real root α, such that the signs of α and a_n are opposite. Prove also that if the degree is even and a_n / a_0 is negative, the equation has a positive and a negative real root.

26. A real number which satisfies an algebraic equation with integral coefficients is called an *algebraic* number.

x and y are algebraic numbers. Prove that $x+y$, $x-y$, xy, x/y are also algebraic numbers. Write $y=z-x$ in the equation satisfied by y and eliminate x from this equation and the equation satisfied by x. Similarly for the other cases.

27. Find the equations with integral coefficients, satisfied by

$$\sqrt[3]{3}+\sqrt[3]{4}, \quad 1+\sqrt{2}+\sqrt{3}.$$

28. Decompose the following expressions into partial fractions:

$$\frac{x^2+1}{x(x^2-1)}, \quad \frac{x^4-2x^2+2}{(x^4-1)(x^2+1)}, \quad \frac{1}{x^4+4}, \quad \frac{1}{x^{2n}+1}, \quad \frac{x^n+1}{x^n-1}.$$

29. Show that if q' is the conjugate of a quaternion q, then q is the conjugate of q'. Show that the conjugate of qq_1 is $q_1'q'$.

30. Prove that the norm of a product is the product of the norms.

31. *A quaternion integer* is a quaternion of the form

$$a/2+(b+(a/2))i+(c+(a/2))j+(d+(a/2))k$$

where a, b, c, d are ordinary integers. Show that for quaternion integers there is a greatest common divisor process.

32. Show that quaternion integers admit of unique factorization into primes, apart from the 24 factors ± 1, $\pm i$, $\pm j$, $\pm k$ and

$$\frac{\pm 1 \pm i \pm j \pm k}{2},$$

which divide unity.

33. *Cubic equations.* By the transformation $z = x - A/3$, the general cubic equation $z^3 + Az^2 + Bz + C = 0$ reduces to

$$(1) \qquad x^3 + ax + b = 0.$$

To solve this equation we put $x = p + q$. Hence (1) is replaced by

$$(2) \qquad p^3 + q^3 + b + (3pq + a)(p + q) = 0,$$

which is satisfied if we determine p and q by the conditions

$$(3) \qquad p^3 + q^3 = -b, \; pq = -a/3.$$

It follows that $p^3q^3 = -(a/3)^3$ and thus p^3 and q^3 are roots of

$$v^2 + bv - (a/3)^3 = 0.$$

Hence

$$\left.\begin{matrix} p^3 \\ q^3 \end{matrix}\right\} = -\frac{b}{2} \pm \sqrt{\left(\frac{b}{2}\right)^2 + \left(\frac{a}{3}\right)^3}$$

i. e.

$$(4) \qquad x = \sqrt[3]{-\frac{b}{2} + \sqrt{\left(\frac{b}{2}\right)^2 + \left(\frac{a}{3}\right)^3}} + \sqrt[3]{-\frac{b}{2} - \sqrt{\left(\frac{b}{2}\right)^2 + \left(\frac{a}{3}\right)^3}}$$

Cardan's formula.

This furnishes 9 values instead of 3, for we replaced pq by p^3q^3. We select the roots by means of (3). If one of the roots is furnished by $x_1 = p + q$, the other two roots are: $x_2 = \epsilon p + \epsilon^2 q$ and $x_3 = \epsilon^2 p + \epsilon q$ where

$$\epsilon = \frac{-1 + \sqrt{-3}}{2}.$$

34. *Biquadratic equations.* Ferrari writes the biquadratic equation $x^4 + Ax^3 + Bx^2 + Cx + D = 0$ in the form

$$(5) \qquad \left(x^2 + \frac{A}{2}x + \frac{y}{2}\right)^2 = \left(\frac{A}{4} - B + y\right)x^2 + \left(\frac{Ay}{2} - C\right)x + \frac{y^2}{4} - D$$

and determines y so that the right-hand side may be a perfect square. The equation for y,

$$(6) \qquad y^3 - By^2 + (AC - 4D)y + D(4B - A^2) - C^2 = 0,$$

is called the *resolvent*. Denoting the right-hand side of (5) by S^2, S is a linear form in x and we get for x two quadratic equations

$$x^2 + \frac{A}{2}x + \frac{y}{2} \pm S = 0,$$

where y is a root of (6).

Thus the solution of a biquadratic equation is reduced to that of a cubic equation, followed by the solution of two quadratic equations.

CHAPTER III

INFINITE SERIES

23. *Convergence, divergence, tests.* An infinite sequence of numbers a_n being given, consider the sequence of their 'partial sums': $s_1 = a_0 + a_1$, $s_2 = a_0 + a_1 + a_2, \ldots, s_n = a_0 + a_1 + \ldots + a_n, \ldots$. If s_n tends to a finite limit s (not ∞), we say that the infinite series of sums, as indicated by the form

$$(1) \qquad \sum_{n=0}^{\infty} a_n \equiv a_0 + a_1 + a_2 + \ldots + a_n + \ldots \text{ ad inf.},$$

converges to s. If $|s_n| \to \infty$ or if s_n has more than one limiting number (proper or not), we say that the infinite series of sums (1) diverges, i.e. does not lead to any definite number. For instance, if $a_0 = 1$, $a_n = a^n$ $(n > 0)$, we obtain

$$s_n = 1 + a + a^2 + \ldots + a^n = (1 - a^{n+1}) / (1 - a),$$

so that when $|a| < 1$, $a^{n+1}/(1-a) \to 0$ and $s_n \to 1/(1-a)$, i.e. the proposed infinite series of sums is convergent, and when $|a| > 1$, $|a^{n+1}| \to \infty$ so that s_n cannot have a proper finite limit; the proposed series of sums is divergent (convergent and divergent infinite geometrical progressions).

The expression 'infinite series of sums' is shortened into *infinite series,* and therefore we do not use the word series in its colloquial sense of sequence. As the idea of infinite series is absolutely fundamental for our presentation of analytic functions, we are going to establish all the properties of infinite series used in the sequel.

We first of all notice that an infinite succession of additions like (1) cannot be carried out, and consequently cannot be thought of as completely carried out. Taking $\lim s_n$ (if it exists) as the sum of (1), we assign a 'sum' to (1) by a more or less arbitrary definition which, at first sight, seems very much like the original infinite succession of sums. The great advantage, however, of our definition of the sum as a limit of a sequence is that *the determination of limit does not involve an infinite succession of operations.*

We have proved in a thoroughly *finite* way that 0 is the only number which is not isolated from the numbers of the form $1/n$, i.e. that $\lim 1/n = 0$. We determine in a similar direct way the limits of certain other concrete sequences and reduce unknown cases to known ones by simple and finite rules.

It is true, on the other hand, that, in general, we have no rules for establishing even the existence of a limit. That is to say, in the majority of cases, a sequence being given, we cannot determine its limit, or we may not be able even to decide whether the sequence has a limit or not. But when this is possible, we attain our aim by an ordinary finite logical inference from the character of the given numbers.

These inferences will appear in the form of 'tests'.

I. *Comparison test for series of positive terms. If, for* $n > m$, *we have* $0 < a_n < b_n$, *the convergence of* Σa_n *follows from that of* Σb_n *and the divergence of* Σb_n *follows from that of* Σa_n.

Proof. If $$b_{n+1} + \dots + b_{n+p} < \epsilon$$

it follows that $$a_{n+1} + \dots + a_{n+p} < \epsilon,$$

which, by 18. VII, proves the first part.

If $$\lim_{n=\infty} (a_{m+1} + \dots + a_{m+n}) = \infty,$$

then, since

$$b_{m+1} + \dots + b_{m+n} > a_{m+1} + \dots + a_{m+n},$$

it follows that $$b_1 + \dots + b_n \to \infty.$$

II. *Test for alternating series. If* $a_n > 0$ *is constantly decreasing to* 0, *the series* $a_0 - a_1 + a_2 - \dots = \Sigma(-1)^n a_n$ *is convergent and its sum* s *satisfies the inequalities* $0 < s < a_0$.

Proof. When $n \to \infty$,

$$s_{2n-1} = (a_0 - a_1) + (a_2 - a_3) + \dots + (a_{2n-2} - a_{2n-1})$$

is constantly increasing,

$$s_{2n} = a_0 - (a_1 - a_2) - \dots - (a_{2n-1} - a_{2n})$$

is constantly decreasing, and $0 < s_{2n-1} < s_{2n} < a_0$. Therefore s_{2n-1} and s_{2n} each tend to a limit, which is the same for both, since $s_{2n} - s_{2n-1} = a_{2n} \to 0$. Thus $s_n \to s$, where $0 < s < a_0$.

III. *The sign of the sum of a convergent alternating series with constantly decreasing terms is that of the first term. The remainder* $R_n = s - a_0 + a_1 - \dots - (-1)^n a_n$ *has the sign preceding* a_{n+1} *and* $|R_n| < a_{n+1}$.

Proof. $\Sigma(-1)^{n+1} a_n = -\Sigma(-1)^n a_n$ is convergent and its sum lies between $-a_0$ and 0. Moreover the sum of

$$a_{n+1} - a_{n+2} + a_{n+3} - \dots$$

lies between 0 and a_{n+1}.

IV. *Comparison test for general series.* Σa_n *is convergent if* $\Sigma |a_n|$ *is convergent, but the converse does not necessarily hold.*

Proof. Since, by hypothesis, $\Sigma |a_n|$ is convergent, we have, for sufficiently large n,

$$|a_{n+1}| + \dots + |a_{n+p}| < \epsilon,$$

i. e.

$$|a_{n+1} + \dots + a_{n+p}| < \epsilon.$$

Thus, by rule 18. VII, the statement is proved.

The same rule shows that for any fixed p, the condition,

$$\lim_{n=\infty} (s_{n+p} - s_n) = 0$$

follows from convergence. In particular

$$\lim (s_{n+1} - s_n) = \lim a_{n+1} = \lim a_n = 0,$$

i. e.

V. $a_n \to 0$ *is a necessary condition of convergence.*

As an application of the above tests consider the series

(2) $\quad 1 - 1/2 + 1/3 - 1/4 + \dots + (-1)^{n+1}/n + \dots$.

By II, it converges to a sum between 0 and 1. On the other hand, the series

(3) $\quad 1 + 1/2 + 1/3 + 1/4 + \dots + 1/n + \dots$

is divergent, since we can write it in the form

$$1 + 1/2 + (1/3 + 1/4) + (1/5 + 1/6 + 1/7 + 1/8) + \dots$$
$$+ [1/(2^n + 1) + 1/(2^n + 2) + \dots + 1/2^{n+1}] + \dots,$$

where every bracket is greater than $1/2$. In fact

$$1/3 + 1/4 > 1/4 + 1/4 = 1/2, \dots, 1/(2^n + 1) + \dots + 1/2^{n+1}$$
$$> 1/2^{n+1} + 1/2^{n+1} + \dots + 1/2^{n+1} = 1/2.$$

Thus the partial sums of (3) tend to ∞. This example shows that the condition $a_n \to 0$ is not sufficient for convergence.

The n-th term of (3) is the absolute value of the corresponding term in (2). Hence it is possible, as stated in IV, that Σa_n

may converge when $\Sigma|a_n|$ diverges. Such a series is said to be *conditionally convergent.* If $\Sigma|a_n|$ also converges, the series is said to be *absolutely convergent.*

For another example we take the *harmonic series*

$$(4) \qquad \Sigma 1/n^\alpha = 1 + 1/2^\alpha + 1/3^\alpha + \dots,$$

convergent for $\alpha > 1$, divergent for $\alpha < 1$. We have just proved that it diverges for $\alpha = 1$. Hence, by test I, it diverges also for $\alpha < 1$ (positive or negative). We will prove that (4) converges for $\alpha > 1$.

For any fixed n, take k such that $2^k > n$. Then

$$s_n \leqslant s_{2^k-1} = 1 + (1/2^\alpha + 1/3^\alpha) + (1/4^\alpha + 1/5^\alpha + 1/6^\alpha + 1/7^\alpha) + \dots \\ + [1/(2^{k-1})^\alpha + 1/(2^{k-1}+1)^\alpha + \dots + 1/(2^k - 1)^\alpha].$$

Replacing every term of a bracket by its first and largest term we obtain

$$s_n < 1 + 2/2^\alpha + 4/4^\alpha + \dots + 2^{k-1}/(2^{k-1})^\alpha \\ = (1 - r^k)/(1 - r) < 1/(1 - r)$$

where $r = 1/2^{\alpha-1}$. Thus s_n is a bounded sequence and, since it is constantly increasing, has a limit.

The same method works as soon as the terms are constantly decreasing. This leads us to the following special test.

VI. *Condensation test. Suppose that the positive numbers a_n are steadily decreasing. Σa_n converges (diverges) if $\Sigma 2^k a_{2^k}$ converges (diverges).* (*Cauchy*, 1821.)

We notice that *the number 2 can be replaced by any greater integer*.

Proof. For any fixed n take k such that $2^k > n$. Then

$$s_n < a_1 + (a_2 + a_3) + \dots + (a_{2^k} + \dots + a_{2^{k+1}-1}) \\ \leqslant a_1 + 2a_2 + 4a_4 + \dots + 2^k a_{2^k} = t_k$$

But if $\Sigma 2^k a_{2^k}$ is convergent, t_k has a limit and thus also the increasing sequence $s_n < t_k$ has a limit. For divergence take k such that $n > 2^k$. Then

$$s_n > a_1 + a_2 + (a_3 + a_4) + \dots + (a_{2^{k-1}+1} + \dots + a_{2^k}) \\ > a_1/2 + a_2 + 2a_4 + \dots + 2^{k-1} a_{2^k} = t_k/2.$$

Thus if $t_k \to \infty$ then $s_n > t_k/2$ tends to infinity.

The extension to integers greater than 2 is obvious.

As an application of the last test, we are going to extend the scale of harmonic series to *Abel's scale of convergent and divergent series.* These series are important in the application of the comparison principle. $\sum_{2}^{\infty} 1/n \log n$ is divergent, for

$$\Sigma 2^k/2^k \log 2^k = \Sigma 1/k \log 2 = (\Sigma 1/k)/\log 2 \text{ is divergent.}$$

Similarly $\Sigma 1/(n \log n . \log\log n)$ is divergent, for

$$\Sigma 2^k/(2^k \log 2^k \log\log 2^k)$$
$$= \frac{1}{\log 2} \Sigma 1/k \log (k . \log 2) > \frac{1}{\log 2} \Sigma 1/k \log k,$$

since $\log 2 < 1$. In general, putting

$$\log\log x = \log_2 x, \ \log\log_2 x = \log_3 x, \ \&c.,$$

we see in this way that $\Sigma 1/(n \log n . \log_2 n \dots \log_p n)$ is divergent.

On the other hand, by the condensation test, we see that $\Sigma 1/(n \log^\alpha n)$ is convergent if $\alpha > 1$. In fact (replacing 2 by 10) it is sufficient to prove that

$$\Sigma(10^{k+1} - 10^k)/(10^k \log^\alpha 10^k) = 9\Sigma 1/(\log 10^k)^\alpha = 9\Sigma 1/k^\alpha$$

is convergent. But as a harmonic series the last series is convergent. Similarly we prove that

$$\Sigma 1/(n \log n \log_2 n \dots \log_p{}^\alpha n)$$

is convergent.

VII. *If the positive a_n are steadily decreasing to zero and Σa_n is convergent, then $na_n \to 0$.* (Olivier, 1827.)

This is included in the following theorem.

VIII. *If the positive a_n are steadily decreasing to zero, then Σa_n is convergent if, and only if, $\sigma_n = s_n - na_n$ converges and, in the case of convergence,* $\lim \sigma_n = \lim s_n$. (Ostrowski, 1925 a.)

Proof. (Knopp, 1928.) We have

(1) $\sigma_n = a_0 + (a_1 - a_n) + (a_2 - a_n) + \dots + (a_\nu - a_n) + \dots + (a_n - a_n)$, so that both s_n and σ_n are increasing, and therefore $s_n \to s$, $\sigma_n \to \sigma$, where s and σ may be $+\infty$. Since $\sigma_n \leqslant s_n$ we have $\sigma \leqslant s$ Taking only the first ν terms in (1), and letting $n \to \infty$, we see that $\lim_{n=\infty} \sigma_n \geqslant s_\nu$, i. e. $\sigma \geqslant s_\nu$, $\sigma \geqslant s$. Hence $\sigma = s$. If both are finite, $s_n - \sigma_n = na_n \to 0$. Q.e.d.

24. *Tests.* In the case of positive series, the general test 23. I readily leads to special but useful forms.

I. $a_n > 0$. *If* Σa_n *is convergent and* $0 \leqslant c_n \leqslant N$, (all may be N), *then* $\Sigma c_n a_n$ *is convergent. If* Σa_n *is divergent and* $c_n > M > 0$, *then* $\Sigma c_n a_n$ *is divergent. In particular if* $a_n/b_n \to l \neq 0$, *the two series* Σa_n *and* Σb_n *converge or diverge together.*

II. *Cauchy's n-th root test. Put* $\overline{\lim_{n=\infty}} | \sqrt[n]{a_n} | = k$. *If* $k < 1$, Σa_n *converges absolutely; if* $k > 1$, Σa_n *diverges.* The test for $k = 1$, is indecisive. (Cauchy, 1821.)

Proof. Taking a number k_1 between k and 1 we have in the first case, for sufficiently large n, $|\sqrt[n]{a_n}| < k_1$, i. e. $|a_n| < k_1^n$. Thus the comparison of the series $\Sigma |a_n|$ with the geometrical progression Σk_1^n establishes the first part. To establish the second we take a number k_2 between 1 and k and we notice that, k being a limiting number of the sequence $|\sqrt[n]{a_n}|$, the sequence has infinitely many numbers greater than $k_2 > 1$, i. e. the sequence $|a_n|$ has infinitely many numbers greater than $k_2^n > 1$. Thus, by 23. V, convergence is impossible.

As a first example of this important special test we readily see that the infinite decimal $a \cdot a_1 a_2 \ldots a_n \ldots$ can be written in the form of an infinite series

$$a + a_1/10 + a_2/10^2 + \ldots + a_n/10^n + \ldots.$$

In fact $a_n \leqslant 9$, and thus $\sqrt[n]{a_n/10^n} < 10^{1/n}/10 \to 1/10 < 1$. The series is therefore convergent.

As another example consider the power series

$$\Sigma a_n z^n = a_0 + a_1 z + a_2 z^2 + \ldots + a_n z^n + \ldots. \tag{1}$$

Fix the value of z and apply test II. Putting

$$\overline{\lim_{n=\infty}} | \sqrt[n]{a_n} | = 1/R \tag{2}$$

and remarking that $\overline{\lim_{n=\infty}} | \sqrt[n]{a_n z^n} | = |z| \overline{\lim_{n=\infty}} | \sqrt[n]{a_n} | = |z|/R$,

we see that (1) converges absolutely for every real or complex z for which $|z| < R$, and diverges for every real or complex z for which $|z| > R$:

III. *The power series* $\Sigma a_n z^n$ *converges absolutely in the circle of radius* R *determined by* (2) *and diverges outside this circle.*

(Cauchy, 1821.)

This result is the basis of the theory of analytic functions founded on power series.

The last special test used in this book is the following:

IV. *Ratio test. If, for sufficiently large* n, $|a_{n+1}/a_n| < k < 1$, Σa_n *converges absolutely; if, for sufficiently large* n, $|a_{n+1}/a_n| > h > 1$, Σa_n *diverges.* (D'Alembert, 1768.)

Proof. In the first case there is an m such that

$$|a_{m+1}| < k|a_m|, |a_{m+2}| < k|a_{m+1}| < k^2|a_m|, \ldots, |a_{m+p}| < k^p|a_m|, \ldots,$$

which shows that $\sum_{p=0}^{\infty} |a_{m+p}| < |a_m| \Sigma k^p$ converges. And the addition of the first m terms does not destroy the absolute convergence. On the other hand, if

$$|a_{m+1}| > h|a_m|, \ldots, |a_{m+p}| > h^p|a_m|, \ldots$$

the terms of Σa_n do not tend to 0, and the series Σa_n diverges.

The case $1/n$ where $a_{n+1}/a_n = n/(n+1) < 1$ and the series diverges shows that the series may diverge when the ratio $|a_{n+1}/a_n|$ tends to 1. The condition that this ratio should be less than a number k less than 1 is thus essential.

As an example consider the series $\Sigma z^n/n!$ In this case $|a_{n+1}/a_n| = |z|/(n+1)$ so that when z is fixed the ratio, for sufficiently large n, will be less than any given small positive number. Thus the series in question is convergent for every real or complex value of z. We put

$$\Sigma z^n/n! = E(z) \tag{3}$$

and call the sum-function $E(z)$ of the series the *exponential function.* This is the first example of the extension of the definition of a real function (the ordinary exponential function) by means of a convergent infinite series to complex values of the independent variable.

Sometimes we use the ratio test in the following form:

IV′. *If* Σa_n *is absolutely convergent and* $|b_{n+1}/b_n| < |a_{n+1}/a_n|$, *then* Σb_n *is absolutely convergent.*

Proof. Write the condition in the form

$$|b_{n+1}/a_{n+1}| < |b_n/a_n| < \ldots < |b_0/a_0|,$$

so that $|b_n| < |a_n| b_0/a_0$. The result follows.

It is easy to show that the ratio test is less general than the n-th root test, i.e. putting

$$l = \varliminf_{n=\infty} |a_{n+1}/a_n|, \quad L = \varlimsup_{n=\infty} |a_{n+1}/a_n|,$$

we have

$$(4) \qquad l \leqslant \varliminf_{n=\infty} |\sqrt[n]{a_n}|, \quad L \geqslant \varlimsup_{n=\infty} |\sqrt[n]{a_n}|.$$

Proof. If $l > 0$, then, for every positive ϵ $(< l)$, there is a fixed m such that $a_m \neq 0$ and

$$l - \epsilon < |a_{n+1}/a_n| < L + \epsilon \text{ for } n \geqslant m,$$

i.e.

$$(l-\epsilon)^{n-m} < |a_n/a_m| < (L+\epsilon)^{n-m}$$

$$|\sqrt[n]{a_m}|(l-\epsilon)^{1-m/n} < |\sqrt[n]{a_n}| < |\sqrt[n]{a_m}|(L+\epsilon)^{1-m/n}.$$

Since m is fixed and $a_m \neq 0$,

$$\lim_{n=\infty} |\sqrt[n]{a_m}| = 1,$$

and so all the limiting numbers of $|\sqrt[n]{a_n}|$ are between $l-\epsilon$ and $L+\epsilon$. Since ϵ is arbitrary (4) is proved. When $l = 0$, the first result is obvious, since $|\sqrt[n]{a_n}| \geqslant 0$ for all values of n. When $L = \infty$, the second result is also obvious. When $l = \infty$, and thus also $L = \infty$, we have

$$|a_{n+1}/a_n| > 1/\epsilon \text{ for } n \geqslant m,$$

i.e.

$$|a_n/a_m| > 1/\epsilon^{n-m}, \qquad |\sqrt[n]{a_n}| > |\sqrt[n]{a_m}|/\epsilon^{1-m/n},$$

i.e. $\lim|\sqrt[n]{a_n}| = \infty$, and in this sense the result also holds in this case.

The ratio test may also be written in the form:

IV″. *If* $\varlimsup |a_{n+1}/a_n| < 1$, *there is absolute convergence; if* $\varliminf |a_{n+1}/a_n| > 1$, *there is divergence.* In the first case, by (4) $\varlimsup|\sqrt[n]{a_n}| < 1$ and in the second case, $\varliminf|\sqrt[n]{a_n}| > 1$. We see also that the n-th root test applies in every case when the ratio test applies, but not conversely.

A useful generalization of the ratio test for *positive* terms is the following.

V. *If, for sufficiently large* n, $n(1-a_{n+1}/a_n)>\alpha>1$, Σa_n *is convergent. If, for sufficiently large* n, $n(1-a_{n+1}/a_n)<1$, Σa_n *is divergent.* (Raabe, 1832.)

Proof. In the first case, for sufficiently large n, $a_{n+1}/a_n \leqslant 1-\alpha/n$, i.e. $na_{n+1}\leqslant(n-1)a_n-\beta a_n$ where $\beta=\alpha-1>0$. Hence $(n-1)a_n-na_{n+1}\geqslant\beta a_n>0$, i.e. from a sufficiently large suffix onwards na_{n+1} is steadily decreasing. Thus, as it remains >0, $na_{n+1}\to\gamma\geqslant 0$. It follows that $\Sigma[(n-1)a_n-na_{n+1}]$ is convergent and thus, since $a_n\leqslant[(n-1)a_n-na_{n+1}]/\beta$, the convergence of Σa_n is established.

In the second case $a_{n+1}/a_n>1-1/n$, i.e. $(n-1)a_n-na_{n+1}\leqslant 0$ and thus na_{n+1} is steadily increasing. Therefore, for sufficiently large n, $na_{n+1}>\gamma$ and, since $a_{n+1}>\gamma/n$, the divergence follows.

In exactly the same way, we obtain a slightly more general form:

VI. *If, for sufficiently large* n, $a_{n+1}/a_n=1-1/n-b_n/n.\log n$, Σa_n *converges when* $b_n\geqslant\alpha>1$ *and diverges when* $b_n\leqslant\alpha<1$. Similarly,

VII. *If, for sufficiently large* n, $a_{n+1}/a_n=1-\alpha/n-\theta_n/n^\lambda$ *where* θ_n *is a bounded sequence and* $\lambda>1$, Σa_n *converges when* $\alpha>1$ *and diverges when* $\alpha\leqslant 1$. (Gauss, 1812.)

Proof. If $\alpha\gtrless 1$, V applies. If $\alpha=1$, we have

$$a_{n+1}/a_n=1-1/n-(\theta_n\log n/n^{\lambda-1})/n\,.\log n,$$

where the expression in the bracket is a zero sequence, and thus VI applies.

The application of all the tests enumerated is considerably widened by the following results.

VIII. *The sum-series* $\Sigma(a_n+b_n)$ *of two convergent series* $\Sigma a_n=A$ and $\Sigma b_n=B$ *is convergent and its sum is* $A+B$.

Proof.

$$a_0+b_0+a_1+b_1+\ldots+a_n+b_n=a_0+a_1+\ldots+a_n+b_0+b_1\ldots+b_n$$

and, by hypothesis,

$$a_0+a_1+\ldots+a_n\to A \text{ and } b_0+b_1+\ldots+b_n\to B.$$

IX. *The sum-series* $\Sigma(a_n+b_n)$ *of two absolutely convergent series is absolutely convergent* (to $A+B$, by VIII).

Proof. $$|a_n+b_n| \leqslant |a_n|+|b_n|,$$

i. e. $$|a_0+b_0+\ldots+a_n+b_n| \leqslant |a_0|+|a_1|+\ldots+|a_n| \\ +|b_0|+|b_1|+\ldots+|b_n|.$$

X. *Maclaurin's Test for positive real series. If the real function $f(x)$ is positive for $x \geqslant a$ and steadily decreases to* 0 *when $x \to +\infty$, then $\sum_{k=0}^{\infty} f(a+k)$ is convergent if $\lim_{t\to\infty} \int_a^t f(x)\,dx$ tends to a finite limit denoted by $\int_a^{\infty} f(x)\,dx$ and is divergent if $\int_a^{\infty} f(x)\,dx$ does not exist.*

Proof. When x is in $(a+p-1,\ a+p)$, (p being a positive integer), it follows from $f(a+p)<f(x)<f(a+p-1)$, by integrating, that $f(a+p)<\int_{a+p-1}^{a+p} f(x)\,dx<f(a+p-1)$.

Putting $p=1, 2, \ldots, n$ and adding we obtain

$$f(a+1)+\ldots+f(a+n)<\int_a^{a+n} f(x)\,dx<f(a)+f(a+1)+f(a+2)+ \\ \ldots+f(a+n-1).$$

Hence if $\int_a^{a+n} f(x)\,dx$ tends to L, say, when $n\to\infty$, then

$$f(a)+f(a+1)+\ldots+f(a+n)<f(a)+L,$$

i.e. $$\sum_{k=0}^{\infty} f(a+k)$$

is convergent.

On the other hand, when $\int_a^{a+n} f(x)\,dx \to \infty$ with n, the left-hand inequality shows that the partial sums of $\Sigma f(a+k)$ also tend to ∞.

For example, if $f(x)=1/x^p$, $p>0$, the conditions are satisfied with $a=1$, and $\int_1^n dx/x^p = n^{1-p}/(1-p)-1/(1-p)$ is convergent when $p>1$ and divergent if $p<1$.

More generally, remarking that

$$1/x \log x \log_2 x \ldots \log_{r-1} x (\log_r x)^p$$

is the differential coefficient of $(\log_r x)^{1-p}/(1-p)$, and that the latter function tends to a finite limit when $p > 1$, and to ∞ when $p < 1$, we obtain a quick proof for Abel's scale of convergent and divergent series.

25. *Derangement of series.* When we add together a finite number of numbers, their sum is independent of the order. Since, formally, an infinite series appears as the sum of infinitely many numbers, one hardly expects to find in their case a contradiction of this fact. It is therefore of importance to show by concrete examples that the sum of an infinite series may depend on the order of its terms.

We have seen that $\sum_{1}^{n} 1/k$ tends to $+\infty$. Hence also $\sum_{1}^{n} 1/2k = \frac{1}{2}\Sigma 1/k$ tends to $+\infty$. On the other hand, $\Sigma(-1)^k/k$ is convergent. Now take any number, A, say. Suppose $A > 0$. From the beginning of the series $\Sigma 1/2k$ we take just as many terms, in their order of occurrence, as is necessary to exceed A, i.e.

$$1/2 + 1/4 + \ldots + 1/2n_1 > A$$

while

$$1/2 + 1/4 + \ldots + 1/(2n_1 - 2) < A.$$

The terms $1/2, 1/4, \ldots, 1/2n_1$ will form the first n_1 terms of the new arrangement. This first group is followed by the first negative term -1, and we have $1/2 + 1/4 + \ldots + 1/2n_1 - 1 < A$. Now take positive terms $1/(2n_1 + 2), \ldots$, as many as are necessary to make the total sum just exceed A, and introduce after them the second negative term $-1/3$, and so on. In this way we exhaust all the terms of $\Sigma(-1)^n/n$ and no other terms are introduced. The new series

(1) $1/2 + 1/4 + \ldots + 1/2n_1 - 1 + 1/(2n_1 + 2) + \ldots + 1/2n_2$ $-1/3 + \ldots$ is a rearrangement of $\Sigma(-1)^n/n$.

But (1) is convergent to the arbitrarily given sum A. In fact its partial sums s_n oscillate about A, the difference $|A - s_n|$ being less than one of the positive or one of the negative terms. Consequently this difference tends to 0 with $1/n$.

If the given number A is negative, we start with the negative terms and insert the positive terms one by one. We notice that

$$\sum_1^n 1/(2k+1) > \sum_1^n 1/(2k+2),$$

i. e. the series of negative terms tends to $-\infty$.

In particular, we can arrange the terms in such a way that the partial sums of the new series tend to $+\infty$ (or to $-\infty$), i. e. a suitable arrangement may make a convergent series divergent. For this purpose we first take enough positive terms just to exceed 1, and insert after that the first negative term. Then we take just enough positive terms to make the total sum exceed 2, and then insert the second negative term, and so on. The same reasoning in the general case leads to the following theorem.

I. *Rearranged in a suitable way a conditionally convergent real series diverges, or converges to any given real number.*

(Riemann, 1854.)

Proof. Put $s_n = p_n - n_n$ where p_n is the sum of positive terms in s_n and $-n_n$ is the sum of negative terms. By hypothesis

$$s_n \to s, \text{ and } \sigma_n = p_n + n_n = \sum_0^n |a_k| \to \infty. \text{ Hence } \sigma_n + s_n = 2p_n$$

and $\sigma_n - s_n = 2n_n$ tend to $+\infty$, i. e. $p_n \to \infty$, $n_n \to \infty$. *The series of positive (negative) terms is divergent.*

Denote the positive terms by α_n and the negative terms by β_n so that if $a_n > 0$, $\alpha_n = a_n$, $\beta_n = 0$, and if $a_n < 0$, $\alpha_n = 0$, $\beta_n = a_n$. By hypothesis $\alpha_n \to 0$, $\beta_n \to 0$. Take any positive or negative number A (we suppose it > 0) and determine the first suffix i_1 such that $\alpha_1 + \alpha_2 + \ldots + \alpha_{i_1} > A$. This is possible, for $\sum_1^n \alpha_i \to \infty$ with n. Now determine the least k_1 such that

$$\alpha_1 + \alpha_2 + \ldots + \alpha_{i_1} + \beta_1 + \beta_2 + \ldots + \beta_{k_1} < A,$$

and proceed in this way to determine the smallest i_2 and k_2 such that $\alpha_1 + \ldots + \alpha_{i_1} + \beta_1 + \ldots + \beta_{k_1} + \alpha_{i_1+1} + \ldots + \alpha_{i_2} > A$, and

$$\alpha_1 + \ldots + \alpha_{i_1} + \beta_1 + \ldots + \beta_{k_1} + \alpha_{i_1+1} \\ + \ldots + \alpha_{i_2} + \beta_{k_1+1} + \ldots + \beta_{k_2} < A,$$

and so forth. Every term a_n of the original series has its place in the new arrangement of terms. On the other hand, denoting by s'_n the partial sum of the new series, we see that $s'_n - A$, if positive, is smaller than the last positive term in s'_n, and, if negative, $A - s'_n$ is smaller than the last negative term in s'_n. But, the series Σa_n being convergent, $a_n \to 0$. Hence $|s'_n - A| \to 0$, which shows that the sum of the rearranged series is the arbitrarily given number A.

Figuratively speaking the result of infinitely many additions depends in that case upon their order. We notice that since

$$\frac{\alpha_1 + \alpha_2 + \dots + \alpha_n}{\beta_1 + \beta_2 + \dots + \beta_n} + 1 = \frac{a_1 + a_2 + \dots + a_n}{\beta_1 + \beta_2 + \dots + \beta_n}$$

and $s_n = a_1 + \dots + a_n$ tends to a finite limit, whereas $\beta_1 + \beta_2 + \dots + \beta_n$ tends to $-\infty$, we have

$$\lim_{n=\infty} \frac{\alpha_1 + \dots + \alpha_n}{\beta_1 + \dots + \beta_n} = -1.$$

In the derangement used so far the order of the positive (negative) terms relative to one another has not been altered. If we split up the given series into two partial series and rearrange the terms so that the relative order of the terms in the two partial series is not altered, we say that we *displace* one part of the series with respect to the other part. To make clear that the *divergence of the two parts* is essential for the validity of our results we are going to prove the following theorem.

II. *The displacement of two convergent complementary parts of a convergent series has no effect on the convergence or on the sum of the series.*

Proof. Imagine the series in the new arrangement and form two complete series by completing the two parts by zeros. By hypothesis we obtain two convergent series with the sums A and B, say. Adding them we obtain, by 24. VIII, another convergent series with the same sum $A + B$. But the sum of the original complete series is also $A + B$. In fact its partial sum s_n, for sufficiently large n, contains the partial sums s'_m and s''_m of the two partial series, and as the original complete series is by hypothesis convergent, $s_n - (s'_m + s''_m) \to 0$ (by 18. VII).

In the case of conditionally convergent complex series we

may rearrange the real or the imaginary part, in order that one of them shall tend to an arbitrary real number (by I). But in this way we also rearrange the other part, and this part in the new arrangement may diverge and thus may make the series divergent.

To clear the position we introduce the idea of *density-direction* of complex terms. The radius vector from the origin of the complex plane making an angle α with the positive real axis is called a direction of density for the given terms a_n, if, for any arbitrarily small ϵ, the angle $(\alpha-\epsilon, \alpha+\epsilon)$ contains an infinity of a_n.

III. *If the complex series* Σa_n *is conditionally convergent, there is a straight line in the complex plane such that the sum of the suitably rearranged series is the affix of any given point of this straight line.* (Levy, 1905, Steinitz, 1913–15.)

Proof. We are going to prove first that there is at least one direction of density for the coefficients. In fact, taking only the terms in one of the four quadrants (sides included) the real parts of the terms as well as the imaginary parts have a constant sign, i. e. if their sum converges, it converges absolutely. Hence, there is at least one quadrant such that the series of terms lying in that quadrant diverges. Halving this quadrant we see, by 24. VIII, that the set of terms lying in one of the half angles diverges. Continuing in this way we establish the existence of a direction of density with the property that *the terms* a_n *taken from any angle* $<\pi/4$ *containing this direction form a divergent series.* If we multiply all the terms of the series by a suitable complex number the corresponding direction of the new series is the positive real axis. Thus we might suppose that for our original series $\Sigma a_n = \Sigma(\alpha_n + i\beta_n)$ the positive real axis is a direction of density.

Consider now the angles $(-\pi/2^{m+1}, \pi/2^{m+1})$, $m = 1, 2, \ldots$, and take terms from the first angle ($m = 1$) such that the sum of their real parts (all positive) exceeds $1/2$ but is less than 1. This is possible since $a_n \to 0$, and so $\alpha_n < 1/2$ for sufficiently large n. Then take from the second angle new terms with the same property and so on. Thus the real part of the selected partial series tends to $+\infty$. On the other hand, the imaginary part converges. In fact if we denote the partial series by $a_{n_1}+a_{n_2}+\ldots$, and suppose a_{n_k} belongs to the m-th angle, we have, since the chord is less than the arc,

$$2\,|\beta_{n_k}|<|a_{n_k}|\,2\pi/2^{m+1}\leqslant\sqrt{2}\,\alpha_{n_k}\,2\pi/2^{m+1},$$

and hence, since the sum of real parts in each angle is less than 1,

$$\Sigma\,|\beta_{n_k}|<\Sigma\,\sqrt{2}\pi/2^{m+1}.$$

Now consider the selected series together with the complementary series. The imaginary part of the latter converges, since this is true for the selected series and the complete series Σa_n. Now displace the two partial series with respect to one another, so that the real part of the complete series converges to an arbitrary real number (by I). Then the convergence and sum of the imaginary part is not disturbed (by II), which proves the statement.

For example, if $\Sigma\,a_n$ is a conditionally convergent *real* series, the complex series $b+\Sigma\,b_n$, where b is any given complex number and $b_n=ca_n$ with the arbitrary complex factor c, converges by a suitable rearrangement of its terms to any complex number lying on the straight line $b+rc$, $-\infty<r<+\infty$.

For the converse of III, viz. that all the possible sums of a conditionally convergent complex series obtained by derangement lie on a straight line or else cover the whole complex plane, see Steinitz, 1913–15. For a further result on conditionally convergent series see Knopp, 1925 a and Jarnik, 1926.

IV. *No derangement of terms affects the convergence and the sum of an absolutely convergent series.*

Proof. Denote by s_n' the partial sum of the deranged series. Since this series contains all the terms of the original series we can take $m>n$ so large that s_m' contains, beside other terms, the first n terms $a_1,\ldots,a_n$ of the original series. Thus

$$|\,s_m'-s_n\,|\leqslant|a_{n+i_1}|+\ldots+|a_{n+i_p}|$$

which, by 18. VII, tends to 0 if Σa_n is absolutely convergent.

26. *Multiplication of series.*

I. *If* $\Sigma a_n=A$ *and* $\Sigma b_n=B$ *are absolutely convergent, the series* Σc_n *formed of all the terms* $a_r\,b_s$ *written in any order is absolutely convergent and its sum is* AB.

Proof. Let μ be the greatest suffix of a_r or of b_s in $s_n = c_0 + \ldots + c_n$. Then

$$|c_0| + |c_1| + \ldots + |c_n| \leqslant \sum_0^\mu |a_r| \sum_0^\mu |b_s|$$

and, by hypothesis, the right-hand side is bounded. Thus Σc_n is absolutely convergent. Consequently we can add its terms in any order without changing its sum. Adding first all the terms c_n resulting from the product $s_n' \, s_n'' = (a_0 + \ldots + a_n)(b_0 + \ldots + b_n)$, then the additional terms resulting from $s_{n+1}' \, s_{n+1}''$ &c., every product $a_r \, b_s$ will be added and s_n formed in this way clearly tends to AB, which proves the statement.

The usual arrangement of the product series is

$$\sum_{n=0}^{\infty} (a_0 b_n + a_1 b_{n-1} + \ldots + a_n b_0),$$

and is called the *Cauchy product.*

Since $\Sigma z^n/n!$ is absolutely convergent for every real or complex z, the multiplication $\Sigma z_1^n/n! \, \Sigma z_2^n/n!$ is legitimate and the Cauchy product is $\Sigma (z_1 + z_2)^n/n!$, i. e. $E(z_1) \, E(z_2) = E(z_1 + z_2)$.

The series $\Sigma (-1)^{n-1}/\sqrt{n}$ is convergent because it is alternating with terms steadily decreasing to 0. In the Cauchy product:

$$\sum \frac{(-1)^{n-1}}{\sqrt{n}} \quad \sum \frac{(-1)^{n-1}}{\sqrt{n}}$$

$$= \sum (-1)^n \left[\frac{1}{\sqrt{1}\,\sqrt{n-1}} + \frac{1}{\sqrt{2}\,\sqrt{n-2}} + \ldots + \frac{1}{\sqrt{n-1}\,\sqrt{1}} \right],$$

the sum in the brackets is $> \dfrac{n-1}{\sqrt{n-1}\,\sqrt{n-1}} = 1$, i. e. the product series is divergent. This shows that the condition of absolute convergence is essential.

In reality the absolute convergence of one of the two series is sufficient.

II. *If* Σa_n *converges absolutely to* A *and* Σb_n *converges to* B, *their Cauchy product converges to* AB. (Mertens, 1875.)

Proof. Putting $a_0 + a_1 + \ldots + a_n = s_n$, $b_0 + b_1 + \ldots + b_n = \sigma_n$, $c_n = a_0 b_n + a_1 b_{n-1} + \ldots + a_n b_0$ we have by definition $s_n \to A$,

$\sigma_n \to B$, and thus $s_n \sigma_n \to AB$. We have to prove that the difference $c_0 + c_1 + \dots + c_n - s_n \sigma_n$ tends to 0. It is sufficient to prove that $\Delta_k = c_0 + c_1 + \dots + c_k - s_m \sigma_m \to 0$, where m is the integral part of $k/2$, for $s_m \sigma_m \to AB$. The proof will be given for n even, that for n odd being similar.

$$\Delta_{2n} = a_0 (b_{n+1} + \dots + b_{2n}) + a_1 (b_{n+1} + \dots + b_{2n-1}) + \dots + a_{n-1} b_{n+1} \\ + a_{n+1} (b_0 + \dots + b_{n-1}) + a_{n+2} (b_0 + \dots + b_{n-2}) + \dots + a_{2n} b_0.$$

Put $\Sigma |a_n| = M$. Since Σb_n is convergent, we have, by 18. VII, for sufficiently large n and for every p, $|b_{n+1} + \dots + b_{n+p}| < \epsilon$ and there is a number N such that $|\sigma_n| < N$. Hence

$$|\Delta_{2n}| < \epsilon(|a_0| + \dots + |a_{n-1}|) + N(|a_{n+1}| + \dots + |a_{2n}|).$$

Since $\Sigma |a_n|$ is, by hypothesis, convergent, we have, for sufficiently large n, $|a_{n+1}| + \dots + |a_{2n}| < \epsilon$, i. e. $|\Delta_{2n}| < \epsilon (M + N)$.

As ϵ is arbitrary and M and N do not depend on n, the only limiting number of the sequence $|\Delta_{2n}|$ is 0.

When both series Σa_n and Σb_n are only conditionally convergent, we have seen by an example that the product series may diverge. Cesàro discovered that the arithmetic means of the partial sums, $S_n = c_0 + c_1 + \dots + c_n$, of the product series necessarily converge to AB. This discovery, as we shall see later on, led to the generalization of the idea of convergency.

III. *If Σa_n and Σb_n converge to A and B respectively, the arithmetic means of the partial sums of their Cauchy product tend to AB.* (Cesàro, 1890.)

Proof. It is readily seen that

$$S_0 + S_1 + \dots + S_n = s_0 \sigma_n + s_1 \sigma_{n-1} + \dots + s_n \sigma_0.$$

It follows from the convergence that there is a number M such that $|s_n| < M, |\sigma_n| < M$. Similarly, as $s_\alpha \sigma_\beta \to AB$, there is a suffix p such that, for $\alpha \geqslant p$ and $\beta \geqslant p$, $|s_\alpha \sigma_\beta - AB| < \epsilon$, with an arbitrarily fixed ϵ.

Now take an $n > 2p$. We have

$$\frac{s_0 \sigma_n + s_1 \sigma_{n-1} + \dots + s_n \sigma_0}{n+1} = \frac{s_0 \sigma_n + \dots + s_{p-1} \sigma_{n-p+1}}{n+1} \\ + \frac{s_p \sigma_{n-p} + \dots + s_{n-p} \sigma_p}{n+1} + \frac{s_{n-p+1} \sigma_{p-1} + \dots + s_n \sigma_0}{n+1}.$$

The first and third terms are less in absolute value than

$pM^2/(n+1)$. Putting $s_\alpha \sigma_\beta = AB + \eta_{\alpha,\,\beta}$ we have

$$\left|\frac{s_0\sigma_n + s_1\sigma_{n-1} + \dots + s_n\sigma_0}{n+1} - AB\right|$$
$$< \frac{2p(M^2 + |AB|)}{n+1} + \frac{|\eta_{p,\,n-p}| + \dots + |\eta_{n-p,\,p}|}{n+1}$$
$$< \frac{2p(M^2 + |AB|)}{n+1} + \frac{(n+1-2p)\epsilon}{n+1}.$$

If p is fixed, the limiting numbers of the last expression are all in the interval $(0, \epsilon)$. Thus the same interval contains all the limiting numbers of the former expression. Since ϵ is arbitrary, 0 is the only limiting number, which proves Cesàro's theorem.

27. *Uniform convergence.* An important application of sequences of functions is the 'representation' of a function as the limit function of simpler functions. By such methods quite complicated functions may be calculated, at least approximately. Since only polynomials and rational functions can be evaluated directly, even the elementary functions like $\sin x$, $\log x$. &c., must be represented as limit functions of polynomials, or rational functions. Such a representation is equally important for the theoretical investigation of the function in question.

The main difficulty of such a representation is that, in general, the properties of $l(x)$, the limit function of $f_n(x)$, are not in close connexion with those of $f_n(x)$. We overcome this difficulty by restricting ourselves largely to representation by *uniformly convergent sequences.*

In order to explain the idea, consider the nil-sequence of functions $f_n(x) = x^n$ in $(-1, 1)$. At every inner point x, $\lim\limits_{n=\infty} f_n(x) = 0$. Hence the name: nil-sequence. If we now fix ϵ as a limit of precision, in order that $|f_n(x_1)| < \epsilon$, we have to take $n > N_1$, say. At x_2, to obtain the same precision, we have, in general, to take $n > N_2$, say, &c. Consider points $x_1, x_2, \dots$ tending to 1. For a fixed n we have $\lim\limits_{x \to 1} x^n = 1$. (See fig. 6.) Consequently the

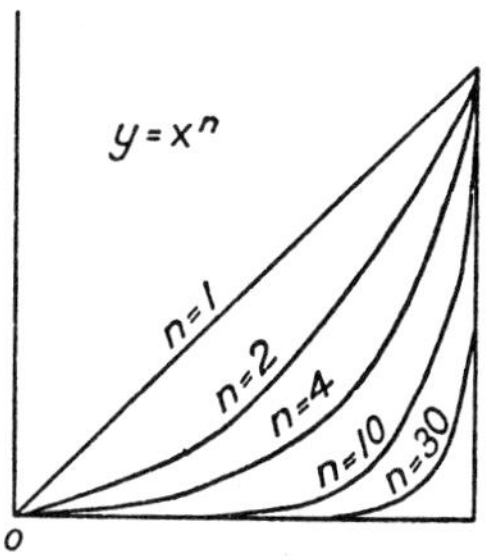

FIG. 6.

values of N corresponding to the points $x_1, x_2, \dots$ cannot have a finite upper bound. *We cannot assign an N good for a given ϵ at every point of* $(-1, 1)$. We say that the convergence of x^n to 0 in the interval $(-1, 1)$ is *not* uniform.

On the other hand, restricting x to the interval $(-k, k)$ $(0<k<1)$ the greatest value of $|x^n|$ will be k^n, so that if we choose N so that $k^N<\epsilon$, we have for $n>N$, *at every point of the interval* $(-k, k)$, $|x^n|<\epsilon$, and we say that in this interval x^n converges uniformly to zero. Similarly for complex values z. If $|z|<\rho<1$, $|z^n|<\rho^n$ at every point of the circle of radius ρ. Thus, choosing N such that $\rho^N<\epsilon$, we have, for $n>N$, $|z^n|<\epsilon$ *at every point of the circle of radius* ρ. We say that z^n converges uniformly to 0 in this circle. The convergence is not uniform, however, in the circle of radius 1.

In general $\epsilon_n(z)$ is said to converge uniformly to 0 in (a, b) or in a region R of the complex plane if, for every given ϵ, there is an N such that, for $n>N$, $|\epsilon_n(z)|<\epsilon$ at every point of (a, b) or R. A sequence of functions $f_n(z)$ is said to converge uniformly to $l(z)$ in (a, b), or in R, if the difference $l(z)-f_n(z)$ converges uniformly to zero in (a, b) or in R.

The definition extends to sequences of functions depending on several real or complex variables. Suppose that the sequence $f_n(x, y, z, \dots)$ has a limit at every point $(x, y, z, \dots)$ of a region $(R_1, R_2, \dots)$ of the respective variables, and denote that limit by $l(x, y, z, \dots)$. If for every positive ϵ there is a fixed suffix N such that, for *every* point of $(R_1, R_2, \dots)$

$$|l(x, y, z, \dots)-f_n(x, y, z, \dots)|<\epsilon,\ n>N,$$

the sequence is said to converge uniformly to $l(x, y, z, \dots)$ in the region $(R_1, R_2, \dots)$.

The limit function of the simple continuous functions x^n is discontinuous at $x=1$ because $l(x)=0$ if $|x|<1$ while $l(1)=1$. Thus the property of continuity may be lost in the limit process. It is therefore important to notice that continuity is passed on to the limit function if the convergence is uniform.

I. *If all the functions $f_n(z)$ are continuous in R, and if the sequence $f_n(z)$ converges uniformly to $l(z)$ in R, $l(z)$ is continuous at every point of R.*

Proof. Put $l(z)-f_n(z)=\epsilon_n(z)$. In virtue of the uniform convergence, for n sufficiently large, $|\epsilon_n(z)| < \epsilon/3$ at every point of R. But $l(z+h) - l(z) = f_n(z+h) - f_n(z) + \epsilon_n(z+h) - \epsilon_n(z)$, i.e. $|l(z+h) - l(z)| < |f_n(z+h) - f_n(z)| + 2\epsilon/3$. Since f_n is continuous at z, $|f_n(z+h) - f_n(z)| < \epsilon/3$ provided h is sufficiently small. Hence, for $|h|$ sufficiently small, $|l(z+h) - l(z)| < \epsilon$, where ϵ is arbitrarily small. This proves the continuity of $l(z)$.

The converse is not generally true though it holds for monotone sequences of real functions.

II. *If at every point of the closed interval (a, b) the real functions $f_n(x)$ are all continuous, $f_{n+1}(x) > f_n(x)$ and $f_n(x)$ does not converge uniformly to $l(x)$ in (a, b), then $l(x)$ is discontinuous at a point of (a, b).*

Proof. Put $\epsilon_n(x) = l(x) - f_n(x)$. Since the convergence is not uniform and $0 < \epsilon_{n+1}(x) < \epsilon_n(x)$, there is an ϵ so small that, whatever n we choose, the condition $|\epsilon_n| < \epsilon$ is *not* satisfied at every point of (a, b). Now divide (a, b) into two equal parts. The same is true of one or both of the parts. In fact if, for $n > N'$, $|\epsilon_n(x)| < \epsilon$ in (a, c) and, for $n > N''$, $|\epsilon_n(x)| < \epsilon$ in (c, b), then, since $0 < \epsilon_{n+1}(x) < \epsilon_n(x)$, we have, for $n > N > N'$ and $N > N''$, $|\epsilon_n(x)| < \epsilon$ in (a, b).

Halving that part for which $|\epsilon_n(x)| < \epsilon$ cannot be satisfied for every x by any value of n, however large, and continuing the process, we determine a succession of intervals each encasing the next. Since their lengths tend to 0, there is one and only one point ξ common to all these intervals and, by hypothesis, $f_n(\xi) \to l(\xi)$, i.e. for $n' > N$, $|\epsilon_{n'}(\xi)| < \eta < \epsilon$. On the other hand, in the neighbourhood of ξ, and as near to it as we like, there are points x such that, *for a fixed suffix n'*, $|\epsilon_{n'}(x)| \geqslant \epsilon$. Thus the oscillation of $\epsilon_{n'}(x)$ in the neighbourhood of ξ is greater than $\epsilon - \eta$. Since η can be taken arbitrarily small independently of ϵ, the oscillation of $\epsilon_n(x)$ at ξ is greater than ϵ (or equal to it). But, $f_n(x)$ being continuous at ξ, the oscillation of $l(x)$ at ξ equals that of $\epsilon_n(x)$. Hence, at ξ, the oscillation of $l(x)$ is not 0, and $l(x)$ is discontinuous at ξ.

We can apply I to infinite series by remarking that in their case $f_n(z) = s_n(z)$ and $\epsilon_n(z) = R_n(z)$:

III. *The sum of a uniformly convergent series of functions continuous in R is a function continuous in R.*

As an application of III consider the power series $f(z) = \Sigma a_n z^n$ with the radius of convergence R. Take R_1 as near to R as we please, but fixed, and R_2 such that $R_1 < R_2 < R$. By 24. III, there is only a finite number (if any) of $|a_n|$ greater than $1/R_2^n$, i. e. after N, say, $|a_n| < 1/R_2^n$. Hence, for $n > N$ and $|z| \leqslant R_1$, we have

$$|R_n(z)| < R_1^{n+1}/R_2^{n+1} + R_1^{n+2}/R_2^{n+2} + \dots$$
$$= (R_1/R_2)^{n+1}/(1 - R_1/R_2).$$

Since $R_1/R_2 < 1$, we have, for a sufficiently large n, $|R_n(z)| < \epsilon$ for *every* z in $|z| \leqslant R_1$:

IV. *A power series with radius of convergence* R *converges uniformly in every circle of radius* $R_1 < R$.

Noticing that $a_n z^n$ is a continuous function of z, we obtain, by I, the result:

V. *The sum function of a power series is a continuous function at every inner point of its circle of convergence.*

It follows, if we put $z = x + iy$ and separate the real and imaginary parts $f(z) = P(x, y) + iQ(x, y)$, that P and Q are continuous functions of (x, y) in the circle $x^2 + y^2 < R^2$, and thus also $|f(z)| = |\sqrt{P^2(x, y) + Q^2(x, y)}|$ *is a continuous function of* (x, y) in the same circle.

An important consequence of this fact is the following theorem.

VI. *The zeros of a regular function are isolated from one another*, i. e. if $f(b) = 0$, there is a circle c, $|z - b| = r$, such that b is the only zero of $f(z)$ in c.

A real or complex function is said to be *regular* (*holomorphic*) at $z = b$ if it can be expanded in a power series about b.

Proof. Expand $f(z)$ in a power series in the neighbourhood of b, $f(z) = b_0 + b_1(z - b) + \dots$. Since $f(b) = 0$, $b_0 = 0$. It may happen that some of the other coefficients are zero. But all of them cannot vanish unless $f(z)$ vanishes for every z. Let b_k be the first non-vanishing coefficient, $k \geqslant 1$. Then

$$f(z) = (z - b)^k [b_k + b_{k+1}(z - b) + \dots].$$

The factor $(z - b)^k$ vanishes only at $z = b$. On the other hand, putting

$$g(z) = b_k + b_{k+1}(z - b) + b_{k+2}(z - b)^2 + \dots,$$

the value of the continuous function $|g(z)|$ at $z=b$ is $|b_k|>0$, so that, by 14. VI, there is a circle c, centre at b, at the points of which $|g(z)|>0$. Thus $g(z)$ does not vanish in c, and hence neither does $f(z)$ except at $z=b$.

The same result applies to any value assumed by a regular function. In fact,

$$f(z)-f(c)=\sum_{1}^{\infty} a_n (z-c)^n$$

vanishes at c and does not vanish elsewhere in a sufficiently small circle round c, i. e. $f(z)$ does not assume again the value $f(c)$ in the neighbourhood of c.

28. *Infinite products.* Put $P_n=(1+a_0)(1+a_1)\dots(1+a_n)$. If $\lim\limits_{n=\infty} P_n = l$ exists and is different from zero, we say that the *infinite product*

$$(1)\qquad (1+a_0)(1+a_1)\dots(1+a_n)\dots \equiv \prod_{n=0}^{\infty}(1+a_n)$$

is *convergent.* If the limit in question does not exist, we call the infinite product *divergent.* The infinite products for which $l=0$ have rather singular properties. We call them *nil-products.* Consequently in a convergent (divergent) infinite product every factor is different from zero. Since $\lim P_n = l$ and $\lim P_{n-1}=l$, we have

$$(2)\qquad \lim_{n=\infty}\frac{P_n}{P_{n-1}}=\lim_{n=\infty}(1+a_n)=1,$$

i. e.

$$\lim_{n=\infty} a_n = 0.$$

Thus the factors of a convergent product tend to 1.

More generally

$$(3)\qquad \lim_{n=\infty}\frac{P_{n+k}}{P_n}=\lim_{n=\infty}(1+a_{n+1})\dots(1+a_{n+k})=1.$$

Similarly, if we write $l=P_n R_n$,

$$(4)\qquad \lim_{n=\infty} R_n = 1.$$

If the product $(1+|a_0|)(1+|a_1|)\ldots(1+|a_n|)\ldots$ is convergent and $a_n \neq -1$ for any n we say that the product (1) is *absolutely* convergent.

I. *An absolutely convergent product is not a nil-product.*

Proof.

$|(1+a_{n+1})\ldots(1+a_{n+k})-1| \leqslant (1+|a_{n+1}|)\ldots(1+|a_{n+k}|)-1.$

But, by (4), $\lim_{n=\infty}(1+|a_{n+1}|)\ldots(1+|a_{n+k}|)\ldots = 1$; therefore if $n>N$, $(1+|a_{n+1}|)\ldots(1+|a_{n+k}|)-1<\epsilon$ for *every* n *and* k. Consequently, if $n>N$, $|(1+a_{n+1})\ldots(1+a_{n+k})\ldots| \geqslant 1-\epsilon$. Since the preceding factors do not contain zero, we have

$$|(1+a_0)(1+a_1)\ldots(1+a_n)\ldots|>0,$$

which was to be proved.

Usually the convergence or divergence of an infinite product is tested by transforming it into a series. For instance, if we put $v_0 = 1+a_0$, $v_n = P_n - P_{n-1} = (1+a_0)\ldots(1+a_{n-1})\,a_n$, the partial sums of the series $\sum_{n=0}^{\infty} v_n$ are just P_n and its sum is P.

In the case where the factors are functions of one or several variables, we say that the product is *uniformly* convergent in an interval or in a region if the sequence $P_n(x, y, z, \ldots)$ tends uniformly to its limit function $l(x, y, z, \ldots)$ for the points of the interval or region in question.

The series Σv_n and the infinite product are uniformly convergent at the same time. It follows that

II. *If all the factors are continuous functions in a region R, the infinite product, uniformly convergent in R, is also continuous in R.*

The usual test of convergence for infinite products is given by the following theorem.

III. *The infinite product*

$$\prod_{n=0}^{\infty}(1+|a_n|) \tag{5}$$

and the infinite series

$$\sum_{n=0}^{\infty}|a_n| \tag{6}$$

are convergent at the same time.

Proof. Putting

$$Q_n = (1+|a_0|)(1+|a_1|)\dots(1+|a_n|),$$

we see that

(7) $$Q_n > 1+|a_0|+|a_1|+\dots+|a_n|,$$

and, since $1+x<e^x$ for $x>0$, we have

(8) $$Q_n < \exp(|a_0|+\dots+|a_n|).$$

The two inequalities (7) and (8) show that if the partial sums of (6) are bounded, in which case this series of positive terms is convergent, then also the partial products of (5) are bounded, and so (5) is convergent and vice versa.

For general infinite products with complex a_n, we have the following test.

IV. *If* (5) *is convergent, then also*

(9) $$\prod (1+a_n)$$

is convergent. Absolute convergence implies ordinary convergence also for infinite products.

Proof. Put

$$v_n = P_n - P_{n-1} = (1+a_0)\dots(1+a_{n-1})\,a_n$$
$$V_n = Q_n - Q_{n-1} = (1+|a_0|)\dots(1+|a_{n-1}|)\,|a_n|.$$

Since, by hypothesis and by III, Q_n tends to a limit, the series ΣV_n is convergent. It follows, since $|v_n| \leqslant V_n$, that Σv_n also is (absolutely) convergent. But the partial sums of the latter series are the partial products of (9), which proves the theorem. This result is not obvious because of the rather arbitrary definition of absolute convergence for infinite products.

29. *Bracketing and decomposition of terms.* If in the divergent series $1-1+1-1+\dots$ we unite consecutive pairs of terms $(1-1)+(1-1)+\dots$ we obtain a series where all the terms vanish, i. e. a convergent series with the sum zero. If we write $1-(1-1)-(1-1)-\dots$ we obtain a convergent series with a sum 1. Similarly, starting with a convergent series Σa_n and putting $a_n = (a_n+1)-1$, we destroy the convergence if we consider a_n+1 and -1 as separate terms, because, writing them out in any order, the terms do not tend to zero. The partial

sums $s_0+1, s_0, s_1+1, s_1, \ldots, s_n+1, s_n, \ldots$ have the two limiting numbers s and $s+1$.

Facts of this kind are of the utmost importance in the theory of analytic functions, since we shall frequently decompose in this way the power series defining the function. Therefore we indicate here the principal properties of such operations.

I. *Bracketing does not destroy convergence or affect sum. Some divergent series may be made convergent by bracketing.*

Proof. If Σa_n is a convergent series and if its partial sums, s_n, tend to s, bracketing amounts to considering only a partial sequence of s_n.

If we start with the terms $a_0+1, -1, a_1+1, -1, \ldots a_n+1, -1, \ldots,$ convenient bracketing leads to Σa_n, i.e. to a convergent series.

In many cases we shall have to replace every term a_n of a series Σa_n by an infinite series $\sum_{k=0}^{\infty} a_{n,k} = a_n$. We obtain an expression of the type

(1) $a_{00}+a_{01}+\ldots+a_{0k}+\ldots$ ad inf. $+a_{10}+a_{11}+a_{12}+\ldots+a_{1k}$ $+\ldots$ ad inf. $+\ldots+a_{n0}+a_{n1}+\ldots+a_{nk}+\ldots$ ad inf. $+\ldots$ ad inf.

According to our convention in art. 6 the term a_{10} is the $(\omega+1)$th term, a_{11} is the $(\omega+2)$th, &c., a_{n0} is the $(n\omega+1)$th, &c. The order displayed by all the terms is of the type ω^2. We shall call such a series a *transfinite series* of ω^2 type, or a *doubly infinite series.*

Performing the same operation on some or all of the terms of the new series, we obtain transfinite series of higher types.

We define the sum of such a transfinite series in the usual way by means of its partial sums. The sum of the first ordinary infinite series will be denoted by s_ω. After that comes

$$s_{\omega+1} = s_\omega + a_{10}, \ldots, s_{2\omega} = s_\omega + \sum_{k=0}^{\infty} a_{1k}, \text{ \&c.}$$

When there is a last term to such a sequence the last term is called the *final limit* of the sequence. This case will not occur in the theory of analytic functions. When there is no last term we say that A is a *final limiting number* of the sequence if after any term there are still terms of the sequence in any neighbourhood of A. Denote by R_n the section of the sequence following the term s_n (n being an ordinary or a transfinite suffix). If R_n is unbounded for every n, we say that the sequence is finally unbounded and that ∞ is an (improper) final limiting number of the sequence. If a transfinite sequence has only one proper or improper final limiting number s, we say that s is the *final limit* of s_n. In symbols, $s_n \twoheadrightarrow s$.

All these definitions are exact copies of the corresponding definitions for ordinary infinite sequences and extend to every type of transfinite sequence (well-ordered set) of numbers (see P. Dienes, 1923).

If we consider the numbers s_n as forming a set, only some of their limiting numbers, perhaps only one, will be final limiting numbers of the same numbers written out in the form of a sequence. Writing them out in different orders, we shall obtain, in general, different final limiting numbers. *The ideas of set and sequence are here clearly separated.*

A transfinite series is said to converge if its partial sums tend to a proper ($\neq \infty$) *final limit.* We shall deal only with absolutely convergent transfinite series for which $\Sigma |a_n|$ is a convergent transfinite series.

Bolzano's theorem, 18. I, extends to transfinite sequences in the following form.

II. *If all the numbers of a transfinite sequence S are in the interval (a, b), or in the region R, S has a final limiting number in (a, b), or in R.*

Proof for real sequences (the extension to complex sequences is obvious). If after a suffix N all the numbers a_n of S are outside the interval (c, d), S has, by definition, no final limiting number in the open (c, d). Hence, halving (a, b), there will be numbers of S after any suffix in at least one of the two halves. Halving this part again, and continuing the process in the usual way, we establish the existence of a number c in the closed (a, b) such that the interval $(c-\epsilon, c+\epsilon)$ contains numbers of S after any suffix for arbitrarily small ϵ.

Cauchy's fundamental test, 18. VII, extends similarly to transfinite sequences:

III. *The necessary and sufficient condition that a transfinite sequence S shall have a final limit is that to every positive* ϵ *shall correspond an ordinary or a transfinite suffix n such that, for every positive p (finite or transfinite),* $|a_{n+p}-a_n|<\epsilon$.

Proof. The condition is *necessary.* In fact, if $a_n \twoheadrightarrow a$, there is a suffix n such that after n there are no numbers of S outside $|z-a| = \epsilon$, for otherwise, by II, S would have a final limiting number outside this circle. Hence $|a_s-a_r| \leqslant 2\epsilon$ when both r and s come after n.

The condition is *sufficient.* In fact, by hypothesis, all the numbers a_{n+p} are in the circle $|z-a_n| = \epsilon$ and thus the final limiting numbers of S are also in the same circle: the diameter d of the set F of final limiting numbers is $\leqslant 2\epsilon$. Since the number ϵ is arbitrarily small and d is a determinate non-negative number, $d = 0$, i.e. F is either empty or it contains only one number. The first case is excluded by II.

It follows that the two important tests, 23. I and 23. IV, are valid for transfinite series Thus, if $\Sigma|a_n|$ converges, then also Σa_n converges.

We notice that, by 6. 1, an absolutely convergent transfinite series has only an enumerable infinity of non-vanishing terms.

Going back to our original problem we shall now prove

IV. *If both the original and the decomposed transfinite series are convergent, they have the same sum.*

Proof. If in general we denote by s_n' the partial sums of the decomposed series, the final limiting numbers of the sequence s_n' contain those of s_n. Thus, if both have only one, it is the same number.

But decomposition may destroy both conditional and absolute convergence.

V. *If the ordinary or transfinite series* Σa_n *is absolutely convergent, then derangement, bracketing, and decomposition into absolutely convergent series do not affect its convergence or its sum.*

Proof. By I, bracketing does not affect convergence or sum. Similarly, by IV, since, by hypothesis, the decomposed series is also convergent, decomposition has no effect on convergence or sum. To establish the result for derangement, suppose first that all the terms a_n are positive real numbers. Since, by hypothesis, Σa_n converges to s, say, we put $s = s_n + R_n$, where s_n is the n-th partial sum, and, after a certain suffix M, $R_n < \epsilon$. Denoting the deranged series and its partial sums by a dash, we have obviously $s_n' \leqslant s$, i.e. s_n' converges to a final limit $s' \leqslant s$. On the other hand, after a certain suffix $R_n' < \epsilon$ also, and thus the terms of s_n figuring also in s_n' give a sum $\leqslant s_n'$ and the other terms (in R_n') give a sum $< \epsilon$, i.e. $s_n < s_n' + \epsilon$. Hence, $s \leqslant s' + \epsilon$ with an arbitrary ϵ, i.e. $s \leqslant s'$, which proves that $s' = s$.

By 6. I, we can write the non-zero moduli of an absolutely convergent complex series in an ordinary series $\Sigma\,|a_i''|$ whose remainder $r_i < \epsilon$ for $i > j$, where i and j are ordinary integers. Now the convergence and sum of a transfinite series are not affected by transferring a finite number of terms to the beginning of the series. Therefore, after a finite or transfinite N,
$s_n = a_1'' + \ldots + a_j'' + \bar{s}_n,\, s_n' = a_1'' + \ldots + a_j'' + \bar{s}_n'$, where $|\bar{s}_n| < \epsilon$, $|\bar{s}_n'| < \epsilon$, so that $|s_n - s_n'| < 2\epsilon$; and, ϵ being arbitrary, our statement is proved.

The result just established is one of the fundamental instruments in the theory of analytic functions.

30. As an application we are going to decompose, rearrange and bracket a power series $f(z) = \Sigma a_n z^n$ convergent in a circle of radius R, centre at the origin. Put $z = (z-a)+a$, i.e. $z^n = (z-a)^n + C_1^n (z-a)^{n-1} a + \ldots + a^n$. Thus we obtain the decomposed power series

$$(1)\quad a_0 + a_1(z-a) + a_1 a + a_2(z-a)^2 + a_2\, 2(z-a)\,a + a_2 a^2$$
$$+ \ldots + a_n(z-a)^n + C_1^n a_n (z-a)^{n-1} a + \ldots + a_n a^n + \ldots.$$

If $|a| > R$, there are infinitely many terms $|a_n a^n| > 1$, i.e. the series is divergent. But a suitable rearrangement and bracketing may still change it into a convergent series. Suppose for the moment that $|a| < R$, i.e. a is an inner point of the circle of convergence. Since

$$|[(z-a)+a]^n| \leqslant [\,|z-a| + |a|\,]^n$$
$$= |z-a|^n + C_1^n |z-a|^{n-1}|a| + \ldots + |a|^n,$$

the decomposed series is absolutely convergent if z satisfies the condition $|z-a| + |a| < R$, i.e. $|z-a| < R - |a|$.

In the geometrical interpretation this means that z is an inner point of the circle of radius $R-|a|$, centre at a. This circle touches the original circle of convergence and lies entirely within it. Thus if z is in this circle we can, by 29. V, rearrange and bracket this series at our will without affecting convergence or sum. Grouping together terms containing the same power of $(z-a)$ and bracketing the group, we obtain first, from the terms not containing $z-a$, $a_0+a_1 a+a_2 a^2+\ldots+a_n a^n+\ldots=f(a)$;

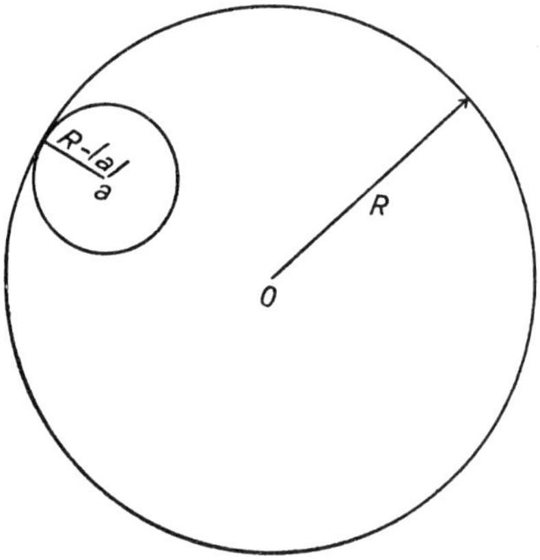

FIG. 7.

then the group containing $z-a$ leads to

$$a_1+2a_2 a+\ldots+na_n a^{n-1}+\ldots=f'(a), \text{ \&c.,}$$

the coefficient of $(z-a)^k$ being

$$(2) \qquad f^{(k)}(a)/k! = \sum_{n=k}^{\infty} \frac{n(n-1)\ldots(n-k+1)}{k!} a_n a^{n-k},$$

where the left-hand side is, for the moment, only a convenient short symbol for the right-hand side.
Hence

$$(3) \qquad f(z) = \Sigma f^{(n)}(a)(z-a)^n/n!$$

in the circle of radius $R-|a|$, centre at a.

If the values of a function in the neighbourhood of a point a can be represented by a convergent power series in $(z-a)$, radius >0, we say that the function is *regular* at a. The function $f(z)$ is obviously regular at the origin $z=0$. The result condensed in (3) is then formulated in the following theorem:

I. *The sum function of a power series is regular at every inner point of the circle of convergence.*

But the rearrangement and bracketing may, in certain cases, turn the divergent series (1) where $|z|>R$ into a convergent one. For example, the sum function of $\Sigma(-1)^n z^n$, convergent in $|z|<1$, is obviously $1/(1+z)$. Moreover the sum function of $\Sigma(-1)^n nz^{n-1} = -\Sigma(-1)^n z^n \Sigma(-1)^n z^n = -1/(1+z)^2$, that is, for x real, $\Sigma(-1)^n nx^{n-1} = [1/(1+x)]'$, and so on. In general

$$\sum_{n=k}^{\infty}(-1)^n n(n-1)\dots(n-k+1)x^{n-k}$$
$$= (-1)^k k!/(1+x)^{k+1} = [1/(1+x)]^{(k)}.$$

Hence, by (3),

$$(4) \qquad 1/(1+z) = \Sigma(-1)^n (z-a)^n/(1+a)^{n+1},$$

provided a is an inner point of $|z|=1$. The general lower bound for the radius of convergence is $1-|a|$. But as a matter of fact the radius of convergence of (4) is $|1+a|$, i.e. if a is $1/2$, say, the series (4) converges in a circle of radius $1+1/2$, centre at $1/2$. The new circle of convergence contains the original one and

$$\sum\frac{(-1)^n}{(1+a)^{n+1}}(z-a)^n = \frac{1}{1+a}\sum\left(\frac{a-z}{1+a}\right)^n = \frac{1}{1+a}\,\frac{1}{1-\dfrac{a-z}{1+a}} = \frac{1}{1+z},$$

i.e. the new series duly represents the function $1/(1+z)$ also at points outside the first circle.

This leads us to the idea of *analytic continuation* of the function defined by a power series in a circle. If we start with the power series, the function (= sum function) is defined first only in the circle of convergence of this power series. Decomposing the terms of this power series in the way indicated, with a inside the circle of convergence, and regrouping them according to the powers of $z-a$, we may succeed in defining the function outside the original circle. By 27. V, the second power series is continuous, i.e. the second function extends the original one in a continuous manner. This is the process of *analytic continuation*.

We may also fail in our effort. For example, taking $a=-1/2$, the radius of convergence of the new series is only $1/2$. In general, if a is between -1 and 0, the new series converges only in a circle contained in the first one. In the direction of -1 the continuation does not succeed. In this case we say that -1 is a *singular point* of the function. In reality, in the neighbourhood of -1 the function assumes as large values as we please — it becomes infinite. It is the singular behaviour of the function which stops the analytic continuation. We shall see later on that this is generally the case.

The second power series may be continued in its turn. The complete function determined by all the continuations of a given power series is called an *analytic function.* The part of it represented by any of the power series used in the process of continuation is called an *element* of the analytic function.

EXERCISES III

1. Establish the existence of the limit

$$\lim (1+1/2+\ldots+1/n-\log n) = c \text{ (Euler's constant).}$$

Put

$$u_n = \int_0^1 t\,dt / n(n+t) = 1/n - \log\frac{n+1}{n};$$

we have $0 < u_n < 1/n^2 = \int_0^1 dt/n^2$, i.e. Σu_n converges. On the other hand, $1+1/2+\ldots+1/n-\log n = \Sigma u_k + \log[(n+1)/n]$ and

$$\log\frac{n+1}{n} \to 0$$

show that the difference $1+1/2+1/3+\ldots+1/n-\log n$ steadily decreases.

2. $\Sigma 1/(an+b)^\alpha$, $a>0$, $b>0$ is convergent for $\alpha>1$ and divergent for $\alpha \leqslant 1$. In fact, $n^\alpha/(an+b)^\alpha = 1/[a+b/n]^\alpha \to 1/a^\alpha$, i.e. $1/(an+b)^\alpha \sim 1/(an)^\alpha$ (apply 24. I).

3. (a) $\Sigma 1/(\log n)^p$ is divergent, for, by Ex. I. 29, for sufficiently large n, $(\log n)^p < n$.

(b) $\Sigma 1/(\log n)^n$ is convergent, for $\sqrt[n]{1/(\log n)^n} = 1/\log n \to 0$.

4. (a) $\Sigma 1/(a+bn+cn^2)$ is convergent, for $|a+bn+cn^2|/n^2 \to |c|$.

(b) $\Sigma n!/n^n$ is convergent, for $n!/n^n < 2/n^2$ if $n>2$.

5. (a) $\Sigma 1/(\log n)^{\log n} = \Sigma 1/n^{\log\log n}$ is convergent, for

$$n^{\log\log n} > n^2 \text{ if } n > a^2,$$

where a is the (arbitrary but positive) base of log.

(b) $\Sigma 1/+\sqrt{a+bn+n^2}$ is divergent, for $\sqrt{a+bn+n^2}/n \to 1$.

6. (a) $\Sigma z^n / n!$ is absolutely convergent for every fixed value of z, for $|a_{n+1} / a_n| = |z| / (n+1) \to 0$.

(b) $\Sigma n^\alpha z^n$ is convergent if $|z| < 1$ and divergent if $|z| > 1$ whatever the fixed value of α. In fact

$$|a_{n+1} / a_n| = (n+1)^\alpha z / n^\alpha \to z.$$

7. r being the radius of convergence of $\Sigma a_n z^n$, determine that of $\Sigma n^\alpha a_n z^n$ and $\Sigma a_n z^n / n!$ $(r, +\infty.)$

8. Put $a_0 + a_1 + \ldots + a_n = s_n$. If $s_n b_{n+1} \to 0$ and $\Sigma s_n (b_n - b_{n+1})$ is convergent, then also $\Sigma a_n b_n$ is convergent. For

$$\sum_{\nu = n+1}^{n+p} a_\nu b_\nu = \sum_{\nu = n+1}^{n+p} s_\nu (b_\nu - b_{\nu+1}) - s_n b_{n+1} + s_{n+p} b_{n+p+1}.$$

9. Show that $\Sigma a_n b_n$ is convergent in the following three cases:

(a) $b_{n-1} > b_n$, $b_n \to 0$ and s_n is bounded.

(b) $b_{n-1} > b_n > \alpha$ and Σa_n is convergent.

(c) $b_n \to 0$, $\Sigma |b_n - b_{n+1}|$ converges and s_n is bounded.

10. Examine the convergence and divergence of $\Sigma z^n / n$ on $|z| = 1$. At $z = 1$ it is known to diverge; at every other point the series converges for, if $|z| = 1$ but $z \neq 1$, then

$$|1 + z + \ldots + z^n| = |1 - z^{n+1}| / |1 - z| < 2 / |1 - z|,$$

i.e. the partial sums of Σz^n are bounded and (a) of Ex. 9 applies.

It follows that $\sum_1^\infty \frac{\sin nx}{n}$ converges for every real x and $\sum_1^\infty \frac{\cos nx}{n}$ converges for every real x except $x = 2k\pi$.

11. Find the points on $|z| = 1$ at which $\Sigma z^{pn} / n$, p an integer, converges (diverges). By the preceding example it diverges only when $z^p = 1$, i. e. at the p-th roots of unity.

12. The radii of convergence of $\Sigma a_n z^n$ and $\Sigma b_n z^n$ are r and R respectively. The radius of convergence of

$$\Sigma (a_0 b_n + a_1 b_{n-1} + \ldots + a_n b_0) z^n$$

is at least as great as the lesser of r and R, but it may be much larger, as shown by Σz^n and $(1 - z) E(z) = 1 - \sum_{n=2}^{\infty} (n-1) z^n / n!$, whose product series converges for every value of z.

13. *Appell's comparison theorem.*

If $p_n > 0$, Σp_n diverges, the radius of convergence of $\Sigma p_n z^n$ is 1, then it follows from $a_n / p_n \to s$ that the radius of convergence of $\Sigma a_n z^n$ is also 1 and $\lim_{r \to 1} \Sigma a_n r^n / \Sigma p_n r^n = s$. (Appell, 1879, usually attributed to Cesàro.)

Proof. Putting $a_n = p_n s + p_n \epsilon_n$, we have

$$\Sigma a_n r^n / \Sigma p_n r^n = s + \Sigma \epsilon_n p_n r^n / \Sigma p_n r^n,$$

i. e. it is sufficient to prove the theorem for $s = 0$. Then for $n > m$, say, $|\epsilon_n| < \epsilon$ and thus $|\Sigma a_n r^n| \leqslant |\sum_0^m a_n r^n| + \epsilon \sum_{n=0}^{\infty} p_n r^n$. The first term on the right-hand side divided by $\Sigma p_n r^n$ tends to 0 when $r \to 1$, for the numerator tends to a finite limit and the denominator tends to $+\infty$. Hence all the limiting numbers of the left-hand side are in $|z| \leqslant \epsilon$, i. e. ϵ being arbitrarily small, the only limiting number is 0. Q. e. d.

This result is of wide application.

14. *Abel's theorem.* If $\sum_{n=0}^{\infty} a_n$ converges to s, then $\lim_{r \to 1} \Sigma a_n r^n = s$.

In fact, applying Appell's theorem to $\Sigma a_n r^n / (1-r) = \Sigma s_n r^n$ and $1/(1-r) = \Sigma r^n$, where, by hypothesis, $s_n = a_0 + a_1 + \dots + a_n$ divided by 1 converges to s, we obtain Abel's theorem.

15. *Frobenius's theorem.* If $\sigma_n = [s_0 + s_1 + \dots + s_n] / n \to s$, then also $\lim_{r \to 1} \Sigma a_n r^n = s$. Apply Appell's theorem to

$$\Sigma \sigma_n r^n = \Sigma a_n r^n / (1-r)^2 \text{ and } \Sigma n r^n = 1/(1-r)^2.$$

16. Extend Appell's theorem to the case $r = \infty$. If $p_n > 0$ and $\Sigma p_n z^n$ converges for every value of z, then it follows from $a_n / p_n \to s$ that $\Sigma a_n z^n$ is convergent for every value of z and

$$\lim_{r \to \infty} \Sigma a_n r^n / \Sigma p_n r^n = s.$$

The same proof as in Ex. 13. The condition that Σp_n should be divergent is replaced here by the fact that, necessarily, $\Sigma p_n r^n \to \infty$ with r.

17. If $p_n > 0$ and $\Sigma p_n z^n$ diverges for $z = 1$ but converges for $|z| < 1$, then it follows from $(a_0 + a_1 + \dots + a_n) / (p_0 + p_1 + \dots + p_n) \to s$ that $\lim_{r \to 1} \Sigma a_n r^n / \Sigma p_n r^n = s$. Apply Ex. 13 to $\Sigma a_n r^n / (1-r) = \Sigma s_n r^n$ and $\Sigma p_n r^n / (1-r) = \Sigma s_n' r^n$ where $s_n = a_0 + \dots + a_n$, $s_n' = p_0 + \dots + p_n$.

18. $0 < r_1 \leqslant r_2 \leqslant \dots \leqslant r_n \leqslant \dots \to \infty$. We say that σ is their *index of convergence* if $\sum_{n=1}^{\infty} 1 / r_n^{\alpha}$ converges for $\alpha > \sigma$ and diverges for $\alpha < \sigma$.

Since the series diverges for $\alpha = 0$, $\sigma \geqslant 0$. If $\Sigma 1/r_n^\alpha$ diverges for every α, we say that the index of convergence is ∞. Prove that

$$\overline{\lim_{n=\infty}} \log n / \log r_n = \sigma.$$

If s is this upper limit we have $\log n < (s+\epsilon) \log r_n$ for sufficiently large n, i.e. $1/r_n^{s+\epsilon} < 1/n$, $1/r_n^{s+2\epsilon} < 1/n^{s+2\epsilon/s+\epsilon}$, i.e. $\Sigma 1/r_n^{s+2\epsilon}$ is convergent and thus, ϵ being arbitrarily small, $\sigma \leqslant s$. On the other hand, by hypothesis, $\Sigma 1/r_n^{\sigma+\epsilon}$ is convergent and thus $n/r_n^{\sigma+\epsilon} \to 0$ (by 23. VII). Hence, for sufficiently large n, $n < r_n^{\sigma+\epsilon}$, i.e. $\log n < (\sigma+\epsilon) \log r_n$ and thus $\log n / \log r_n < \sigma + \epsilon$, which shows that $\sigma \geqslant s$.

19. If x_n are real non-vanishing numbers and $|x_i - x_k| \geqslant d > 0$, the index of convergence of $|x_n|$ is $\leqslant 1$.

20. If $0 < r_1 \leqslant r_2 \leqslant \dots$, the moduli of the terms of $1 + \Sigma z^n / r_1 r_2 \dots r_n$ steadily increase up to the m-th term for which $r_m < |z| < r_{m+1}$ and steadily decrease after the 'maximum term'. *The index of the maximum term*, or the greatest of the indices having the same maximum modulus, is called the *central index*.

If $\Sigma a_n z^n$ converges for every z, the central index does not remain constantly the same when $|z| \to \infty$. In fact for $n > m$,

$$|a_n z^n| > |a_m z^m| \text{ if } |z| > \sqrt[n-m]{|a_m / a_n|}.$$

21. a_n is real, $s_n = a_0 + a_1 + \dots + a_n$. Show that

$$\underline{\lim_{n=\infty}}\, s_n \leqslant \overline{\lim_{r\to 1}}\, (\Sigma a_n r^n) \leqslant \overline{\lim_{n=\infty}}\, s_n.$$

22. $a_n > 0$, $\lim_{r \to 1} \Sigma a_n r^n = s$. Show that $s_n \to s$, i.e. in this case the converse of Abel's theorem is true.

23. $p_n > 0$, Σp_n convergent. Show that

$$(p_1 + 2p_2 + \dots + np_n)/n \to 0.$$

24. $p_n > 0$ is steadily increasing to infinity. If Σa_n is convergent, then

$$(1) \qquad (p_0 a_0 + p_1 a_1 + \dots + p_n a_n)/p_n \to 0,$$

and conversely if (1) is true for every positive p_n steadily increasing to infinity, Σa_n is convergent. (Kronecker.)

25. $a_n \to 0$, (real), L and U are the least and greatest limiting numbers of the sequence of partial sums $s_n = a_0 + a_1 + \dots + a_n$. Then every value between L and U is a limiting number of the sequence (s_n).

26. If every partial series of Σa_n is convergent, the series is absolutely convergent.

27. The Cauchy product of the *two divergent* series

$$1-3/2-(3/2)^2-\dots \text{ and } 1+(2+1/2^2)-(2^2+1/2^3)3/2 \\ +(2^3+1/2^4)(3/2)^2+\dots \text{ is } 1+3/4+(3/4)^2+(3/4)^3+\dots,$$

i. e. is *absolutely convergent.* How do you explain this result?

28. *The hypergeometric series*

$$1+\frac{\alpha}{1}\frac{\beta}{\gamma}z+\frac{\alpha(\alpha+1)}{1.2}\frac{\beta(\beta+1)}{\gamma(\gamma+1)}z^2+\dots.$$

Since $a_{n+1}/a_n = z(\alpha+n)(\beta+n)/(1+n)(\gamma+n)\to z$, the series is absolutely convergent if $|z|<1$ and divergent if $|z|>1$. If $z=1$, by Gauss's test, 24. VII, the series converges if $\alpha+\beta<\gamma$ and diverges if $\alpha+\beta\geqslant\gamma$.

29. *Pringsheim's theorem.* Putting $A_n=a_1+a_2+\dots+a_n$ where $a_n\geqslant 0$ and Σa_n diverges, $\sum_{n=2}^{\infty} a_n/A_nA_{n-1}^{\rho}$ is convergent if $\rho>0$.

Proof. Choose an integer $p>1/\rho$. It is sufficient to prove the theorem for $\tau=1/p$. As $\Sigma(1/A_{n-1}^{\tau}-1/A_n^{\tau})$ is obviously convergent, it is sufficient to prove that

$$(A_n-A_{n-1})/(A_nA_{n-1}^{\tau})<\frac{1}{\tau}(1/A_{n-1}^{\tau}-1/A_n^{\tau}),$$

i.e. $1-A_{n-1}/A_n<\frac{1}{\tau}(1-A_{n-1}^{\tau}/A_n^{\tau})$. But $1-x^p<p(1-x)$, since $1-x^p=(1-x)(1+x+\dots+x^{p-1})$, i.e. putting $x=(A_{n-1}/A_n)^{1/p}$ we establish the result.

30. *Dini's theorem.* Notation and conditions as in the preceding example. $\Sigma a_n/A_n^{\rho}$ converges if $\rho>1$ and diverges if $\rho\leqslant 1$. If $\rho=1$, we have

$$a_{n+1}/A_{n+1}+\dots+a_{n+k}/A_{n+k}\geqslant(a_{n+1}+\dots+a_{n+k})/A_{n+k} \\ =1-A_n/A_{n+k}.$$

Since, by hypothesis, $A_n\to\infty$, to every n belongs a k such that the $A_n/A_{n+k}<1/2$. This proves the divergence for $\rho\leqslant 1$. The convergence for $\rho>1$ is proved by Pringsheim's theorem.

31. Deduce Abel's scale by Dini's theorem.

32. If $a_n / A_n \to 0$, then $a_1 / A_1 + a_2 / A_2 + \dots + a_n / A_n \sim \log A_n$ (Cesàro). Putting $a_n / A_n = x_n$, we have, from Ex. I. 32,

$$x_n / \log [1 / (1 - x_n)] \to 1, \text{ i.e. } \frac{a_n / A_n}{\log \dfrac{A_n}{A_{n-1}}} \to 1.$$

Hence also, putting $A_0 = 1$,

$$\frac{a_1 / A_1 + a_2 / A_2 + \dots + a_n / A_n}{\log A_1 + \log A_2 / A_1 + \dots + \log A_n / A_{n-1}}$$
$$= \frac{1}{\log A_n} \left[\frac{a_1}{A_1} + \frac{a_2}{A_2} + \dots + \frac{a_n}{A_n} \right] \to 1.$$

33. Prove that $\Sigma 1 / n \log n \sim \log \log n$, and that more generally $\Sigma 1 / n \log n \log_2 n \dots \log_p n \sim \log_{p+1} n$.

CHAPTER IV

ELEMENTARY FUNCTIONS

31. *Exponential and trigonometrical functions.* We have seen in Art. 24 that the series

(1) $$\Sigma z^n/n! = E(z)$$

is convergent at every point z of the complex plane and (Art. 26) that

(2) $$E(z_1)\,E(z_2) = E(z_1 + z_2).$$

It follows that, $E(1)$ being denoted by e and m being a positive integer, $E(m) = eE(m-1) = e^2 E(m-2) = \ldots = e^m$. Moreover if m/n is any positive fraction,

$$[E(m/n)]^n = E(m/n + \ldots + m/n) = E(m) = e^m,$$

i.e., as $E(m/n)$ is positive, $E(m/n) = |\,e^{m/n}\,|$. Since $E(z)$ is continuous, by 27. IV, the same equation holds for real irrational values: $E(x) = |\,e^x\,|$. Finally for negative real values

$$E(-x)\,E(x) = E(0) = 1, \text{ i. e. } E(-x) = |\,e^{-x}\,|.$$

In general, an expression like $e^{m/n}$ has more than one value, but only one which is real and positive. If, in the case of base e, we make the special convention to denote by e^x the positive value of the expression, we can write, for real x, $E(x) = e^x$. Accordingly, $E(x)$ is called the *exponential* function. For complex values we define the exponential function by putting $e^z = E(z)$, and for any positive base a and complex index b,

(3) $$a^b = E(b \log_e a).$$

The property (2) shows that $a^{b_1} a^{b_2} = a^{b_1 + b_2}$, $a_1{}^b a_2{}^b = (a_1 a_2)^b$.

We decompose the exponential function into two parts by putting

(4) $$C(z) = \sum_0^\infty (-1)^n z^{2n}/(2n)!, \quad S(z) = \sum_0^\infty (-1)^n z^{2n+1}/(2n+1)!.$$

Since $(-1)^n = i^{2n}$ we have, for every value of z, real or complex,

(5) $$e^{iz} = C(z) + iS(z).$$

The properties of $C(z)$ and $S(z)$. $C(z)$ is obviously an even function, and $S(z)$ is an odd function, i. e.

(6) $$C(-z) = C(z),\ S(-z) = -S(z).$$

Moreover $C(0) = 1$, $S(0) = 0$. We readily verify also, by multiplying the infinite series in question, that

(7) $$\begin{aligned} C(z)\,C(z') \mp S(z)\,S(z') &= C(z \pm z'),\\ S(z)\,C(z') \pm C(z)\,S(z') &= S(z \pm z'). \end{aligned}$$

Putting in (7), with the lower signs, $z' = z$, we have

(8) $$C^2(z) + S^2(z) = 1.$$

Restricting ourselves to real values x of the variable, $C(x)$ and $S(x)$ are real functions with the following properties.

I. *$C(x)$ vanishes between $\sqrt{2}$ and $\sqrt{3}$.*

Proof. Since $\quad x^{2n}/(2n)! > x^{2n+2}/(2n+2)!$
provided $\quad x^2 < (2n+1)\,(2n+2)$,

the terms of the alternating series $C(x)$ are constantly decreasing from the very first term on, provided $x < \sqrt{2}$. By 23. IV, the sign of the sum of such a series is that of its first term, here 1. Thus, $C(x) > 0$ between 0 and $\sqrt{2}$. Similarly $S(x) > 0$ in $(0, \sqrt{6})$. On the other hand the moduli of the same series are constantly decreasing from the second term $(n = 1)$ on, provided $x < \sqrt{12}$. But $|1 - x^2/2| > x^4/24$ and $1 - x^2/2 < 0$ if $\sqrt{3} < x < 2{\cdot}5$. Thus, taking for first term $1 - x^2/2!$, the series $(1 - x^2/2!) + x^4/4! - x^6/6! + \ldots$ is alternating and constantly decreasing for the specified range of values of x. Since the first term is negative, $C(x) < 0$. Since $C(x)$ is continuous, it vanishes between $\sqrt{2}$ and $\sqrt{3}$. The zeros of a regular function being isolated, $C(x)$ has only a finite number of zeros in a finite interval. Denote its smallest positive zero by $\pi/2$. Its smallest negative zero is $-\pi/2$ because $C(-\pi/2) = C(\pi/2) = 0$.

II. *$C(x)$ and $S(x)$ are periodic functions with the period 2π.*

Proof. From (8), $S^2(\pi/2) + C^2(\pi/2) = 1$, i. e. $S(\pi/2) = \pm 1$ and, as $S(x) > 0$ in $(0, \sqrt{6})$, we have $S(\pi/2) = 1$. Hence by (7),

$$C(\pi)\,C\Big(-\frac{\pi}{2}\Big) - S(\pi)\,S\Big(-\frac{\pi}{2}\Big) = C\Big(\pi - \frac{\pi}{2}\Big) = 0, \text{ i.e. } S(\pi) = 0.$$

Similarly from

$$C(\pi)S\left(-\frac{\pi}{2}\right)+C\left(-\frac{\pi}{2}\right)S(\pi)=S\left(\pi-\frac{\pi}{2}\right)=S\left(\frac{\pi}{2}\right),$$

it follows that

$$C(\pi) = -S(\pi/2)/S(\pi/2) = -1.$$

Finally the equations

$$C(x+\pi) = C(x)\,C(\pi)-S(x)\,S(\pi) = -C(x)$$

and $S(x+\pi) = -S(x)$ lead to $C(x+2\pi) = -C(x+\pi) = C(x)$ and $S(x+2\pi) = S(x)$, which proves the statement.

This result leads to a fundamental property of the exponential function.

III. *$E(z)$ is a periodic function with the period $2\pi i$.* In fact $E(z+2\pi ki) = E(z)E(2\pi ki)$ and $E(2\pi ki) = C(2\pi k)+iS(2\pi k) = 1$.

We are now going to examine the behaviour of the two functions $C(x)$ and $S(x)$ as x increases from 0 to 2π.

If x and $x+h$, $h>0$, are both in $\left(0, \frac{\pi}{2}\right)$, $S(x)>0$ and thus

$$C(x+h) = C(x)C(h)-S(x)S(h) < C(x)\,C(h) < C(x),$$

i.e. $C(x)$ is constantly decreasing in $(0, \pi/2)$. The relation $C(\pi-x) = -C(x)$ shows that $C(x)$ keeps on decreasing from $\pi/2$ to π also. Consequently in $(0, \pi)$ $C(x)$ assumes every value between 1 and -1, *but only once.* Finally $C(x+\pi) = -C(x)$ shows that $C(x)$ is constantly increasing from π to 2π, i.e. in $(\pi, 2\pi)$ $C(x)$ assumes again every value between -1 and 1, but only once. Briefly $C(x)$ *increases and decreases in the same way as* $\cos x$. Similarly $S(x)$ *increases and decreases in the same way as* $\sin x$.

32. Let us take a real number c between -1 and 1. From the last remark there are two and only two values of x in the interval $(0, 2\pi)$ such that $C(x) = c$, and if x_1 is one of them, the other is $2\pi-x_1$. For these two values $S(x_1) = \sqrt{1-C^2(x_1)} = \pm\sqrt{1-c^2}$ and $S(2\pi-x_1) = \pm\sqrt{1-c^2}$. As $S(2\pi-x_1) = -S(x_1)$, there is one and only one value, x_1, say, of x for which $C(x_1) = c$ and $S(x_1) = |\sqrt{1-c^2}|$; then for $2\pi-x_1$ we have $C(2\pi-x_1) = c$, $S(2\pi-x_1) = -|\sqrt{1-c^2}|$.

If $a = a_1 + i a_2$ is a point on the unit circle we have, by hypothesis, $a_1^2 + a_2^2 = 1$, i. e. $a_2 = \pm\sqrt{1 - a_1^2}$. From the preceding remark we have

I. *If* $a_1^2 + a_2^2 = 1$, *there is one and only one real value* x, $0 \leqslant x < 2\pi$, *for which* $C(x) = a_1$ *and* $S(x) = a_2$, i. e. *for which*

$$(1) \qquad a_1 + i a_2 = C(x) + iS(x) = e^{ix}.$$

To every point on this circumference corresponds a single value of x satisfying (1), and conversely, for every value of x, $C^2(x) + S^2(x) = 1$, i. e. there is a corresponding point on the unit circle. Equation (1) establishes a one-one correspondence between the interval $0 \leqslant x < 2\pi$ and all the points on the circumference of the unit circle.

Multiplying (1) by a positive number r, we see that

II. *Every number* $A + iB$ *on the circle of radius* r, i. e. *whose absolute value is* r, *can be written in the form*

$$(2) \qquad A + iB = re^{ix}.$$

Since every complex number, except $0 + i0$, has an absolute value $r > 0$, *every complex number other than* 0 *can be written in the above form* (2). The real number x, $0 \leqslant x < 2\pi$, is called the *argument* of $A + iB$.

Consider the n points $1, e^{2\pi i/n}, e^{4\pi i/n}, \ldots, e^{(n-1)2\pi i/n}$ on the unit circle. Since

$$e^{k2\pi i/n} - e^{(k+1)2\pi i/n} = e^{k2\pi i/n}(1 - e^{2\pi i/n}),$$

the absolute value of the difference between two consecutive numbers is the same for all values of k, viz.: $|1 - e^{2\pi i/n}|$.

Interpreted geometrically, the n points in question form a regular polygon of n sides with vertices on the unit circle. The total length of this polygon is

$$n\,|1 - e^{2\pi i/n}| = n\left|\frac{2\pi i}{n} + \left(\frac{2\pi i}{n}\right)^2\frac{1}{2!} + \ldots + \left(\frac{2\pi i}{n}\right)^\nu\frac{1}{\nu!} + \ldots\right|$$
$$= \left|2\pi i + \frac{(2\pi i)^2}{n}\frac{1}{2!} + \ldots\right| \to 2\pi,$$

as $1/n \to 0$. Therefore the length of the unit circle is 2π, i. e. our symbol π introduced as the double of the first positive real zero of $C(x)$ is the number usually denoted by π, viz. the length of the semicircle of radius 1.

Hence the argument of $A+iB$ may be interpreted geometrically as the *angle in radians* between the positive real axis and the segment $(0+i0,\ A+iB)$. We shall use the symbols $\cos z$ and $\sin z$ for $C(z)$ and $S(z)$ respectively on the understanding that $\cos z$ and $\sin z$ are defined by the two infinite series, (31. 4), for $C(z)$ and $S(z)$ respectively.

III. $\cos z$ *and* $\sin z$ *have no complex roots.*

Proof. $\cos(x+iy) = \cos x(e^y+e^{-y})/2 - i\sin x\,(e^y-e^{-y})/2.$

Hence

$$|\cos(x+iy)|^2 = \cos^2 x\,(e^y+e^{-y})^2/4 + \sin^2 x\,(e^y-e^{-y})^2/4$$
$$= (e^y-e^{-y})^2/4 + \cos^2 x,$$

and this expression can vanish only when $y=0$. Q. e. d.

IV. *The equation* $e^z=0$ *has no root.*

Proof. $e^{x+iy} = e^x(\cos y + i\sin y)$. But e^x does not vanish for any real value of x, since for x positive all the terms of the series $\Sigma x^n/n!$ are positive and $E(-x) = 1/E(x)$. Moreover $\cos y$ and $\sin y$ never vanish for the same value of y.

From (31. 5) and $e^{-iz} = \cos z - i\sin z$ we obtain, for all values of z, $\cos z = (e^{iz}+e^{-iz})/2$, $\sin z = (e^{iz}-e^{-iz})/2i$. The other trigonometrical functions are defined for the complex variable by the usual relations

$$\tan z = \sin z/\cos z,\ \cot z = \cos z/\sin z,\ \&c.$$

We notice also that for purely imaginary values ix,

$$\sin ix = (e^{-x}-e^x)/2i,\ \cos ix = (e^{-x}+e^x)/2.$$

Thus $\cos ix$ and $i\sin ix$ are real functions, called *hyperbolic functions*; in symbols $\cos ix = \cosh x$, $i\sin ix = \sinh x$.

The class of elementary functions may be represented as follows:

The seven algebraic operations lead directly to polynomials, rational functions, algebraic functions like root and logarithmic functions. The inverse of the logarithm is the exponential function. And here the series stops for real variables. The definition of the exponential function for complex values leads to the incorporation of trigonometrical functions with their inverses. Any finite combination of these functions is said to be an *elementary function.*

Formulae for trigonometrical functions:

(3) $\cos mz + i\sin mz = e^{miz} = (e^{iz})^m = (\cos z + i\sin z)^m$ (De Moivre, 1706–7.)

Hence

(4) $\cos mz = \cos^m z - C_2^m \cos^{m-2} z \sin^2 z + \ldots$

(5) $\sin mz = C_1^m \cos^{m-1} z \sin z - C_3^m \cos^{m-3} z \sin^3 z + \ldots .$

Eliminating $\sin z$ or $\cos z$ by $\sin^2 z + \cos^2 z = 1$ we see that

(6)
$$\begin{aligned} \cos mz &= P(\cos z) \\ \sin mz &= Q(\sin z), \text{ for odd } m, \\ &= \cos z\, Q(\sin z), \text{ for even } m, \end{aligned}$$

where $P(z)$ and $Q(z)$ are polynomials.

The function $\sin mz$ vanishes for $z = l\pi/m$, where l is any positive or negative integer or zero. By (31. 4),

$$\sin z = z\left(1 - \frac{z^2}{3!} + \ldots\right),$$

i. e. $z = 0$ is a simple zero of $\sin z$, and thus, since

$$\sin(z + 2k\pi) = \sin z \text{ and } \sin[z + (2k+1)\pi] = -\sin z,$$

all the zeros of $\sin z$ are simple. The same remark applies to $\sin mz$.

Suppose, for simplicity, that m is odd. The polynomial $Q(u)$ vanishes for $u = \sin l\pi/m$, i. e. for the m distinct values

$$u = 0,\ \pm\sin\pi/m, \ldots,\ \pm\sin\left(\frac{m-1}{2}\frac{\pi}{m}\right).$$

Therefore, expressing $Q(u)$ in the form

$$Au\left(1 - \frac{u}{u_1}\right)\left(1 - \frac{u}{u_2}\right)\cdots\left(1 - \frac{u}{u_{m-1}}\right)$$

we obtain, uniting the factors belonging to $\pm\sin k\pi/m$,

$$\sin mz = A\sin z\left[1 - \frac{\sin^2 z}{\sin^2\frac{\pi}{m}}\right]\cdots\left[1 - \frac{\sin^2 z}{\sin^2\frac{m-1}{2}\frac{\pi}{m}}\right].$$

Since, for small values of z, $\sin mz \backsim mz$, the right-hand side $\backsim Az$, and we see that $A = m$. Replacing z by $\pi z/m$ we obtain

$$\sin\pi z = m\sin\frac{\pi z}{m}\left[1 - \frac{\sin^2\frac{\pi z}{m}}{\sin^2\frac{\pi}{m}}\right]\cdots\left[1 - \frac{\sin^2\frac{\pi z}{m}}{\sin^2\frac{m-1}{2}\frac{\pi}{m}}\right].$$

As $m \to \infty$, $m \sin \frac{\pi z}{m} \to \pi z$, $\sin^2 \frac{\pi z}{m} / \sin^2 \frac{p\pi}{m} \to z^2/p^2$. Thus the product of the first $k+1$ factors tends to

$$\pi z\,(1-z^2/1)\,(1-z^2/4)\ldots(1-z^2/k^2).$$

We are going to prove that, for sufficiently large k, the product of factors after the $(k+1)$-th differs from 1 by as little as we please. Take a p between k and $(m-1)/2$. We have

$$\sin^2 \frac{\pi z}{m} = \frac{\pi^2 z^2}{m^2}(1+\epsilon).$$

Moreover, by Taylor's theorem for real variables,

$$\sin \frac{p\pi}{m} = \frac{p\pi}{m} - \left(\frac{p\pi}{m}\right)^3 \frac{1}{3\,!} \cos \frac{\theta p \pi}{m}, \quad 0<\theta<1.$$

As p/m is between 0 and $1/2$, we have $0 < \cos \frac{\theta p\pi}{m} < 1$, i.e.

$$\sin \frac{p\pi}{m} = \pi p A_p/m, \text{ where } 1-\pi^2/24 < A_p < 1.$$

Hence
$$1 - \frac{\sin^2 \frac{\pi z}{m}}{\sin^2 \frac{p\pi}{m}} = 1 - \frac{z^2(1+\epsilon)}{p^2 A_p^2} = 1 - \frac{B_p}{p^2}$$

where, if z is in a finite region, $|B_p|$ is between fixed limits. Thus, by 28. III, the infinite product

$$\left[1 - \frac{B_{k+1}}{(k+1)^2}\right]\left[1 - \frac{B_{k+2}}{(k+2)^2}\right]\cdots$$

is absolutely convergent and its value approaches 1 as $k \to \infty$. Therefore

$$\sin \pi z = \pi z\,(1-z^2/1^2)\ldots(1-z^2/k^2)\,K(k),$$

where $\lim_{k=\infty} K(k) = 1$, i.e.

(7) $$\sin \pi z = \pi z \prod_1^\infty (1-z^2/n^2).$$

For example, for $z = 1/2$, (7) gives

(8) $$\pi/2 = \prod_1^\infty 4n^2/(4n^2-1) \qquad \text{(Wallis's formula)}$$

Moreover

$$(9) \qquad \cos \pi z = \frac{\sin 2\pi z}{2\sin \pi z} = \frac{2\pi z \prod_{n=1}^{\infty}\left(1-\frac{4z^2}{n^2}\right)}{2\pi z \prod_{m=1}^{\infty}\left(1-\frac{z^2}{m^2}\right)}.$$

The factors for which $n = 2m$ are cancelled by the denominator and thus we obtain

$$(10) \qquad \cos \pi z = \prod_{0}^{\infty}\left[1-\frac{4z^2}{(2n+1)^2}\right].$$

33. *The Gamma function.* Put

$$(1) \qquad \Pi(n,z) = \frac{1\,.\,2\,.\dots(n-1)\,n^z}{z(z+1)\dots(z+n-1)},$$

$z \neq$ a negative integer.

Since

$$\Pi(n+1,z)/\Pi(n,z) = \frac{n}{n+z}\frac{(n+1)^z}{n^z}$$
$$= \left(1-\frac{z}{n}+\frac{z^2}{n^2}-\dots\right)\left(1+\frac{z}{n}+\frac{z(z-1)}{2n^2}+\dots\right)$$
$$= 1+\frac{z(z-1)}{2n^2}+\dots = 1+\frac{A_n}{n^2}$$

where $\lim_{n=\infty} A_n = z(z-1)/2$, the infinite product

$$\Pi(2,z)\frac{\Pi(3,z)}{\Pi(2,z)}\dots\frac{\Pi(n+1,z)}{\Pi(n,z)}\dots$$

converges absolutely, i. e. the limit $\lim_{n=\infty}\Pi(n,z)$ exists if z is not a negative integer. In any finite region R of z not containing negative integers the convergence is uniform. Thus we put

$$(2) \qquad \Gamma(z+1) = \lim_{n=\infty}\Pi(n,z). \qquad \text{(Euler's formula.)}$$

We are going to deduce from (2) some remarkable properties of $\Gamma(z)$.

$$\Pi(n,z)\,\Pi(n,-z) = -\frac{[(n-1)!]^2}{z^2(1^2-z^2)\dots[(n-1)^2-z^2]}$$
$$= -\frac{\pi}{z}\frac{1}{\pi z\left(1-\frac{z^2}{1}\right)\dots\left[1-\frac{z^2}{(n-1)^2}\right]},$$

i. e. by (32. 7),

$$(3) \qquad \Gamma(z)\Gamma(-z) = -\frac{\pi}{z\sin\pi z}$$

and

$$(4) \qquad \Gamma(z)\Gamma(1-z) = -z\Gamma(z)\Gamma(-z) = \frac{\pi}{\sin\pi z}.$$

For $z = 1/2$

$$(5) \qquad [\Gamma(1/2)]^2 = \pi, \ \Gamma(1/2) = \sqrt{\pi}.$$

We readily verify that the ratio

$$\frac{m^{mz}\Pi(n,z)\Pi\left(n,z+\frac{1}{m}\right)\dots\Pi\left(n,z+\frac{m-1}{m}\right)}{\Pi(mn,mz)} = \frac{m^{mn}[(n-1)!]^2 n^{(m-1)/2}}{(mn-1)!} \equiv k_n$$

is independent of z. For $n = \infty$ we obtain

$$(6) \qquad \frac{m^{mz}\Gamma(z)\Gamma\left(z+\frac{1}{m}\right)\dots\Gamma\left(z+\frac{m-1}{m}\right)}{\Gamma(mz)} = \lim_{n=\infty} k_n = C.$$

In order to determine C we put $z = 1/m$, i. e.

$$m\Gamma\left(\frac{1}{m}\right)\dots\Gamma\left(\frac{m-1}{m}\right) = C.$$

Multiplying the left-hand side by itself (the order of factors being inverted), we find

$$m^2\frac{\pi}{\sin\frac{\pi}{m}}\frac{\pi}{\sin\frac{2\pi}{m}}\dots\frac{\pi}{\sin\frac{(m-1)\pi}{m}} = C^2.$$

But

$$z^{2m}-1 = \prod_{k=0}^{2m-1}\left(z-e^{\frac{2k\pi i}{2m}}\right) = \prod_{0}^{m-1}\left(z-e^{\frac{2k\pi i}{2m}}\right)\left(z-e^{\frac{2(m+k)\pi i}{2m}}\right)$$

$$= (z^2-1)\left(z^2-2z\cos\frac{2\pi}{2m}+1\right)\dots\left(z^2-2z\cos\frac{2(m-1)\pi}{2m}+1\right).$$

Putting $z = 1+h$ and equating the coefficients of h, we obtain

$$2m = 2\left(2\sin\frac{\pi}{2m}\right)^2\dots\left(2\sin\frac{(m-1)\pi}{2m}\right)^2.$$

Putting $z = -1+h$ we obtain similarly

$$2m = 2\left(2\cos\frac{\pi}{2m}\right)^2 \dots \left(2\cos\frac{(m-1)\pi}{2m}\right)^2.$$

Multiplying the last two equations and taking the square root we have

$$m = 2^{m-1}\sin\pi/m \dots \sin\pi(m-1)/m, \text{ i.e.}$$

(7) $$C = (2\pi)^{(m-1)/2}\sqrt{m}.$$

$\Gamma(z)$ may also be defined as an integral. Consider the integral

(8) $$I(a) = \int_0^\infty x^{a-1}e^{-x}\,dx,\quad a = \alpha+i\beta,\ \alpha>0,\ x \text{ real}.$$

For a sufficiently large x we have $e^x > x^{\alpha+1}$, i.e. $x^{\alpha-1}e^{-x} < 1/x^2$. Hence

$$\left|\int_l^{l'} x^{a-1}e^{-x}\,dx\right| < \int_l^{l'} x^{\alpha-1}e^{-x}\,dx < \epsilon$$

for $l' > l > l_0$. Also $\int_\epsilon^1 x^{\alpha-1}e^{-x}\,dx$ tends to a limit when $\epsilon \to 0$ provided $1-\alpha < 1$, i.e. $\alpha > 0$. It follows that $I(a)$ is perfectly determinate when $\alpha > 0$.

In particular if $\alpha > 1$, by partial integration,

$$I(a) = -\left[x^{a-1}e^{-x}\right]_0^\infty + (a-1)\int_0^\infty x^{a-2}e^{-x}\,dx,$$

i.e. $$I(a) = (a-1)\,.\,I(a-1).$$

Moreover

$$I(1) = \int_0^\infty e^{-x}dx = 1, \text{ i.e. for an integer } a,\ I(a) = (a-1)\,!,$$

which shows that $I(n)$ is a generalization of the factorial symbol $n!$ for non-integral (also irrational and complex) values of n.

We are going to prove that $I(a) = \Gamma(a)$ when $\mathrm{Rl}(a) > 0$.

Since $I(a) = \int_0^\infty x^{a-1}e^{-x}dx$, putting $x = y^2$, we have

$I(a) = \int_0^\infty 2y^{2a-1}e^{-y^2}dy$. Again, putting $x = \log 1/z$, where z is a real positive variable, we obtain

$$I(a) = \int_0^1 (\log 1/z)^{a-1}dz,$$

i.e.

$$I(a) = \lim_{\mu=\infty}\int_{e^{-\sqrt{\mu}}}^1 (\log 1/z)^{a-1}dz$$

Putting $1-z^{1/\mu} = h$, i. e. $\mu = \log z/\log(1-h)$ and

$$\mu(1-z^{1/\mu}) = h\log z/\log(1-h) = -\frac{h}{\log(1-h)}\log 1/z,$$

where $-h/\log(1-h) = h/(h+h^2/2+\ldots) \to 1$ when $h \to 0$, i. e. when $\mu \to \infty$, we have

$$I(a) = \lim_{\mu=\infty}\int_{e^{-\sqrt{\mu}}}^{1} \mu^{a-1}(1-z^{1/\mu})^{a-1}\,dz.$$

From

$$\left|\int_0^{e^{-\sqrt{\mu}}} \mu^{a-1}(1-z^{1/\mu})^{a-1}\,dz\right| < \int_0^{e^{-\sqrt{\mu}}} \mu^{a-1}\,dz < \mu^{a-1}e^{-\sqrt{\mu}} \to 0,$$

we see that $\quad I(a) = \lim_{\mu=\infty}\mu^{a-1}\int_0^1 (1-z^{1/\mu})^{a-1}\,dz.$

Putting $z = y^{\mu}$, we have

$$I(a) = \lim_{\mu=\infty}\mu^{a}\int_0^1 y^{\mu-1}(1-y)^{a-1}\,dy.$$

By partial integration

$$\int_0^1 y^{\mu-1}(1-y)^{a-1}\,dy$$

$$= \left[-\frac{1}{a}y^{\mu-1}(1-y)^{a}\right]_0^1 + \frac{\mu-1}{a}\int_0^1 y^{\mu-2}(1-y)^{a}\,dy$$

$$= \frac{\mu-1}{a}\int_0^1 y^{\mu-2}(1-y)^{a}\,dy.$$

Continuing the reduction we obtain

$$I(a) = \lim_{\mu=\infty}\frac{\mu^{a}(\mu-1)(\mu-2)\ldots 1}{a(a+1)\ldots(a+\mu-1)} = \Gamma(a) \qquad \text{Q. e. d.}$$

34. *Cyclometric functions. Root and logarithm.* The inverse functions of $\cos z$, $\sin z$, $\tan z$ and $\cot z$ are called $\arccos z$, $\arcsin z$, $\arctan z$ and $\operatorname{arccot} z$. Consider them for the time being only for real values of the independent variable. By definition $\arccos x$ is the function $y(x)$ defined by $x = \cos y$. Thus x cannot assume values outside $(-1, 1)$, i. e. $y(x)$ is defined only in the interval $(-1, 1)$. Moreover if x and y satisfy $x = \cos y$ then x and $y + 2k\pi$ as well as x and $-y+2k\pi$ also satisfy it. Thus to one and the same value of the independent variable belong

infinitely many different values of the function $\arccos x$. It is *a multiform* function with infinitely many branches. We remark, however, that if we know one value belonging to x we know every value belonging to the same x. When x varies from 0 to 1, the branch of $\arccos x$ which is $-\pi/2$ at $x = -1$ constantly increases from $-\pi/2$ to $\pi/2$. This one-valued branch is the 'principal branch' of our function and we make the convention that, if we do not state it otherwise, the symbol $\arccos x$ will denote the principal branch. The other branches form two groups $2k\pi + \arccos x$ and $2k\pi - \arccos x$.

From $x = \cos y = \sin\left(\frac{\pi}{2} - y\right)$, we see that

$$(1) \quad \frac{\pi}{2} - \arccos x = \arcsin x.$$

The 'principal branch' of $\arcsin x$ is thus the branch which increases from $-\frac{\pi}{2}$ to $\frac{\pi}{2}$ when x increases from -1 to $+1$. The symbol $\arcsin x$ will denote this branch, the other branches are $2k\pi + \arcsin x$ and

$$2k\pi + \pi - \arcsin x.$$

The principal branch of $\arctan x$ is the branch which increases from $-\frac{\pi}{2}$ to $\frac{\pi}{2}$ when x increases from $-\infty$ to $+\infty$. The other branches are given by the formula

$$y = k\pi + \arctan x.$$

We notice finally that

$$\arctan x + \operatorname{arccot} x = \frac{\pi}{2}$$

$$\operatorname{arcsec} x = \arccos 1/x$$

$$\operatorname{arccosec} x = \arcsin 1/x.$$

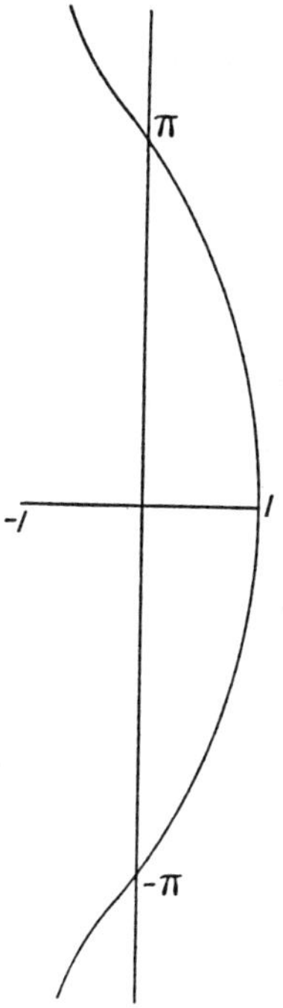

FIG. 8.

But in this book we shall hardly ever make use of sec and cosec and their inverses. The arc-functions are sometimes referred to as *cyclometric functions* or inverse circular functions. We shall define these functions for a complex variable in Art. 37.

Root and logarithm. We define $y = \log x$ by the equation $e^y = x$. In order to show that the equation has a solution for every x (except $x = 0$) put $x = a + ib$ and determine ϕ such that $\tan\phi = b/a$. It follows that

$$\sin\phi = \frac{\tan\phi}{\sqrt{1+\tan^2\phi}} = \frac{b}{\sqrt{a^2+b^2}},\ \cos\phi = \frac{a}{\sqrt{a^2+b^2}}.$$

Then $y = \log\sqrt{a^2+b^2} + i\phi$ satisfies the equation, because

$$e^{\log\sqrt{a^2+b^2}+i\phi} = \sqrt{a^2+b^2}\,(\cos\phi + i\sin\phi) = a + ib.$$

Thus the logarithm of $x = a + ib$ is $\log\sqrt{a^2+b^2} + i \arctan b/a$ where $\arctan b/a$ denotes the principal value of $\arctan b/a$, i.e. $-\pi/2 \leqslant \arctan b/a \leqslant \pi/2$. Geometrically this means that the real part of the logarithm is the ordinary logarithm of the distance (modulus) of $a + ib$ from the origin and the imaginary part y is its *argument* i.e. the angle between $(0, a + bi)$ and the positive real axis.

As the exponential function is periodic, this solution is not the only one. In fact, $e^{\log\sqrt{a^2+b^2}+i\arctan b/a+2\pi ki} = a + bi$. For example $\log 1 = 0,\ 2\pi i,\ -2\pi i,\ 4\pi i,\ -4\pi i, \ldots$ Thus every number has infinitely many logarithms, but these numbers differ only in their imaginary part and always by integral multiples of $2\pi i$, so that if we know one value of $\log(a + ib)$ we know all its values.

The fundamental property of $\log z$, namely

$$\log z_1 + \log z_2 = \log(z_1 z_2)$$

follows immediately from (31. 2).

So far we have defined root and, in general, power only for positive integral indices $a^m = a \,.\, a \ldots a$ (a real or complex) or, in Art. 31, for complex indices: $a^b = E(b \log a)$ but only for $a > 0$. As we have now defined log also for negative and complex numbers, we can extend the last definition to any base and index by putting

$$(1) \qquad a^b = E(b \log a).$$

More exactly we shall call the 'principal logarithm' of a, and denote by $\log a$, that log whose imaginary part is positive and less than 2π. Similarly the 'principal value' of a^b means the value given by $E(b \log a)$ when $\log a$ is the principal log of a. Since

$$E(b_1 \log a)\, E(b_2 \log a) = E[(b_1 + b_2) \log a],$$

we have
$$a^{b_1} a^{b_2} = a^{b_1+b_2}.$$

Similarly from

$$E(b \log a_1)\, E(b \log a_2) = E[b(\log a_1 + \log a_2)] = E[b \log (a_1 a_2)],$$

we have

$$a_1{}^b\, a_2{}^b = (a_1 a_2)^b.$$

Finally

$$(a^b)^c = a^{bc}.$$

In fact, by the definition of log,

$$\log E(z) = z \text{ and } c \log E(b \log a) = bc \log a,$$

and so

$$(a^b)^c = [E(b \log a)]^c = E[c \log E(b \log a)] = a^{bc}.$$

Thus our definition of power for any complex base and complex index is entirely justified. All the formal properties of the power have been preserved in the generalization.

35. *The linear function.* $u = (az+b)/(cz+d)$ establishes a one-one correspondence between the points of the z- and u-planes, provided $ad \neq bc$, i. e. to every z corresponds one and only one u, to $z = -d/c$ corresponding the improper point $u = \infty$, and conversely, as $z = (-du+b)/(cu+a)$, to every u corresponds one and only one z, and to $u = -a/c$ corresponds the improper point $z = \infty$. In the spherical representation improper points become ordinary points.

We are going to examine the correspondence established by a linear function *for which $ad \neq bc$.*

1. $u = z + a$ is a translation of the complex plane as a whole (without rotation) such that the origin is displaced to $z = -a$.

2. $u = e^{ia} z$. The two origins correspond to each other and the whole complex plane is turned about the origin, $u = re^{i(\phi+\alpha)}$ corresponding to $z = re^{i\phi}$.

3. $u = pz, p > 0$. $u = pre^{ia}$, corresponds to $z = re^{ia}$, i.e. the arguments of corresponding points are the same and the absolute value of u is p times that of z. This correspondence may be described as a stretching of the whole complex plane along the radii issuing from the origin.

We can obviously decompose the correspondence or mapping established by $u = az+b$ into the preceding three particular cases.

4. $u = 1/z$. From fig. 9, where the angle OQz' is a right angle and the triangles OQz and OQz' are similar, we have

$$|z|/R = R/|z'|, \text{ i.e.}$$

(1) $$|z|\,|z'| = R^2.$$

Taking a circle of radius $R = 1$, we see that $1/|z| = |z'|$ and we know that $\arg 1/z = -\arg z$. Thus $|u|$ is determined by

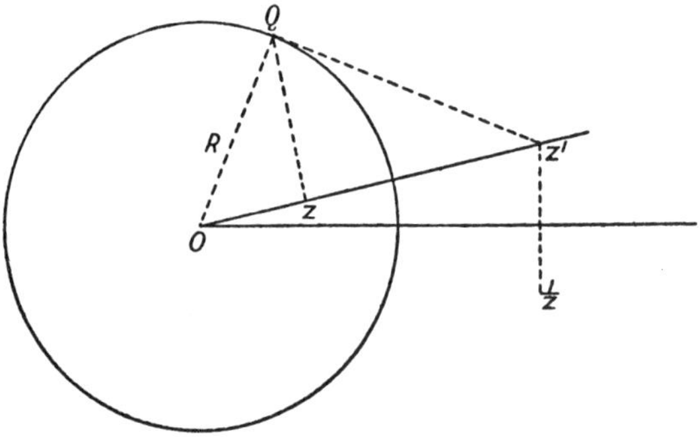

FIG. 9.

a 'reflexion' in the unit circle. The point z' is said to be the *inverse* of z with respect to the circle $|z| = R$ and vice versa.

The general mapping $u = (az+b)/(cz+d)$ may be decomposed into five consecutive mappings of the types just discussed, viz. into $z_1 = z + d/c$, $z_2 = c^2 z_1$, $z_3 = 1/z_2$, $z_4 = (bc-ad)z_3$, $u = z_4 + a/c$.

A general property of the mapping by linear functions is the following:

I. *In the mapping* $u = (az+b)/(cz+d)$ *circles and straight lines correspond to circles and straight lines*, but a circle may correspond to a straight line. As we may consider a straight line as an infinite circle we call this property the *circular affinity* displayed by the mapping.

Proof. The equation of a circle is

$$(x-\alpha)^2 + (y-\beta)^2 - r^2 = x^2 + y^2 - 2\alpha x - 2\beta y + \alpha^2 + \beta^2 - r^2 = 0.$$

Conversely, an equation of the form

(2) $$\alpha x^2+\alpha y^2+2\beta x+2\gamma y+\delta=0$$

represents a straight line if $\alpha=0$. If $\alpha\neq 0$, it may be written in the form $$\left(x+\frac{\beta}{\alpha}\right)^2+\left(y+\frac{\gamma}{\alpha}\right)^2+\frac{\delta\alpha-\beta^2-\gamma^2}{\alpha^2}=0.$$

Hence it is a circle if $\delta\alpha-\beta^2-\gamma^2<0$.

Putting $x+iy=z$, (2) assumes the form

(3) $$\alpha z\bar{z}+B\bar{z}+\bar{B}z+\delta=0, \text{ where } B=\beta+i\gamma.$$

It is a straight line if $\alpha=0$ and a circle if $\alpha\neq 0$ and

(4) $$\alpha\delta-B\bar{B}<0.$$

If $\alpha\delta-B\bar{B}=0$, (3) is satisfied by a single point; if $\alpha\delta-B\bar{B}<0$, (3) is an imaginary circle.

Similarly in the u-plane:

(5) $$\alpha u\bar{u}+B\bar{u}+\bar{B}u+\delta=0$$

represents a circle or a straight line (or a point or nothing). Replacing u by $az+b$ and $\bar{u}$ by $\bar{a}\bar{z}+\bar{b}$ we obtain

$$|a|^2\alpha z\bar{z}+(\alpha a\bar{b}+\bar{B}a)z+(\alpha\bar{a}b+B\bar{a})\bar{z}+\alpha|b|^2+B\bar{b}+\bar{B}b+\delta=0,$$

which is of the type (3), i.e. the coefficients of $z\bar{z}$ and of the absolute term are real, and the coefficients of z and $\bar{z}$ respectively are conjugate complex numbers. The condition replacing (4) reduces exactly to (4) multiplied by $|a|$. Thus *for* $u=az+b$ *circles correspond to circles and straight lines correspond to straight lines.*

For $u=1/z$, (5) changes into $\alpha+Bz+\bar{B}\bar{z}+\delta z\bar{z}=0$ which is a circle if $\delta\neq 0$, i.e. when the corresponding circle on the u-plane does not pass through the origin, and is a straight line if $\delta=0$.

As the general linear mapping is composed of five consecutive elementary mappings all of them displaying circular affinity, the theorem is proved.

Another general property of linear mapping refers to inverse points. We say that z_1 and z_2 are *inverse* with respect to the circle $(z-c)(\bar{z}-\bar{c})=R^2$ of radius R, centre at c, if they satisfy the equation

$$(z_1-c)(\bar{z}_2-\bar{c})=R^2,$$

i.e. if z_1-c and z_2-c have the same argument and their moduli satisfy the condition $|z_1-c|\,|z_2-c| = R^2$. If the circle reduces to a straight line, inversion is defined as meaning reflexion in the straight line (see Fig. 10).

II. *In the special linear mapping* $u = az+b$, *the property of two points being inverse is conserved. In the general linear mapping the same holds for points* z_1, z_2 *inverse with respect to a circle centre at* $z = 0$ *if the centre of the corresponding circle is* $u = 0$.

Proof. In the mapping $u = az+b$, the point $\gamma = ac+b$ corresponds to the centre c and, from $u-\gamma = a(z-c)$, it follows that, for inverse points z_1, z_2,

$$(u_1-\gamma)(\bar{u}_2-\bar{\gamma}) = a\bar{a}(z_1-c)(\bar{z}_2-\bar{c}) = a\bar{a}R^2.$$

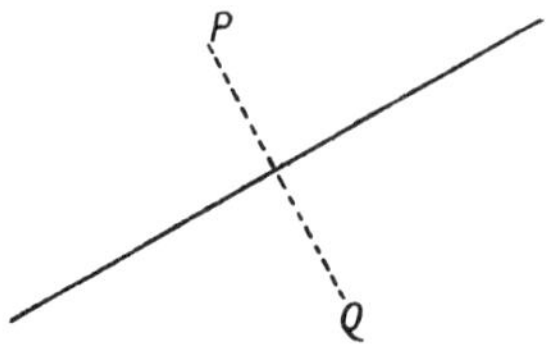

FIG. 10.

Therefore, by

$$(u-\gamma)(\bar{u}-\bar{\gamma}) = a\bar{a}R^2,$$

u_1 and u_2 are inverse with respect to the corresponding circle of the u-plane.

If, in the general linear mapping, the circle $C: z\bar{z} = R^2$ corresponds to the circle $u\bar{u} = \rho^2$, we have, *for every* z *on* C,

$$(az+b)(\bar{a}\bar{z}+\bar{b}) = \rho^2(cz+d)(\bar{c}\bar{z}+\bar{d}),$$

i. e.

$$a\bar{a}R^2+b\bar{b} = \rho^2(c\bar{c}R^2+d\bar{d})$$

$$a\bar{b} = \rho^2 c\bar{d}. \tag{6}$$

It results from (6) that

$$(az_1+b)(\bar{a}\bar{z}_2+\bar{b}) = \rho^2(cz_1+d)(\bar{c}\bar{z}_2+\bar{d})$$

provided $z_1\bar{z}_2 = R^2$, i. e. the points u_1, u_2, corresponding to z_1, z_2 satisfy the condition $u_1\bar{u}_2 = \rho^2$. Q. e. d.

We are going to apply this result to an important particular case.

III. *The necessary and sufficient condition that in a linear mapping the circumference of the unit circle centre at the origin should correspond to itself is that the linear function have the form*

$$u = (az-b)/(\bar{b}z-\bar{a}), \tag{7}$$

where a *and* b *are arbitrary complex numbers.*

Proof. We write the linear function in the form $u = \frac{a}{c}\frac{z-\alpha}{z-\beta}$. The points 0 and ∞ are inverse with respect to the unit circle in the z-plane, centre at the origin. Thus, by II, the corresponding points α and β are inverse in the u-plane with respect to the same circle. Hence $|\alpha\beta| = 1$. As inverse points with respect to any circle centre at the origin have the same argument, $\arg\alpha = \arg\beta = \phi$. Therefore $\beta = e^{i\phi}/|\alpha| = 1/\bar{\alpha}$ and

$$(8) \qquad u = \frac{a}{c}\frac{z-\alpha}{z-1/\bar{\alpha}} = \frac{a\bar{\alpha}}{c}\frac{z-\alpha}{\bar{\alpha}z-1}.$$

On the other hand, when $|z| = 1$ and thus also $|\bar{z}| = 1$, we have $|z-\alpha| = |\bar{z}-\bar{\alpha}| = |\bar{z}-\bar{\alpha}|/|\bar{z}| = |1-\bar{\alpha}/\bar{z}| = |1-\bar{\alpha}z|$. Therefore in order that the circumference of the unit circle be mapped on itself it is necessary and sufficient that $|a\bar{\alpha}|/|c| = 1$. Since $|a/\bar{a}| = 1$, it follows that (8) may be written in the form (7).

We have still to notice that *the whole unit circle,* and not its circumference alone, *is mapped on the whole unit circle if* $a\bar{a}-b\bar{b}>0$. In fact, u being a continuous function of z, the whole circle $z\bar{z}<1$ corresponds either to $u\bar{u}<1$ or to $u\bar{u}>1$. Thus the pole (∞) of the mapping must lie outside the circle, i. e. we must have

$$|\bar{a}|/|\bar{b}| = |a|/|b| > 1, \ |a|^2 > |b|^2, \text{ or } a\bar{a}-b\bar{b}>0.$$

$z = 0$ corresponds to $u = b/\bar{a}$. As a and b can be taken arbitrarily we can choose them in such a way that an arbitrary point u_0 corresponds to $z = 0$. Since we have two arbitrary constants we can still take an arbitrary z_1 on the circumference $|z| = 1$ and require that z_1 correspond to $u_1 = e^{i\alpha}$ on the circumference $|u| = 1$. In fact, putting $b/\bar{a} = A$ (given), we have $(az_1 - A\bar{a})/(\bar{A}az_1 - \bar{a}) = e^{i\beta}$ (of modulus 1). Multiplying the linear function corresponding to a and $b = \bar{a}A$ by $e^{i(\alpha-\beta)}$, we obtain the linear function in which z_1 corresponds to u_1.

MULTIFORM FUNCTIONS

36. *The idea of multiform functions.* The equation $y^2 = x$ is satisfied by two real continuous functions $y_1 = |\sqrt{x}|$ and $y_2 = -|\sqrt{x}|$, defined for $x \geqslant 0$. These two functions are connected in two ways. (a) They satisfy the same equation.

(b) they continue each other, i. e. $y_1(0) = y_2(0)$. Now take any two functions $y_1 = f(x)$ and $y_2 = g(x)$ such that $f(a) = g(a)$. Both satisfy the equation $y^2 - (f+g)y + fg = 0$, and they piece together at a. Are they two 'branches' of the same function?

To show the complexity of the question we notice that

$$y_3(x) = \begin{cases} y_1 \text{ if } x \text{ is rational} \\ y_2 \text{ if } x \text{ is irrational,} \end{cases}$$

and infinitely many other one-valued functions satisfy $y^2 = x$ for $x \geqslant 0$. The reason for this is that an equation determines only local couples (x, y), and every collection of these couples constitutes a function satisfying the same equation. The solutions y_1 and y_2 are distinguished from the infinity of solutions by being the only *continuous* solutions pieced together. But the first remark shows that, in the domain of real variables, even this condition does not rule out the joining of two arbitrary functions together as a two-valued continuous solution of an equation. For real variables the distinction between uniform and multiform functions cannot be settled in a satisfactory way and as a matter of fact, in the investigations on real functions, multiform functions are mostly disregarded.

We are going to show that the extension of the definition of functions to the complex variable furnishes an elegant method of solving the problem of multiformity.

We have seen that every complex number can be written in the form $a + bi = re^{i\alpha}$ where $r = |\sqrt{a^2+b^2}|$ and $\alpha = \arctan b/a$ (called the argument of $a+bi$). Now put $z = re^{i\alpha}$ and $u = Re^{i\beta}$. The equation $u^2 = z$ assumes the form $R^2 e^{i2\beta} = re^{i\alpha}$. For given r and $\alpha < 2\pi$, two obvious solutions are $u_1 = |\sqrt{r}|e^{i\frac{\alpha}{2}}$ and $u_2 = |\sqrt{r}|e^{i(\frac{\alpha}{2}+\pi)} = -|\sqrt{r}|e^{i\frac{\alpha}{2}}$, and they are the only continuous solutions for a fixed α, for $|\sqrt{r}|$ and $-|\sqrt{r}|$ are the only continuous solutions of the real equation $x^2 = r$, $r > 0$.

In particular, for a positive real z, i. e. when $\alpha = 0$, $u_1 = |\sqrt{r}|$ and $u_2 = -|\sqrt{r}|$. Both u_1 and u_2 are one-valued functions of z defined for every value of z.

Now follow the change in u_1 when α varies from 0 to 2π, i. e. when the variable z describes a circle of radius r about the origin. As the exponential function $e^{i\alpha}$ is a continuous function of α, the variation of u_1 is continuous. Its final value is $|\sqrt{r}|e^{i\frac{2\pi}{2}} = -|\sqrt{r}| = u_2$. The function u_1 is apparently discontinuous along the positive real axis because the values just above and just below this real axis differ in sign and are not 0 (save at the origin). Moreover u_1 pieces together with u_2 along the positive real axis, so that when z describes the circle round the origin for a second time, the values of u_1 continue those of u_2 and finally, at the end of the second round, $u_2 = u_1$ along the positive real axis.

The equation $u^2 = z$ has no continuous, one-valued solution defined for the whole complex plane.

But, as a matter of fact, when α passes through the critical value 2π, u_1 changes *continuously* into u_2, so that the discontinuity of u_1 is highly artificial and due only to our desire to assign only one value of u to every complex number z. If we remove this restriction by uniting u_1 and u_2 into one functional body we obtain a continuous function which is necessarily two-valued.

The equation $u^2 = z$ has a unique continuous solution defined for the whole complex plane and this solution is a two-valued function.

Now take the equation

$$(2) \qquad u^2 - [f(z) + g(z)]u + f(z)g(z) = 0,$$

$f(z)$ and $g(z)$ being two continuous one-valued complex functions. Put, for $0 \leqslant \alpha \leqslant 2\pi$, $u_1 = f(z)$ and $u_2 = g(z)$. When z describes a circle round the origin, u_1, for $\alpha = 2\pi$, assumes its old value u_1, and u_2 will also remain unaltered, i. e. *u_1 and u_2 do not piece together along the real axis*, though they may assume here and there the same values. The test of continuity all over the complex plane splits up the solutions of equation (2) into two separate functions which are continuous and one-valued.

37. *Riemann surfaces.* To construct an accurate geometrical picture of the functional relation $u = \sqrt{z}$, take two complex planes I and II and imagine the values of $u_1(z)$ attached (written) to the corresponding value of z on I and the values of $u_2(z)$ on II. Along the positive real axis both $u_1(z)$ and $u_2(z)$

are discontinuous and, along the lower edge of I, i. e. the side of the positive real axis corresponding to the argument 2π, $u_1 = u_2$

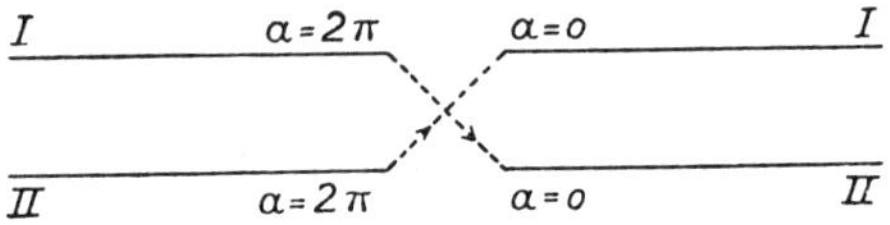

FIG. 11.

while, along the lower edge of II, $u_2 = u_1$. Therefore we cut the two complex planes along the positive real axis, from 0 to $+\infty$, and make the convention that the lower edge of I should be continued by the upper edge of II (following the continuity of attached values) and the lower edge of II should be continued by the upper edge of I. If a more concrete picture is wanted, we might imagine the edges as bridged over by fine threads leading cross-ways from $\alpha = 0$ on I to $\alpha = 2\pi$ on II and from $\alpha = 2\pi$ on I to $\alpha = 0$ on II.

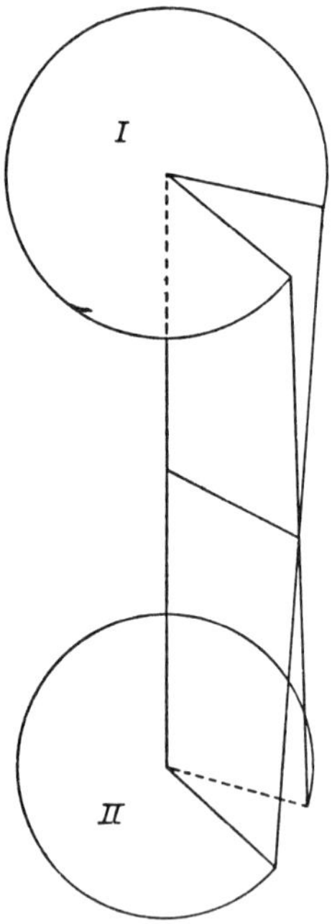

FIG. 12.

Thus, if we want to go round 0, i. e. if we want to describe a closed circuit about 0, we describe a circle $z = re^{i\alpha}$, α varying from 0 to 2π on I, say, then we descend slantwise to the point of II just under our initial point on I and describe a circle under our first circle and ascend slantwise again to $\alpha = 0$ on I. If in the geometrical picture we make use of bridges, our mathematical convention amounts to the prohibition of the passage from one cross-bridge to the other while on a bridge.

On the two-sheeted complex plane so constructed the function $u = \sqrt{z}$ is uniform (since it was constructed for this very purpose). This two-sheeted plane is called the *Riemann surface* of the function $u = \sqrt{z}$. Notice that we obtain a similar result if, instead of the positive real axis, we cut the two planes and cross-bridge them *along any argument*, i. e. along complex numbers of the type $re^{i\alpha}$ where α is fixed. The positive real axis is distinguished in no way from any other direction.

On the other hand, as we are going to explain, the point $z = 0$ is distinguished, for $u = \sqrt{z}$, from all the other points.

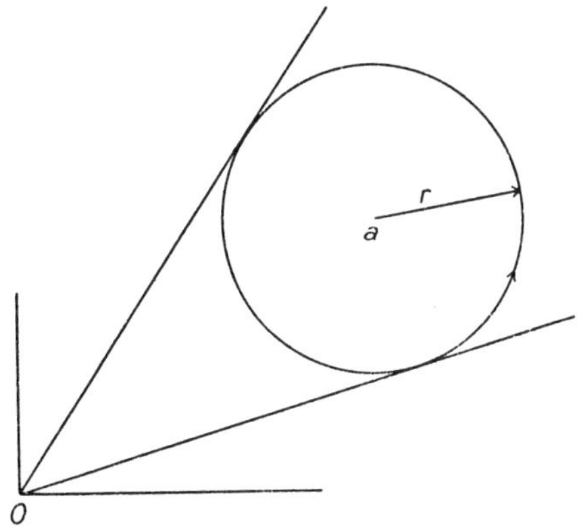

FIG. 13.

We first notice that *when z describes a circle about the point a of radius $r < |a| = \rho$, its argument is not increased by 2π, in fact, it re-assumes its initial value.*

Proof. Putting $a = \rho e^{i\alpha_0}$, $z = re^{i\alpha}$, $\rho e^{i\alpha_0} + re^{i\alpha} = Re^{i\beta}$, we have $\beta(\alpha) = \arctan\,[(\rho \sin\alpha_0 + r\sin\alpha)/(\rho\cos\alpha_0 + r\cos\alpha)]$. For simplicity's sake we put $\alpha_0 = 0$; $\beta(\alpha)$ is thus a real function of the real variable α and

$$\beta'(\alpha) = (r^2 + r\rho\cos\alpha)/(\rho + r\cos\alpha)^2.$$

Since the numerator of $\beta'(\alpha)$ vanishes when $\cos\alpha = -r/\rho$, i. e. when $\alpha = \alpha' < \pi$, say, and $2\pi - \alpha'$, and the denominator never vanishes, we see that $\beta'(\alpha) < 0$, for $\alpha' < \alpha < 2\pi - \alpha'$ and $\beta'(\alpha) \geqslant 0$ elsewhere in $(0, 2\pi)$. Thus $\beta(\alpha)$ is an increasing function along the first arc and its maximum value (at α') is $\arctan\,[r/+\sqrt{\rho^2 - r^2}]$, i. e. the tangent of the maximum argument is $r/+\sqrt{\rho^2 - r^2}$; its minimum value (at $2\pi - \alpha'$) is $\arctan\,[r/-\sqrt{\rho^2 - r^2}]$, i. e. the tangent of the minimum angle is $r/-\sqrt{\rho^2 - r^2}$. Thus if $r < \rho$, as we suppose, the tangent never becomes infinite and thus the argument is, *for every value of α, between $-\pi/2$ and $\pi/2$.* It increases from $-\alpha'$ to $\alpha' < \pi$ and then decreases again to $-\alpha'$.

Consequently *the values of* u_1 *and* u_2 *are exchanged only when* z *turns about the origin.* Therefore $z=0$ is said to be a *branch-point* of $u=\sqrt{z}$, and $u_1(z)$ and $u_2(z)$ are called its two *branches.*

We notice finally that turning about $z=\infty$ means, by definition, describing a very large circle about the origin. Therefore $z=\infty$ is also a (conventional) branch-point. In the spherical representation $z=\infty$ is the north pole. To the two-sheeted Riemann surface corresponds a surface composed of two spherical shells cut along a semicircle through the poles and cross-bridged along this cut.

We can repeat our construction for $u=\sqrt{z-1}$ by putting $z-1=z'$. To a simple (double) circle about $z'=0$ corresponds a simple (double) circle about $z=1$ and to the cut on the z'-plane from 0 to ∞ (along the real axis) corresponds a cut on the z-plane from 1 to ∞ (along the real axis).

To construct a geometrical picture of the functional relation $u=\sqrt[n]{z}$, we have to take n planes and attach to the points $re^{i\alpha}$ (α fixed) the values of the n continuous functions of r:

$$u_1=|\sqrt[n]{r}|e^{i\alpha}, u_2=|\sqrt[n]{r}|e^{i\frac{\alpha+2\pi}{n}}, \ldots, u_n=|\sqrt[n]{r}|e^{i\frac{\alpha+(n-1)2\pi}{n}}.$$

By turning once about the origin, i.e. increasing α by 2π, u_i becomes u_{i+1} and u_n becomes u_1. Thus the cross-section of the

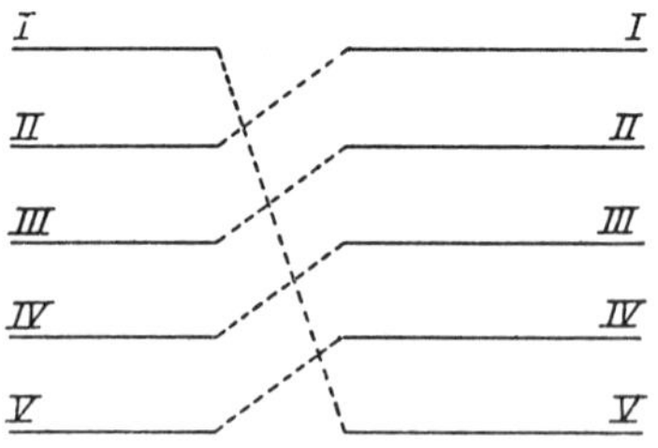

FIG. 14.

connecting bridges between the planes (along the positive real axis, say,) is as shown by fig. 14.

$u=\log z$. Putting $z=re^{i\alpha}$ we have, $u=\log r+i(\alpha+2k\pi)$. First with $k=0$, this equation defines, for a fixed α, a continuous function of $r>0$. Thus for $\alpha=0$, we obtain the ordinary $\log r$. As the expression is a linear function of α, we define in this way a continuous function u_1 of r, except at the origin where $u = \infty$, and along the positive real axis where, for $\alpha = 2\pi$, we obtain $\log r + i\,2\pi$ instead of the initial function $\log r$. Now, starting with the determination $\log r + i\,2\pi$ (along the positive real axis), we define on a new complex plane a second function $u_2 = \log r + i(\alpha + 2\pi)$ which becomes, for $\alpha = 2\pi$, i.e. after a complete turn about the origin, $\log r + i\,4\pi$. Continuing

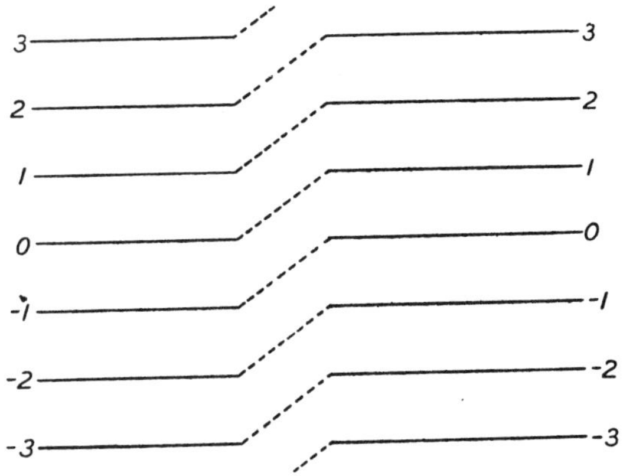

FIG. 15.

in this way, for negative integral values of k also, we see that infinitely many branches of $\log z$ are pieced together along the positive real axis, say, in a screw-like way. The values at points directly under one another on the successive planes differ only by $2\pi i$. The origin is the only finite branch-point and we notice that any succession of points $z_1, z_2, \dots, z_k$, with increasing arguments $\alpha_1, \alpha_2, \dots, \alpha_k = \alpha_1 + 2\pi$ leads from $\log z$ to the next branch $\log z + 2\pi i$. As $\log 1/z' = -\log z'$, $z = \infty$ is also a branch-point. For the function $a \log(z-b) + c$, $z = b$ is the only finite branch-point and the jump from one branch to another is $a\,2\pi i$.

We are going to discuss the functional relation $u = \sqrt{z(z-1)}$. As $\log u = \frac{1}{2}\log z + \frac{1}{2}\log(z-1)$, we see that, if z turns about the origin, $\frac{1}{2}\log z$ becomes $\frac{1}{2}\log z + \pi i$ and, if z turns about 1, $\frac{1}{2}\log(z-1)$ becomes $\frac{1}{2}\log(z-1) + \pi i$. Thus, if z turns about 0 and 1 at the same time, $\log u$ changes into $\log u + 2\pi i$, i.e. the argument of u is increased by 2π and thus there is no change in its value. Consequently, for the construction of the corresponding Riemann's surface, we take two complex planes and cut them along the real axis from 0 to 1. Starting with one of the values of our two-valued function $u(z)$ and not crossing the cut we cover the first plane with the values of a uniform function $u_1(z)$, and the second plane with the values of $u_2 = u_1 e^{\pi i}$.

The cross-bridge now simply stretches along the cut from 0 to 1. Infinity is not a branch-point. In the spherical repre-

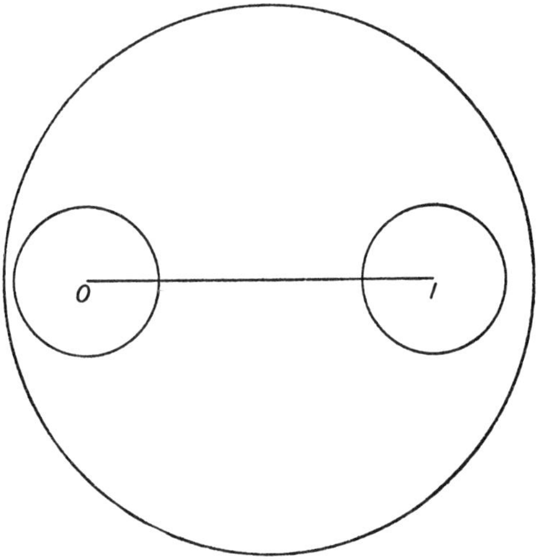

FIG. 16.

sentation the two shells are distinct at the north pole. They communicate only along (0, 1).

The same method applies to $u = \sqrt{(z-a_1)(z-a_2)\ldots(z-a_k)}$. We take two planes (or spherical shells), mark the points $a_1, \ldots, a_k$ and join them by polygonal lines, (simple segments if possible), not cutting one another. If k is odd, one of them has to be joined to ∞ (as in the case $k=1$). Along a circuit enclosing an even number, $2m$, of points a_i, the increase in the argument of $(z-a_1)\ldots(z-a_k)$ is $2m\pi$ which, if we take the square root, becomes $m\pi$. Hence the two values of u are exchanged only along circuits enclosing an odd number of branch-points.

Turning about a_i on one of the two planes we turn about one, i. e. an odd number of branch-points. Hence, if along one edge of (a_i, a_{i+1}) we have u_1, along the other edge we have

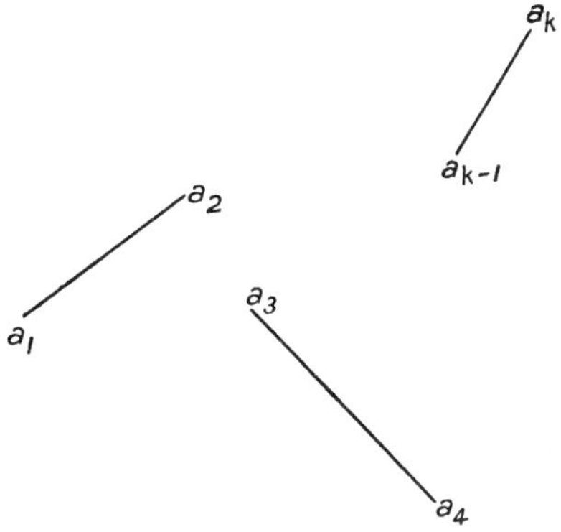

FIG. 17.

$u_2 = e^{i\pi} u_1$; similarly on the second plane. Hence the cross-bridges along the cuts have to be constructed in the usual way.

The connexion between $\log z$ *and* $\arctan z$ is given by the equation

$$z = \tan u = \frac{1}{i}\frac{e^{iu}-e^{-iu}}{e^{iu}+e^{-iu}}, \quad iz = \frac{e^{2iu}-1}{e^{2iu}+1}, \quad e^{2iu} = \frac{1+iz}{1-iz} = \frac{i-z}{i+z},$$

$$u = \arctan z = \frac{1}{2i}\log\frac{i-z}{i+z} = \frac{1}{2i}[\log(i-z) - \log(i+z) + 2k\pi i].$$

Since we divide by $2i$, the various branches of u differ by a multiple of π. The points $z = \pm i$ are singular points. By a small circuit about $z = i$ (in the direct sense) the value of $\log(i-z)$ increases by $2\pi i$, while that of $\log(i+z)$ is not changed, so that the initial value of u is increased by π. By a small circuit about $z = -i$, u is decreased by π. Thus u is unaltered by a circuit about both i and $-i$, and along the cut between i and $-i$ the branches are successively connected as in the case of $\log z$.

The connexion between $\log z$ *and* $\arcsin z$ is given by the equations $z = \sin u = (e^{iu} - e^{-iu})/2i$, i. e. $e^{iu} = iz \pm \sqrt{1-z^2}$ and $u = \arcsin z = \frac{1}{i}\log(iz \pm \sqrt{1-z^2})$. If iu_0 is one of the logarithms of $iz + \sqrt{1-z^2}$, the others are $iu_0 + 2k\pi i$. On the other hand,

$iz-\sqrt{1-z^2} = -1/(iz+\sqrt{1-z^2})$, so that one of its logarithms is $i\pi - iu_0$, i. e.

$$u = \begin{cases} u_0 + 2k\pi \\ \pi - u_0 + 2k\pi. \end{cases}$$

The second range of values coincides with the first only if u_0 is an odd multiple of $\pi/2$, and in this case

$$\frac{1}{i}\log(iz+\sqrt{1-z^2}) = (2k'+1)\tfrac{1}{2}\pi,$$

$$iz+\sqrt{1-z^2} = e^{\frac{2k'+1}{2}\pi i} = (-1)^{k'} i,$$

i. e.
$$z = (-1)^{k'} = \pm 1.$$

Connexion of branches. A branch is sufficiently characterized by its value assumed at 0 (or at any other point): viz. $k\pi$. Denote this branch by $u_k(z)$. By a turn about $z=1$, the argument of $1-z^2 = (1-z)(1+z)$ is increased by 2π, i. e. the two values of $\sqrt{1-z^2}$ are exchanged. The value assumed by this new branch at the origin is $u_k(0) + \frac{1}{i}\log(-1) = (k+1)\pi = u_{k+1}(0)$. Thus the branches are exchanged along $(1, +\infty)$ and $(-1, -\infty)$ in the logarithmic way.

From
$$\cos u = \sin(\pi/2+u),$$
we have
$$\arccos z = -\pi/2 + \arcsin z.$$

38. *Cycles.* The function $u(z)$ defined by the equation

(1)
$$u^6 = z^3(z-1)$$

is obviously a 6-valued function with the finite branch-points $z=0$ and $z=1$. Putting $z = re^{i\alpha}$, $z-1 = Re^{i\phi}$, let us consider the functions $u_1(r,\alpha) = |r^{1/2}(r-1)^{1/6}|\, e^{i\left(\frac{\alpha}{2}+\frac{\phi}{6}\right)}$, $u_{k+1} = \epsilon_k u_1$, where $1, \epsilon_1, \epsilon_2, \epsilon_3, \epsilon_4, \epsilon_5$ are the six roots of unity, viz. $\epsilon_k = e^{i\frac{2k\pi}{6}}$ $k = 0, 1, \ldots, 5$.

When α varies from 0 to 2π and $r<1$, the final value of ϕ is the same as its initial value. Hence,

$u_1(r,2\pi) = -u_1(r,0) = \epsilon_4 u_1(r,0) = u_4(r,0)$ and $u_4(r,2\pi) = u_1(r,0)$.

The two branches u_1 and u_4 form a *cycle* about the origin. Similarly, $u_2(r,2\pi) = u_5(r,0)$, $u_5(r,2\pi) = u_2(r,0)$,

and,
$$u_3(r,2\pi) = u_6(r,0),\; u_6(r,2\pi) = u_3(r,0).$$

When z turns about 1 and $R<1$, the final and initial values of α are the same, whereas ϕ is increased by 2π. Therefore the argument of u is increased by $2\pi/6$, i. e. the initial value of u is multiplied by $e^{i\frac{2\pi}{6}} = \epsilon_1$. Thus

$$u_1(R, 2\pi) = \epsilon_1 u_1(R, 0) = u_2(R, 0)$$

and $u_2(R, 2\pi) = \epsilon_1 u_2(R, 0) = u_1(R, 0)\,\epsilon_1^2 = \epsilon_2 u_1 = u_3(R, 0)$,

and so on; u_3 pieces with u_4; u_4 with u_5; u_5 with u_6 and u_6

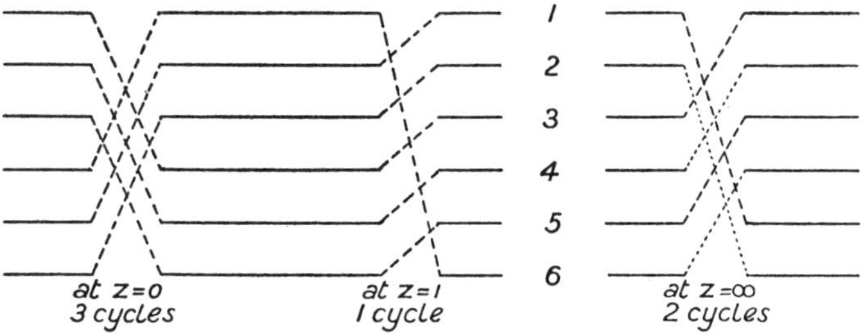

FIG. 18.

with u_1. Thus the cross-section of the Riemann surface is as shown in fig. 18.

At $z = \infty$. Putting $z = 1/z'$, we have $u^6 = (1-z')/z'^4$. Consider now a circle of radius $r' < 1$ centre at $z' = 0$. When $z' = r' e^{i\alpha'}$ describes this circle, $\sqrt[6]{1-z'}$ resumes its initial value, so that the exchange of branches is determined by

$$\sqrt[6]{1/z'^4} = \frac{e^{-i\frac{4\alpha'}{6}}}{|\sqrt[6]{r'^4}|} = \frac{1}{|\sqrt[6]{r'^4}|} e^{i\frac{4\alpha}{6}},$$

where the factor $1/|\sqrt[6]{r'^4}|$ is a fixed number. When α varies from 0 to 2π, one of the six determinations of $u(1/z')$ coincides with $u_1(r, \alpha)$, say. For $\alpha = 2\pi$, $e^{i\frac{4.2\pi}{6}} = \epsilon_4$, i. e. u_1 pieces with u_5. Similarly, u_5 pieces with $u_{5+4} = u_3$ and u_3 with $u_{3+4} = u_1$. In the same way u_2, u_4, u_6 form a second cycle at $z = \infty$.

Consider the function $u(z)$ determined by the equation $u^3 - 3u + 2z = 0$. By Cardan's formula, Ex. II. 33,

$$u = \sqrt[3]{-z+\sqrt{z^2-1}} + \sqrt[3]{-z-\sqrt{z^2-1}} = p+q,$$

where the determination of the cube root is subjected to the condition $pq = 1$. As $\sqrt{z^2-1} = \sqrt{(z-1)(z+1)}$, we see that if we turn about $z = 1$ (or $z = -1$) the initial determination of $\sqrt{z^2-1}$ becomes $-\sqrt{z^2-1}$, i.e. $-z+\sqrt{z^2-1}$ becomes $-z-\sqrt{z^2-1}$.

Hence the turn about 1 (or -1) changes any of the three determinations of p into one of the three determinations of q, and vice-versa. Putting $\eta = e^{i\frac{2\pi}{3}}$, the three roots of our equation are $u_1 = p_1+q_1$, $u_2 = \eta p_1+\eta^2 q_1$, $u_3 = \eta^2 p_1+\eta q_1$ where p_1 and q_1 have been so chosen that $p_1 q_1 = 1$. Therefore, if the turn about $z = 1$ changes p_1 into q_1, q_1 is changed into p_1, for we obtain one of the roots u_1, u_2, u_3. In this case u_1 is *not altered by turning about* $z = 1$. If p_1 changes into ηq_1, q_1 changes into $\eta^2 p_1$ and, after a second turn, into $\eta^3 p_1 = p_1$ and $\eta^3 q_1 = q_1$ respectively, i.e. the branches u_1 and u_3 are exchanged, but u_2 is *not altered*, for $\eta(\eta q_1)+\eta^2(\eta^2 p_1) = \eta p_1+\eta^2 q_1 = u_2$; similarly if p_1 changes into $\eta^2 q_1$.

This example shows that *a point may be a branch-point for some branches of the function and may not be a branch-point for other branches.*

The corresponding Riemann surface is shown by fig. 19. When

FIG. 19.

z is near 1 and we want to pass continuously from $u_1(z)$ to $u_3(z)$, it is necessary for z to go down to the second plane and then go round $z = -1$ and come back on the third plane to the original position of z.

Our last example is the function $u = z^\alpha$, where α is an irrational number. By definition $u = e^{\alpha \log z}$ so that, starting with a definite branch of $\log z = \log r + i(\alpha + 2k\pi)$ and turning about $z = 0$, we have $z = r + i[\alpha + 2(k+1)\pi]$, i.e. the next branch of u is $e^{\alpha \log 2 + i\alpha 2\pi} = ue^{i\alpha 2\pi}$. After m turns we obtain the factor $e^{im\alpha 2\pi}$ and, as α is not a fraction p/q, $m\alpha 2\pi$ never reduces to a multiple of 2π: we obtain *infinitely many branches* both in the positive and negative directions. The branches and the corresponding sheets are connected about the origin in a screw-like way, as in the case of logarithms. The difference between the two cases is that just as the real part of $\log z$ is the same for all branches, so in the case of $u = z^\alpha$ the modulus is the same for all branches, i. e. $|z^\alpha|$ *is a uniform function.*

EXERCISES IV

1. For every z, $|e^z - 1| \leqslant e^{|z|} - 1 \leqslant |z| e^{|z|}$ and for $0 < |z| < 1$, $|z|/4 < |e^z - 1| < 7|z|/4$.

2. x real and $\neq 0$.

(a) For positive x, $e^x > 1 + x$.
(b) For $x < 1$, $e^x < 1/(1-x)$.
(c) For $x > -1$, $1 + x > e^{\frac{x}{1+x}}$ (replace, in (b), x by $x/(1+x)$).
(d) For $0 < x < 1$, $e^{-x} < 1 - x/2$.
(e) For $x > 0$ and $y > 0$, $e^{\frac{xy}{x+y}} < (1 + x/y)^y < e^x$ [by (c) and (a) replacing x by x/y and raising to the y-th power].

3. For every z, $\lim\limits_{n=\infty} (1 + z/n)^n = e^z$. Proof. If $z = re^{i\alpha}$ is fixed we choose an m such that $\sum\limits_{n=m+1}^{\infty} r^n/n! < \epsilon$, and we notice that in

$$(1 + z/m)^m = 1 + z + \left(1 - \frac{1}{m}\right)\frac{z^2}{2!}$$
$$+ \dots + \left(1 - \frac{1}{m}\right)\left(1 - \frac{2}{m}\right)\dots\left(1 - \frac{m-1}{m}\right)\frac{z^m}{m!},$$

the coefficient of z^k tends to the coefficient of z^k in $\Sigma z^n/n!$ and thus the limiting numbers of

$$\left|\sum_0^\infty \frac{z^n}{n!} - \left(1 - \frac{z}{n}\right)^n\right|$$

are all less than ϵ.

In particular, the number e defined in Ex. I. 31, as the limit of $(1 + 1/n)^n$ is the same as the sum of $\Sigma 1/n!$

4. Show that if $z_n \to z$, $(1+z_n/n)^n \to e^z$. Take an r such that $|z_n| < r$ and thus also $|z| \leqslant r$. Then, by Ex. 3, for a sufficiently large n, $|(1+z/n)^n - e^z| < \epsilon$ for every $|z| \leqslant r$. In particular

$$|(1+z_n/n)^n - e^{z_n}| < \epsilon.$$

As e^z is continuous, $e^{z_n} \to e^z$ and thus the limiting numbers of

$$(1+z_n/n)^n - e^z$$

are all in the circle of radius ϵ.

5. Determine the directions in which e^z tends to a limit when $z \to \infty$ in the direction in question. From $e^z = e^{r\cos\alpha} e^{ir\sin\alpha}$, when $\cos\alpha > 0$, $|e^z| \to \infty$; when $\cos\alpha < 0$, $e^z \to 0$; for $\alpha = \pi/2$ or $3\pi/2$, e^z and $|e^z|$ have no limits.

6. $\lim\limits_{z\to\infty} |z+e^z| = \infty$ (in every direction).

7. Establish the following properties of hyperbolic functions defined for the complex variable in Art. 32:

(a) $\cosh^2 z - \sinh^2 z = 1$;
(b) $\sinh(z_1+z_2) = \sinh z_1 \cosh z_2 + \cosh z_1 \sinh z_2$;
(c) $\cosh(z_1+z_2) = \cosh z_1 \cosh z_2 + \sinh z_1 \sinh z_2$.

8. Find the lines along which $\sinh z$, $(\cosh z)$, is real.

9. Show that i^i is real. Determine its values.

10. Every point of the circumference of the unit circle $|z| = 1$ is a limiting point of $n^{i\alpha}$ where α is any fixed real number. We put $n^{i\alpha} = e^{i\alpha \log n}$, $\log n = x_n + \epsilon_n$ with $x_n = -c + 1 + 1/2 + \ldots + 1/n$ (by Ex. III. 1) and apply Ex. I. 22.

11. Every point of the circle $|z| = 1/\sqrt{1+\alpha^2}$ is a limiting point of $z_n = (1^{i\alpha} + 2^{i\alpha} + \ldots + n^{i\alpha})/n$ where α is any real number. We write $z_n = n^{i\alpha} \sum\limits_{\nu=1}^{n} (\nu/n)^{i\alpha}/n$ where the second factor converges to $\int_0^1 x^{i\alpha}\,dx = 1/(1+i\alpha)$ and the limiting numbers of the first factor, by the preceding example, cover $|z| = 1$.

12. Solve the equations:

(a) $\sin z = 10$; (b) $\sin z = 1 - i$; (c) $\cos z = 2i$.

13. *Division by a power series.* As $|a_1 + a_2 z + \ldots + a_n z^{n-1} + \ldots|$ is

bounded in any circle inside the circle of convergence of $\Sigma a_n z^n$, there is a circle of radius R such that

$$\left|\frac{z}{a_0}\right| |a_1 + a_2 z + \ldots + a_n z^{n-1} + \ldots| < p < 1.$$

Thus

$$\frac{1}{a_0 + a_1 z + \ldots} = \frac{1}{a_0} \frac{1}{1 - \frac{z}{a_0} \sum_1^\infty -a_n z^{n-1}} = \frac{1}{a_0} \sum_{m=0}^\infty \left(-\sum_{n=1}^\infty a_n z^{n-1}\right)^m$$

and the G. P. on the right-hand side is cgt. in $|z| < R$. Since the double series $\sum_m \left[\sum_n (a_n z^{n-1})\right]^m$ is *absolutely* cgt. we can rearrange the terms as we like without changing the value of the sum. Hence putting $\left(\sum_{n=1}^\infty -a_n z^{n-1}\right)^m = \sum_1^\infty c_k z^k$, we can determine $c_1, c_2, c_3, \ldots$ step by step: $c_1 = -a_1$, $c_2 = a_1 a_2 + a_1^2$, &c.

Calculate c_3, c_4, c_5.

14. *Bernoulli's numbers.* Expand $z/(e^z - 1)$ in power series. Putting (for historical reasons)

$$\left(1 + \frac{z}{2!} + \frac{z^2}{3!} + \ldots\right)\left(B_0 + \frac{B_1}{1!} z + \frac{B_2}{2!} z^2 + \ldots\right) \equiv 1$$

we find
$$B_0 = 1, \frac{1}{2!}\frac{B_0}{0!} + \frac{1}{1!}\frac{B_1}{1!} = 0, \ldots,$$

$$\frac{1}{n!}\frac{B_0}{0!} + \frac{1}{(n-1)!}\frac{B_1}{1!} + \ldots + \frac{1}{1!}\frac{B_{n-1}}{(n-1)!} = 0,$$

i. e. multiplying by $n!$

$$C_0^n B_0 + C_1^n B_1 + \ldots + C_{n-1}^n B_{n-1} = 0,$$

or in symbolic form: $(B+1)^{[n]} - B^{[n]} = 0$.

The numbers B_n are called *Bernoulli's numbers.*

15. Calculate the first fifteen numbers B_n.

16. *Inversion of a power series. If $u = a_0 + a_1(z - z_0) + \ldots$ is cgt. in $|z| < R$, $z - z_0$ can be expressed as a power series in $u - a_0$.* Put for simplicity's sake $a_0 = 0$, $z_0 = 0$, $a_1 = 1$ and write $z = \sum_1^\infty c_n u^n$.

Then the identity $\sum c_n u^n = \sum_n c_n \left(\sum_k a_k z^k\right)^n$ determines the coefficients c_n. Calculate the first five coefficients and determine their recurrence formula.

17. *Expansion of* $\tan z$ *and* $\cot z$ *into power series.* In Ex. 14 we have seen that $z/(e^z-1)+z/2 = 1+B_2z^2/2!+B_3z^3/3!+\dots$. The left-hand side is $\frac{z}{2}(e^{\frac{z}{2}}+e^{-\frac{z}{2}})/(e^{\frac{z}{2}}-e^{-\frac{z}{2}})$. Since this is an even function, $B_{2n+1}=0$, for $n>0$. Hence

$$z\,\frac{1+\dfrac{z^2}{2!}+\dfrac{z^4}{4!}+\dots}{z+\dfrac{z^3}{3!}+\dfrac{z^5}{5!}+\dots} = 1+\frac{B_2}{2!}(2z)^2+\frac{B_4}{4!}(2z)^4+\dots.$$

Changing z^2 into $-z^2$ the left-hand side is $z\cos z/\sin z = z\cot z$. Hence

$$(1)\qquad z\cot z = 1-\frac{B_2}{2!}(2z)^2+\frac{B_4}{4!}(2z)^4+\dots+(-1)^n\frac{2^{2n}B_{2n}}{(2n)!}z^{2n}+\dots.$$

As $\tan z = \cot z - 2\cot 2z$, we get

$$(2)\qquad \tan z = \sum_1^\infty (-1)^{n+1}\frac{2^{2n}(2^{2n}-1)B_{2n}}{(2n)!}z^{2n-1}.$$

Calculate the first five coefficients of (1) and (2).

18. Prove that, for $x>0$,

$$(1)\qquad I(x)\equiv\int_0^\infty (e^{-t}-e^{-tx})\frac{dt}{t} = \log x.$$

We have

$$I(x) = \lim_{\delta\to0,\,\rho\to\infty}\left\{\int_\delta^\rho \frac{e^{-t}}{t} - \int_\delta^\rho \frac{e^{-tx}}{t}\,dt\right\}.$$

The second integral is equal to

$$\int_{\delta x}^{\rho x}\frac{e^{-u}}{u}\,du,$$

so that

$$I(x) = \lim_{\delta\to0,\,\rho\to\infty}\left\{\int_\delta^{\delta x}\frac{e^{-t}}{t}\,dt-\int_\rho^{\rho x}\frac{e^{-t}}{t}\,dt\right\}.$$

Now, if $x>0$,

$$\lim_{\rho\to\infty}\int_\rho^{\rho x}\frac{e^{-t}}{t}\,dt = 0,$$

and

$$\int_\delta^{\delta x}\frac{e^{-t}}{t}\,dt = \log x - \int_\delta^{\delta x}\frac{1-e^{-t}}{t}\,dt \to \log x,$$

for

$$\lim_{t\to0}\frac{1-e^{-t}}{t} = 1$$

19. Prove that, for $x>0$,

$$\int_0^\infty \left(\frac{xe^{-t}}{t}+\frac{e^{-tx}}{t^2}\right)dt = x\log x - x.$$

In formula (1) Ex. 18, integrate under the sign of integration with respect to x and also integrate the right-hand side. Verify that the two functions of x so obtained have the same value at $x=0$.

20. Prove that

$$w(n)=\int_0^\infty \left[\frac{1}{1-e^{-x}}-\frac{1}{x}-\frac{1}{2}\right]e^{-nx}\frac{dx}{x},$$

decreases to zero with $1/n$.

It is easily verified that the integrand is positive for $x>0$ and so decreases with $1/n$. From the expansion of $\dfrac{z}{e^z-1}$ in Ex. 14 we see that

$$\phi(x)\equiv\left[\frac{1}{1-e^{-x}}-\frac{1}{x}-\frac{1}{2}\right]\frac{1}{x}=\frac{B_2}{2!}+\ldots$$

is a power series convergent in $|x|<\rho$, so that the integrand $\phi(x)e^{-nx}\leqslant\phi(x)$ is bounded in $(0,\rho')$, $\rho'<\rho$, and thus there is a δ such that

$$\int_0^\delta \phi(x)e^{-nx}\,dx<\epsilon.$$

Moreover

$$\lim_{n=\infty}\int_\delta^c \phi(x)e^{-nx}\,dx=0.$$

Finally, $\phi(x)$ being bounded in (c,∞), the rapidity of the decrease of e^{-nx} to zero makes this part of the integral also a zero sequence.

21. Find the value of $w(\frac{1}{2})$.

Changing x into $2x$ we have

$$w(\tfrac{1}{2})=\int_0^\infty \left[\frac{1}{1-e^{-2x}}-\frac{1}{2x}-\frac{1}{2}\right]e^{-x}\frac{dx}{x}.$$

From the two forms of $w(1)$, viz.

$$w(1)=\int_0^\infty \left[\frac{1}{1-e^{-x}}-\frac{1}{x}-\frac{1}{2}\right]e^{-x}\frac{dx}{x}=\int_0^\infty \left[\frac{1}{1-e^{-2x}}-\frac{1}{2x}-\frac{1}{2}\right]e^{-2x}\frac{dx}{x},$$

we obtain by subtraction

$$0=\int_0^\infty \left[\frac{1}{1-e^{-2x}}-\frac{2-e^{-x}}{2x}-\frac{1-e^{-x}}{2}\right]e^{-x}\frac{dx}{x}.$$

Subtracting this from $w(\frac{1}{2})$ we have

$$w(\tfrac{1}{2})=\tfrac{1}{2}\int_0^\infty \left[\frac{e^{-x}-e^{-2x}}{x^2}-\frac{e^{-2x}}{x}\right]dx.$$

The integrand may be written

$$\left(\frac{e^{-2x}-e^{-x}}{x}\right)' - \frac{e^{-x}-e^{-2x}}{x}.$$

Integrating the second part we obtain log 2, by Ex.18. The value of

$$\frac{e^{-2x}-e^{-x}}{x},$$

at $x = \infty$ is obviously 0. Its value at $x = 0$ is -1. Thus

$$w(\tfrac{1}{2}) = \tfrac{1}{2} - \tfrac{1}{2}\log 2.$$

22. *Stirling's formula.* From (33. 8) we obtain

$$\Gamma'(m) = \int_0^\infty x^{m-1} e^{-x} \log x \, dx.$$

Substituting $\log x = \int_0^\infty (e^{-z} - e^{-xz}) \frac{dz}{z}$ (see Ex. 18) and inverting the order of integration, we obtain

$$\Gamma'(m) = \int_0^\infty \frac{dz}{z} \int_0^\infty x^{m-1} e^{-x} (e^{-z} - e^{-xz}) \, dx.$$

Since

$$\int_0^\infty x^{m-1} e^{-x} e^{-z} \, dx = e^{-z} \Gamma(m)$$

and by the substitution $x(1+z) = y$,

$$\int_0^\infty x^{m-1} e^{-x} e^{-xz} \, dx = \int_0^\infty \frac{y^{m-1} e^{-y}}{(1+z)^m} \, dy = (1+z)^{-m} \Gamma(m),$$

we have

$$\Gamma'(m) / \Gamma(m) = \int_0^\infty dz \left[e^{-z} - (1+z)^{-m} \right] / z.$$

Integrating with respect to m from $m = 1$ to $m = n$ and inverting the order of integration we obtain

$$\log \Gamma(n) = \int_0^\infty \frac{dz}{z} \left[(n-1) e^{-z} - \frac{(1+z)^{-1} - (1+z)^{-n}}{\log(1+z)} \right].$$

Putting $n = 2$ we have

$$0 = \int_0^\infty dz \left[\frac{e^{-z}}{z} - \frac{(1+z)^{-2}}{\log(1+z)} \right],$$

i.e., multiplying the last equation by $n-1$ and subtracting from the preceding formula,

$$\log \Gamma(n) = \int_0^\infty \left[(n-1)(1+z)^{-2} - \frac{(1+z)^{-1} - (1+z)^{-n}}{z} \right] \frac{dz}{\log(1+z)}.$$

Putting $\log(1+z) = x$, i.e. $z = e^x - 1$, we have finally

$$\log \Gamma(n) = \int_0^\infty \left[(n-1) e^{-x} - \frac{e^{-x} - e^{-nx}}{1 - e^{-x}} \right] \frac{dx}{x}.$$

We might also write

$$\log \Gamma(n) = \int_0^\infty \left[(n-1)e^{-x} - \frac{e^{-x}}{1-e^{-x}} + \left(\frac{1}{x}+\frac{1}{2}\right)e^{-nx}\right]\frac{dx}{x}$$
$$+\int_0^\infty \left[\frac{1}{1-e^{-x}} - \frac{1}{x} - \frac{1}{2}\right]e^{-nx}\frac{dx}{x} = F(n)+w(n).$$

[In the expansion of $1/(1-e^{-x})$ in powers of x the first terms are $1/x+1/2$].

$F(n)$ can be evaluated precisely in the following way:

$$F(n)-F\left(\frac{1}{2}\right) = \int_0^\infty \left(n-\frac{1}{2}\right)e^{-x}+\left(\frac{1}{x}+\frac{1}{2}\right)(e^{-nx}-e^{-x/2})\frac{dx}{x}$$
$$= \left(n-\frac{1}{2}\right)\log n - n + \frac{1}{2}, \quad \text{(by Ex. 19)},$$

and

$$F\left(\frac{1}{2}\right) = \log \Gamma\left(\frac{1}{2}\right) - w\left(\frac{1}{2}\right) = \frac{1}{2}\log \pi - \frac{1}{2}(1-\log 2), \quad \text{(by Ex. 21.)}$$

Thus
$$F(n) = \left(n-\frac{1}{2}\right)\log n - n + \frac{1}{2}\log 2\pi,$$

and
$$\log \Gamma(n+1) = \left(n+\frac{1}{2}\right)\log n - n + \frac{1}{2}\log 2\pi + w(n)$$

where $w(n)$ decreases to zero with $1/n$, by Ex. 20. This asymptotic expression for $\Gamma(n+1)$ is known as *Stirling's formula.*

23. *Euler's integral of the first kind.*

$$\Gamma(p)\,\Gamma(q) = \int_0^\infty 2x^{2p-1}e^{-x^2}\,dx \int_0^\infty 2y^{2q-1}e^{-y^2}\,dy$$
$$= \int_0^\infty \int_0^\infty 4x^{2p-1}y^{2q-1}e^{-x^2-y^2}\,dx\,dy.$$

Putting $x = \rho\cos\phi$, $y = \rho\sin\phi$,

$$\Gamma(p)\,\Gamma(q) = \int_0^{\frac{\pi}{2}}\int_0^\infty 4\cos^{2p-1}\phi\,\sin^{2q-1}\phi\,\rho^{2p+2q-1}e^{-\rho^2}\,d\rho\,d\phi$$
$$= \int_0^{\frac{\pi}{2}} 2\cos^{2p-1}\phi\,\sin^{2q-1}\phi\,d\phi \int_0^\infty 2\,\rho^{2p+2q-1}e^{-\rho^2}\,d\rho.$$

Putting $\cos^2\phi = x$, $-2\sin\phi\cos\phi\,d\phi = dx$, we have

$$B(p,q) = \int_0^{\frac{\pi}{2}} 2\cos^{2p-1}\phi\,\sin^{2q-1}\phi\,d\phi = \int_0^1 x^{p-1}(1-x)^{q-1}\,dx,$$

and thus

(1) $$\Gamma(p)\,\Gamma(q) = B(p,q)\,\Gamma(p+q).$$

$B(p,q)$ is called Euler's integral of the first kind.

CHAPTER V

COMPLEX DIFFERENTIATION

39. *Differential coefficient of a complex function.* Let $f(z)$ be a uniform function of $z = x+iy$, and consider the ratio

$$(1) \qquad \frac{f(z+\Delta z)-f(z)}{\Delta z},$$

where $\Delta z = \Delta x + i\Delta y$. If (1) tends to a definite limit when Δx and Δy both tend to zero *in any manner*, $f(z)$ is said to be *differentiable* and the limit is its *differential coefficient.*

To show that there are uniform functions which are not differentiable, suppose $f(z) = x-iy$ (when $z = x+iy$ is given $x-iy$ is perfectly determinate). Form the ratio (1), and now suppose Δx and Δy tend to zero in such a way that $\Delta y = \alpha\Delta x$ (α being any real constant). Then we have

$$\lim_{\Delta z\to 0}\frac{\Delta x - i\Delta y}{\Delta x + i\Delta y} = \frac{1-i\alpha}{1+i\alpha} = \frac{1-\alpha^2}{1+\alpha^2} - i\frac{2\alpha}{1+\alpha^2},$$

so that for this function (1) has infinitely many limiting values, which depend on the way in which Δy decreases compared with Δx, i.e. $f(z)$ is nowhere differentiable.

On the other hand z^n is differentiable at every point. In fact, by the binomial theorem, n a positive integer,

$$(z+\Delta z)^n - z^n = nz^{n-1}\Delta z + C_2^n z^{n-2}\Delta z^2 + \ldots + \Delta z^n.$$

Hence

$$\lim_{\Delta z\to 0}\frac{(z+\Delta z)^n - z^n}{\Delta z} \equiv \frac{dz^n}{dz} = nz^{n-1},$$

independently of the way in which $\Delta z \to 0$.

Complex functions which are not differentiable have not yet been studied.

The rules for differentiation of real functions readily extend to differentiable complex functions.

I. *Rules for differentiation:*

$$[u(z)\pm v(z)]' = u'(z)\pm v'(z), \qquad (uv)' = u'v+uv',$$
$$(u/v)' = (u'v-uv')/u^2, \qquad (v[u(z)])' = v_u{}'u'.$$

If $z = g(u)$ *is the inverse function of* $u = f(z)$, *then*

$$\frac{dz}{du} = 1 \Big/ \frac{du}{dz}.$$

The proofs are identical reproductions of the corresponding proofs for real variables. Similarly for partial differentiation.

When $z = x + iy$, i.e. x and y are fixed, the real and imaginary parts of every uniform function $u = f(z)$ are determinate. Hence we can write $u = P(x, y) + iQ(x, y)$. We are going to express u' in terms of P and Q. We have

$$\frac{\Delta u}{\Delta z} = \frac{\Delta P}{\Delta z} + i\frac{\Delta Q}{\Delta z},$$

where $\Delta z = \Delta x + i\Delta y$, $\Delta P = P(x+\Delta x, y+\Delta y) - P(x, y)$, and $\Delta Q = Q(x+\Delta x, y+\Delta y) - Q(x, y)$. Hence

$$\frac{\Delta u}{\Delta z} = \frac{\Delta P \, . \, \Delta x + \Delta Q \, . \, \Delta y}{\Delta x^2 + \Delta y^2} + i\frac{\Delta Q \, . \, \Delta x - \Delta P \, . \, \Delta y}{\Delta x^2 + \Delta y^2}.$$

Since we suppose that $\Delta u / \Delta z$ tends to a definite limit when Δz approaches 0, independently of the way in which Δz, i.e. Δx and Δy, decrease to zero, we can fix the value of Δy and let Δx tend to 0. Putting $\Delta y = 0$ we get

$$\frac{du}{dz} = \frac{\partial P}{\partial x} + i\frac{\partial Q}{\partial x} \tag{2}$$

Similarly, putting $\Delta x = 0$ and letting Δy tend to 0, we get

$$\frac{du}{dz} = \frac{\partial Q}{\partial y} - i\frac{\partial P}{\partial y}. \tag{3}$$

It follows that *for every differentiable function*

$$u = P(x, y) + iQ(x, y)$$

we have

$$\frac{\partial P}{\partial x} = \frac{\partial Q}{\partial y} \quad \textit{and} \quad \frac{\partial P}{\partial y} = -\frac{\partial Q}{\partial x}. \tag{4}$$

These equations are called *Cauchy's conditions.*

The integral of a complex function $f(x) = u(x) + iv(x)$ of a real variable x, (e.g. when only the real or only the imaginary part of z varies) is defined by putting

$$\int_\alpha^\beta f(x)\,dx = \int_\alpha^\beta u(x)\,dx + i\int_\alpha^\beta v(x)\,dx. \tag{5}$$

All the ordinary rules for integration hold good for such pairs of integrals. For a complex variable, the integral will be defined in Chapter VII.

The first important consequence of Cauchy's conditions is that if $du/dz = 0$ at every point of a region R, we have, by (2) and (3)

$$\frac{\partial P}{\partial x} = 0, \quad \frac{\partial Q}{\partial x} = 0, \quad \frac{\partial P}{\partial y} = 0, \quad \frac{\partial Q}{\partial y} = 0,$$

in R, i. e. P and Q are constants:

II. *The differential coefficient of a constant function is* 0 *and conversely if* $du/dz = 0$ *in* R, $u = \text{const.}$ *in* R.

Applying this result to the difference $u-v$ of two functions, we obtain

III. *If* $\dfrac{du}{dz} = \dfrac{dv}{dz}$ *in* R, $u = v + \text{const.}$ *in* R.

We see also that the real and imaginary parts of differentiable complex functions are closely connected with one another.

We are going to establish some simple consequences of (4).

If $P = \text{const.}$ for every point in the region considered, then also $Q = \text{const.}$, since, from (4), $\dfrac{\partial Q}{\partial x} = 0$ and $\dfrac{\partial Q}{\partial y} = 0$. On the other hand, if $P^2 + Q^2 = \text{const.}$, we have

$$P\frac{\partial P}{\partial x} + Q\frac{\partial Q}{\partial x} = 0, \quad P\frac{\partial P}{\partial y} + Q\frac{\partial Q}{\partial y} = 0,$$

i. e. by (4),

$$P\frac{\partial P}{\partial x} - Q\frac{\partial P}{\partial y} = 0, \quad Q\frac{\partial P}{\partial x} + P\frac{\partial P}{\partial y} = 0.$$

Solving this homogeneous system of simultaneous linear equations for $\dfrac{\partial P}{\partial x}$ and $\dfrac{\partial P}{\partial y}$ we find that the determinant is $P^2 + Q^2 = \Delta$. If this determinant is 0, we have $P = 0$ and $Q = 0$, i. e. $f(z) = 0$ at every point of R. If the determinant differs from 0, the only solution of the system is $\dfrac{\partial P}{\partial x} = 0$, $\dfrac{\partial P}{\partial y} = 0$, i. e. $P = \text{const.}$ Hence also $Q = \text{const.}$, i. e. $f(z) = \text{const.}$ Thus

IV. *If the real or imaginary part of a differentiable complex function* $f(z)$ *is constant at every point of a region, then*

$f(z) = \text{const.}$ *in the region. If* $|f(z)| = \text{const.}$, *then also* $f(z) = \text{const.}$ *in the same region.*

40. *Taylor series. Cauchy's inequalities.* If z is a fixed inner point of the circle of convergence (of radius R) of $\Sigma a_n z^n = f(z)$, then, for a sufficiently small h, $z+h$ is also inside the circle. Thus, for $|h| \leqslant k < R - |z|$, $\Sigma a_n(z+h)^n - \Sigma a_n z^n$, even if the terms $a_n(z+h)^n$ are decomposed, is an absolutely and uniformly convergent series in h. Therefore, in this circle, we can rearrange it in ascending powers of h:

$$\Sigma a_n(z+h)^n - \Sigma a_n z^n = h\Sigma n a_n z^{n-1} + \frac{h^2}{2!}\Sigma n(n-1)a_n z^{n-2} + \dots,$$

and thus

$$\frac{f(z+h)-f(z)}{h} = \Sigma n a_n z^{n-1} + \frac{h}{2}\Sigma n(n-1)a_n z^{n-2} + \dots .$$

Since the right-hand side is a continuous function of h, (being a power series), its limit as $h \to 0$ is the value of the sum function at 0. Thus we obtain the result

$$f'(z) = \Sigma n a_n z^{n-1},$$

i. e. *the differentiation term by term leads to the differential coefficient of the sum function.* We notice that, since $\sqrt[n]{n} \to 1$, $\overline{\lim_{n=\infty}} |\sqrt[n]{n a_n}| = \overline{\lim_{n=\infty}} |\sqrt[n]{a_n}|$, i. e. the radius of convergence of the differentiated series is the same as that of the original series.

I. *Differentiating a convergent power series term by term we obtain another power series which converges in the same circle and represents the differential coefficient of the sum function of the first series.*

As the differentiated power series is also a power series, *the sum function of a convergent power series is indefinitely differentiable and all the successive differentiated series have the same radius of convergence.*

We also notice that in the decomposition and regrouping leading to a new power series at a,

$$f(z) = \Sigma a_n[(z-a)+a]^n = \Sigma b_n(z-a)^n,$$

the coefficient b_n is just the n-th differential coefficient of $f(z)$ at a divided by $n!$, i. e.

$$(1) \qquad f(z) = \Sigma \frac{f^{(n)}(a)}{n!}(z-a)^n,$$

where $f^{(n)}(a)$ is now not only a notation for the sum of a series, but has in addition the usual meaning.

Differentiating $\Sigma a_n z^n$ and putting $z=0$, we see that $a_1 = f'(0)$ and so on, giving

$$(2) \qquad a_n = f^{(n)}(0)/n!.$$

Thus the coefficients and also the power series itself appear to be determined by a function. If we start with a given function like $1/(1+z)$ and form the coefficients $a_n = f^{(n)}(a)/n!$, the series so constructed is called *the Taylor series of* $f(z)$ *at* a. Such a series as $\Sigma \frac{f^{(n)}(a)}{n!}(z-a)^n$ may be divergent at every point except at $z=a$, in which case the series reduces to its first term. But if it is convergent at a point different from a, it is convergent in a circle about a (for it is a power series). In this case *its sum function is the function* $f(z)$ *used in the construction of its coefficients.* In fact, if we expand it about any inner point b of its circle of convergence the first term will be $f(b)$. Expansion about b means putting $z-a=(z-b)+(b-a)$ and rearranging in powers of $z-b$.

On the other hand, if we start with coefficients a_n, chosen independently of any function, and put $\Sigma a_n z^n = s(z)$, this sum function $s(z)$ may be taken for a given function, and we can construct the Taylor series corresponding to this function. But $a_0 = s(0)$, and we have seen that in general $a_n = s^{(n)}(0)/n!$, so that every power series converging in more than one point is the Taylor series of its sum function. We shall say that a power or Taylor series is convergent only if its radius of convergence is greater than zero. Thus

II. *A convergent power series is the Taylor series of its sum function.*

There is no point therefore in distinguishing between power and Taylor series, and we shall keep to the historical name of Taylor series.

If $F'(z) = f(z)$, we say that $F(z)$ is a primitive of $f(z)$. By 39. III, two primitives of $f(z)$ differ only by a constant, i.e. if $F(z)$ is a primitive of $f(z)$, all its primitives are of the form $F(z) + \text{const.}$

Since $[\Sigma a_n z^{n+1}/(n+1)]' = \Sigma a_n z^n$, *the primitives of an analytic function can be obtained by integrating the series term by term.*

III. *A primitive of* $\Sigma a_n z^n$ *is* $\Sigma a_n z^{n+1}/(n+1)$.

A fundamental property of Taylor coefficients is expressed by the following result:

IV. *If in the circle C of radius R, and centre at a,*

$$f(z) = \Sigma a_n (z-a)^n$$

and $|f(z)| \leqslant M$ in $|z-a| \leqslant R$, *then*

$$|a_n| \leqslant M/R^n, \quad \text{(Cauchy's inequalities)} \tag{3}$$

and equality takes place only for the function

$$f(z) = e^{i\alpha} M(z-a)^n/R^n, \quad (\alpha \text{ real}).$$

Proof. Denoting by $\bar{z}$ the conjugate of z we have, for any point z in C,

$$|f(z)|^2 = \Sigma a_n (z-a)^n \Sigma \bar{a}_n (\bar{z}-\bar{a})^n = g(r, \phi) \tag{4}$$

where $z-a = re^{i\phi}$, and

$$\begin{aligned}\int_0^{2\pi} |f(z)|^2 d\phi \\ = \int_0^{2\pi} (a_0 + a_1 re^{i\phi} + \dots + a_n r^n e^{in\phi} + \dots) \\ (\bar{a}_0 + \bar{a}_1 re^{-i\phi} + \dots + \bar{a}_n r^n e^{-in\phi} + \dots)\, d\phi.\end{aligned} \tag{5}$$

Since, for every positive or negative m, $\int_0^{2\pi} e^{mi\phi} d\phi = 0$, the only surviving terms are those for which, after multiplication, the coefficient of $i\phi$ is 0. Thus

$$\frac{1}{2\pi}\int_0^{2\pi} |f(z)|^2 d\phi = |a_0|^2 + |a_1|^2 r^2 + \dots + |a_n|^2 r^{2n} + \dots. \tag{6}$$

Since, by hypothesis, $|f(z)|^2 \leqslant M^2$, the left-hand side is $\leqslant M^2$. Hence $|a_0|^2 + |a_1|^2 r^2 + \dots + |a_n|^2 r^{2n} + \dots \leqslant M^2$. As the right-hand side is independent of r, we have also

$$|a_0|^2 + |a_1|^2 R^2 + \dots + |a_n|^2 R^{2n} + \dots \leqslant M^2. \tag{7}$$

Therefore the same inequality holds separately for every term. But, if $|a_n| = M/R^n$, all the terms but $|a_n|^2 R^{2n}$ must vanish. This remark proves the complete statement.

A simple application of Cauchy's inequality is the important result known as Liouville's theorem. We say that $f(z) = \Sigma a_n z^n$

is an *integral function* if the series converges for every finite value of z. Suppose now that an integral function is bounded, i.e. $|f(z)| \leqslant M$ throughout the complex plane. Then, by IV, $|a_n| \leqslant M/R^n$ for every R. The left-hand side is independent of R. Thus taking a larger and larger R, we see that

$$a_1 = 0,\ a_2 = 0,\ \ldots,\ a_n = 0,\ \ldots,$$

i.e.

$$f(z) = a_0.$$

The function $f(z)$ reduces to a constant.

If $f(z)/z^m$ is bounded (by M, say), similarly $|a_{m+p}| \leqslant M/R^p$, i.e. $f(z)$ is a polynomial of degree less than or equal to m.

V. *Liouville's theorem. If an integral function is bounded, it reduces to a constant. If $f(z)/z^m$ is bounded, $f(z)$ is a polynomial of degree less than or equal to m.* (Cauchy, 1844.)

Borel showed that Cauchy's inequalities can be made more precise in the following way. Putting $z = re^{i\phi}$, $a_n = a_n' + ia_n''$, $f(z) = P(r, \phi) + iQ(r, \phi)$, we have

$$(8) \qquad P(r, \phi) = a_0' + \sum_1^{\infty} (a_n' \cos n\phi - a_n'' \sin n\phi) r^n,$$

where the series converges uniformly for $r \leqslant R - \epsilon$. Hence, multiplying by $\cos n\phi$ or by $\sin n\phi$ and integrating, we find

$$\pi r^n a_n' = \int_0^{2\pi} P(r, \phi) \cos n\phi\, d\phi, \quad \pi r^n a_n'' = -\int_0^{2\pi} P(r, \phi) \sin n\phi\, d\phi,$$

i.e.

$$\pi r^n a_n = \int_0^{2\pi} P(r, \phi) e^{-in\phi} d\phi.$$

Hence

$$\pi r^n |a_n| \leqslant \int_0^{2\pi} |P(r, \phi)|\, d\phi.$$

Also

$$(9) \qquad 2\pi a_0' = \int_0^{2\pi} P(r, \phi) d\phi.$$

Therefore

$$\pi(|a_n| r^n + 2a_0') \leqslant \int_0^{2\pi} [|P(r, \phi)| + P(r, \phi)] d\phi.$$

As the bracket under the sign of integration vanishes if P is negative or zero and $= 2P$ when P is greater than zero, we have, for $r < R$, $n > 0$, denoting by $A(r)$ the algebraic maximum of $P(r, \phi)$ for $0 \leqslant \phi < 2\pi$,

$$|a_n| r^n + 2a_0' \leqslant 4A(r)$$

if $A(r)$ is positive. If $A(r) \leqslant 0$, then $P(r, \phi) \leqslant 0$ for every ϕ, $a_0' \leqslant 0$ and thus

$$|a_n| r^n + 2a_0' \leqslant 0.$$

Therefore, in every case,

$$(10) \qquad |a_n| \leqslant \frac{4C(r) + 2|a_0'|}{r^n},$$

where $C(r) = A(r)$ if $A(r) \geqslant 0$ and $C(r) = 0$ if $A(r) \leqslant 0$. It follows that, for $\rho < r$,

$$(11) \qquad |f(\rho e^{i\theta})| \leqslant \sum_{n=0}^{\infty} |a_n| \rho^n$$

$$\leqslant |a_0| + [4C(r) + 2|a_0'|] \frac{r}{r-\rho}.$$

Similarly for $Q(r, \phi)$.

The last inequality plays an important part in the modern theory of analytic functions.

41. *The principle of the maximum.* We shall now discuss a property of analytic functions which is of fundamental importance for the whole theory. We begin with a kind of mean-value theorem used in the theory of harmonic functions.

I. *If $f(r, \phi)$ is a real, continuous function and if, for every $r < \rho$ it satisfies the equation*

$$(1) \qquad \int_0^{2\pi} f(r, \phi)\, d\phi = 2\pi f(0),$$

$f(r, \phi)$ has no extremum (maximum or minimum) at the origin, unless it reduces to a constant.

Proof. We first notice that if $f(r_0, \phi)$ has a constant value $f(r_0)$ along the circumference of radius r_0,

$$\int_0^{2\pi} f(r_0, \phi)\, d\phi = 2\pi f(r_0),$$

and thus, by (1), $f(r_0) = f(0)$.

Now suppose that $f(0)$ is a local (or general) maximum, i.e. that

$$(2) \qquad f(r, \phi) \leqslant f(0), \quad \text{if } r < \rho.$$

If $f(r, \phi)$ is not a constant, there is a point (r_0, ϕ_0) such that $f(r_0, \phi_0) < f(0)$. It follows from our first remark that $f(r_0, \phi)$ is not a constant; therefore, since $f(r, \phi)$ is continuous, there is an arc, $(0, \alpha)$, say, on the circumference of radius r_0 along which

$$f(r_0, \phi) \leqslant A < f(0), \text{ if } 0 \leqslant \phi \leqslant \alpha,$$

and thus

$$\int_0^\alpha f(r_0, \phi)\, d\phi < \alpha f(0).$$

Moreover from (2),

$$\int_\alpha^{2\pi} f(r_0, \phi)\, d\phi \leqslant (2\pi - \alpha) f(0),$$

so that

$$\int_0^{2\pi} f(r_0, \phi)\, d\phi < 2\pi f(0),$$

which contradicts (1). A similar argument establishes the result for minima.

II. *If $f(z)$ is regular and uniform in a domain D, its real and imaginary parts have no extrema in D unless $f(z)$ is a constant.*

Proof. Near any point a of D we have, by hypothesis,

(3) $$f(z) = \Sigma a_n (z-a)^n$$

where the series on the right-hand side converges in a certain circle $|z-a| \leqslant \rho$. Putting $z - a = re^{i\phi}$, $a_n = a_n' + ia_n''$, we obtain $f(z) = P(r, \phi) + iQ(r, \phi)$ where the two series

$$P(r, \phi) = \Sigma (a_n' \cos n\phi - a_n'' \sin n\phi) r^n,$$
$$Q(r, \phi) = \Sigma (a_n' \sin n\phi + a_n'' \cos n\phi) r^n$$

are absolutely and uniformly convergent with respect to both r and ϕ in every circle of radius $r < \rho$. Therefore, integrating with respect to ϕ from 0 to 2π, we see that

$$\int_0^{2\pi} P(r, \phi)\, d\phi = 2\pi a_0' = 2\pi P(0),$$

$$\int_0^{2\pi} Q(r, \phi)\, d\phi = 2\pi a_0'' = 2\pi Q(0),$$

so that I applies and proves II.

III. (*Principle of the maximum*). *If a uniform function $f(z)$ is regular in a domain D, or if all the determinations of a multiform function $f(z)$ are regular at any point of D and*

$|f(z)|$ is uniform in D, $|f(z)|$ has no maximum in D unless $f(z)$ is a constant. If $f(z)$ is not a constant, the only possible minimum value for $|f(z)|$ in D is zero. (Cauchy.)

Proof. Suppose first that $f(z)$ is uniform in D. Take any point a in D and suppose $f(z)$ is given by (3) in a circle about a. Denote the right-hand side of (40. 6) by $h(r)$. Then it follows from (3) and (40. 4) that, as $r \to 0$, $h(r)$ steadily decreases, unless $f(z)$ is a constant, and tends to $g(0) = |a_0|^2$.

Excluding the case $f(z) = \text{const.}$, let us suppose that $|f(z)|$ and thus also $|f(z)|^2$ has a maximum at a, i.e. for $r = 0$. If $g(r, \phi) = \text{const.}$, then also $f(z)$ is a constant (by 39. IV), which is not the case. Therefore there is a point (r_0, ϕ_0) such that $g(r_0, \phi_0) < A < g(0)$, and thus there is an arc, $(0, \alpha)$, say, on the circumference of radius r_0 along which $g(r_0, \phi) < A < g(0)$. It follows that

$$\int_0^\alpha g(r_0, \phi)\, d\phi < \alpha g(0).$$

On the other hand, $g(0)$ being a maximum,

$$\int_\alpha^{2\pi} g(r_0, \phi)\, d\phi \leqslant (2\pi - \alpha)\, g(0).$$

The two inequalities show that

$$\frac{1}{2\pi}\int_0^{2\pi} g(r_0, \phi)\, d\phi = h(r_0) < g(0),$$

which contradicts the fact that $h(r) > g(0)$.

If $f(z)$ is not uniform in D, (3) only represents one determination of $f(z)$. However, if $|f(z)|$ is uniform, as in the case of $u = z^\alpha$, i.e. if $|f(z)|$ is the same for all the branches, the result still holds.

To prove the second statement of the theorem let us suppose that $f(z)$ does not vanish in D. Then $1/f(z)$ satisfies the conditions of the theorem and thus has no maximum in D. Therefore $|f(z)|$ has no minimum in D. Moreover if, at a point of D, $f(z_0) \neq 0$, then $f(z) \neq 0$ in a sufficiently small circle c about z_0 and thus $|f(z)|$ has no minimum in c, i.e. has no local minimum at z_0. This proves the second statement.

If we imagine $|f(x+iy)|$ as a height at (x, y) normal to the (x, y) plane, we obtain a surface sometimes called the *analytic landscape* of $f(z)$. *There is no peak in this landscape.*

As a first application of the principle of the maximum consider a Taylor series $f(z) = \Sigma a_n z^n$, convergent in $|z| < R$, and put

$$M(r) = \max_{|z|=r} |f(z)|, \; r < R$$

$$A(r) = \max_{0 \leqslant \phi < 2\pi} P(r, \phi), \quad B(r) = \max_{0 \leqslant \phi < 2\pi} Q(r, \phi),$$

where $A(r)$ and $B(r)$ are algebraic maxima, i.e. they may be negative. $M(r)$ is called the *maximum modulus* of $f(z)$ along $|z| = r$.

IV. *$M(r)$, $A(r)$, and $B(r)$ are steadily increasing (and not only non-decreasing) functions of r unless $f(z)$ is a constant.*

Proof. Along $|z| = r$, $|f(z)|$ is a continuous function of ϕ. Therefore, there is a point z_0 of this circumference at which $|f(z)|$ assumes its maximum, i.e. $|f(z_0)| = M(r)$. Now, if there were a circle $|z| = \bar{r} > r$ in which $|f(z)| \leqslant M(r)$, $|f(z)|$ would have a maximum at the *inner* point z_0, and thus, by III, $f(z)$ would be a constant.

Similar reasoning holds for $A(r)$ and $B(r)$.

V. *If the real or the imaginary part of $f(z) = \Sigma a_n z^n$ is constant along the circle $|z| = r < R$, $f(z)$ reduces to a constant. If $f(z) \neq 0$ in $|z| < r$ and $|f(z)|$ is constant along $|z| = r < R$, $f(z)$ reduces to a constant.*

Proof. If $P(r, \phi)$ is independent of ϕ, its maximum and its minimum on $|z| = r$ coincide. But, by II, the value of P at any inner point is between the maximum and minimum assumed on the boundary. Therefore $P(r, \phi)$ is a constant throughout $|z| \leqslant r$, and thus, by the first part of 39. IV, $f(z)$ is also a constant. The second statement follows in a similar way from III and from the second statement of 39. IV.

We notice that in the result so obtained the circle may be replaced by very general boundaries. In reality, besides the general conditions of II or III and 39. IV, it is sufficient for the validity of the argument that $P(r, \phi)$ or $Q(r, \phi)$ or $|f(z)|$ as the case may be, should tend to a definite value as z approaches a boundary point in any manner from inside, and that this value should be the same for all the boundary points.

We have formulated the principle of the maximum in a negative form 'no maximum modulus inside R' because the positive form: '$|f(z)|$ assumes its maximum at a boundary point', is less general. In fact, $f(z)$ may not exist at some (or all) points of the boundary, in which case the maximum modulus may not be assumed.

If $f(z)$ is regular not only inside R but also at its boundary points, and if $|f(z)| \leqslant M$ at the boundary points, we conclude, by the principle of the maximum, that $|f(z)| \leqslant M$ throughout R. We shall make frequent use of this argument.

In many cases, however, we do not possess such complete information about $f(z)$ at the boundary points and, in some cases, we may know definitely that $f(z)$ is not regular at certain boundary points. If z_0 is such a boundary point, $f(z)$ is defined only in that part of the neighbourhood of z_0 which lies inside R, called the 'inner neighbourhood' of z_0 with respect to R. Phragmen and Lindelöf have established a positive form of the principle of the maximum which has been much used in recent researches on analytic functions.

VI. *The Phragmen-Lindelöf principle of the maximum. Suppose* (a) $f(z)$ *is regular and* $|f(z)|$ *is uniform in the finite domain* D, (b) *for an arbitrarily given* $\epsilon > 0$, *and in a certain inner neighbourhood of every boundary point* ζ (*depending on* ϵ),

$$\text{(A)} \qquad |f(z)| < M + \epsilon.$$

Then $|f(z)| \leqslant M$ *at every inner point, and equality at any inner point implies that* $f(z) =$ const. *throughout* D.

(Phragmen and Lindelöf, 1908.)

Proof. Denote by G the upper bound of $|f(z)|$ inside D. The case $G = +\infty$ is not excluded as a possibility. By the definition of the upper bound, there are inner points z_k such that $|f(z_k)| \to G$.

(1) Suppose that a limiting point $\bar{z}$ of z_k is an inner point of D, and consider a part of the sequence z_k, also denoted by z_k, tending to $\bar{z}$. Then, $|f(z)|$ being continuous inside D,

$$\lim_{k=\infty} |f(z_k)| = |f(\bar{z})| = G,$$

i.e. $|f(z)|$ assumes its maximum at the inner point $\bar{z}$, and thus, by III, $|f(z)| =$ *const. throughout* D.

(2) Suppose that all the limiting points of the sequence z_k are boundary points, and again consider a part of the sequence z_k, also denoted by z_k, tending to the boundary point $\bar{z}$. Now, by (A), there is a square q centre $\bar{z}$ such that $|f(z)| < M + \epsilon$ in the

common part of q and D. Since, for a sufficiently large k, the points z_k tending to $\bar{z}$ are all in q, $G \leqslant M+\epsilon$, i.e. ϵ being arbitrary, $G \leqslant M$, which proves the first statement of the theorem. The second follows by III.

42. *Some consequences of the principle of the maximum.* We are going to deduce from the result of the preceding article some theorems of wide application.

I. *Schwarz's lemma. If* $\sum_1^\infty a_n z^n = f(z)$ *is convergent and* $|f(z)| \leqslant M$ *in* $|z| < R$, *then* $|f(z)| \leqslant M|z|/R$ *in* $|z| < R$ *and equality takes place only for functions of the type* $Me^{i\alpha}z/R$ (α *real*).

Proof. Since $a_1 + a_2 z + \ldots = f(z)/z = g(z)$ is convergent in $|z| < R$ and the maximum modulus of $g(z)$ on $|z| = r$ is $M(r)/r$, we have, for $r < R$

$$|f(z)|/|z| \leqslant M(r)/r.$$

Since, as $r \to R$, $M(r)/r$, the maximum modulus of a regular function, is a non-decreasing function of r, we have also

$$|f(z)|/|z| \leqslant M/R$$

in $|z| < R$, which proves the first part of the statement.

But the equality $|f(z)|/|z| = M/R$ for a z *inside* $|z| = R$ means that the maximum is assumed inside, and thus the left-hand side cannot effectively increase when $|z| \to R$, i.e. $|f(z)/z|$ and, by 39. IV, $f(z)/z$ also, is a constant; which establishes the second part.

II. *Hadamard's three circles theorem. Suppose* $0 < r_1 < r_2 < r_3$ *and that* $f(z)$ *is uniform and regular in the ring region* $r_1 \leqslant |z| \leqslant r_3$; *let* M_1, M_2, M_3 *denote the maximum of* $|f(z)|$ *on the circles* $|z| = r_1, r_2, r_3$ *respectively. Then*

(2) $$M_2^{\log(r_3/r_1)} \leqslant M_1^{\log(r_3/r_2)} M_3^{\log(r_2/r_1)}.$$ (Hadamard, 1896.)

Proof. If $f(z)$ is constant in the ring region, (2) is satisfied with the equality sign. Excluding the case in which $f(z)$ is identically zero, we suppose that $M_1, M_2, M_3 > 0$. For any real number α, the function z^α is in general multiform, but $|z^\alpha f(z)|$ is *uniform and continuous*. On $|z| = r_1$ we have $|z^\alpha f(z)| \leqslant r_1^\alpha M_1$; on $|z| = r_3$, we have $|z^\alpha f(z)| \leqslant r_3^\alpha M_3$, i.e. on the boundary of our ring domain $|z^\alpha f(z)|$ is less than the greater of $r_1{}^\alpha M_1$ and $r_3{}^\alpha M_3$. In symbols,

$$(3) \qquad |z^\alpha f(z)| \leqslant \max (r_1{}^\alpha M_1, \ r_3{}^\alpha M_3).$$

Now, any branch of $z^\alpha f(z)$ is uniform and regular in the domain enclosed by *akablba* of Fig. 20, so that $|z^\alpha f(z)|$ assumes its

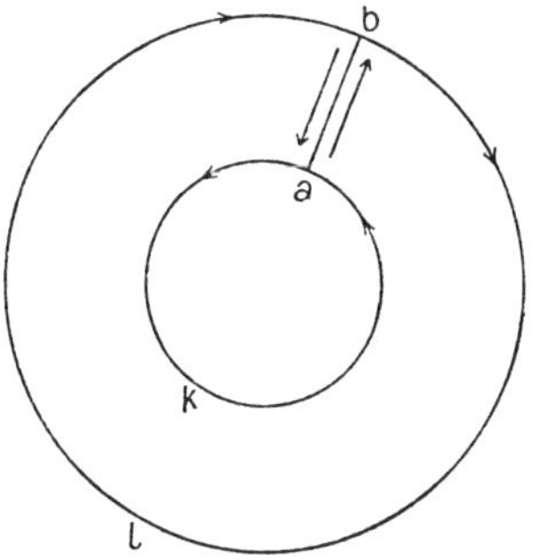

FIG. 20.

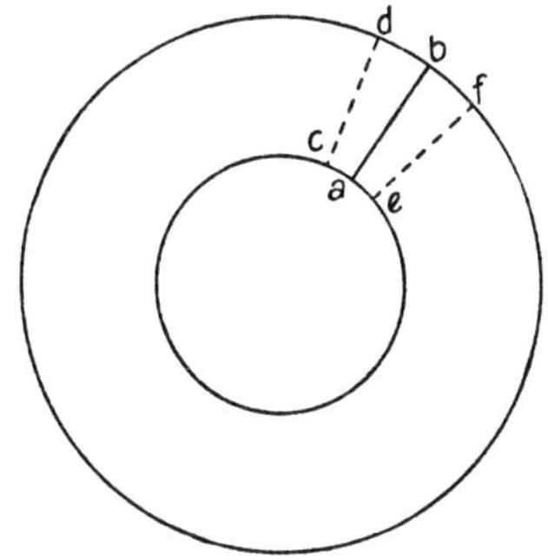

FIG. 21.

maximum on its boundary. But in the domain enclosed by *acdbfea* in Fig. 21 any of the branches is uniform and regular, so that $|z^\alpha f(z)|$ cannot assume its maximum at a point on ab. Thus (3) holds good for every point of the ring region. In particular $r_2{}^\alpha M_2 \leqslant \max (r_1{}^\alpha M_1, \ r_3{}^\alpha M_3)$, or $M_2 \leqslant$ the greater of $(r_1/r_2)^\alpha M_1$ and $(r_3/r_2)^\alpha M_3$. If $\alpha = \log \ (M_3/M_1) \div \log \ (r_1/r_3)$ these two numbers are equal and thus

$$M_2 \leqslant M_1 (r_1/r_2)^{\log (M_3/M_1) \div \log (r_1/r_3)} = M_1 (M_3/M_1)^{\log (r_2/r_1) \div \log (r_3/r_1)}$$
$$= M_1{}^{\log (r_3/r_2) \div \log (r_3/r_1)} M_3{}^{\log (r_2/r_1) \div \log (r_3/r_1)},$$

which when raised to the power $\log (r_3/r_1)$, leads to Hadamard's theorem.

Remark. Equation (2) may be written in the form

$$\begin{vmatrix} \log M_1 & \log r_1 & 1 \\ \log M_2 & \log r_2 & 1 \\ \log M_3 & \log r_3 & 1 \end{vmatrix} \leqslant 0.$$

The geometrical meaning of this condition is as follows:—We say that the real function $g(t)$ of the real variable t is *convex* in the interval (a, b) if all the values of $g(t)$ assumed between two arbitrary points t_1 and t_3 of (a, b) lie below or on the chord between $[t_1, \ g(t_1)]$ and $[t_3, \ g(t_3)]$. In mathematical terms, if

$t_1 < t_2 < t_3$, ve must have $g(t_2) \leqslant g(t_1) + \dfrac{t_2 - t_1}{t_3 - t_1}[g(t_3) - g(t_1)]$, i.e.

$$\begin{vmatrix} g(t_1) & t_1 & 1 \\ g(t_2) & t_2 & 1 \\ g(t_3) & t_3 & 1 \end{vmatrix} \leqslant 0.$$

Thus Hadamard's three circles theorem can be stated in the form $\log M(r)$ *is a convex function of* $\log r$.

Hardy proved a similar theorem for

$$I(r) = \frac{1}{2\pi}\int_0^{2\pi} |f(re^{i\theta})|\, d\theta.$$

III. *If $f(z)$ is regular and not a constant in $|z| < R$, $I(r)$ steadily increases with r and* $\log I(r)$ *is a convex function of* $\log r$. (Hardy, 1915 b.)

Proof. Let $0 < r_1 < r_2 < r_3 < R$, and define $\epsilon(\theta)$ and $F(z)$ by putting

$$\epsilon(\theta) f(r_2 e^{i\theta}) = |f(r_2 e^{i\theta})|, \quad F(z) = \frac{1}{2\pi}\int_0^{2\pi} f(ze^{i\theta})\epsilon(\theta)\, d\theta.$$

Since $F(z)$ is regular in and on $|z| = r_3$, we may suppose that it assumes its maximum modulus at $r_3 e^{i\theta_3}$. Then

$$I(r_2) = F(r_2) \leqslant |F(r_3 e^{i\theta_3})| \leqslant I(r_3),$$

which proves that $I(r)$ is steadily increasing.

Now determine the real number α by the condition that $r_1{}^{\alpha} I(r_1) = r_3{}^{\alpha} I(r_3)$. The function $z^{\alpha} F(z)$ is regular in the ring $r_1 \leqslant z \leqslant r_3$ and its modulus is uniform. Hence, by 41. III,

$$r_2{}^{\alpha} I(r_2) = r_2{}^{\alpha} F(r_2) \leqslant \max_{r_1 \leqslant |z| \leqslant r_3} |z^{\alpha} F(z)| \leqslant r_1{}^{\alpha} I(r_1) = r_3{}^{\alpha} I(r_3),$$

and thus we can finish the proof as in II.

As an application of our previous results we are going to establish two very important theorems on sequences of regular functions.

IV. *Vitali's theorem. Suppose $f_\nu(z)$ is regular and uniform and $|f_\nu(z)| \leqslant M$ in the finite domain D ($\nu = 1, 2, 3, \ldots$) and $\lim_{\nu=\infty} f_\nu(z)$ exists for infinitely many points $z = z_a$ in D having a limiting point in D. Then $f_\nu(z)$ converges uniformly in every region R within D to a function regular in R.* (Vitali, 1903.)

Proof. We suppose first that D is a circle of radius R centre at the origin. We can also assume that 0 is a limiting number of the sequence z_a, which thus contains a sequence tending regularly to 0. We denote the sequence again by z_a so that $z_a \to 0$. Therefore the functions $f_\nu(z)$ satisfy the following conditions: (a) the functions $f_\nu(z)$ are uniform and regular in $|z| < R$, (b) $|f_\nu(z)| \leqslant M$ in $|z| < R$, (c) the limit $\lim f_\nu(z)$ exists for every point of the sequence z_a where $|z_a| < R$ and $\lim\limits_{a=\infty} z_a = 0$.

The proof consists of the following steps. Putting

$$f_1(z) = a_{0,1} + a_{1,1}z + a_{2,1}z^2 + \dots + a_{k,1}z^k + \dots$$
$$\cdot \quad \cdot \quad \cdot \quad \cdot \quad \cdot \quad \cdot \quad \cdot \quad \cdot \quad \cdot$$
$$f_\nu(z) = a_{0,\nu} + a_{1,\nu}z + a_{2,\nu}z^2 + \dots + a_{k,\nu}z^k + \dots \tag{4}$$
$$\cdot \quad \cdot \quad \cdot \quad \cdot \quad \cdot \quad \cdot \quad \cdot \quad \cdot \quad \cdot$$

we first prove that every column in the table of coefficients has a limit, i.e. that the coefficients of the same power k of z in the successive Taylor series tend to a definite limit a_k, say. The second step consists in proving that the Taylor series formed by the columnal limits a_k, i.e. $\Sigma a_k z^k$ is convergent in $|z| < R$, and so represents a function $f(z)$ regular in $|z| < R$. The final step is to show that the functions $f_\nu(z)$ tend uniformly to this function $f(z)$ in $|z| \leqslant R - \epsilon$, for an arbitrary positive ϵ.

By (4) and (b),

$$|f_\nu(z) - f_\nu(0)| \leqslant |f_\nu(z)| + |f_\nu(0)| \leqslant 2M,$$

so that, by Schwarz's lemma,

$$|f_\nu(z) - f_\nu(0)| \leqslant 2M|z|/R$$

in $|z| < R$. Hence

$$\begin{aligned} &|f_n(0) - f_{n+m}(0)| \\ &\quad \leqslant |f_n(0) - f_n(z_a)| + |f_n(z_a) - f_{n+m}(z_a)| + |f_{n+m}(z_a) - f_{n+m}(0)| \\ &\quad \leqslant 4M|z_a|/R + |f_n(z_a) - f_{n+m}(z_a)|. \end{aligned}$$

From $z_a \to 0$ and from the convergence of $f_\nu(z_a)$ for $\nu = \infty$, we see that the limit

$$\lim_{\nu=\infty} f_\nu(0) = \lim_{\nu=\infty} a_{0,\nu}$$

exists. We put

$$\lim_{\nu=\infty} a_{0,\nu} = a_0.$$

Now consider the functions

$$(5)\qquad f_{\nu,1}(z) = [f_\nu(z) - a_{0,\nu}]/z = a_{1,\nu} + a_{2,\nu}z + \dots .$$

We are going to prove that the sequence of functions $f_{\nu,1}(z)$ satisfies the conditions (a), (b), (c) with conveniently chosen M and R. It will follow that $a_{1,\nu}$ tends to a limit as $\nu \to \infty$.

Since the radius of convergence of the Taylor series on the right-hand side of (5) is R, condition (a) is satisfied. Moreover, by Cauchy's inequalities (40. 3),

$$(6)\qquad |a_{k,\nu}| \leqslant M/R^k,$$

i. e. in $|z| \leqslant \mathrm{R} - \epsilon$, we have

$$|f_{\nu,1}(z)| = |a_{1,\nu} + a_{2,\nu}z + \dots|$$
$$\leqslant M[1 + (R-\epsilon)/R + \dots]/R = M/\epsilon,$$

which proves that (b) is satisfied in $|z| \leqslant R - \epsilon$ if we replace M by M/ϵ. Finally, the limit $\lim\limits_{\nu=\infty} f_{\nu,1}(z)$ exists for every $z_a \neq 0$, since it exists for $f_\nu(z)$.

By repeating this reasoning we complete the first step, i. e. we establish the existence of the limits

$$\lim_{\nu=\infty} a_{k,\nu} = a_k$$

for every value of $k = 1, 2, \dots$.

For the second part we have only to remark that, by (6)

$$|a_k| \leqslant M/R^k,$$

and thus the sum of the series $\Sigma a_k z^k$ is regular in $|z| < R$.

For the third part of the proof, we have, for $|z| \leqslant R - \epsilon$,

$$|f(z) - f_\nu(z)| \leqslant |(a_0 - a_{0,\nu}) + \dots + (a_m - a_{m,\nu})z^m|$$
$$+ \left|\sum_{k=m+1}^{\infty} a_k z^k\right| + \left|\sum_{k=m+1}^{\infty} a_{k,\nu} z^k\right|,$$

and so

$$|f(z) - f_\nu(z)| \leqslant \sum_{\lambda=0}^{m} |a_\lambda - a_{\lambda,\nu}|\,|z^\lambda| + [2M/R^{m+1}](R-\epsilon)^{m+1} R/\epsilon.$$

To prove the uniform convergence of $f_\nu(z)$ to $f(z)$ in $|z| \leqslant R - \epsilon$ we first choose m, δ being arbitrarily given, such that

$$2M(R-\epsilon)^{m+1}/\epsilon R^m < \delta/2$$

and then $\nu > \nu(\delta, m)$ so large that all the $m+1$ numbers $|a_0 - a_{0,\nu}|$, $|a_1 - a_{1,\nu}|$, ..., $|a_m - a_{m,\nu}|$ are less than

$$\frac{\delta}{2} \frac{1-(R-\epsilon)}{1-(R-\epsilon)^{m+1}}.$$

Thus $|f(z) - f_\nu(z)| < \delta$, which proves the theorem for a circle.

To prove the general statement, consider any region R in D. Since, by hypothesis, all the functions $f_\nu(z)$ are regular at every point of R, the result just established shows that there is a circle about every point of R in which all the functions $f_\nu(z)$ are regular. Hence, by Borel's lemma, we can cover R with a finite number of these circles: $C_1, \ldots, C_p$.

One of these circles, C_1, say, contains a limiting point $\bar{z}$ of z_a. Consider a sub-sequence z_a' of z_a tending to $\bar{z}$ and apply our preceding result to C_1. We find that the functions $f_\nu(z)$ tend uniformly to a limit function $f(z)$ in every region inside C_1. Now take a second circle C_2 overlapping C_1 and denote their common part by K. For any sequence z_a in K leading to $\bar{z}$ in K we have

$$\lim_{\nu=\infty} f_\nu(z_a) = f(z_a),$$

and thus our result applies to C_2, i.e. the functions $f_\nu(z)$ tend, in C_2, uniformly to a limit function as $\nu \to \infty$. Since in K the limit function obtained for C_1 and the limit function obtained for C_2 are identical (they are the limit functions of the same sequence of functions), the latter is the analytic continuation of the former. In this way, step by step, we extend the theorem to all the p circles, i.e. to R. This completes the proof.

The great interest of the result just established lies in the fact that the conditions involve very little knowledge of the sequence, while the conclusion gives most useful and tangible information about it.

Now suppose only that $f_\nu(z)$ is regular and that $|f_\nu(z)| < M$ in D. Take any sequence z_a of inner points tending to the inner point $\bar{z}$. Since $|f_\nu(z_1)| < M$ there are suffixes μ such that $f_\mu(z_1)$ tends to a regular limit (selecting first the moduli tending to a limit and then selecting converging arguments). Similarly there is a sub-sequence of $f_\mu(z_2)$ tending to a limit and so on. The diagonal method determines in the usual way a sequence tending to a limit at all the points z_a in question, and then we can apply Vitali's theorem.

The converse of this general result is also true. Suppose that the functions $f_\nu(z)$, regular in D, are such that any sub-sequence contains a sub-sequence converging uniformly in D. We may show that the sequence is bounded in every region of D. If this were not so, we could find functions $f_{n_a}(z)$ such that $|f_{n_a}(z)| > N_a$ at some point of R, for $a = 1, 2, 3, \ldots$, where $N_a \to \infty$. The sequence $f_{n_a}(z)$ contains by hypothesis a sub-sequence $f_{n_q}(z)$ tending to a function $f(z)$ regular in R. Hence, for a sufficiently large q,

$$|f(z) - f_{n_q}(z)| < \epsilon, \text{ i.e. } |f_{n_q}(z)| < |f(z)| + \epsilon$$

in R. As $f(z)$ is regular in R, $|f(z)| < M$ in R, which contradicts the hypothesis that $|f_{n_q}(z)| > N_a$ at some point of R. Thus we have

V. *If a family of functions, regular in D, is collectively bounded, it contains a sequence tending uniformly to a regular function in every region of D. And conversely, if every sub-class of a family of uniform functions regular in D contains a sequence tending uniformly to a limit function in every region of D, the family is collectively bounded in every region of D.* (Montel, 1907.)

43. *Taylor series of elementary functions.* Since $e^z = \Sigma z^n/n!$, we readily verify that $(e^z)' = e^z$. Putting $z = e^u$ we have by rule 39. I, $\dfrac{du}{dz} = 1\Big/\dfrac{dz}{du} = 1/e^u = 1/z$, i.e. $(\log z)' = 1/z$. Hence

$$(1) \qquad [\log(1+z)]' = 1/(1+z) = \Sigma(-1)^n z^n.$$

Thus, by 40. III,

$$\log(1+z) = \sum_0^\infty (-1)^n z^{n+1}/(n+1) + \text{const.}$$

Putting $z = 0$ on both sides, the left-hand side becomes $\log 1 = 0$, and the right-hand side becomes $0 + \text{const.}$ Hence the constant is 0. Therefore

$$(2) \quad \log(1+z) = z - z^2/2 + z^3/3 - \ldots + (-1)^{n+1} z^n/n + \ldots,$$

as for real variables. The radius of convergence is 1.

Similarly $(\tan z)' = 1/\cos^2 z$. Hence, putting $z = \tan u$, u is the inverse function of the tangent, called $\arctan z$, and

$$\frac{du}{dz} = 1/\frac{dz}{du} = \cos^2 u = 1/(1+\tan^2 u) = 1/(1+z^2),$$

i. e.

(3) $$(\arctan z)' = 1/(1+z^2) = \Sigma(-1)^n z^{2n}.$$

Hence $\arctan z = \Sigma(-1)^n z^{2n+1}/(2n+1) + \text{const.}$, and for the principal branch $\arctan 0 = 0$, i. e.

(4) $\arctan z = z - z^3/3 + z^5/5 - \dots$, radius of convergence 1. The differential coefficient of $\arcsin z$ is $1/\sqrt{1-z^2}$. Thus, to expand it in a Taylor series, we have first to expand $(1-z^2)^{-1/2}$, i. e. we have to establish the binomial theorem for negative and fractional indices. We are going to establish it for a general real index m:

(5) $$(1+z)^m = 1 + \sum_{n=1}^{\infty} \frac{m(m-1)\dots(m-n+1)z^n}{1.2\dots n}.$$

The radius of convergence of the series on the right-hand side is 1. For, putting

$$m_n = m(m-1)\dots(m-n+1)/n!,$$

we have $m_{n+1}z^{n+1}/m_n z^n = (m-n)z/(n+1)$, and so, by the ratio test, 24. IV, the series is absolutely convergent for $|z| < 1$ and divergent for $|z| > 1$. Now put $f(z) = \Sigma m_n z^n$. We readily verify that $(n+1)m_{n+1} - (m-n)m_n = 0$. On the other hand, since $zf'(z) = \Sigma n m_n z^n$, we have

$$(1+z)f'(z) - mf(z) = \Sigma[(n-m)m_n + (n+1)m_{n+1}]z^n \equiv 0.$$

It follows that

$$\left(\frac{f(z)}{(1+z)^m}\right)' = \frac{f'(z)(1+z)^m - f(z)m(1+z)^{m-1}}{(1+z)^{2m}}$$
$$= \frac{f'(z)(1+z) - mf(z)}{(1+z)^{m+1}} = 0,$$

therefore $f(z)/(1+z)^m$ is a constant. Since $f(0) = 1$, this constant is 1, i. e. $f(z)$, the sum function of the series on the right-hand side of (5), is really $(1+z)^m$.

Putting $m = -1/2$ and replacing z by $-z^2$ we find that

$$\frac{1}{\sqrt{1-z^2}} = 1 + z^2 + \frac{1\,.\,3 z^4}{2\,.\,4} + \frac{1\,.\,3\,.\,5 z^6}{2\,.\,4\,.\,6} + \ldots ,$$

and hence

$$(6) \qquad \arcsin z = z + \frac{z^3}{2\,.\,3} + \frac{1\,.\,3\,.\,z^5}{2\,.\,4\,.\,5} + \frac{1\,.\,3\,.\,5\,.\,z^7}{2\,.\,4\,.\,6\,.\,7} + \ldots ,$$

for the principal branch.

For the expansion of $\tan z$ and $\cot z$ see Ex. IV. 17.

44. *Conformal representation.* Suppose $z_1(t)$, $z_2(t)$ are two curves, in the z-plane, passing through the point a: $z_1(t_1) = a$ and $z_2(t_2) = a$. The argument of $b-a$ is the angle between the straight segment from a to b and the positive real axis. Thus the argument of $z_1(t_1+\Delta t) - z_1(t_1)$ is the angle α of the secant passing through $z_1(t_1)$ and $z_1(t_1+\Delta t)$. As Δt has the argument 0, multiplication or division by Δt does not alter the argument. Hence

$$\alpha = \text{argument of } \frac{z_1(t_1+\Delta t) - z_1(t_1)}{\Delta t},$$

and, in the limit as $\Delta t \to 0$, the argument of the tangent to the curve $z_1(t)$ at t_1 is $\arg\left(\frac{dz_1}{dt}\right)_{t_1}$. Similarly the argument of the tangent to $z_2(t)$ at t_2 is $\arg\left(\frac{dz_2}{dt}\right)_{t_2}$. The angle between the two curves at $z_1(t_1) = z_2(t_2)$ is thus $\arg\left(\frac{dz_1}{dt}\right)_{t_1} - \arg\left(\frac{dz_2}{dt}\right)_{t_2}$. Suppose that $u = f(z)$ is an analytic function, and $f'(a) \neq 0$. The corresponding curves in the u-plane are $u_1 = f[z_1(t)]$, $u_2 = f[z_2(t)]$.

Therefore their angle of intersection is

$$\begin{aligned} &\arg\left(\frac{du_1}{dt}\right)_{t_1} - \arg\left(\frac{du_2}{dt}\right)_{t_2} \\ &\qquad = \arg\left[f'[z_1(t_1)]\left(\frac{dz_1}{dt}\right)_{t_1}\right] - \arg\left[f'[z_2(t_2)]\left(\frac{dz_2}{dt}\right)_{t_2}\right] \\ &\qquad = \arg f'(a) + \arg\left(\frac{dz_1}{dt}\right)_{t_1} - \arg f'(a) - \arg\left(\frac{dz_2}{dt}\right)_{t_2} = \alpha, \end{aligned}$$

since $\arg ab = \arg a + \arg b$. We prove in this way that *angles are preserved.*

On the other hand, if $z = a + re^{i\alpha}$, $u = b + Re^{i\phi}$, then

$$|u-b|/|z-a| = R/r.$$

Hence, when $z \to a$ (so that both r and $R \to 0$) the ratio of the corresponding lengths becomes $\left|\dfrac{du}{dz}\right|_{z=a}$. For very small distances in the neighbourhood of a we have, independently of α,

$$R = \left|\left(\frac{du}{dz}\right)_a\right| r \text{ provided } \left(\frac{du}{dz}\right)_a \neq 0,$$

i.e. the ratio of the corresponding lengths (called the *linear magnification at* $z = a$) does not depend upon the orientation of the length r. Therefore a very small triangle in the neighbourhood of a becomes a very small *similar* triangle in the neighbourhood of b. The form of infinitesimal figures is not altered. Hence the name *conformal representation.*

At points at which $\dfrac{du}{dz} = 0$, the result in general does not hold; for example, if $u = z^2$, $\arg u = 2 \arg z$, i.e. the angle between $(0, u)$ and the positive real axis is double the angle between $(0, z)$ and the positive real axis. Corresponding angles are not equal because $\left(\dfrac{du}{dz}\right)_{z=0} = 0$.

When $z = re^{i\theta}$ describes the circle $|z| = r$, the rate of change, which we may call the velocity, of $f(z)$ with respect to θ is

$$\frac{df(z)}{d\theta} = \frac{df(z)}{dz}\frac{dz}{d\theta} = f'(z)iz.$$

The rate of change of the argument of $f(z)$ [the angular velocity of $f(z)$] is determined as follows: $\arg f(z) = \text{Im}\,[\log f(z)]$,

$$\frac{d[\arg f(z)]}{d\theta} = \text{Im}\left[\frac{d\log f(z)}{d\theta}\right] = \text{Im}\left[\frac{f'(z)}{f(z)}iz\right] = \text{Rl}\left[z\frac{f'(z)}{f(z)}\right].$$

A simple closed curve C is said to be *starlike* with respect to one of its inner points a, if all the radii from a meet C in one point only (all the points of C are *visible* from a). If $u = f(z)$ maps the inner domain D of the u-plane, enclosed by C, upon $|z| < r$,

C is starlike (visible) from $u = 0$ if and only if $\mathrm{Rl}\left[\frac{zf'(z)}{f(z)}\right] > 0$ for $|z| = r$, because then and only then is $\arg f(z)$ constantly increasing.

The picture of $|z| = r$ in the mapping, $u = f(z)$, is convex if and only if the picture of $|z| = r$ by $u = zf'(z)$ is starlike with respect to $u = 0$. In fact, the angle between du and the positive real axis is the transform by $u = f(z)$ of $\arg[izf'(z)]$. Convexity means that this argument varies always in the same direction, i. e. that $u = izf'(z)$ or $u = zf'(z)$ maps $|z| = r$ on a curve C' starlike with respect to $u = 0$.

We are going to establish the chief properties of conformal mapping.

I. (1) $$u = \rho(z-a)/(\rho^2 - \bar{a}z)$$

maps $|z| = \rho$ *on* $|u| = 1$. *If* $|a| < \rho$, *it maps* $|z| < \rho$ *on* $|u| < 1$ *and* $|z| > \rho$ *on* $|u| > 1$. *If* $|a| > \rho$, *it maps* $|z| > \rho$ *on* $|u| < 1$ *and* $|z| < \rho$ *on* $|u| > 1$.

Proof. Putting $z = \rho e^{i\phi}$, we have

$$u = \rho\,\frac{\rho e^{i\phi} - a}{\rho^2 - \bar{a}\rho e^{i\phi}} = \frac{e^{i\phi} - \dfrac{a}{\rho}}{1 - \dfrac{\bar{a}}{\rho}e^{i\phi}},$$

and, independently of A and ϕ, $\left|\dfrac{e^{i\phi} + A}{1 + \bar{A}e^{i\phi}}\right| = 1,$

since $$|1 + \bar{A}e^{i\phi}| = |1 + Ae^{-i\phi}|.$$

Conversely,

(2) $$z = \frac{\rho^2 u + \rho a}{\rho + \bar{a}u} = \rho\,\frac{u + \dfrac{a}{\rho}}{1 + \dfrac{\bar{a}}{\rho}u},$$

i. e. when $|u| = 1$, then $|z| = \rho$, which proves the first proposition if we remark that, both (1) and (2) being linear expressions, the mapping is necessarily biuniform. Since the right-hand side of (1) is a continuous function, $|z| < \rho$ is mapped either on the inside or on the outside of $|u| = 1$. But, if $|a| = |\bar{a}| < \rho$, u is bounded in $|z| < \rho$, i. e. $|z| < \rho$ cannot be mapped on $|u| > 1$. Similarly for the other cases.

Since $$\frac{du}{dz} = \rho\frac{\rho^2-\bar{a}z+(z-a)\bar{a}}{(\rho^2-\bar{a}z)^2} = \rho\frac{\rho^2-a\bar{a}}{(\rho^2-\bar{a}z)^2},$$

we have $$\left(\frac{du}{dz}\right)_{z=a} = \frac{\rho}{\rho^2-|a|^2},$$

and if we divide by the latter quantity the linear magnification at $z=a$ becomes unity. The function

$$u = [\rho^2-|a|^2]\frac{z-a}{\rho^2-\bar{a}z} \tag{3}$$

so obtained is said to be *the mapping function of* $|z|<\rho$ *normed with respect to* $z=a$.

Since (1) maps $|z|<\rho$ on the unit circle, (3) maps it on the circle of radius $\dfrac{\rho^2-|a|^2}{\rho}$. We say that the *inner conform-radius* of $|z|<\rho$ *with respect to* $z=a$ is $r(a)=\dfrac{\rho^2-|a|^2}{\rho}$.

We notice that $r(0)=\rho, \lim\limits_{|a|\to\rho} r(a)=0$. Since $u=z$ maps $|z|>\rho$ on $|u|>\rho$, $z=\infty$ corresponding to $u=\infty$, and the mapping is normed with respect to $z=\infty$, we say that the *outer conform-radius* $\bar{r}=\rho$.

When $|a|>\rho$, (3) maps $|z|\geqslant\rho$ on the circle $|u|\leqslant\dfrac{|a|^2-\rho^2}{\rho}$. Since the mapping is normed with respect to $z=a$ when we replace the square bracket by $|a|^2-\rho^2$, we see that the inner conform-radius of $|z|>\rho$ is $\dfrac{|a|^2-\rho^2}{\rho}$. This tends to ∞ with $|a|$.

II.

$$w=(z-i)/(z+i) \tag{4}$$

maps $\operatorname{Im}(z)>0$ *upon* $|w|<1$.

Proof. Put $z=x+iy$. Since the formula is bilinear, it establishes a biuniform mapping of the two planes on each other. We have only to show that when $y>0$, $|w|<1$, and conversely. But writing $|z-i|\leqslant|z+i|$ we are led to

$$x^2+(y-1)^2\leqslant x^2+(y+1)^2,$$

i.e. to $4y\geqslant 0$. Conversely, $z=i(1+w)/(1-w)$,

i.e. $$\operatorname{Im}(z)=(1-u^2-v^2)/[(1-u)^2+v^2],$$

i.e. $\operatorname{Im}(z)\geqslant 0$ when $|w|\leqslant 1$, while $\operatorname{Im}(z)=0$ and $|w|=1$ correspond to each other.

Since

$$dw/dz = [z+i-(z-i)]/(z+i)^2 = 2i/(z+i)^2$$

and
$$(dw/dz)_{z=i} = 1/2i,$$

the inner conform-radius of $\mathrm{Im}\,(z) > 0$ with respect to $z = i$ is 2.

Similarly

(5) $$w = (z-a-i)/(z-a+i)$$

maps $\mathrm{Im}\,(z) > \mathrm{Im}\,(a)$ *upon* $|w| < 1$. In fact if $z = x+iy$ and $a = \alpha + i\beta$, $|z-a-i| \leqslant |z-a+i|$ is fully equivalent to $0 \leqslant 4\,(y-\beta)$ while $|w| = 1$ corresponds to $y = \beta$. We can also formulate it in the following way:

$$w = (z-b)/(z-b+2i)$$

maps the half plane $\mathrm{Im}\,(z) > \mathrm{Im}\,(b) - 1$ on the circle $|w| < 1$.

III. *If* $u = f(z)$ *maps* $|z| < 1$ *biuniformly on a domain* D *and* $g(u)$ *is biuniform in* D, *then* $g[f(z)]$ *is biuniform in* $|z| < 1$.

Proof. Let z_1 and z_2 be two points in $|z| < 1$ and $f(z_1) = u_1$, $f(z_2) = u_2$. If $g[f(z_1)] = g[f(z_2)]$, i. e. $g(u_1) = g(u_2)$, then by hypothesis $u_1 = u_2$, i. e. $z_1 = z_2$.

IV. *If* $w = f(z) = \sum_{n=-\infty}^{+\infty} a_n z^n$ *is regular in* $r \leqslant |z| \leqslant R$, *the area of the domain* D *corresponding to the inside of this ring (multiply covered parts being counted multiply) is* $\pi \Sigma n\,|a_n|^2\,(R^{2n} - r^{2n})$.

Proof. Putting $w = f(x+iy) = u+iv$, the area

$$A = \iint\limits_{r^2 < x^2+y^2 < R^2} du dv = \iint \left|\frac{\partial(u,v)}{\partial(x,y)}\right| dx dy = \int_r^R \int_0^{2\pi} \left|\frac{\partial(u,v)}{\partial(x,y)}\right| \rho\, d\rho\, d\theta.$$

But

$$\frac{\partial(u,v)}{\partial(x,y)} \equiv \frac{\partial u}{\partial x}\frac{\partial v}{\partial y} - \frac{\partial u}{\partial y}\frac{\partial v}{\partial x} = \left(\frac{\partial u}{\partial x}\right)^2 + \left(\frac{\partial v}{\partial x}\right)^2$$
$$= \left|\frac{\partial(u+iv)}{\partial x}\right|^2 = |f'(z)|^2.$$

(Hence $|f'(z)|^2$ is called *the coefficient of superficial magnification*). Therefore

$$A=\int_r^R\int_0^{2\pi}|f'(\rho e^{i\theta})|^2\rho d\rho d\theta = 2\pi\int_r^R\Big(\sum_{n=-\infty}^{+\infty} n^2|a_n|^2\rho^{2n-1}\Big)d\rho$$

$$= \pi\sum_{n=-\infty}^{+\infty} n|a_n|^2(R^{2n}-r^{2n}).$$

If $r=0$, we obtain for $w=\sum_0^\infty a_nz^n$, $A=\pi\sum_0^\infty n|a_n|^2R^{2n}$.

V. *If* $w=f(z)=\sum_{-\infty}^{+\infty} a_nz^n$ *is regular on* $|z|=r$ *and does not assume the same value twice on this circle, the area enclosed by the curve* L *corresponding to the circle* $|z|=r$ *is*

$$\pi\sum_{-\infty}^{+\infty} n|a_n|^2r^{2n}.$$

Proof. From Fig. 22, where P is the affix of $w=f(z)$ and Q is that of

$$w+dw=f(z)+\frac{df(z)}{dz}\frac{dz}{d\theta}d\theta$$
$$=f(z)+izf'(z)d\theta,$$

we have

$$\text{area } OPQ=\tfrac{1}{2}PQ\,.\,OR$$
$$=\tfrac{1}{2}|izf'(z)|\;|f(z)|\sin\omega\,d\theta.$$

Decomposing the area enclosed by L into positive and negative triangles and integrating, we obtain

$$A=\tfrac{1}{2}\int_0^{2\pi}|izf'(z)|\;|f(z)|\sin\omega\,d\theta.$$

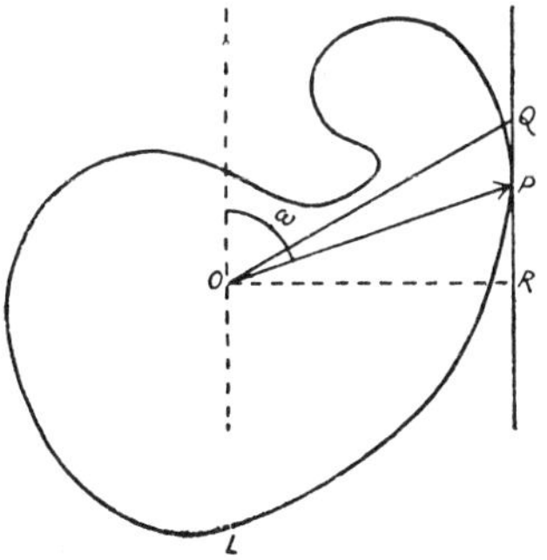

FIG. 22.

Now put $v=izf'(z)=v_1+iv_2$, $w=w_1+iw_2$ and denote the arguments of v and w by α and β respectively. Then we have, from

$$\sin\beta=\frac{w_2}{|w|},\ \cos\beta=\frac{w_1}{|w|}\ \&c.,$$

$$\sin\omega=\sin(\alpha-\beta)=\frac{v_2}{|v|}\frac{w_1}{|w|}-\frac{v_1}{|v|}\frac{w_2}{|w|}.$$

But

$$\operatorname{Im}\frac{v}{w}=\operatorname{Im}\frac{v\bar{w}}{|w|^2}=\frac{v_2w_1-v_1w_2}{|w|^2}.$$

Therefore,

$$\sin \omega = \frac{\operatorname{Im}\dfrac{v}{w}}{\left|\dfrac{v}{w}\right|}.$$

Hence,

$$|f(z)| \sin \omega = |f(z)| \frac{\operatorname{Im}\left[\dfrac{izf'(z)}{f(z)}\right]}{\left|\dfrac{izf'(z)}{f(z)}\right|} = \frac{\operatorname{Rl}[zf'(z)\bar{f}(z)]}{|zf'(z)|},$$

and therefore

$$A = \tfrac{1}{2} \operatorname{Rl} \int_0^{2\pi} \sum_{-\infty}^{+\infty} k a_k r^k e^{ik\theta} \sum_{-\infty}^{+\infty} \bar{a}_s r^s e^{-is\theta} d\theta,$$

which proves the statement.

VI. *If the concentric circles C and c (contained in C) are mapped on the domains D and d (contained in D) respectively and if we denote the areas by $|C|$, $|c|$, $|D|$, $|d|$ respectively, we have $|D|/|d| \geqslant |C|/|c|$, equality holding only for linear polynomial mapping.*

Proof. Let us suppose that the common centre of C and c is $z = 0$ and that this corresponds to $u = 0$. Denote the radii by R and r and the mapping function by $u = f(z) = a_1 z + \ldots$. Then, by the definition of the inner area of a domain,

$$|D| = \pi \sum_1^{\infty} n |a_n|^2 R^{2n}, \quad |d| = \pi \sum_1^{\infty} n |a_n|^2 r^{2n},$$

$$|C| = \pi R^2, \; |c| = \pi r^2,$$

and thus

$$\frac{|D|}{|d|} - \frac{|C|}{|c|} = \frac{r^2 R^2 \sum_{n=2}^{\infty} n |a_n|^2 (R^{2n-2} - r^{2n-2})}{\sum_1^{\infty} n |a_n|^2 r^{2n-2}} \geqslant 0,$$

and $= 0$ only if $a_2 = 0, \ldots, a_n = 0, \ldots$

VII. *If the circle C is mapped biuniformly on the domain D and a^2 is the superficial magnification at the centre of C, then $D|/|C| \geqslant a^2$ (equality only for linear polynomials).*

Proof. With the notation of VI, we have

$$|D| = \pi \sum_{1}^{\infty} n\,|a_n|^2 R^{2n} \geqslant \pi\,|a_1|^2 R^2 = \pi a^2 R^2.$$

EXERCISE V

1. Determine the domain of convergence of $\Sigma 1/n^z$. From $|n^z| = n^{\mathrm{Rl}\, z}$, the series is convergent if $\mathrm{Rl}\, z > 1$. When $\mathrm{Rl}\, z < 1$, i. e. $\mathrm{Rl}\,(1-z) = d > 0$,

$$|1/n^{1-z} - 1/(n+1)^{1-z}| \leqslant |(1+1/n)^{1-z} - 1|/n^d$$

and, by Ex. IV. 1,

$$|(1+1/n)^{1-z} - 1| = |e^{(1-z)\log(1+1/n)} - 1| \leqslant |1-z|\,K/n,$$

where the constant K is $\leqslant 2^{|1-z|}$. Hence,

$$\Sigma\,|b_n - b_{n+1}|,\; b_n = 1/n^{1-z},$$

is convergent, and thus, by Ex. III. 9 (c), if $\Sigma 1/n^z$ were convergent, $\sum \frac{1}{n^z} \cdot \frac{1}{n^{1-z}} = \Sigma 1/n$ would also be convergent. Therefore $\Sigma 1/n^z$ diverges if $\mathrm{Rl}\, z < 1$.

2. Same for
(a) $\Sigma z^n/(1-z^n)$;
(b) $\Sigma z^n/a^n(1-z^n)$.

3. Same for $\Sigma \sin nz/n$.
By Ex. III. 10, the series converges if $\mathrm{Im}\, z$ is 0. On the other hand it diverges if $\mathrm{Im}\, z = y \neq 0$. In fact $\sin nz = (e^{inx-ny} - e^{-inx+ny})/2i$, i.e. $|\sin nz| \geqslant (e^{n|y|} - e^{-n|y|})/2$ and thus $\sin nz/n$ does not tend to 0 as $n \to \infty$.

4. Same for $\Sigma \cos nz/n^2$.

5. Same for $\Sigma a_n z^n/(1-z^n)$. If Σa_n converges, series converges for $|z| \neq 1$, for $|z^n/(1-z^n)| \to 1$ or 0. If Σa_n diverges: (a) series diverges for $|z|>1$. In fact if $\Sigma a_n z^n/(1-z^n)$ converges for $|z|>1$, then also $\Sigma a_n/(1-z^n)$ converges and thus also their difference Σa_n; (b) series converges for $|z|<1$ if, and only if, $\Sigma a_n z^n$ converges, i.e. its domain of convergence is that of $\Sigma a_n z^n$.

6. Examine the series of Exx. 1–5 from the point of view of uniform convergence.

7. $f(z)$ and $g(z)$ are regular in $|z|<1+d$. Prove that

$$g(z)+[f(z)-g(z)]\left\{1/2+\sum_{1}^{\infty}[1/(1+z^n)-1/(1+z^{n-1})]\right\}$$

represents $f(z)$ for $|z|<1$ and $g(z)$ for $1<|z|<1+d$. The partial sums of the series in the brackets are $1/(1+z^n)$ and thus the series converges to 1 in $|z|<1$ and to 0 in $|z|>1$.

8. Expand into Taylor series the function $f(z)=\log(a+\sqrt{a^2+z^2})$, where $a>0$ and $\sqrt{a^2+z^2}$, for small values of $|z|$, denotes the branch tending to a when $z\to 0$. Choosing a determinate value of $\log 2a$ and the corresponding branch of $f(z)$, we have

$$\begin{aligned} f'(z) &= z(\sqrt{a^2+z^2}-a)/z^2\sqrt{a^2+z^2} \\ &= 1/z-1/z\sqrt{1+(z/a)^2} = -\sum_{1}^{\infty} C_n^{-\frac{1}{2}} z^{2n-1}/a^{2n}, \end{aligned}$$

and thus $$f(z)=\log 2a+\sum_{1}^{\infty} C_n^{-\frac{1}{2}}(z/a)^{2n}/2n.$$

9. Expand into Taylor series $f(z)=\frac{1}{2}\left(\log\frac{1}{1-z}\right)^2$.

$$\frac{1}{2}\left(z+\frac{z^2}{2}+\dots\right)^2=\frac{1}{2}\sum_{n=2}^{\infty}\left(\frac{1}{1\,.\,(n-1)}+\dots+\frac{1}{k\,.\,(n-k)}+\dots+\frac{1}{(n-1)\,.\,1}\right)z^n$$

$$=\sum_{n=2}^{\infty}\frac{1}{n}\left(1+\frac{1}{2}+\dots+\frac{1}{n-1}\right)z^n.$$

10. Same for $\cos^2 z$ and $\sin^2 z$.

11. Same for $1/\cos z$. Putting

$$1/\cos z=\sum_{0}^{\infty}(-1)^n E_{2n} z^{2n}/(2n)!$$

where the numbers E_{2n} are called *Euler's integers*, we obtain from

$$(1-z^2/2!+z^4/4!-\dots)(E_0-E_2z^2/2!+\dots)\equiv 1,\ E_0=1$$

the recurrence formulae

$$E_0+C_2^{2n}E_2+C_4^{2n}E_4+\dots+C_{2n}^{2n}E_{2n}=0.$$

12. Same for $z/\sin z$. By $1/\sin z=\cot z+\tan(z/2)$.

13. $a_n\to 0$ and $\Sigma|a_n-a_{n-1}|$ is convergent. Prove that the radius of convergence of $\Sigma a_n z^n$ is at least 1 and that if it is 1 the

Taylor series converges at every point of $|z|=1$ except maybe at $z=1$. Apply Ex. III. 9 (c).

14. At which points on their circle of convergence are the series

(a) $$\sum_0^\infty (-1)^n z^{2n+1} / (2^n+1),$$

(b) $$\sum_3^\infty z^n / \log\log n,$$

convergent? Apply Ex. 13.

15. Determine the fixed points of the transformation

$$u = (az+b) / (cz+d).$$

From $z=(az+b)/(cz+d)$, i.e. from $cz^2+(d-a)z-b=0$, we have

$$z = \frac{a-d \pm \sqrt{(a-d)^2+4bc}}{2c}$$

If $c=0$, the only finite fixed point is $b/(d-a)$. The other is ∞. If $(a-d)^2+4bc=0$, the two fixed points coincide.

16. Show that if the transformation $u=(az+b)/(cz+d)$ has two finite fixed points z_1 and z_2, the relation between u and z can be written in the form $(u-z_1)/(u-z_2) = A(z-z_1)/(z-z_2)$.

17. Calculate the value of A in Ex. 16. Putting $u'=(u-z_1)/(u-z_2)$ and $z'=(z-z_1)/(z-z_2)$, the fixed points of the transformation leading from z' to u' are 0 and ∞, so that $u=Az'$.

$$A = \frac{a+d+\sqrt{(a-d)^2+4bc}}{a+d-\sqrt{(a-d)^2+4bc}}.$$

The linear transformations with *two* fixed points are called

(a) *Hyperbolic* if A is real,
(b) *Elliptic* if $A=e^{i\alpha}$;
(c) *Loxodromic* in the other cases.

18. Show that if the transformation $u=(az+b)/(cz+d)$ has only one fixed point z_1 (finite or not), called *parabolic* transformation, the relation between u and z can be written in the form

$$1/(u-z_1) = 1/(z-z_1)+A.$$

We notice that putting $u-z_1=u'$ and $z-z_1=z'$, the relation is expressed in terms of a simple *translation*.

19. Determine the transforms of the lines

(a) $|z-1/3|=1/9$;
(b) $|z-a|=|a|$;

(c) $\text{Rl}\, z = d$ (real, $\gtreqless 0$), three examples;

(d) the concentric circle, centre a, by the transformation $u = 1/\bar{z}$ called *reflexion in the unit circle.*

20. Map the sector $|z| \leqslant 1, 0 \leqslant \arg z \leqslant \pi/3$ on the unit circle. $z_1 = z^3$ maps it on a half circle, $z_2 = (1+z_1)/(1-z_1)$ on a first quadrant, $z_3 = (z_2)^2$ on a half plane and $u = (z_3 - i)/(z_3 + i)$, i.e.

$$u = \frac{(1+z^3)^2 - i(1-z^3)^2}{(1+z^3)^2 + i(1-z^3)^2}$$

maps it on the unit circle.

21. $f(0) = 0, f(z)$ is biuniform in $|z| < 1$. Then both branches of $g(z) = \sqrt{f(z^2)} = z\sqrt{f(z^2)/z^2}$ are biuniform in $|z| < 1$. Similarly for $\sqrt[n]{f(z^n)}$.

Proof. As $f(z)$ vanishes only for $z = 0$, $f(z^2)/z^2$ is regular and $\neq 0$ in $|z| < 1$; $g(z)$ is obviously an odd function: $g(-z) = -g(z)$. Now if $g(z_1) = g(z_2)$, then $f(z_1^2) = f(z_2^2)$, i.e. $z_1^2 = z_2^2$ and the case $z_1 = z_2 \neq 0$ is ruled out since

$$g(z_1) = g(z_2) \neq 0$$

is impossible for an odd function, for it leads to

$$g(z_2) = -g(z_1) = g(z_1).$$

22. $f(z)$ is regular and $|f(z)| < M$ in $|z| < 1$ and vanishes at $z_1, z_2, \ldots, z_n$. Then

$$|f(z)| \leqslant M \left| \frac{z-z_1}{1-\bar{z}_1 z} \frac{z-z_2}{1-\bar{z}_2 z} \cdots \frac{z-z_n}{1-\bar{z}_n z} \right| \quad \text{in } |z| < 1.$$

Since along the circle $|z| = 1$, $|z - z_n|/|1-\bar{z}_n z| = 1$, in a sufficiently small neighbourhood of $z = e^{i\alpha}$ the function

$$\phi(x) = f(x) \Bigg/ \prod_{\nu=1}^{n} \frac{z-z_\nu}{1-\bar{z}_\nu z}$$

satisfies the inequality $|\phi(z)| < M + \epsilon$. Apply 41. VI.

23. If $f(z)$ is meromorphic in $|z| < 1$ and $|f(z)|$ is constant along $|z| = 1$, $f(z)$ is a rational function. Proof. If $a_1, a_2, \ldots, a_n$ are the zeros and $b_1, b_2, \ldots, b_m$ the poles of $f(z)$ in $|z| < 1$, the function

$$f(z) \prod_{\mu=1}^{n} \frac{1-\bar{a}_\mu z}{z - a_\mu} \prod_{\nu=1}^{m} \frac{z - b_\nu}{1-\bar{b}_\nu z}$$

is regular in $|z| \leqslant 1$ and its modulus is constant on $|z| = 1$. Hence it is a constant, by 41. V.

24. If $f_1(z), f_2(z), \ldots, f_n(z)$ are regular and uniform in the domain D, the function $Q(z) = |f_1(z)| + |f_2(z)| + \ldots + |f_n(z)|$ assumes its maximum at a boundary point of D. Take an inner point z_0 of D and put $|f_\nu(z_0)| = \epsilon_\nu f_\nu(z_0)$, $\nu = 1, 2, \ldots, n$. The function

$$F(z) = \epsilon_1 f_1(z) + \epsilon_2 f_2(z) + \ldots + \epsilon_n f_n(z)$$

is regular and uniform in D and thus assumes its maximum modulus at a boundary point z_1. Hence $Q(z_1) \geqslant |F(z_1)| \geqslant |F(z_0)| = Q(z_0)$.

25. If $u = f(z)$ is regular in $|z| < R$ and maps the circle $|z| = r < R$ biuniformly on the rectifiable curve C (see Art. 51) in the u-plane, the length l of C is given by

$$l = \int_0^{2\pi} |f'(re^{i\theta})| \, r d\theta.$$

Writing $u = P(x,y) + iQ(x,y)$ we have

$$l = \int_0^{2\pi} \left\{ \left(\frac{dP}{d\theta}\right)^2 + \left(\frac{dQ}{d\theta}\right)^2 \right\}^{\frac{1}{2}} d\theta.$$

Now

$$\frac{dP}{d\theta} = \frac{\partial P}{\partial x}\frac{dx}{d\theta} + \frac{\partial P}{\partial y}\frac{dy}{d\theta} = \frac{\partial P}{\partial x}\frac{dx}{d\theta} - \frac{\partial Q}{\partial x}\frac{dy}{d\theta},$$

$$\frac{dQ}{d\theta} = \frac{\partial Q}{\partial x}\frac{dx}{d\theta} + \frac{\partial Q}{\partial y}\frac{dy}{d\theta} = \frac{\partial Q}{\partial x}\frac{dx}{d\theta} + \frac{\partial P}{\partial x}\frac{dy}{d\theta}.$$

Therefore

$$\left(\frac{dP}{d\theta}\right)^2 + \left(\frac{dQ}{d\theta}\right)^2 = \left\{ \left(\frac{\partial P}{\partial x}\right)^2 + \left(\frac{\partial Q}{\partial x}\right)^2 \right\} \left\{ \left(\frac{dx}{d\theta}\right)^2 + \left(\frac{dy}{d\theta}\right)^2 \right\}, \text{ \&c.}$$

CHAPTER VI

GEOMETRICAL LANGUAGE

45. *The idea of curve.* As complex numbers cover a two-dimensional plane, it is natural in complex function theory, as in the theory of real functions of two variables, to use the language of two-dimensional analytical geometry. Our imagination is helped by this to retain more easily the data of a problem or to represent the various stages of the reasoning. But in no way can geometrical intuition replace mathematical proof. In fact geometrical intuition means visualization, the precision of which breaks down as soon as the 'infinite' (infinitely great or infinitely small) comes in.

We could not pretend, for example, to foresee an essential difference between the infinity of the rational and that of the irrational numbers, for there is no finite break in either range. As we have seen, however, rational numbers are enumerable, irrationals are not. Again, our geometrical intuition is completely upset by the fact that a square contains just 'as many' points as one of its sides. Why? Because we seem to reason like this: either infinities are all alike (any distinction between infinities seems artificial, i. e. foreign to our geometrical intuition) or, if there are various infinities, their dimensions ought to separate them. We may, of course, take this remark as a hint that our way of splitting infinities into classes does not seem to be 'practical', but it shows, at the same time, that geometrical intuition alone cannot cope with an abstract notion like one-one correspondence, which is as fundamental in mathematics as in geometry.

On the other hand, geometrical language is very convenient. Thus, in order to have its advantages without its drawbacks, we have to establish the precise mathematical meaning of every geometrical term used, so that, in reasoning, our imagination will proceed by images (which is a great help) and our reason by the corresponding abstract ideas. This process is very much the same as the use, in elementary geometry, of necessarily imperfect figures to prove precise abstract theorems.

To show the very real difficulties in establishing such a dictionary of the mathematical and geometrical languages, we shall try to construct the mathematical meaning of *curve* (a *point* being defined as usual as a pair of real numbers in a certain order). We restrict ourselves to unbroken, i. e. 'continuous' curves. Thus we may propose *a one-dimensional continuous succession of points* as the mathematical definition of a curve, i. e., in formulae, $x = f(t)$, $y = g(t)$, where $f(t)$ and $g(t)$ are continuous functions of a real variable t, referred to as the parameter of the mathematical representation.

Peano showed that there are curves of this description passing through every point of a square—a rather embarrassing fact. We are going to give Hilbert's ingenious construction of such a Peano-curve.

Divide an arbitrary square into four equal squares by parallels to the axes (as we have seen, a square and its division in such a

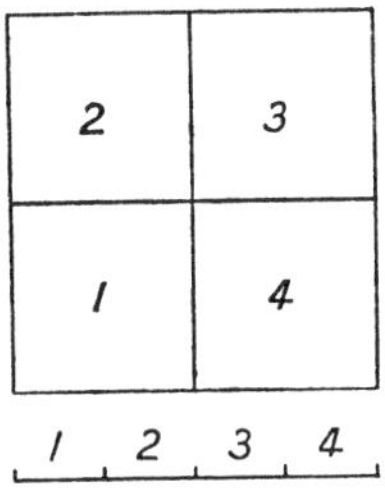

FIG. 23.

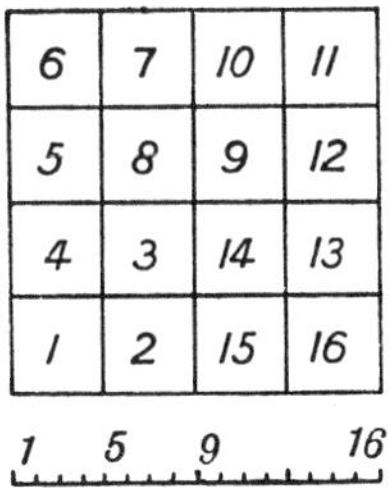

FIG. 24.

way are purely mathematical notions), and number the four squares in such a way that squares with consecutive suffixes have a common side belonging to the square with the higher suffix. Also divide an arbitrary interval, (0, 1) say, into four equal sub-intervals, closed on the left and open on the right, and number the sub-intervals from left to right, say. We shall say that the square and interval with the same number correspond to each other.

Repeat the operation for every square and interval as shown in fig. 24; and so on indefinitely. The points on the side between squares 2 and 15, say, belong to 2. Those on the side between

2 and 3 belong to 3. The square p is open along its side in common with $p+1$. A vertex belongs to the square with the least index meeting at the vertex in question.

Now consider any point t of the interval (0, 1). It can be considered as the only common point of an infinite sequence of our sub-intervals each encased in the preceding ones. The corresponding squares are also each encased in the preceding ones and have only one point (x, y) in common (since the lengths of the sides tend to 0). We say that the point (x, y) corresponds to t. This means mathematically that x and y are uniform functions of t: $x = f(t)$, $y = g(t)$, defined for every value of t between 0 and 1.

Conversely, every point (x, y) is the only common point of a sequence of our squares each encased in the preceding ones, and the corresponding intervals have also a common point (they may have several). Hence to every point of the square corresponds a value of t, i.e. the 'curve' $x = f(t)$, $y = g(t)$ passes through every point of the square.

We have yet to prove that $f(t)$ and $g(t)$ are continuous functions. But t and $t+h$ are contained in one of our intervals or, if $t+h$ is an extremity, in two consecutive intervals, whose lengths tend to zero with h. The corresponding squares or pairs of consecutive squares (having by construction a common side) contain all the following ones, as $h \to 0$, and thus dwindle to a definite point. More precisely, if the interval, or pair of intervals, still containing t and $t+h$ corresponds to the n-th step in halving, the length of the double interval, and also the longer side of the corresponding rectangle, is $1/2^{n-1}$, which establishes continuity.

Our first attempt to construct a mathematical definition of curve is not satisfactory. To our geometrical intuition a set of points filling a whole square is not a curve. The chief difficulty in this problem is that we cannot 'discover' the relation between geometrical curves and mathematical functions, because the former are not well defined. All that our geometrical intuition can do is to put down certain more or less vague requirements, ruling out 'fancy' mathematical constructions. It follows that the mathematician has to propose several exact definitions and the geometer has to choose one. For mathematical purposes, however, we may retain, under specific names, the whole series of definitions of curves and make use of them according to our problem.

As a matter of fact the preceding general definition, one-dimensional continuous succession of points, is seldom used. Jordan discovered that the restriction of having no double and multiple points, i. e. $f(t)+ig(t) \neq f(t')+ig(t')$ for

$$t_0 \leqslant t \leqslant t_1,\ t_0 \leqslant t' \leqslant t_1,\ t' \neq t,$$

provides the curve with a good many of its intuitive properties. Hence *in the definition of Jordan curves, $f(t)$ and $g(t)$ are continuous functions in the interval (t_0, t_1) and the two equations $f(t)=f(t')$ and $g(t)=g(t')$ are not simultaneously satisfied for any pair of values t and t' taken from (t_0, t_1).* The set of points (x, y) defined by the equations $x=f(t)$, $y=g(t)$ is called an *open Jordan curve.*

If the equation $f(t)+ig(t)=f(t')+ig(t')$ $(t \neq t')$ is satisfied for the pair of values t_0 and t_1 but for no pair of values between t_0 and t_1 (no multiple point), *the curve is called a closed Jordan curve.*

One of the most fundamental results in the theory of analytic functions, as in the modern foundations of geometry, is Jordan's famous theorem.

I. *Jordan's theorem. A closed Jordan curve divides the plane into two domains having the Jordan curve for their common boundary.* More than half a dozen different proofs of this theorem are available, though at first sight it seems to be a truism. [Jordan, 1893–96, I. p. 90; Ames, 1905; Hartogs, 1925; Kerékjártó, 1919 and 1923; E. Schmidt, 1923; Schönfliesz, 1924. The text follows Kerékjártó's proof.]

To understand clearly the import of the statement we have to express it in mathematical terms or mathematized geometrical terms, and to be able to follow the proof we must get well acquainted with the mathematical meaning of the geometrical language used in the reasoning. (Without geometrical terms, which provide shortened symbols for complicated mathematical constructions, the proof would be too cumbersome.) Thus, as a preliminary to the proof, we shall deal at first with definitions and particular cases.

46. *Definitions of geometrical terms.* We begin with a summary and extension of the terminology given at the end of Art. 11.

Point = pair of real numbers in a certain order. Complex plane = all the pairs $x+iy$, where x and y are real. Straight line = all the pairs $x+iy$, where the real x and y satisfy an equation of the type $Ax+By+C=0$, with real coefficients. We notice that two straight lines $Ax+By+C=0$ and $A'x+B'y+C'=0$ meet either (i) at a single point, when $AB'-A'B\neq 0$, or (ii) nowhere, when $AB'-A'B=0$, but either $CA'-C'A$ or $CB'-C'B$ is different from 0, or (iii) everywhere, i.e. they coincide, when the three determinants all vanish; in the second case we say that the two straight lines are *parallel*. If x_1+iy_1 and x_2+iy_2 are two points of a straight line we can write its equation in the form

$$\begin{vmatrix} x & y & 1 \\ x_1 & y_1 & 1 \\ x_2 & y_2 & 1 \end{vmatrix} = 0,$$

or in the parametric form $x=t(x_2-x_1)+x_1$, $y=t(y_2-y_1)+y_1$ (the elimination of t leads to a linear equation in x and y). When t assumes the values between 0 and 1 only, the set of the corresponding points is called the *segment* from x_1+iy_1 to x_2+iy_2.

Distance. The distance d_{12} between two points x_1+iy_1 and x_2+iy_2 is the positive value of $\sqrt{(x_2-x_1)^2+(y_2-y_1)^2}$. It is readily seen that $d_{12}<d_{13}+d_{32}$, provided x_3+iy_3 is *not* a point of the segment between x_1+iy_1 and x_2+iy_2, and $d_{12}=d_{13}+d_{32}$ if x_3+iy_3 is a point of this segment. We also say that the distance d_{12} is the *length* of the segment between x_1+iy_1 and x_2+iy_2. If, in the parametric equations of a segment, t varies only from 0 to $1/n$, from $1/n$ to $2/n$, &c., the length of each part is d/n, where d is the total length of the original segment. In this way we can divide a segment into partial segments of arbitrarily small length.

Taking the parametric form of the equations to a straight line, the distance between $a+bi$ and the point of the line corresponding to the value t of the parameter is given by the formula

$$d^2=[a-x_1-t(x_2-x_1)]^2+[b-y_1-t(y_2-y_1)]^2,$$

which is a quadratic expression in t, tending to $+\infty$ as $|t|\to\infty$. Therefore the expression assumes its minimum for a determinate finite value of t. This minimum distance is called the distance of $a+ib$ from the straight line. We notice that this distance vanishes only when $a+ib$ is on the line.

In the latter case we may put $a = x_1$, $b = y_1$, and thus $d^2 = t^2 d^2_{12}$, i. e. the distances of the points of a line from the point of it corresponding to $t = 0$ are proportional to t.

It is readily proved that the distance between two parallel straight lines is the distance of any point of one of the lines from the other line.

A finite number of segments, $(1, 2)$, $(2, 3)$, $(3, 4)$, ..., $(n-1, n)$, where the last point of a segment (except maybe that of the last segment) is the first point of the next, is said to form a *polygon.* A polygon with no multiple points is called a *simple polygon.* If the first and last points of a polygon are the same the polygon is *closed*; otherwise it is *open.* The points $x+iy$, satisfying the equation $(x-a)^2+(y-b)^2 = r^2$, (a, b, r are real), are said to form the *circumference of a circle* of radius r, centre at $a+bi$.

For a given set of points, S, the point $x+iy$ is either an *inner point* (if there is an open square containing $x+iy$ and contained in S), or an *outer point*, (if there is an open square containing $x+iy$ and not containing any point of S), or a *boundary* point, (if every neighbourhood of $x+iy$ contains points of S as well as points not belonging to S).

I. *The set B of all the boundary points of a set S is closed.*

Proof. If every square q, centre at P, contains boundary points of S, then every square q' within q, centre at a boundary point, contains, by definition, points of S as well as points not belonging to S, and thus q possesses the same property, i. e. P is a boundary point, which proves I.

A set is said to be *open* if it has only inner points. We notice that a set may be neither closed nor open, e. g. an open interval together with one of its extremities. 'Closed' really means completely closed (*all* the boundary points are included in the set) and 'open' means completely open (*no* boundary point is included in the set). An open set together with its boundary points is called a *region*, so that a region is necessarily closed.

Two points of a set S are said to be *connected* (cf. Art. 11) if S contains a finite chain of overlapping circles joining the two points, and S is said to be *connex* if every pair of points of S is connected in this way. This definition implies that

S has inner points, since it contains complete circles. According to this definition the points of a circumference do not form a connex plane set.

II. *If two points of an open set S lie on a Jordan curve C (e.g. on a simple polygon) entirely in S, the two points are connected.*

Proof. If $f(t)+ig(t)$, $t_0 \leqslant t \leqslant t_1$ is the arc C of a Jordan curve between $a+bi = f(t_0)+ig(t_0)$ and $a_1+ib_1 = f(t_1)+ig(t_1)$, the points of C form a closed set, for $f(t)$ and $g(t)$ are continuous functions of t. Since, by hypothesis, every point of C is an inner point of S (for S is open), there is a circle about every point of S, entirely in S and, by Borel's lemma, 11. III, a finite number of these circles covers C, i.e. there is a finite chain of circles connecting the two points in question.

This result furnishes a very useful test for connex sets, but it applies only to open sets. In fact, every pair of points of the set S consisting of the points of two non-intersecting circles, and a segment joining the two circles can be joined by a polygon; but S is not connex, for there is no chain of circles lying entirely in S and connecting points of the two circles.

A connex open set is called a *domain* (Gebiet,—connex open domain in Hobson 1921–6, I, p. 143). The idea of a domain is one of the most fundamental notions in modern function theory. If we add to a domain all its boundary points, we obviously obtain a connex region.

If the two domains D_1 and D_2 have a common point, the united set D_1+D_2 is a domain. If R is a connex region in the domain D, the points of D outside R form a domain $D-R$, where R may be empty.

The set of all the finite points of the complex plane (i.e. the point at infinity excluded) is a domain. In fact, it consists of inner points alone, and the segment between any pair of these points lies in the set. The same set, together with the point at infinity, also forms a (conventional) domain.

Similarly, the points $x+iy$ for which

$$(1) \qquad (x-a)^2+(y-b)^2 < r^2$$

form a domain. In fact, if (1) is satisfied for (x, y), it is satisfied also in a certain neighbourhood of (x, y), for $(x-a)^2+(y-b)^2$ is a continuous function of (x, y). To prove that it is connex, we have only to notice that, if $x'+iy'$ is another point of the domain, the two segments $(x+iy,\ a+ib)$ and $(a+ib,\ x'+iy')$ lie wholly in the set.

A similar proof holds for the open rectangle $[a+ib,\ c+id]$.

We are going to establish some elementary results concerning domains.

III. *A straight line divides the plane into two domains, the straight line constituting their common boundary.*

Proof. The expression $Ax+By+C$ is positive, negative, or zero. The points $x+iy$ for which $Ax+By+C>0$ form a domain. In fact, if

$$Aa+Bb+C>0, \quad Aa'+Bb'+C>0$$

we have, for the whole segment $x=t(a'-a)+a$, $y=t(b'-b)+b$,

$$Ax+By+C>0,$$

for this expression is linear in t, so that, if it vanishes for $t=t_0$, its sign is constant for $t<t_0$ and for $t>t_0$. Similarly the points for which $Ax+By+C<0$ form a domain.

Finally, as $Ax+By+C$ is a continuous function of (x, y), every point $x+iy$ satisfying the equation $Ax+By+C=0$ is a boundary point of the two domains.

IV. *The circumference of a circle divides the plane into two domains, the circumference constituting their common boundary.*

Proof. We have already seen that the points for which

$$(2) \qquad (x-a)^2+(y-b)^2<r^2$$

form a domain. Therefore we have only to prove the same for the set S of points $x+iy$ satisfying the inequality

$$(x-a)^2+(y-b)^2>r^2.$$

If $c+id$ and $c'+id'$ are any two points of S, we consider the circle centre $a+ib$ passing through the nearer (to $a+ib$) of these two points $c+id$, say. The points of this circumference form a closed set and thus there is a point $\alpha+i\beta$ of this circumference having the least distance from $c'+id'$. By the general properties of distance the segment $(\alpha+i\beta, c'+id')$ is entirely outside the circle passing through $c+id$. Hence the arc $(c+id, \alpha+i\beta)$ of this circumference plus the segment $(\alpha+i\beta, c'+id')$ lie entirely in S, which completes the proof.

V. *The boundary points of any rectangle* $[a+ib,\ c+id]$ *divide the plane into two domains whose common boundary is constituted by the four sides of the rectangle.*

Proof. We have already seen that the points of the rectangle $[a+ib, c+id]$, i.e. the points for which $a<x<c$, $b<y<d$ form a domain. Thus we have only to prove that the set S of the points $x+iy$ *not* satisfying

$$(3) \qquad a\leqslant x\leqslant c, \qquad b\leqslant y\leqslant d$$

is a domain.

To prove that every point of S is an inner point we have only to remark that, if (3) is not satisfied for a particular point $x+iy$, it is not satisfied in a sufficiently small square centre $x+iy$. To prove that S is connex we consider two arbitrarily given points $A = a'+ib'$ and $B = a''+ib''$ of S and the rectangle p_ϵ

$$[a-\epsilon+i(b-\epsilon),\ c+\epsilon+i(d+\epsilon)],$$

where $\epsilon>0$ and less than the least of the four numbers

$$|a'-a|,\ |a''-a|,\ |b'-b|,\ |b''-b|.$$

We readily verify that both A and B are outside p_ϵ. If the segment $(a'+ib', a''+ib'')$ does not meet p_ϵ, A and B are connected in S by this segment. If this segment meets p_ϵ at z_1 and z_2 (z_1 may coincide with z_2), the two points are connected in S by the segments (A, z_1) [or (A, z_2)] and (z_2, B) [or (z_1, B)] linked up along p_ϵ. This completes the proof.

As an example of putting geometrical results into mathematical form, we are going to prove that every straight line L, passing through any inside point $m+in$ of a rectangle $[a+ib, c+id]$, meets the boundary p of this rectangle in just two points. If the equation of L is $x = m$, L meets p at $m+ib$ and at $m+id$. A similar result holds when the equation is $y = n$. If L is not 'parallel' to one of the sides, i.e. if its equation is

$$\alpha(x-m)+\beta(y-n) = 0,$$

where both α and β are different from 0, L meets the straight line $x = a$ at (a, g), say. Therefore, if $b\leqslant g\leqslant d$, L meets p at $a+ig$. If $g>d$, y assumes the value d for a value x' of x between a and m because, along L, y is a continuous function of

x; thus L meets p at $x'+id$. For the second intersection, let us vary x between m and c, and denote by y' the value of the decreasing function y, ($\leqslant n$ in the interval), assumed at $x = c$. If $y' \geqslant b$, L meets p at $c+iy'$. If $y' < b$, there is a value x'' for which y is just b, and thus L meets p at $x''+ib$. In the case $g<b$, y is an increasing function of x; otherwise we reason as before.

47. *Triangle and polygonal domains.* We are now going to discuss the triangle. For this purpose we have to define mathematically the inside and outside points of the triangle whose vertices are x_1+iy_1, x_2+iy_2, x_3+iy_3, where

$$(1) \qquad \Delta = \begin{vmatrix} x_1, & y_1, & 1 \\ x_2, & y_2, & 1 \\ x_3, & y_3, & 1 \end{vmatrix} \neq 0.$$

By definition, the points of the segment $(x_1+iy_1,\ x_3+iy_3)$ are

$$x = t_1(x_3-x_1)+x_1,\quad y = t_1(y_3-y_1)+y_1,\quad 0 \leqslant t_1 \leqslant 1.$$

Those of $(x_2+iy_2,\ x_3+iy_3)$ are

$$x = t_2(x_3-x_2)+x_2,\quad y = t_2(y_3-y_2)+y_2,\quad 0 \leqslant t_2 \leqslant 1.$$

Hence the segment between any point of the first segment and any point of the second is

$$(2) \qquad \begin{aligned} x &= t_3[t_2(x_3-x_2)+x_2-t_1(x_3-x_1)-x_1]+t_1(x_3-x_1)+x_1, \\ y &= t_3[t_2(y_3-y_2)+y_2-t_1(y_3-y_1)-y_1]+t_1(y_3-y_1)+y_1, \end{aligned}$$

i.e.

$$(3) \qquad \begin{aligned} x &= (1-t_1-t_3+t_1t_3)x_1+(t_3-t_2t_3)x_2+(t_1-t_1t_3+t_2t_3)x_3 \\ &= \tau_1x_1+\tau_2x_2+\tau_3x_3 \\ y &= (1-t_1-t_3+t_1t_3)y_1+(t_3-t_2t_3)y_2+(t_1-t_1t_3+t_2t_3)y_3 \\ &= \tau_1y_1+\tau_2y_2+\tau_3y_3. \end{aligned}$$

These equations seem to contain three parameters t_1, t_2, t_3, or τ_1, τ_2, τ_3, but

$$(4) \qquad \tau_1+\tau_2+\tau_3 = 1,$$

which reduces their number to two. We notice also that *for inside points* $0<t_1<1$, $0<t_2<1$, $0<t_3<1$, i.e.

$$\tau_1 = (1-t_1)(1-t_3)>0,\ \tau_2 = t_3(1-t_2)>0,\ \tau_3 = t_1(1-t_3)+t_2t_3>0,$$

so that *the three coefficients are all positive* (>0).

On the other hand, if $\tau_3 = 0$, the equations $x = \tau_1x_1+\tau_2x_2$,

$y = \tau_1 y_1 + \tau_2 y_2$, and $\tau_1 + \tau_2 = 1$ lead to $x = \tau_1(x_1 - x_2) + x_2$. $y = \tau_1(y_1 - y_2) + y_2$, i. e. they represent the side (1, 2). Similarly for the other two sides. If two of the τ's vanish, we obtain a vertex, while, by (4), all three cannot vanish.

Consider now, irrespective of the geometrical considerations involved in the preceding remarks, the set A of points for which $\tau_1 > 0$, $\tau_2 > 0$, $\tau_3 > 0$ and the set B of points for which one at least of the τ's is negative (less than 0). We are going to prove that both A and B are domains. For this purpose we shall show (a) that every point of A and B is an inner point; (b) that every pair of points a and a' of A is connected by a polygon lying wholly in A and similarly for B.

From (3) and (4), since the determinant (1) does not vanish, the τ's may be expressed as linear functions of x and y. In particular, these functions are continuous. If then, at a point P, the three functions τ are all positive, there will also be a square q, centre at P, at all points of which they are positive (by 14. VI), i. e. every point of q is in A; A is thus an open set. The same is true if any one of the functions τ is negative at a point, so that B also is an open set.

To show that A is connex, we take two points of A. At these points each of the functions τ will be positive and, since they are linear functions of x and y, they will also be positive at every point of the segment joining the points (see the proof of III). All these points belong to A and thus, by II, A is connex.

We have only to show that B is connex. At all points of B one of the functions τ is negative. If P and Q are two points of B, either there is a τ_i ($i = 1, 2$, or 3) which is negative at both points, or there is a τ_i negative at P and a τ_j negative at Q. In the first case, at all points of the segment PQ, τ_i is negative. In the second case, putting $\tau_i = -a$ at P and $\tau_j = -b$ at Q, the equations $\tau_i = -a$ and $\tau_j = -b$ represent two straight lines, all points of which will be in B, and which will intersect in a definite point R. Thus, P and Q can be connected by the segments PR and RQ in B. Therefore B is connex and both A and B are domains.

Thus we have proved the following result:

I. *A triangle divides the plane into two domains having the three sides of the triangle for their common boundary.*

One of these domains can be connected with ∞. We call it the outer domain. The other, the inner domain, is separated from the first, in the sense that no polygonal path connects a point of the outer domain B with a point of the inner domain A without passing through their common boundary.

We notice finally that one extremity of a segment which cuts only one side of the triangle is necessarily an inside point or a boundary point.

II. *A simple closed polygon p divides the plane into two domains whose common boundary is the polygon p.*

Proof. Since we have proved the theorem for a triangle, we shall use the principle of mathematical induction to prove it for a polygon of n sides. A segment joining two vertices of the polygon and not meeting it in any other point is called a *diagonal.* We are going to show that there is a diagonal dividing the given simple closed polygon into two simple closed polygons with the diagonal for their common side and having each a smaller number of sides than the given polygon.

Let AB and AC be any adjacent sides and join BC. Suppose first that there are no vertices of our polygon inside the triangle ABC. Then, by the last remark preceding II, there can be no point of the sides inside ABC. If there is no other vertex on BC, BC is a diagonal. If there are vertices on BC, let H be the one nearest to B. Then BH is a diagonal, unless it is a side of the polygon, in which case either HC or the segment joining H to the nearest vertex along BC is a diagonal.

Now suppose that there are vertices within ABC and let G be a vertex at the greatest distance from BC. Through G draw EF parallel to BC. There is no vertex in the triangle AEF, for its distance from BC would be greater than that of G (see the remarks on distance in Art. 46) and therefore there are no points of the polygon within AEF. Therefore AG is a diagonal. We have thus shown how to find a diagonal in every case.

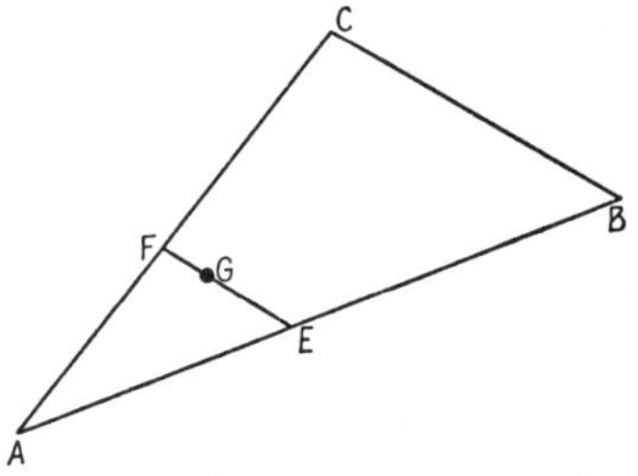

FIG. 25.

Suppose we have a polygon p with n sides and a diagonal AG. The polygon may be described in two ways from A to G. Suppose that the number of sides along these two paths, u_1 and u_2, are r and s. Then $r+s = n$, $r>1$, $s>1$, so that u_1 and the side AG form a polygon p_1 with less than n sides, and u_2 and AG form another such polygon p_2.

Suppose now these polygons have definite interiors and exteriors. Then either one is interior to the other or each is exterior to the other. In the first case, p_2 contained in p_1, say, the domains of points exterior to both and of points interior to both, together with the common side AG (extremities excluded) form a domain called the *exterior* of the polygon p. The points interior to p_1 and exterior to the connex region formed by p_2 and its boundary is a domain called the *interior* of p. In the second case, the interiors of p_1 and p_2, together with AG (the points A, G excluded), form the interior of p, and the points exterior to both p_1 and p_2 form the exterior of p. The theorem now follows by induction from the case of a triangle.

48. *Jordan's theorem.* In a one-one correspondence, corresponding points, arcs, &c., are called 'homologues'. As a rule, they are denoted by the same letter, accented for the elements of one side of the correspondence, and unaccented for those of the other side. We say that a one-one correspondence is *topological* if $P_n \to P$ implies $P_n' \to P'$, and vice versa. For example, the correspondence between the points of the circumference of a circle $(x-a)^2+(y-b)^2 = r^2$ and the points of the interval $(0, 2\pi)$, by means of the formulae $x-a = r\cos\theta$ and $y-b = r\sin\theta$, is topological, as it is a one-one correspondence, with the exception of the point $x = a+r$, $y = b$ corresponding to $\theta = 0$ and $\theta = 2\pi$, and the functions $\sin\theta$ and $\cos\theta$ are continuous. Similarly $t = 2\pi(t-t_0)/(t_1-t_0)$ is a topological correspondence between the two intervals (t_0, t_1) and $(0, 2\pi)$. Therefore, *there is a topological correspondence between a closed Jordan curve and the points of the circumference of a circle.*

Conversely, if there is a topological correspondence between a curve $x = f(t)$, $y = g(t)$, $t_0 \leqslant t \leqslant t_1$ and the circumference of a circle, $f(t)$ and $g(t)$ are continuous. In fact, if one of them, $f(t)$ say, were discontinuous at $t = t_0$, $f(t_n)$ would not tend to $f(t_0)$

for every $t_n \to t_0$, whereas on the circumference of the circle $x(t_n) \to x(t_0)$, $y(t_n) \to y(t_0)$, since $\sin\theta$ and $\cos\theta$ are continuous; and thus the correspondence would not be topological. From this arises the usual *definition of a closed Jordan curve as a topological picture of the circumference of a circle* and, from its definition, *an open Jordan curve is the topological picture of an interval.*

By the topological mapping of a Jordan curve, j, on the circumference of a circle we order its points. The point A of j precedes B if the angle $\theta > 0$ corresponding to A is less than the angle $\theta' < 2\pi$ of B. This ordering helps a good deal in the following proof of 45. I.

Let j' denote a circle, j its topological picture (Jordan curve). As j is bounded, there is a square q containing it. Join a point R of

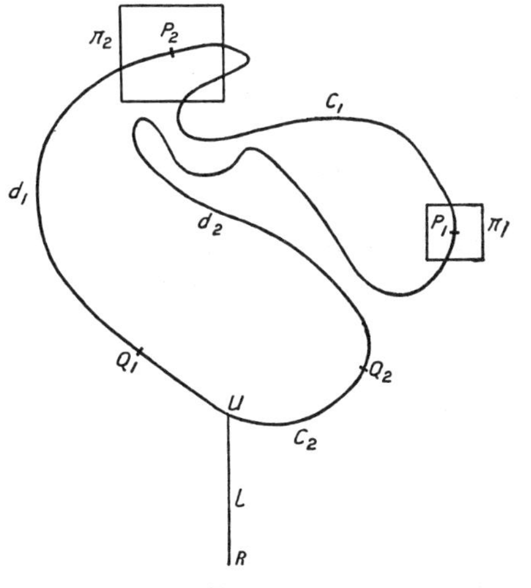

Fig. 26.

the boundary of q to a point of j by a segment, and let U be the first point of j on the segment. RU will be denoted by l. If U' is the homologue of U on j', choose four points on j' such that $(P_1'P_2'Q_1'U'Q_2')$ form a cyclic order. The arcs $P_1'P_2'$, $P_2'Q_1'$, $Q_1'Q_2'$, $Q_2'P_1'$ (end points included) will be denoted by c_1', d_1', c_2', d_2'; the homologues on j, as usual, by unaccented letters. If two sets have no common point, we say that they are *distinct.*

Since d_1' and d_2' are distinct from each other, d_1 and d_2 are also distinct and, being closed sets, they have a positive (>0) distance. Similarly for c_1 and c_2. Let δ denote the smaller of these two distances and subdivide q into squares (parallel to the axes) with sides $<\delta/4$. We suppose that P_1 and P_2 are inner points of two squares π_1 and π_2 respectively.

π_1 and π_2 are necessarily distinct, since π_1 contains points of d_2, π_2 those of d_1 and the distance of d_1 and d_2 is $>\delta$. For the same reason π_1 is distinct from d_1+c_2+l and π_2 is distinct from d_2+c_2+l. The points of c_1, d_1 and d_2 outside or on the boundary of π_1 and π_2 will be denoted by $\bar{c}_1$, $\bar{d}_1$, $\bar{d}_2$. As P_2 is the only common point of c_1 and d_1, it follows that $\bar{c}_1$ and d_1 and similarly $\bar{c}_1$ and d_2 are distinct. The sets $\bar{c}_1$ and d_1+d_2, being closed and distinct, their distance $\bar{d}$ is positive.

Subdivide q, *but not* π_1 *and* π_2, into squares whose sides are $<\bar{d}/4$ and denote by μ the set of closed squares containing, inside or on their boundary, the points of $\bar{c}_1$; the region μ is distinct from $d_1+d_2+c_2+l$. *The region of squares* $\mu+\pi_1+\pi_2$ *has a polýgonal boundary* π *such that* c_1 *is inside* π, c_2 *is outside* π, for c_2+l is distinct from the polygonal line π and its point R is outside π.

We are going to divide π into four sections. There is at least one point of π_1 on π, for the (connex) part of $\bar{d}_2$ which contains Q_2 is outside π and has a limiting point on π_1. Similarly there is a point of π_2 on π.

Take a point C of π on π_1 (Fig. 27). Going from C along π in one direction to the first point A of π_2 and coming back along the same path to the first point B of π_1, we obtain the simple polygonal path $u_1(BA)$ uniting π_1 and π_2. Similarly we construct $u_2(DE)$. Since c_1 is completely inside π, u_1 and u_2, parts of π, do not meet c_1, and, since μ is distinct from $d_1+d_2+c_2$, they do not meet j at all. The part of π between B and D, containing C, is denoted by v_1 and the remaining part, between A and E, by v_2. We notice that v_1 is distinct from d_1, for v_1 is part of π_1, which is distinct from d_1. Similarly v_2 is distinct from d_2. Thus π *consists of four sections* u_1, u_2, v_1, v_2 *such that* u_1 *and* u_2 *do not meet* j, v_1 *is distinct from* d_1, *and* v_2 *is distinct from* d_2; c_1 *is wholly inside* π, c_2 *is wholly outside* π.

We are going to prove that *every simple polygonal path*

joining a point M_1 of u_1 to a point M_2 of u_2 meets j. Suppose in fact, that this is not so and denote by w that part of the simple polygonal path joining M_1 to M_2 without meeting j, between the last intersection M_1' with u_1 and the first intersection M_2' with u_2, and by w_1, w_2, the two parts of π between M_1' and M_2' containing v_1 and v_2 respectively. Then, since π does not

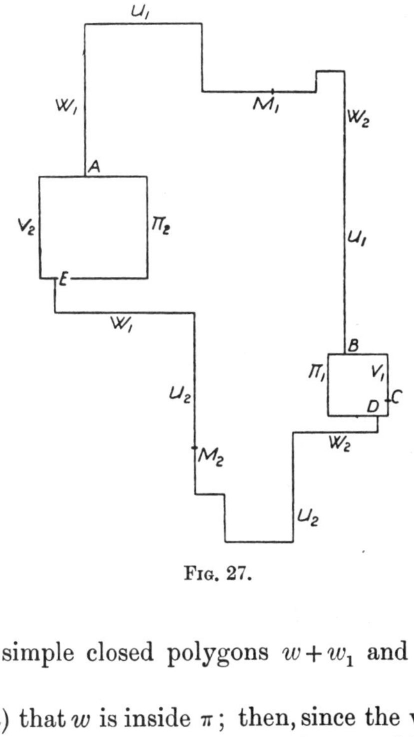

FIG. 27.

meet c_2, the simple closed polygons $w+w_1$ and $w+w_2$ do not meet c_2.

Suppose (*a*) that w is inside π; then, since the whole of c_1 is in one piece, either $w+w_1$ or $w+w_2$ contains c_1, while c_2 is outside both. Therefore either $w+w_1$ or $w+w_2$ separates c_1 from c_2. Next, suppose (*b*) that w is outside π; then c_1 is inside one of $w+w_1$ and $w+w_2$ and outside the other, while c_2 is either outside both or inside both. Therefore either $w+w_1$ or $w+w_2$ separates c_1 from c_2. Thus *in every case either $w+w_1$ or $w+w_2$ separates c_1 from c_2*. Suppose that it is $w+w_1$. Since $c_1+d_1+c_2$ is distinct from $\bar{w}$ and w_1, we can pass from any point of c_1 to any point of c_2 along $c_1+d_1+c_2$ without meeting

$w+w_1$ and thus they cannot be separated by $w+w_1$, and the contradiction proves the statement. Hence

I. *A closed Jordan curve determines in the plane at least two distinct domains.*

We notice that, in our construction of π, c_1 may be any arc of j in any arbitrary neighbourhood of any fixed point of j, and π may be contained in any neighbourhood of the point. Hence

II. *In the neighbourhood of every point of a Jordan curve j there are points of at least two distinct domains.*

49. *Jordan's theorem* (concluded). We are now going to prove that j *determines at most two distinct domains.* The boundary points of q are separated by j either from u_1 or from u_2. Take any two points M_1 and M_2, each separated from q by j. We are going to show that M_1 *and* M_2 *can be joined by a simple polygonal path not meeting* j.

We join two points of the contour q by a segment and denote the first and last intersections with j by U_1 and U_2 respectively. There is such a segment for which $U_1 \neq U_2$. In fact, if every segment meets j at most once, any pair of points in q may be connected by a polygon not meeting j, in contradiction with 48. I. We draw two segments, h_1 and h_2, through M_1 and M_2 parallel to l and denote their first intersections with j in both directions by S_1, T_1 and S_2, T_2.

In this construction we can suppose that the arcs $U_1 U_2$ and $U_2 U_1$ of j contain (each) one of the members of the pairs S_1, T_1 and S_2, T_2. In fact, if all the four points lie on the arc $U_1 U_2$, say, we take a point of the arc $U_2 U_1$ and in its neighbourhood take a point M_3 separated from the contour q and join it to two points of the arc $U_2 U_1$ by segments. Then our reasoning, applied to M_1 and M_3 as well as to M_2 and M_3, will prove that M_1 and M_3, M_2 and M_3 are contained in the same domain, and thus also M_1 and M_2 will be contained in the same domain. Thus we can determine four arcs c_1, d_1, c_2, d_2 of j (as above) such that c_1 contains U_1, S_1, T_1 (say) and c_2 contains U_2, S_2, T_2. We now construct π, separating c_1 from c_2, and notice that π can be decomposed (as above) into two parts w_1 and w_2 such that w_1 is distinct from d_1 and w_2 from d_2.

We can also suppose that π has only one point in common

with each of l_1, h_1, h_2; viz. L_1, H_1, H_2. In fact, retaining the three squares which contain S_1, S_2, U_1 respectively, the points of c_1 outside these three squares are at a finite distance δ from the points of l_1, h_1, h_2 outside the three squares. The subdivision by squares with sides $< \delta/4$ leads to a modified π

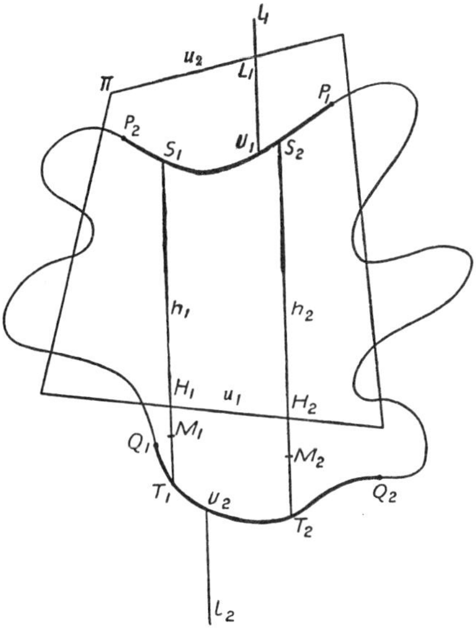

FIG. 28.

satisfying the required condition. Now put $\pi = u_1 + v_1 + u_2 + v_2$, where v_1 is distinct from d_1, v_2 from d_2, and u_1 and u_2 do not meet j.

Then H_1, H_2 *and* L_1 *are on* $u_1 + u_2$. But, by hypothesis, M_1, M_2, and hence H_1, H_2 are separated from the contour q, and L_1 is not. Thus H_1 and H_2 lie both on u_1 or both on u_2; on u_1 say. The path $(M_1 h_1 H_1 u_1 H_2 h_2 M_2)$ is thus a path connecting M_1 and M_2 without meeting j. Since this is true of any two such points, *there is only one domain separated from every point of the contour* q. On the other hand, the points which are not separated from the contour q are not separated from each other. Hence the points outside j form a single domain and j is, by II, the common boundary of the inner and outer domains. Q.e.d.

50. *Connectivity of domains.* The most delicate part in pro-

blems involving the idea of domain is the consideration of the boundary of the domain. As our examples will show us, the adequate description of the boundary requires a more general notion than that of a Jordan curve. So far we have only proved that the boundary of a domain is a closed set (46. I). For further characterization of this set we introduce the notion of a *continuum*.

If between two points $a+ib$ and $a'+ib'$ of a set S we can insert a finite number of points P_i from S such that the distance between two consecutive points P_i and P_{i+1}, ($P_0 = a+bi$, $P_n = a'+ib'$) is less than ϵ, we say that $a+ib$ and $a'+ib'$ are connected in S by an ϵ-chain (of points). If any two points of a *closed* set are connected by an ϵ-chain, however small ϵ be, we say that S is a *continuum*. We notice that the idea of a continuum does not depend on the dimensions. All the points of a closed segment form a (linear) continuum, all the points of a closed circle form a (plane) continuum, &c.

We have said that two sets of points are *distinct* if they have no common point. *The united set K_1+K_2 of two continua is a continuum if and only if K_1 and K_2 are not distinct.*

Proof. By 11. I, if the closed sets K_1 and K_2 have no common point, their distance d is positive. Thus, taking $\epsilon < d$, we see that not every two points of K_1+K_2 are connected by an arbitrary ϵ-chain. Conversely, if K_1 and K_2 have a common point P, every point p_1 of K_1 can be connected to any point p_2 of K_2 by an ϵ-chain through P for any arbitrary ϵ.

Two closed squares q_1 and q_2 having only one common point P, e. g. a vertex, form a continuum, because the ϵ-chain works through P, but the inner points form two distinct domains in spite of the fact that every inner point of q_1 is connected with every inner point of q_2 by an ϵ-chain for every ϵ (since there are points of q_1 and of q_2 as near to P as we like). The reason of this fact is that the connexion constituting a domain implies a chain of *circles* lying entirely in the set, whereas the connexion constituting a continuum implies only a chain of points.

We give two examples to show the complexity of the problem of the boundary. Fig. 29 shows the division of a circle into two complementary domains such that every point of the circumference is a boundary point for both domains. It is a spiral domain narrowing indefinitely as it approaches the circumference.

FIG. 29.

In the second example the circular bands approach indefinitely (a) the shaft leading to the inner circle $|z| = r_0$, (b) the larger

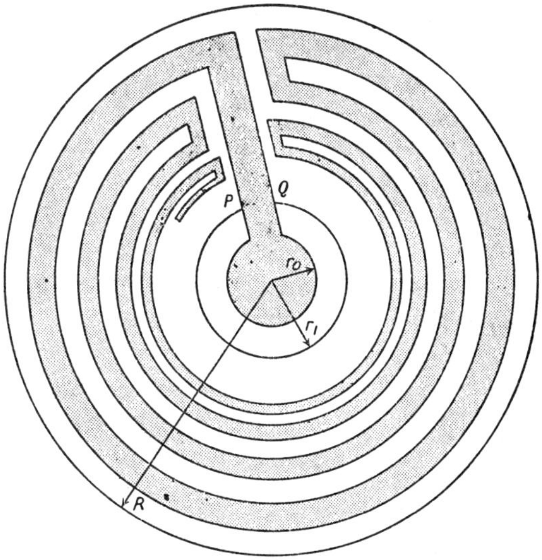

FIG. 30.

inner circle $|z| = r_1$, except the small arc PQ. Thus every point of $|z| = r_1$, the arc PQ omitted, is a boundary point of the shaded domain. We may even combine the two examples by producing the shaft towards $|z| = R$ and letting the circumference $|z| = R$ be approached by a spiral band as in the first example, but starting from the shaft. We obtain thus a domain including among its boundary points parts, or the whole of three concentric circumferences, together with a complicated curve. In view of this example we shall be able to appreciate the following result.

I. *If the complementary set K of a finite domain D is a continuum, the boundary B of D is also a continuum.*

The proof is based on the following lemma.

Lemma 1. *If S is a bounded closed set but not a continuum, there is a closed polygon π distinct from S and such that there are points of S inside and outside π.*

Proof of the lemma. By hypothesis, S can be decomposed into two or more distinct closed sets, S_1 and S_2, with a distance $d > 0$. Divide the plane into squares of side $< d/4$, and consider the closed squares containing points of S_1. They form one or more polygonal regions R_i, with the following obvious properties: (a) No point of S is on the boundary of these regions, (b) every point of S_1 is an inner point of some R_i (if a point of S_1 is on the side A of a square, R_i contains also, by construction, the next square having the side A, and similarly for the vertices), (c) every R_i contains a point of S_1, (d) every point of S_2 lies outside the regions R_i. If there is only one polygon, this polygon satisfies the conditions of the lemma, by (c) and (d). If there are several polygons and two of them are outside one another, either of these two polygons satisfies the conditions. Finally if the polygons are such that each contains the next, then (1) S_2 may lie outside all of them, in which case any of the polygons satisfies the conditions of the lemma; (2) S_2 lies inside the second, (for R_1 is formed by the area between the first and second polygons) in which case the second polygon satisfies the requirements.

Proof of Theorem I. By 46. I, the boundary points of a domain D form a closed set B. Moreover B is finite, since, by hypothesis, D is contained in a sufficiently large square and thus B is also contained in the same closed square. Now if B is not a continuum, there is, by Lemma 1, a polygon π

not meeting B and such that there are points of B inside as well as outside π. Therefore, as there are points of D as near to any point of B as we like, there are points of D inside and outside π. Any path joining such an inside point to an outside point meets π, i.e. at least one point of D lies on π, and, as π does not meet the boundary B of D, π is entirely in D. Therefore π is distinct from the complementary region K of D;

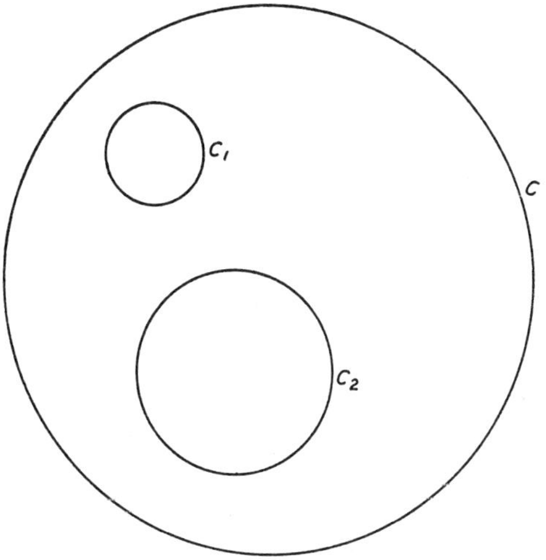

FIG. 31.

but there are points of K inside as well as outside π, which is absurd, since K is by hypothesis a continuum.

The condition that the complementary set K is a continuum is indispensable, as shown by the example of a domain inside a circle C and outside two circles, C_1 and C_2, contained in C. Here the boundary consists of three distinct continua, i.e. B is not a continuum. The reason for this is that the complementary set K consists of three distinct parts, i.e. K is not a continuum.

Going back to our combined example (p. 194) where the boundary does not seem to be a continuum, we remark that *for every* given $\epsilon < 0$ there is an ϵ-chain, vertices on B, connecting any point of $|z| = R$ to a point of $|z| = r_1$, since there is only a finite number of bands whose width is $> \epsilon$, i.e. an infinity of these bands can be crossed in one step by jumping from a point on $|z| = r_1$ to a boundary point on a band at a distance $\delta < \epsilon$.

Afterwards we must go round and jump again where necessary to $|z| = R$. Thus the complete boundary is a continuum as required by Theorem I and forms a good example of possible occurrences in a continuum.

In function theory the most important type of domain is a domain D inside the Jordan curve J and outside one or more Jordan curves j_i contained in J. The most important general

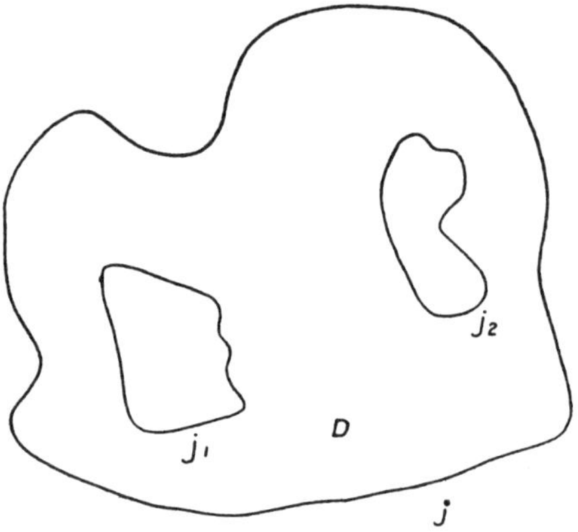

Fig. 32.

feature of such a domain is its *connectivity*, explained as follows: In fig. 32 joining a point of J to a point of j_1, and similarly for j_2, and excluding the points of the joining curves from D (by two 'cross-cuts') we obtain a domain D'. On the other hand, if we exclude from D' the points of a curve in D' joining two points of the boundary we obtain two distinct domains. We say that D is triply connected. In general, we say that *a domain is simply connected if its boundary is a continuum, doubly connected if its boundary is formed by two distinct continua and so on.*

II. *If the infinite sequence of simply connected domains* D_1, D_2, ... *is such that* D_{i+1} *contains* D_i, *the set of all points belonging to one at least of these domains forms a simply connected limit domain* D. *Every simply connected domain* D *is a limit domain of simply connected polygonal domains.*

Proof. If a point P belongs to D_i, then also a complete neighbourhood of P belongs to D_i and thus to D_{i+1}, ..., which proves that all the points belonging to any of the domains D_i

form a domain D. Suppose now that the limit domain D is not simply connected. This means that its boundary B consists of two or more distinct continua, and thus, by Lemma 1, there is a polygon π in D separating one of the continua B', say, from the rest. For sufficiently large i, π is entirely in D_i, otherwise one point at least of π would be missing in all the D_i and thus also in D. But there are points not belonging to D_i inside as well as well as outside π, for otherwise the whole inside or the whole outside of π would belong to D_i and thus ultimately to D, which contradicts the given construction for π. It follows that there are boundary points of D_i inside as well as outside π, which contradicts the hypothesis that D_i is simply connected.

To prove the last statement of the theorem, we consider the points of the given D whose distances from the boundary are $\geqslant 1/n$ and whose distance from the origin is $< n$. By Lemma 1, we can construct a polygon π_n separating this portion from the boundary. For a sufficiently large n, π_n is the boundary of a simply connected domain which tends to D when $n \to \infty$. The above proof applies to bounded or unbounded domains. Notice also that, *every Jordan curve can be indefinitely approached by polygons.*

Similar considerations lead to the general statement:

III. *Every domain is the limit domain of polygonal domains.*

The important thing for us is, however, the reduction of a multiply connected domain to a simply connected one by means of *cross-cuts*, i. e. by means of simple polygonal lines in the domain joining two distinct portions of the boundary. Thus, by definition, every point of a cross-cut is an inner point except its two extremities.

IV. *A simple cut joining two points of the same portion of the boundary and distinct from the other portions decomposes the domain into two domains.*

Simple means 'no multiple points'.

For brevity's sake we give the proof for simply connected domains. A simple polygonal line π inside D will not split D into more than two domains, as all the points along either side of it belong to one and the same domain. Thus we have to prove that D does not remain one domain.

Suppose that D remains one domain. We are going to show that this hypothesis is in contradiction with a property of continua.

Consider a circle in D, with a portion of π for its diameter, containing no other points of π and also a segment QR through the centre P, not reaching the circumference. As we know, such lines do not split the semicircles into two domains. It follows that if, as we suppose, D is not split by π, then D is not split by π together with QR.

Therefore we can join the points Q and R in D by a polygon π' not meeting π, B or the segment QR, for these three

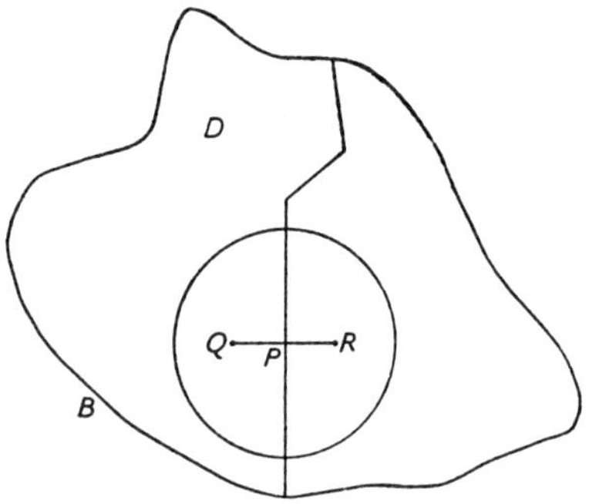

FIG. 33.

continua form the new boundary. But π' and QR together form a simple closed polygon π'', such that there are points of π inside as well as outside π'', viz. points of the diameter of our original circle near P. Thus π breaks into two polygons, π_1 and π_2, one inside, the other outside π'', i. e. π'' separates the continua π_1+B and π_2+B, which is absurd, since B cannot be both inside and outside π''. This proves the theorem.

V. *A cross-cut reduces the connectivity of the domain by one.* It is understood, of course, that the connectivity is finite.

Proof. Let the cross-cut QR join two portions of the boundary B_1 and B_2, and let the segment $Q'R'$ be removed. The part QQ' of the cross-cut and B_1 form a continuum C. The part RR' and the remaining portions of the complete boundary B form a closed set S (several continua). By Lemma 1, there is a closed polygon π separating C from S, and QR joins an inner point of π with an outer point, i. e. meets π or may even have a portion in common with π. If Q'' and R'' are the first and last points of intersection (perhaps coincident), and Q''' a point of π before Q'', R''' a point of π after R'', the two points Q''' and R''' split π into two open polygons π_1 and π_2 uniting two points on different sides of the cross-cut, of which one, π_1 say, does not meet the cross-cut. Therefore, after the points of the cross-cut

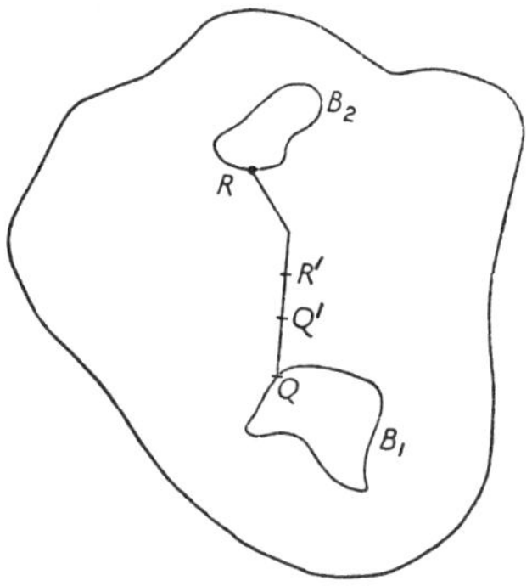

FIG. 34.

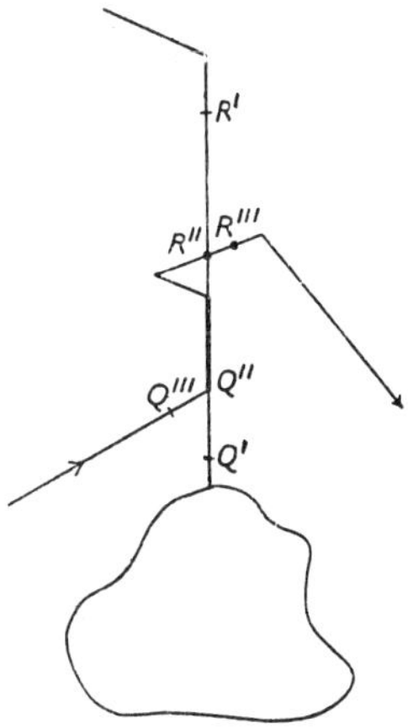

FIG. 35.

have been removed from D, the points on its two sides can still be joined by a polygon entirely in D, i. e. D is not cut into distinct domains. On the other hand, the cross-cut reduces by one the number of distinct continua in B, since the cross-cut $+ B_1 + B_2$ form a single contour, and the rest is unaffected. Q.e.d.

51. *Rectifiable curves and line integrals.* The idea of a Jordan curve is too general for many practical purposes. We readily verify this when we try to define the length of a curve between two of its points.

Geometrically we define length as the limit length of polygons approaching the curve. We are going to put this into mathematical language. The curve C: $x(t)$, $y(t)$ and its two points a: $x(t_0)$, $y(t_0)$ and b: $x(t)$, $y(t)$ being given, we divide the arc of C between a and b by the points corresponding to $t_0 (= a)$, t_1,

$t_2, \ldots, t_{n-1}, t_n (= b)$ and add the distances of these points. Putting $|x(t_i) - x(t_{i-1})| = \Delta_i x, |y(t_i) - y(t_{i-1})| = \Delta_i y$, the length l of the polygon corresponding to our division of the arc is

$$l = \sum_{i=1}^{n} \sqrt{(\Delta_i x)^2 + (\Delta_i y)^2}.$$

Such a polygon of chords of a given arc is said to be *inscribed* in the arc. We define the *length of an arc* as the upper bound of the lengths of all inscribed polygons [Peano, 1890 b]. If this upper bound is finite, we say that the arc is *rectifiable.* If the upper bound is infinite, we say that the arc is *not rectifiable* or that its length is *infinite.*

I. *The necessary and sufficient condition that the arc of a curve $x(t)$, $y(t)$ between $t = a$ and $t = b$ be rectifiable is that $x(t)$ and $y(t)$ be of bounded variation in (a, b).* (Jordan, 1893–6, I, p. 100.)

Proof. From $\sqrt{x^2 + y^2} < x + y$ for positive x and y, we see that

$$(1) \qquad \Sigma \sqrt{(\Delta_i x)^2 + (\Delta_i y)^2} < \Sigma |\Delta_i x| + \Sigma |\Delta_i y|,$$

and obviously

$$(2) \qquad \begin{aligned} \Sigma \sqrt{(\Delta_i x)^2 + (\Delta_i y)^2} &> \Sigma |\Delta_i x|, \\ \Sigma \sqrt{(\Delta_i x)^2 + (\Delta_i y)^2} &> \Sigma |\Delta_i y|. \end{aligned}$$

Therefore if the arc in question has a finite length, i.e. if the left-hand sides of (2) are bounded, the right-hand sides are also bounded, and thus $x(t)$ and $y(t)$ are of bounded variation. Conversely, if $x(t)$ and $y(t)$ are of bounded variation, the right-hand side of (1) is bounded and so is the left-hand side, whose upper bound is, by definition, the length of the curve.

Theorem I shows that the existence of a finite length, according to Peano's definition, only requires that $x(t)$ and $y(t)$ should be of bounded variation. Continuity even is not necessary. Still, in the sequel, we shall restrict the use of the word *curve* to indicate *a chain of a finite number of open Jordan curves.* We shall now prove that for Jordan curves the upper bound is replaced by a simple limit, provided we only admit successions of inscribed polygons whose maximum sides tend to 0.

II. *If L is the length of an open Jordan curve $x(t)$, $y(t)$ between $t = a$ and $t = b$, the lengths l_n of any succession of inscribed* *polygons* π_n *tend to* L, *provided their maximum sides tend to* 0.

Proof. By hypothesis, the arc j in question has the length L. Therefore, there is an inscribed polygon π, corresponding to the division Δ, $(t_0 = a, t_1, \ldots, t_{p+1} = b)$, say, such that its length $\lambda > L - \epsilon/2$. Consider now any succession of inscribed polygons π_n of length l_n, corresponding to the divisions d_n, say, such that the length δ_n of the maximum side tends to 0.

It follows from the last condition that, after a sufficiently large suffix N, the lengths of all the sides of π_n are less than η, where η is an arbitrary positive number. Now consider the subdivision d'_n obtained by adding to d_n the points of Δ. Let π'_n be the polygon corresponding to d'_n and let δ'_n be the length of its longest side. Then, since π'_n contains at most p vertices which do not belong to π_n, we have $l'_n - l_n < 2p\delta'_n$. We notice that if we subdivide a given division, the polygonal length is increased or perhaps remains the same. If now it be true that $\delta'_n \to 0$ as $n \to \infty$, it follows that $l'_n - l_n < \epsilon/2$ if n is large enough. And hence, since $L \geqslant l'_n \geqslant \lambda$, we have, for sufficiently large n, $L - l_n < \epsilon$, i.e. $l_n \to L$.

To complete the proof we observe that

(a) It follows from the continuity of $x(t)$ and $y(t)$ that

$$\sqrt{\{[x(t'') - x(t')]^2 + [y(t'') - y(t')]^2\}} < \eta$$

provided $|t'' - t'| < \zeta$, say.

(b) Since the curve is an open Jordan curve, when the points P'_n and P''_n, corresponding to t'_n and t''_n respectively, tend to the same point P, corresponding to t, then $t'_n \to t, t''_n \to t$. But the length

$$\sqrt{\{[x(t''_n) - x(t'_n)]^2 + [y(t''_n) - y(t'_n)]^2\}}$$

of the chord $P'_n P''_n$ does not tend to 0 unless $x(t''_n) - x(t'_n) \to 0$ and $y(t''_n) - y(t'_n) \to 0$. Thus, with the lengths of chords $P'_n P''_n$ those of the corresponding intervals $t''_n - t'_n$ tend to 0.

Now, for every n, any fixed point P of j, corresponding to the value t, is an inner point of an arc $A_i A_{i+1}$ or of a double arc $A_i A_{i+2}$ corresponding to the interval (t^n_i, t^n_{i+1}) or (t^n_i, t^n_{i+2}), say, of the division d_n. Hence there is a least N such that, for $n > N$, $|t^n_{i+1} - t^n_i| < \zeta$ or $|t^n_{i+2} - t^n_i| < \zeta$, as the case may be. The suffix N varies with t, but, by Borel's lemma, 11. III, there are a finite number of the *same* intervals possessing the same property. Therefore, we can find an N suitable for *all* the points of (a, b), i.e. such that, if $n > N$, all the intervals of d_n are shorter than ζ. Since we obtain d_n' from d_n by inserting new points of division, the intervals of d_n' are $< \zeta$, and thus, by (a), the corresponding chords are less than the arbitrary η. In particular, $\delta_n' < \eta$. This proves that $\delta_n' \to 0$.

We shall use II to prove the following result, indispensable for the definition of length of general curves.

III. *If, by an intermediate point, we split an open Jordan curve into two parts j_1 and j_2, we have $L = L_1 + L_2$, where L, L_1, L_2 are the lengths of j, j_1, j_2 respectively.*

Proof. Let $t = c$ correspond to the common part of j_1 and j_2, and let l_n' and l_n'' be the polygonal lengths corresponding to any division of (a, c) and (c, b) respectively, and such that the longest chord tends to 0. The two divisions together make up a division of (a, b) with the same property, and for which the polygonal length is $l_n' + l_n''$ tending to L as $n = \infty$. Since $l_n' \to L_1$, $l_n'' \to L_2$, the statement is proved.

We might also say that length is additive.

This leads us to the definition of the length of a curve or succession of open Jordan curves, e.g. that of a closed Jordan curve, as the *sum of lengths of the component curves.* A *rectifiable curve* will also be referred to as a *path.*

52. *Stieltjes' integral.*

Consider (a) the real function $f(x)$ of the real variable x defined and bounded in the interval (a, b), (b) the real and increasing function $g(x)$, and form for a given subdivision $x = a, x_1, \dots, x_{n-1}, x_n = b$ of the interval (a, b) the sums

$$(1) \qquad \begin{aligned} S &= \sum_{i=0}^{n} M_i[g(x_i) - g(x_{i-1})] \\ s &= \sum_{i=0}^{n} m_i[g(x_i) - g(x_{i-1})], \end{aligned}$$

where M_i and m_i are the upper and lower bounds respectively of $f(x)$ in the i-th interval. We call S and s the *upper* and *lower sums* corresponding to the subdivision. We suppose first that $f(x) \geqslant 0$ in (a, b). As the differences in the brackets are, by hypothesis, positive, we have $S \geqslant s$.

If we insert a new point of division x', e. g. in the i-th interval, the term $M_i[g(x_i) - g(x_{i-1})]$ is replaced by

$$M_i'[g(x') - g(x_{i-1})] + M_i''[g(x_i) - g(x')]$$

where M_i' is the upper bound of $f(x)$ in (x_{i-1}, x') and M_i'' in (x', x_i). Since $M_i' \leqslant M_i$ and $M_i'' \leqslant M_i$, it follows that

$$M_i'[g(x') - g(x_{i-1})] + M_i''[g(x_i) - g(x')] \leqslant M_i[g(x_i) - g(x_{i-1})].$$

Consequently, if S' corresponds to the new subdivision (with the point x' inserted),

$$S' \leqslant S.$$

Similarly $$s' \geqslant s.$$

Let us now compare two arbitrary divisions $(a, x_1, \ldots, x_{n-1}, b)$ and $(a, x_1', x_2' \ldots, x'_{n'-1}, b)$ and denote the corresponding sums by S, s and S', s'. Uniting the two divisions, we get a third one $(a_n, x_1'', x_2'', \ldots, x''_{n''-1}, b)$ with the sums S'' and s''.

According to our previous remark

$$S'' \leqslant S \quad S'' \leqslant S'$$
$$s'' \geqslant s \quad s'' \geqslant s',$$

since the third division is the continuation of the first as well as of the second division. Hence $S \geqslant S'' \geqslant s'' \geqslant s'$ and similarly $S' \geqslant s$, i. e. any upper sum, belonging to any division, is greater than or equal to any lower sum, belonging to any other (or to the same) division.

The lower bound of upper sums S formed for every possible division of (a, b) is called the upper integral of $f(x)$ in (a, b) with respect to $g(x)$. The upper bound of lower sums s formed for every possible division of (a, b) is called the lower integral of $f(x)$ in (a, b) with respect to $g(x)$. In symbols,

$$\underline{\lim}\, S = \underline{S} = \overline{\int_a^b} f(x)dg(x), \quad \overline{\lim}\, s = \bar{s} = \underline{\int_a^b} f(x)dg(x).$$

If, for the function $f(x)$, these two numbers are the same, we say that $f(x)$ is integrable with respect to $g(x)$, and we call their common value *the (Stieltjes) integral of $f(x)$ with respect to $g(x)$*;

in symbols $\int_a^b f(x)dg(x)$.

We notice that, if $g(x)$ is differentiable in (a, b), we have

$$\int_a^b f(x)\,dg = \int_a^b fg'\,dx,$$

where the right-hand side is an ordinary integral.

If $f(x)$ also assumes negative values in (a, b) but $|f(x)| \leqslant M$ in (a, b), we put

$$f = (f+M) - M \quad \text{and} \quad S(f) = S(f+M) - M[f(b) - f(a)].$$

Since $f+M$ is > 0, the preceding reasoning applies and the lower bound of $S(f)$ is that of $S(f+M)$ diminished by $M[f(b)-f(a)]$. Similarly for the lower sum. Thus, the upper and lower integrals exist for every bounded function.

By Art. 15, if $g(x)$ is of bounded variation in (a, b),

$$g(x) = g_1(x) - g_2(x),$$

where both $g_1(x)$ and $g_2(x)$ are increasing functions. Thus in this case we define the Stieltjes integral of $f(x)$ with respect to $g(x)$ by putting

$$\int_a^b f(x)\,dg(x) = \int_a^b f(x)\,dg_1(x) - \int_a^b f(x)\,dg_2(x),$$

whenever the two integrals on the right-hand side exist. It is readily seen that in establishing the general properties of Stieltjes integrals we can restrict ourselves to the former case.

In the calculation of upper and lower integrals we can restrict ourselves to series of divisions d_n, for which the greatest sub-interval tends to 0. In fact, the upper sums $S_1, S_2, \ldots, S_n, \ldots$ corresponding to a series of subdivisions d_n, for which the greatest sub-interval does not tend to 0, are not greater than the sums S_n' corresponding to subdivisions d_n', obtained by adding to d_n new points of subdivision in such a way that the greatest sub-interval tends to 0. Similarly for s_n.

The simplification thus obtained is considerable for, as we are going to prove, any infinite sequence S_n, corresponding to a series of divisions d_n for which the length of the maximum interval tends to 0, tends in the ordinary sense to $\underline{S}$ ($\underline{S}$ is not merely the lower bound of the upper sums). The proof is an exact repetition of the reasoning used in the case of rectifiable curves.

By hypothesis, there is a division Δ $(a, \tau_1, \ldots, \tau_p, b)$ with the corresponding S such that $S-\underline{S}<\epsilon/2$. On the other hand, if $d_1, d_2, \ldots, d_n, \ldots$ is a sequence of divisions for which the greatest sub-interval tends to 0, there is an N such that for $n>N$, the lengths of all the sub-intervals of $d_n, d_{n+1}, \ldots$ are less than η, where η is an arbitrary positive number. Now consider the subdivision d_n' obtained by adding to d_n the points of Δ and let S_n' correspond to d_n'. Suppose $|f(x)| \leqslant M$, $g(x)$ continuous in (a,b) and let δ_n be the length of the greatest increment $|g(x_i)-g(x_{i-1})|$ in d_n. Then, since d_n' contains at most p points which do not belong to d_n, $S_n - S_n' \leqslant 2pM\delta_n < \epsilon/2$ if n be large enough. But $S \geqslant S_n' \geqslant S$. Therefore, for sufficiently large n, $|S_n - S| < \epsilon$, which prove the following statement:

I. *If the upper (lower) sums $S_n(s_n)$ of a Stieltjes integral with respect to a function $g(x)$ which is continuous and of bounded variation correspond to divisions for which the maximum interval tends to* 0, *$S_n(s_n)$ tends regularly to the lower (upper) bound S, (s), of the upper (lower) sums.* (Darboux for $g(x) \equiv x$.)

functions.

II. ***If $f(x)$ is integrable in (a, b) with respect to $g_1(x)$ and $g_2(x)$, then it is also integrable with respect to g_1+g_2 and we have***

$$\int_a^b f(x)\,d\,(g_1+g_2) = \int_a^b f(x)\,dg_1 + \int_a^b f(x)dg_2.$$

Proof. Suppose g_1 and g_2 are increasing. If $f(x)$ is integrable with respect to g (increasing),

$$S_n - s_n = \Sigma(M_i - m_i)\,[g(x_i)-g(x_{i-1})] \to 0$$

for a succession of divisions with the greatest interval tending to 0. Hence in (1) we can replace M_i and m_i by any numbers between these two without altering the limit, i. e. the integral. Thus

$$\int_a^b f(x)\,d(g_1+g_2) = \lim_{n=\infty}\sum_{i=0}^{n} f(\xi_i)\,[g_1(\xi_i)+g_2(\xi_i)-g_1(\xi_{i-1})-g_2(\xi_{i-1})]$$

$$= \lim_{n=\infty}\left\{\sum_0^n f(\xi_i)[g_1(\xi_i)-g_1(\xi_{i-1})] + \sum_0^n f(\xi_i)[g_2(\xi_i)-g_2(\xi_{i-1})]\right\}$$

$$= \int_a^b f(x)dg_1 + \int_a^b f(x)dg_2.$$

In general, if g_1 and g_2 are of bounded variation g_1+g_2 has the same property and all three functions can be expressed as the difference of two increasing functions. Thus the proof is completed by using the first part of the argument. Q. e. d.

Exactly similar reasoning proves the following theorem.

III. *If f_1 and f_2 are integrable in (a, b) with respect to g, then also f_1+f_2 is integrable with respect to g and we have*

$$\int_a^b (f_1+f_2)dg = \int_a^b f_1 dg + \int_a^b f_2 dg.$$

IV. *If $f(x)$ is continuous and $g(x)$ is of bounded variation in (a, b), $f(x)$ is integrable in (a, b) with respect to $g(x)$.*

Proof. We shall first suppose that $g(x)$ is increasing. We have to show that $|S_n - s_n| \to 0$ provided $S_1, S_2, \ldots; s_1, s_2, \ldots$ correspond to a succession of divisions of (a, b) with the maximum interval tending to 0. But

$$S_n - s_n = \Sigma(M_i - m_i)\,[g(x_i) - g(x_{i-1})].$$

Since, by hypothesis, $f(x)$ is continuous at every point x of the closed interval (a, b), there is an interval containing x such that the oscillation of $f(x)$ in that interval is $<\epsilon/2$ (ϵ fixed arbitrarily). Thus to every point in (a, b) corresponds an interval covering this point. Applying Borel's lemma we see that there is a finite number of the same set of intervals, $i_1, \ldots, i_p$, say, covering (a, b). Now, if n be taken sufficiently large, all the intervals of the division d_n are less than the least of $i_1, \ldots, i_p$, i. e. the intervals of d_n are continued subdivisions of $i_1, \ldots, i_p$, except perhaps p of them containing the points of division of $i_1, \ldots, i_p$. For a subdivision of d_n containing a point of division of $i_1, \ldots, i_p$, $M_i - m_i < \epsilon$, while, for the remainder, $M_i - m_i < \epsilon/2$. Hence

$$S_n - s_n < \epsilon\,\Sigma[g(x_i) - g(x_{i-1})] = \epsilon[g(b) - g(a)],$$

which proves the statement for increasing $g(x)$.

If $g(x)$ is of bounded variation, $g(x) = g_1(x) - g_2(x)$, where both g_1 and g_2 are increasing functions. Thus, by the above reasoning, $f(x)$ is integrable with respect to g_1 and g_2 separately and so, by II, it is integrable with respect to their difference.

We are going to make use of the last result in the definition of line integrals.

If $C: x(t), y(t)$ is a path from $a: x(t_0), y(t_0)$ to $b: x(t), y(t)$, and $f(x, y)$ is a continuous function of the two variables along C, i.e. if $f[x(t), y(t)] = F(t)$ is continuous, we put

$$(4) \qquad \int_C f(x, y)\, dx = \int_{t_0}^{t} F(t)\, dx(t),$$

where the right-hand side is a Stieltjes integral. By IV and 51. I our hypotheses secure the existence of the Stieltjes integral in question. Generally we have two functions $f(x, y)$ and $g(x, y)$ given and we put

$$(5) \quad \int_C f(x, y)\, dx + g(x, y)\, dy$$

$$= \int_{t_0}^{t} f[x(t), y(t)]\, dx(t) + \int_{t_0}^{t} g[x(t), y(t)]\, dy(t).$$

For example,

$$\int_{t_0}^{t} dx(t) = \int_{t_0}^{t} dx_1(t) - \int_{t_0}^{t} dx_2(t)$$

where both $x_1(t)$ and $x_2(t)$ are increasing, and thus we have

$$(6) \quad \int_{t_0}^{t} dx(t) = x_1(t) - x_1(t_0) - [x_2(t) - x_2(t_0)] = x(t) - x(t_0).$$

Also

$$(7) \qquad \int_{t_0}^{t} x(t)\, dx(t) = \tfrac{1}{2}[x^2(t) - x^2(t_0)].$$

Proof.

$$\int_{t_0}^{t} x(t)\, dx(t)$$

$$= \lim_{n=\infty} \sum_{i=1}^{n} x(t_{i-1})\, [x(t_i) - x(t_{i-1})]$$

$$= \lim \Sigma x(t_i) [x(t_i) - x(t_{i-1})]$$

$$= \lim \tfrac{1}{2} \{\Sigma x(t_i) [x(t_i) - x(t_{i-1})] + \Sigma x(t_{i-1}) [x(t_i) - x(t_{i-1})]\}$$

$$= \lim \Sigma \tfrac{1}{2} [x^2(t_i) - x^2(t_{i-1})]$$

and, for increasing $x(t)$,

$$\Sigma \tfrac{1}{2} [x^2(t_i) - x^2(t_{i-1})] = \tfrac{1}{2}[x^2(t) - x^2(t_0)].$$

By II and III, the same result holds for any $x(t)$ of bounded variation.

CHAPTER VII

COMPLEX INTEGRATION

53. *Cauchy's fundamental theorem.* Putting $x(t)+iy(t)=z(t)$, a curve on the complex plane is represented by $z(t)$. Similarly, we put $dx(t)+idy(t)=dz(t)$. Hence, if $f(z)=P(x,y)+iQ(x,y)$, we define the integral of the uniform complex function $f(z)$ along a rectifiable Jordan curve C, when z describes C in the counter-clockwise direction, by putting

$$(1) \qquad \int_C f(z)dz = \int_C (P+iQ)\,d(x+iy)$$

$$= \int_C P(x,y)\,dx(t) - Q(x,y)\,dy(t) + i\int_C Q(x,y)dx(t) + P(x,y)\,dy(t).$$

Integration in the clockwise direction is indicated if necessary by $\int_{-C}$. Since the integrand is the same in each case and the signs of dx and dy are opposite,

$$\int_{-C} = -\int_C.$$

Thus equations (52. 6) and (52. 7) applied separately to the real and imaginary parts give

$$(2) \qquad \int_{t_0}^{t} dz = z(t) - z(t_0),$$

$$(3) \qquad \int_{t_0}^{t} zdz = \tfrac{1}{2}\left[z^2(t) - z^2(t_0)\right].$$

In particular if $z(t_0)$ and $z(t_1)$ coincide, we have *for closed curves*

$$(4) \qquad \int_C dz = 0, \quad \int_C zdz = 0.$$

The fundamental theorem of complex integration is a generalization of (4). For brevity, a rectifiable closed Jordan curve will be called a *simple contour.*

I. *Cauchy's fundamental theorem of complex integration. If $f(z)$ is uniform and differentiable at every point of a region R, limited by a simple contour C, then*

$$\int_C f(z)\,dz = 0. \qquad (5) \qquad \text{(Cauchy 1825, 1831 b, 1846)}$$

Proof. (Goursat, 1900.) Consider any point z of R and a point z' of R on a small square q centre at z. Since, by hypothesis, $f(z)$ is differentiable at z, if the side of this small square tends to 0, the expression $[f(z')-f(z)]/(z'-z)$ tends to $f'(z)$, i. e. there is a small square such that, for every z' of R on its side (or even in the square),

$$\left|\frac{f(z')-f(z)}{z'-z}-f'(z)\right|<\eta, \qquad (6)$$

where η is fixed beforehand. We can write this inequality in the form

$$[f(z')-f(z)]/(z'-z)=f'(z)+\epsilon,$$

where $|\epsilon|<\eta$.

Hence

$$f(z')=f(z)+z'f'(z)-zf'(z)+\epsilon z'-\epsilon z. \qquad (7)$$

To satisfy (6) at various points z, squares of different sizes must be taken. Imagine, however, that by parallels to the axes we subdivide a square containing C into equal squares. Some of the small squares may satisfy (6) for a conveniently chosen z in the square in question. If we continue the subdivision into equal squares, more and more squares will satisfy (6) for a convenient z always in the square in question; if a square reaches beyond C, we only retain the part contained in C and call the square irregular.

After a finite number of steps all the regular or irregular squares so obtained satisfy (6). In fact, if it were not so, there would be regular or irregular squares, each encasing the next, and dwindling to a point z with the property that, however far we go with the subdivision into squares, there are points z' in the square containing z for which (6) is not satisfied. But we have seen that there is a square, centre at z, such that (6) is satisfied. This contradiction establishes the remark. We denote the regular (complete) squares so obtained by $q_1, \dots, q_r$, and the irregular (incomplete) squares by $q'_1, \dots, q'_s$.

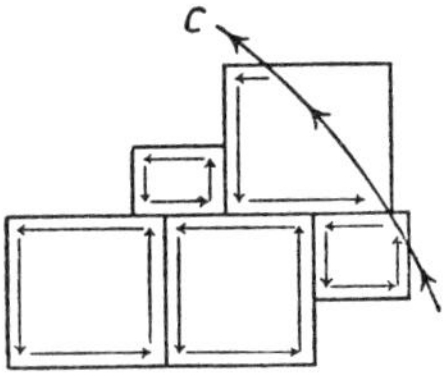

FIG. 36.

On the other hand, the integral along C can be replaced by the sum of integrals along $q_1, \dots, q_r$, and $q'_1, \dots, q'_s$, tne enclosed area lying always on our left. In fact all the integrals along straight segments cancel one another, because we integrate along every straight segment twice and in opposite directions so that, $f(z)$ being the same [$f(z)$ is supposed to be uniform in C] and dz being replaced by $-dz$ the second time, they destroy one another. Only the integrals along the arcs of C remain.

But, by (7) and (4),

$$\int_{q_i} f(z')dz' = f(z)\int_{q_i} dz' + f'(z)\int_{q_i} z'dz' - zf'(z)\int_{q_i} dz' + \int_{q_i} \epsilon(z'-z)dz' = \int_{q_i} \epsilon(z'-z)dz'.$$

Similarly

$$\int_{q'_i} f(z')dz' = \int_{q'_i} \epsilon(z'-z)dz'.$$

Hence

$$\left|\int_{q_i} f(z')dz'\right| < \eta\sqrt{2}l_i 4l_i = 4\eta\sqrt{2}a_i,$$

where l_i is the length of the side of q_i and a_i is its area. Similarly, denoting by L_i the length of C in q'_i (L_i may be much longer than the four sides of the complete square taken together) and by l'_i and a'_i the side and area of q'_i, we have

$$\left|\int_{q'_i} f(z')dz'\right| < \eta l'_i\sqrt{2}(4l'_i + L_i) = 4\eta\sqrt{2}a'_i + \eta l'_i\sqrt{2}L_i.$$

Adding all the integrals along regular and irregular squares, we obtain

$$\left|\int_C f(z')dz'\right| < \eta[4\sqrt{2}(\Sigma a_i + \Sigma a'_i) + \lambda\sqrt{2}L],$$

where λ is the side of the square containing C and L is the total length of C. As $\Sigma a_i + \Sigma a_i'$ is less than the area A of the first square containing C, we obtain

$$\left| \int_C f(z') dz' \right| < B\eta,$$

where B is independent of the subdivision. As η is arbitrarily small, the left-hand side is 0. Q.e.d.

When the function $f(z)$ is not defined (or not known) beyond C, the condition that $f(z)$ is differentiable at the points of C has no clear meaning. The theorem however remains true, i.e. $\int_C f(z) dz = 0$, where $f(z)$ is uniform and differentiable in the domain D enclosed by C and is continuous in the complete region $R = D + C$.

We establish this result only for contours C starlike with respect to an inner point c, i.e. when every radius vector from c meets C at a single point. In such a case, when z describes C, $c + \theta(z-c)$, $0 < \theta < 1$, describes a contour C' entirely inside C and

$$\int_C f(z) dz - \int_{C'} f(z) dz = \int_C \{f(z) - \theta f[z-(z-c)(1-\theta)]\} dz.$$

The integrand equals

$$f(z) - f[z-(z-c)(1-\theta)] + (1-\theta) f[z-(z-c)(1-\theta)]$$

whose modulus can be made $< \epsilon$ by choosing θ sufficiently near 1.

As $\int_{C'} f(z) dz = 0$, it follows that

$$\left| \int_C f(z) dz \right| < \epsilon L,$$

where L is the length of C. Since the left-hand side is a determinate positive number or zero and the right-hand side is as small as we please, the result is established.

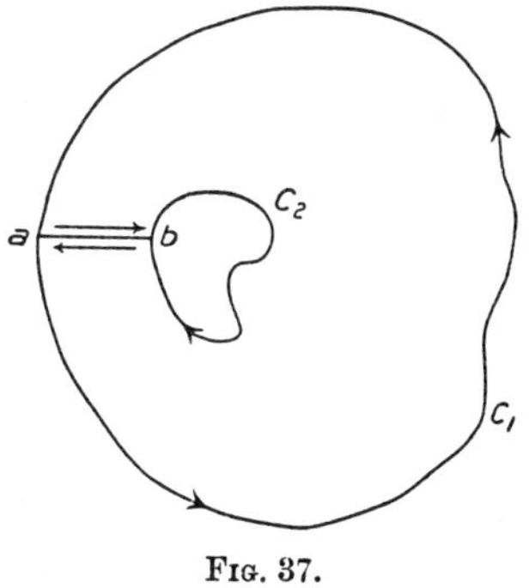

FIG. 37.

The fundamental theorem readily extends to domains limited by several contours like C. For example, consider the domain inside C_1 and outside C_2. Joining C_1 and C_2 by a rectifiable curve (straight segment if possible), we have by the fundamental theorem

$$\int_{C_1} f(z)\,dz + \int_a^b - \int_{C_2} + \int_b^a = 0.$$

As

$$\int_a^b + \int_b^a = 0,$$

we obtain

$$\int_{C_1} f(z)\,dz - \int_{C_2} f(z)\,dz = 0.$$

More generally

II. *If D is a finite domain limited by a finite number of simple contours, $C_1, \dots C_p$, and $f(z)$ is uniform and differentiable in the region $D + C_1 + \dots + C_p$, the integral of $f(z)$ along the whole contour of D is* 0 (the area D lying always on the left when we proceed along the contour).

Since, taken along the same curve, $\int_a^b = -\int_b^a$, the above result leads to

III. *If $f(z)$ is uniform and differentiable in a simply connected domain D, the value of the integral*

$$I(z) = \int_a^z f(z)\,dz$$

is independent of the path c followed from a to z in D, i.e. *$I(z)$ is a uniform function of the upper limit of integration.*

Proof. Since, by hypothesis, c has only a finite number of loops, all limited by simple contours, the same is true of c continued by another path c' from z to a. The result follows by applying I to the simple contours making up $c + c'$.

The above result is sometimes stated in the following form:

IV. *If we deform the path C leading from a to z in such a way that, in the area swept over, $f(z)$ is uniform and differentiable at every point, the value of $\int f(z)\,dz$ is not altered, i.e. is the same for all the paths considered.*

By *deformation* of C we simply mean choosing another rectifiable curve between a and z.

54. *Cauchy's fundamental formula.* Apply 53. II to the function $f(z)/(z-x)$, where x is a fixed inner point of the domain D enclosed by C. Since, at $z = x$, the function is not differentiable, (it is not even continuous), we have to exclude x from D by a small circle c entirely in D. We shall denote by C the complete contour of D, consisting of a finite number of simple contours. Joining c to a point of C (see Fig. 38) and integrating along

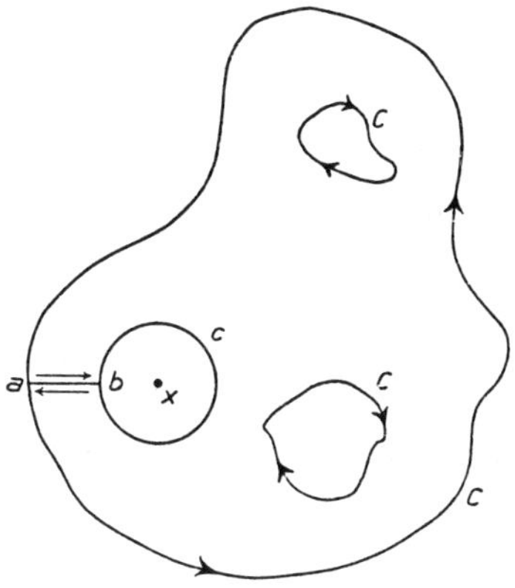

FIG. 38.

$$C + (a, b) - c + (b, a),$$

we see as before that, since the integrand is uniform in D, the integrals from a to b and from b to a cancel one another. By 53. II we have thus

$$(1) \qquad \int_{C-c} \frac{f(z)}{z-x}\, dz = 0,$$

i. e.

$$(2) \qquad \int_C \frac{f(z)dz}{z-x} = \int_c \frac{f(z)dz}{z-x}.$$

To evaluate the right-hand side we put $z - x = re^{i\alpha}$. Thus $dz = ire^{i\alpha}d\alpha = i(z-x)d\alpha$. Hence,

$$(3) \qquad \int_c \frac{f(z)dz}{z-x} = i\int_0^{2\pi} f(x+re^{i\alpha})\,d\alpha.$$

This is true for every sufficiently small value of r and the left-hand side is independent of r. But $f(z)$ is by hypothesis continuous at $z = x$, i. e. for $|z-x| = r$ sufficiently small, $< \delta$, say, we have $f(x+re^{i\alpha}) = f(x) + \epsilon(r, \alpha)$, where $|\epsilon(r, \alpha)| < \epsilon$ (fixed arbitrarily), when $r < \delta$. Hence

$$\int_0^{2\pi} f(x+re^{i\alpha})\,d\alpha = f(x)\int_0^{2\pi} d\alpha + \int_0^{2\pi} \epsilon(r, \alpha)\,d\alpha,$$

and, for $r < \delta$,

$$\left|\int_0^{2\pi} \epsilon(r, \alpha)\,d\alpha\right| \leqslant \epsilon \int_0^{2\pi} d\alpha = 2\pi\epsilon,$$

which proves that the right-hand side of (3) tends to $2\pi if(x)$ as $r \to 0$. Since this is also the value of the left-hand side,

$$(4) \qquad f(x) = \frac{1}{2\pi i}\int_C \frac{f(z)\,dz}{z-x}.$$

This is Cauchy's fundamental formula. The value of the uniform function $f(z)$ at an inner point is expressed in terms of its values along the boundary of a domain in which and on the boundary of which $f(z)$ is differentiable. Moreover, by III, we can replace C by other rectifiable closed contours in D, enclosing x and only points of D, without altering the value of the integral. This freedom in the choice of contours gives a great flexibility to complex integrals.

By our remark on the generalization of the fundamental theorem, formula (4) remains valid when $f(z)$ is uniform and differentiable in D (but not necessarily on C) and continuous in $D+C$.

Another interesting feature of (4) is that, if x is outside C, the integrand is uniform and differentiable in C, i.e. by the fundamental theorem the integral vanishes. *Thus the integral on the right-hand side represents $f(x)$ inside C and the function* 0 *outside C.*

If C is a circle $|z| = R$ and $f(z)$ is uniform and differentiable in $|z| < R$ and continuous in $|z| \leqslant R$, we put $z = Re^{i\phi}$, $x = re^{i\psi}$, so that (4) assumes the form

$$f(z) = \frac{1}{2\pi}\int_0^{2\pi} f(Re^{i\phi})\frac{Re^{i\phi}\,d\phi}{Re^{i\phi}-re^{i\psi}}.$$

Take the point $z' = R^2e^{i\psi}/r$ outside $|z| = R$. Since $f(z)/(z-z')$ is regular in $|z| = R$,

$$0 = \frac{1}{2\pi}\int_0^{2\pi} f(Re^{i\phi})\frac{Re^{i\phi}\,d\phi}{Re^{i\phi}-\dfrac{R^2}{r}e^{i\psi}}$$

$$= \frac{1}{2\pi}\int_0^{2\pi} f(Re^{i\phi})\frac{re^{i\phi}\,d\phi}{re^{i\phi}-Re^{i\psi}}.$$

Subtracting the last equation from the first and noticing that

$$\frac{Re^{i\phi}}{Re^{i\phi}-re^{i\psi}} - \frac{re^{i\phi}}{re^{i\phi}-Re^{i\psi}} = \frac{R^2-r^2}{R^2-2Rr\cos(\phi-\psi)+r^2},$$

we obtain *Poisson's formula*:

$$(5)\quad f(z)=\frac{1}{2\pi}\int_0^{2\pi} f(Re^{i\phi})\frac{R^2-r^2}{R^2+r^2-2Rr\cos(\phi-\psi)}\,d\phi.$$

Applying (4) also to the point $x+\Delta x$ we see that

$$\frac{f(x+\Delta x)-f(x)}{\Delta x}=\frac{1}{2\pi i}\int_C\frac{f(z)dz}{(z-x)(z-x-\Delta x)}$$

$$=\frac{1}{2\pi i}\int_C\frac{f(z)dz}{(z-x)^2}+\frac{1}{2\pi i}\int_C\frac{\Delta x f(z)dz}{(z-x)^2(z-x-\Delta x)}.$$

Hence, if M is the upper bound of $|f(z)|$ along C, L the length of C and δ is less than the lower bound of $|z-x|$ along C, the second integral, for sufficiently small Δx, is $<ML|\Delta x|/\delta^3$, so that it tends to 0 with $|\Delta x|$. Thus

$$(6)\qquad f'(x)=\frac{1}{2\pi i}\int_C\frac{f(z)dz}{(z-x)^2},$$

i.e. the differentiation under the sign of integration with respect to the parameter x leads to the differential coefficient of the integral as a function of the parameter.

But, what is much more remarkable, the same reasoning applies to the new integral and proves that

$$f''(x)=\frac{2!}{2\pi i}\int_C\frac{f(z)dz}{(z-x)^3}$$

exists and so on. Thus

$$(7)\qquad f^{(n)}(x)=\frac{n!}{2\pi i}\int_C\frac{f(z)dz}{(z-x)^{n+1}}.$$

Hence the theorem

I. *If $f(z)$ is uniform and differentiable in a domain D without any restriction on its boundary, it is indefinitely differentiable in the same domain. The successive differential coefficients are given by* (7), *where C is any simple contour in D enclosing x and only points of D.*

Proof. Apply the above reasoning to the contour C.

This is one of the most curious facts in function theory. It shows that differentiability in two dimensions is a very strong condition, since it requires the existence of a unique limit for $[f(z+\Delta z)-f(z)]/\Delta z$ as Δz approaches 0 *in any manner.*

The reasoning leading to (6) applies word for word in the case of the function

$$\int_C \frac{f(z)\,dz}{z-x} = F(x), \tag{8}$$

where C is any rectifiable curve, closed or not, and $f(z)$ is uniform and continuous along C. It is sufficient that $f(z)$ be defined only along C. Thus we see that

II. *If $f(z)$ is uniform and continuous but not necessarily differentiable along the open or closed rectifiable curve C, the integral* (8) *determines an obviously uniform function $F(x)$ differentiable for every value of x except perhaps the points of C. Moreover,*

$$F^{(n)}(x) = n!\int_C \frac{f(z)\,dz}{(z-x)^{n+1}}. \tag{9}$$

The same reasoning leads to *the rule of differentiation under the sign of integration*:

III. *If the uniform function $f(z, x)$ is differentiable in x and continuous in z as x varies in D and z varies along a rectifiable curve L, the function*

$$\int_L f(z, x)\,dz = g(x)$$

is differentiable in D and

$$g'(x) = \int_L \frac{\partial f}{\partial x}\,dz.$$

Proof. If c is a circle in D of radius R centre x, we have

$$f(z, x) = \frac{1}{2\pi i}\int_c \frac{f(z, z')\,dz'}{z'-x},$$

i. e.

$$g(x) = \frac{1}{2\pi i}\int_L dz \int_c \frac{f(z, z')\,dz'}{z'-x}.$$

Similarly,

$$g(x+\Delta x) = \frac{1}{2\pi i}\int_L dz \int_c \frac{f(z, z')\,dz'}{z'-x-\Delta x}$$

i. e.

$$\frac{g(x+\Delta x)-g(x)}{\Delta x} = \frac{1}{2\pi i}\int_L dz \int_c \frac{f(z, z')\,dz'}{(z'-x)^2}$$

$$+\frac{\Delta x}{2\pi i}\int_L dz \int_c \frac{f(z, z')\,dz'}{(z'-x)^2\,(z'-x-\Delta x)}.$$

If M is the maximum modulus of $f(z, z')$ when z and z' describe L and c respectively, l the length of L, $\rho = |\Delta x|$, the modulus of the second integral is less than

$$\frac{\rho}{2\pi} \frac{M}{R^2(R-\rho)} 2\pi R l = \frac{\rho M l}{R(R-\rho)} \to 0 \text{ with } \rho.$$

Thus

$$g'(x) = \frac{1}{2\pi i} \int_L dz \int_c \frac{f(z, z')\, dz'}{(z'-x)^2} = \int_L \frac{\partial f}{\partial x}\, dz.$$

Q. e. d.

We are now going to apply our general results to series of uniform and differentiable functions.

IV. *Suppose the functions $f_n(z, z')$ are all continuous and the series*

$$\sum_{n=1}^{\infty} f_n(z, z') = F(z, z')$$

is uniformly convergent when z is on the rectifiable curve C and z' is in the region R' of z'. Then

$$\sum_{n=1}^{\infty} \int_C f_n(z, z')\, dz = \int_C F(z, z')\, dz,$$

i. e. term-by-term integration is legitimate, and the integrated series converges uniformly.

Proof. Putting $F(z, z') = s_n(z, z') + R_n(z, z')$, where $s_n(z, z')$ is the sum of the first n terms, we have, by hypothesis, for every suffix n after a certain N, $|R_n(z, z')| < \epsilon$ along C, with z' in R', i.e., if L is the length of C,

$$\left| \int_C R_n(z, z')\, dz \right| < \epsilon L.$$

Hence

$$\left| \int_C F(z, z')\, dz - \int_C f_1(z, z')\, dz - \dots - \int_C f_n(z, z')\, dz \right| < \epsilon L,$$

which proves the proposition.

As uniform functions, differentiable in a domain D limited by a simple contour C, are in general determined by their boundary values, we shall see that uniform convergence in any region R of D follows from the uniform convergence along C.

V. *Suppose D is a domain enclosed by the simple contour C,* *the functions* $f_n(z)$ *are all uniform and differentiable in* D *and continuous in* $D+C$, *and the series*

$$\sum_{n=1}^{\infty} f_n(z) = F(z)$$

is uniformly convergent on C. *Then*

$$\sum_{n=1}^{\infty} f_n(z)$$

converges uniformly in any region R *of* D, *its sum function* $F(z)$ *is uniform and differentiable in* D *and*

$$F^{(k)}(z) = \sum_{n=1}^{\infty} f_n^{(k)}(z),$$

i.e. term-by-term differentiation is legitimate.

Proof. Since, by 27. III, $F(x)$ is continuous on C, the integral

$$G(x) = \frac{1}{2\pi i}\int_C \frac{F(z)\,dz}{z-x}$$

is, by II, a uniform function of x, differentiable at every point of D, and its k-th derivative is given by

$$G^{(k)}(x) = \frac{k!}{2\pi i}\int_C \frac{F(z)\,dz}{(z-x)^{k+1}}.$$

But if x varies in R and z on C and $\delta > 0$ is the shortest distance between R and C, we have $|z-x| \geqslant \delta$ and, from the hypotheses, the series

$$\sum_{n=1}^{\infty} \frac{f_n(z)}{z-x} = \frac{F(z)}{z-x} \quad \text{and} \quad \sum_{n=1}^{\infty} \frac{f_n(z)}{(z-x)^{k+1}} = \frac{F(z)}{(z-x)^{k+1}}$$

are uniformly convergent *on* C. Therefore, by IV and by the fundamental formula,

$$G(x) = \sum_{n=1}^{\infty} \frac{1}{2\pi i}\int_C \frac{f_n(z)\,dz}{z-x} = \sum_{n=1}^{\infty} f_n(x) = F(x),$$

where the series $\sum_{n=1}^{\infty} f_n(x)$ converges uniformly in R to a function, $G(x) = F(x)$, differentiable in D. Similarly

$$F^{(k)}(x) = G^{(k)}(x) = \sum_{n=1}^{\infty} \frac{k!}{2\pi i}\int_C \frac{f_n(z)\,dz}{(z-x)^{k+1}} = \sum_{n=1}^{\infty} f_n^{(k)}(x).$$

Q. e. d.

A simple consequence of this result is the following theorem, valid for quite general domains with any kind of boundary.

VI. *Suppose the functions* $f_n(z)$ *are uniform and differable in a domain* D *and* $\Sigma f_n(z) = F(z)$ *is uniformly convergent in every region of* D. *Then* $F(z)$ *is regular in* D *and*

$$F^{(k)}(z) = \Sigma f_n^{(k)}(z).$$

(Weierstrass.)

Proof. z being a point of D we apply V to a circle about z.

55. *Differential coefficient of the indefinite integral.* Consider a general domain D and a rectifiable curve c leading, in D, from a to z, and suppose that $f(z)$ is uniform and differentiable in D. The value of the integral

$$(1) \qquad F(z) = \int_a^z f(z)dz,$$

depends, in general, on the path c leading from a to z in D, so that $F(z)$ is in general a multiform function. Since differentiation has been defined only for uniform functions, we have to specify a uniform branch of $F(z)$.

A function $\phi(z)$, uniform and differentiable (therefore also continuous) in a domain Δ is said to be a *branch* of the multiform function $F(z)$ if, at every point z of Δ, $\phi(z)$ is equal to one of the values of $F(z)$ attached to that point z. As a rule, a branch is only defined in a simply connected domain Δ.

In our case we specify the branch of $F(z)$ as follows. We fix any point z_0 of c and consider a circle K, $|z-z_0| \leqslant \rho$, within D. Since the integrand $f(z)$ is uniform and differentiable in K, the value of its integral, by 53. III, does not depend on the way we produce c in k from z_0 to any point z_0+h in K. We choose for the path the straight segment from z_0 to z_0+h. Thus

$$F(z_0+h)-F(z_0) = \int_a^{z_0+h} f(z)dz - \int_a^{z_0} f(z)dz = \int_{z_0}^{z_0+h} f(z)dz.$$

Since by hypothesis $f(z)$ is continuous in the neighbourhood of z_0, we can take $|h|$ so small, $< \eta$, say, that $|f(z_0+\theta h)-f(z_0)| < \epsilon$ for every positive $\theta \leqslant 1$. Thus the functional values entering the integral are of the form $f(z_0)+\epsilon(z)$ where, between z_0 and z_0+h (on the segment), $|\epsilon(z)| < \epsilon$. Hence

$$\int_{z_0}^{z_0+h} f(z)dz = f(z_0)h + \int_{z_0}^{z_0+h} \epsilon(z)dz,$$

i. e. $$\left|\frac{F(z_0+h)-F(z_0)}{h}-f(z_0)\right| \leqslant \frac{1}{|h|}\left|\int_{z_0}^{z_0+h} \epsilon(z)dz\right| \leqslant \epsilon.$$

As ϵ is arbitrary, we see that $F(z)$ is a differentiable function at z_0 and its differential coefficient is $f(z_0)$:

I. *If $f(z)$ is uniform and differentiable in a domain D, every branch of the function* (1), *specified in a domain Δ of D by a rectifiable curve c in D, is at every point of Δ a differentiable function of the upper limit of integration and $F'(z) = f(z)$.*

By 39. III, if $G(z)$ is a primitive of $f(z)$, $G(z) = F(z) + \text{const.}$ It follows, as usual, that

$$(2) \qquad {}_{(c)}\int_a^z f(z)dz = G(z) - G(a),$$

provided we follow the change of G, if it is multiform, along c, i. e. if we mean by $G(z)$ the value of G at z obtained along c.

For example, we know that $(\log z)' = 1/z$. But $\log z$ is not differentiable at the origin. Thus we have to consider a domain excluding the origin, e. g. a ring domain about the origin.

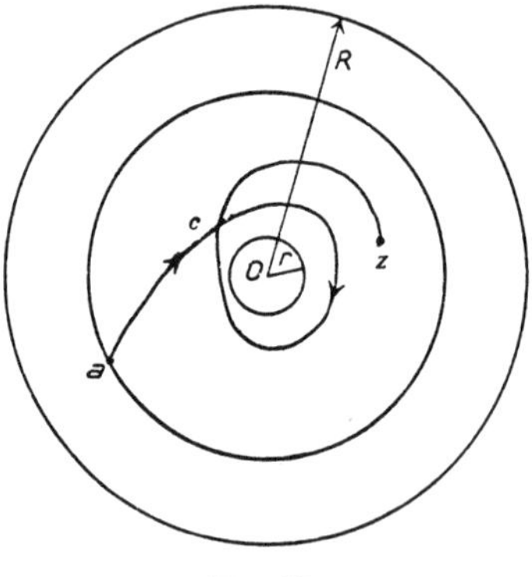

FIG. 39.

By (2) (see figure for c), we have

$$(3) \qquad {}_{(c)}\int_a^z dz/z = \log z - \log a,$$

so that we might believe that

$$\int_c dz/z = \log a - \log a = 0.$$

We are going to show that this is incorrect. To evaluate this integral directly, we take a circle about the origin, of radius $|a|$, and put $z = |a|e^{i\alpha}$, i. e. $dz = |a|ie^{i\alpha}d\alpha$,

$$\int_c dz/z = i\int_0^{2\pi} d\alpha = 2\pi i,$$

i.e. not zero (though it is a closed path). If we turn twice about the origin we obtain the same integral twice, and so on, and in the opposite direction $-2\pi i$.

More generally

$$(4) \qquad {}_{(c)}\int_a^z f'(z)\,dz/f(z) = \log f(z) - \log f(a),$$

provided $\log f(z)$ means the value of $\log f(z)$ obtained along c (from a).

As an example we have for any real or complex $m \neq -1$

$$\int_a^z z^m dz = (z^{m+1} - a^{m+1})/(m+1).$$

If m is an integer, $\int_c z^m dz = 0$. But if m is not an integer, the meaning of z^{m+1} is given by $e^{(m+1)\log z}$, which is a multiform function. Thus the result depends on how many times we turn about the origin, which is again a branch point of the function.

With this proviso, the formula (2) can be used very much as in the real calculus.

Theorem I leads to the inversion of Cauchy's fundamental theorem.

II. *If $f(z)$ is continuous in a domain D and $\int_c f(z)dz = 0$ for any simple contour in D, then $f(z)$ is differentiable in D.*

(Morera, 1902.)

Proof. By hypothesis

$$F(z) = \int_a^z f(z)\,dz$$

is, in D, independent of the path, i. e. $F(z)$ is a uniform function. Hence, by an argument identical with that used in I, we see that $F'(z)$ exists and equals $f(z)$. It follows, by 54. I, that $f(z)$, being the differential coefficient of a uniform function, is itself differentiable.

III. *Partial integration.*

$$(5) \qquad \int_C f' g\,dz + \int_C f g'\,dz = [fg]_C,$$

where $[F]_C$ means the difference between the value of F at the end of C, arrived at along C, and its value at the initial point of C, whether C is closed or not.

Proof. A primitive of $f'g + fg'$ is fg, Hence the result by I.

IV. *Darboux's mean value theorem.* *If $g(z)$ is continuous along the straight segment between a and b, $|a|<|b|$, and $f(r)$ is real and positive for $|a| \leq r \leq |b|$, we have, if $|z| = r$,*

$$(6) \qquad \int_a^b f(r) g(z) dz = \lambda g(\xi) \int_a^b f(r) |dz|, \quad |\lambda| \leq 1.$$

where on the left-hand side we integrate along the straight segment between a and b and ξ is a number of this segment.

Proof. Denoting the left-hand side by I, we have obviously

$$(7) \qquad |I| \leq \int_a^b f(r) |g(z)| |dz|.$$

Applying the ordinary mean value theorem of the integral calculus to the real integral on the right-hand side of (7) we obtain

$$\int_a^b f(r) |g(z)| |dz| = |g(\xi)| \int_a^b f(r) |dz|,$$

which establishes the theorem.

If $f(r) \equiv 1$, we obtain in particular

$$(8) \qquad \int_a^b g(z) dz = \lambda (b-a) g(\xi).$$

When $g(z)$ is the derivative of $F(z)$, the left-hand side is $F(b)-F(a)$, i. e.

$$(9) \qquad F(b)-F(a) = \lambda |b-a| F'(\xi), \quad |\lambda| \leq 1,$$

which exactly corresponds to the mean value theorem of the real differential calculus.

56. *Taylor and Laurent series.* We have seen that if $f(z)$ is uniform and differentiable in a two-dimensional domain, $f(z)$ is indefinitely differentiable in the same domain. We are going to prove that the Taylor expansion of $f(z)$ about any inner point a is a convergent series, and represents $f(z)$ in a circle about a. In such a case we shall say that $f(z)$ is *regular* (or *holomorphic*) at a.

I. *If $f(z)$ is uniform and differentiable in a domain D and a is any point of D, then, in a sufficiently small circle about a,*

$$(1) \qquad f(z) = \Sigma f^{(n)}(a) (z-a)^n / n!$$

i.e. $f(z)$ is regular at every point of D. (Cauchy 1831 a.)

Proof. We take a circle c of radius R, centre a, throughout which, circumference included, $f(z)$ is uniform and differentiable. By the fundamental formula

(2) $$f(x) = \frac{1}{2\pi i}\int_c \frac{f(z)\,dz}{z-x}.$$

Putting

$$\frac{1}{z-x} = \frac{1}{z-a-(x-a)} = \sum \frac{(x-a)^n}{(z-a)^{n+1}},$$

the last series, multiplied by $f(z)$, is uniformly convergent when z is on c and $|x-a| < R' < R$. Hence, by 54. IV,

$$f(x) = \Sigma\, a_n (x-a)^n,$$

where

(3) $$a_n = \frac{1}{2\pi i}\int_c \frac{f(z)\,dz}{(z-a)^{n+1}}, \quad n = 0, 1, \ldots$$

and, by 54. I, $a_n = f^{(n)}(a)/n!$

Thus, *for complex functions, 'uniform and differentiable' in any small neighbourhood of a point and 'regular' at that point are equivalent expressions.*

It follows from (3) that

(4) $$|a_n| \leqslant M/R^n,$$

where M is the maximum modulus of $f(z)$ in $|z-a| \leqslant R$.

Consider now the ring domain D between the concentric circles c_1 and c_2 (of radius ρ and $r < \rho$ respectively), centre a, and suppose that $f(z)$ is uniform and differentiable in and on the boundary of D. If x is any point of D, we have, by the fundamental formula,

$$f(x) = \frac{1}{2\pi i}\int_{c_1} \frac{f(z)\,dz}{z-x} - \frac{1}{2\pi i}\int_{c_2} \frac{f(z)\,dz}{z-x}.$$

We apply the preceding reasoning to the first integral and obtain

$$\frac{1}{2\pi i}\int_{c_1} \frac{f(z)\,dz}{z-x} = \Sigma a_n (x-a)^n,$$

convergent when x is in c_1. To evaluate the second integral we write

$$\frac{1}{x-z} = \sum \frac{(z-a)^n}{(x-a)^{n+1}},$$

uniformly convergent when z is on c_2 and $|x-a| > r' > r$, i. e. x is outside c_2.

Thus, by 54. IV, we obtain *Laurent's expansion* (1843) in the ring domain

$$(5) \qquad f(x) = \sum_0^\infty A_n (x-a)^n + \sum_1^\infty B_n (x-a)^{-n},$$

where

$$(6) \quad A_n = \frac{1}{2\pi i} \int_{c_1} \frac{f(z)dz}{(z-a)^{n+1}}, \quad B_n = \frac{1}{2\pi i} \int_{c_2} f(z)(z-a)^{n-1} dz.$$

If $f(z)$ is uniform and regular in c_1, except at its centre a, the expansion (5) is valid for every ring domain in c_1 excluding the point a, i. e. is valid in c_1 except at a itself.

In this case, (a) if the second series, called the *principal part* of Laurent's expansion at a, consists of a finite number of terms (the greatest negative index of $x-a$ being k), we say that the point a is a *pole* of $f(z)$ of order k, (b) if the principal part contains infinitely many non-vanishing coefficients, a is said to be an *essential point* of $f(z)$.

We notice also that

$$(7) \qquad |A_n| < M/\rho^n \text{ and } |B_n| < M' r^n.$$

It follows that the regular part of Laurent's expansion converges at least in c_1. Similarly the principal part converges for every x outside c_2. If $f(x)$ is regular in c_1 except at a, we can take for c_2 any small circle about a, i. e. in this case the principal part converges for every value of $x \neq a$.

The inequalities (4) are logically more general than the apparently identical inequalities (40. 3). In fact (4) simply follows from the fact that $f(z)$ is uniform and differentiable in $|z-a| \leqslant R$ whereas we established (40. 3) by assuming that the function is given by one and the same Taylor series throughout the whole circle in question. In reality, however, this logical difference in their generality does not exist, as is shown by the following important consequence of (4).

II. *If the radius of convergence r of $\Sigma a_n(z-a)^n = f(z)$ is finite, there is a direction in which $f(z)$ cannot be continued beyond the circle of radius r.* In other words $f(z)$ has a *singular point* (Art. 61) on the circumference of its circle of convergence.

Proof. Suppose that the theorem is not true for a function $f(z)$. This means that every point of the circumference $|z| = r$ is an inner point of a circle with centre at some inner point of the circle $|z| < r$. Thus by Borel's lemma there are a finite number of these overlapping circles covering the whole circumference and it follows that there is a circle c' of radius $r' > r$ in which the function is regular, i. e. in (3) we can replace c by c' without altering the value of the integral. Then, by (4), we should have for every n

$$(8) \qquad |a_n| < M/r'^n.$$

But the radius of convergence r of $\Sigma a_n(z-a)^n$ is defined as the reciprocal of the greatest limiting number of $|\sqrt[n]{a}|$, i. e. for every $r' > r$ there are infinitely many suffixes n such that $|a_n| > 1/r'^n$. This shows that (8) is impossible. We can formulate our result by saying that *the convergence of a Taylor series $\Sigma a_n(z-a)^n$ is stopped only by the nearest singular point to $z = a$.* Thus it follows from the regularity in the circle $|z-a| = r$ that the function is given by one and same Taylor series in the whole circle.

This result leads to an interesting remark due to Poincaré and Volterra (independently). To exhaust all possible ways of continuation of a Taylor series we have to consider its expansions about *every* inner point of its circle of convergence. Denote by D_1 the united domain of all the open circles thus obtained. Thus if z is an inner point of D_1, there is a circle about the point a, say, of the original circle of convergence, containing z. Now, there are points as near to a as we please with rational coordinates (rational points). As the distance between the singular points and a is a continuous function of a (see Art. 11), the radius of convergence varies continuously when a varies. Therefore there is a point b near a such that the circle of convergence about b contains z. We see thus that for the complete analytic continuation of a given Taylor series, it is sufficient to consider expansions about rational points. Since the same remark applies to the continuation beyond D_1, if this is possible, and since, by definition, the complete analytic continuation consists of all the continuations obtained by a finite but arbitrary number of similar steps, we see that

III. *At any fixed point of the complex plane an analytic function assumes only an enumerable set of values.*

(Poincaré, 1888. Volterra, 1888.)

57. *Test for singular points on the circle of convergence. Non-continued Taylor series.* When $c = a + re^{i\alpha}$ is a point inside the circle of convergence of $\Sigma a_n (z-a)^n$, of radius R, the continuation along the radius ac is possible if and only if the radius of convergence of the expansion about c is greater than $R-r$, i.e. if for every ϵ there is an N such that for $n > N$,

$$(1)\qquad |a_n + C_1^{n+1} a_{n+1} re^{i\alpha} + \ldots$$
$$+ C_p^{n+p} a_{n+p} r^p e^{ip\alpha} + \ldots | < \left(\frac{1-\epsilon}{R-r}\right)^n.$$

Similarly $\Sigma a_n (z-a)^n$ cannot be continued along ac if for every ϵ there are infinitely many suffixes n such that

$$(2)\qquad |a_n + C_1^{n+1} a_{n+1} re^{i\alpha} + \ldots$$
$$+ C_p^{n+p} a_{n+p} r^p e^{ip\alpha} + \ldots | > \left(\frac{1-\epsilon}{R-r}\right)^n.$$

We shall apply this test to the case in which all the coefficients after a certain suffix are positive, and for simplicity's sake we put $a = 0$.

I. *If, after a certain suffix, a_n is real and $\geqslant 0$, then $z = R$ is a singular point of $\Sigma a_n z^n$,* R being the radius of convergence of the latter series. (Vivanti, 1893.)

Proof. If $f(z)$ can be continued along the real axis, then $z = R$ is an inner point of an expansion about $z = r < R$, so that there is no singular point in the vicinity of the point $z = R$. Thus all the Taylor expansions about points on the real axis between 0 and R contain $z = R$ as an inner point. In particular, the expansion about $z = R/2$ contains $z = R$ and $z = 0$ as inner points. Thus there is a point $R + \eta$ on the real axis beyond $z = R$ for which

$$(3)\qquad \sum_0^\infty \left[a_n + C^{n+1} a_{n+1} \frac{R}{2} + \ldots\right.$$
$$\left. + C_p^{n+p} a_{n+p} \left(\frac{R}{2}\right)^p + \ldots\right] (R/2 + \eta)^n$$

is convergent. Since all but a finite number of the terms are positive, the double series is absolutely convergent and thus we can rearrange it at will. Fixing the value of $n + p = m$, and collecting the terms containing $a_{n+p} = a_m$, we obtain for the coefficient of a_m

$$\sum_{p=0}^m C_p^m (R/2 + \eta)^{m-p} (R/2)^p = (R/2 + \eta + R/2)^m.$$

Hence $\Sigma a_m (R+\eta)^m$ would be convergent, which is absurd, for the original series diverges outside $|z| = R$.

The result also extends to certain series with complex coefficients.

II. *If, after a certain suffix, the argument of a_n is between $-\alpha$ and $\alpha < \pi/2$, $z = R$ is a singular point of $\Sigma a_n z^n$.*

(Dienes, 1909 c.)

Proof. If $a_n = \alpha_n + i\beta_n$, we have $|a_n| < \alpha_n \sec\alpha$. Hence the absolute convergence of $\Sigma a_n x^n$ $(x > 0)$ follows from its convergence and thus the rearrangement is valid. The proof follows as before.

Consider now the series $f(z) = \Sigma a^n z^{b^n}$ (Weierstrass), where $a > 0$ and b is an integer > 1. Since $\lim a^{n/b^n} = 1$, the radius of convergence is 1, and by I, $z = 1$ is a singular point. Putting

$$f_m(z) = \sum_{n=m}^{\infty} a^n z^{b^n},$$

the difference $f - f_m$ is a polynomial, i.e. regular at every finite point, in particular at $z = 1$. It follows that 1 is singular also for $f_m(z)$. On the other hand $f_m(ze^{2\pi i h/b^m}) = f_m(z)$ for any integer h, i.e. $f_m(z)$ is reproduced along the radii with the arguments $0, 2\pi/b^m, 4\pi/b^m, \ldots, (b^m - 1)\,2\pi/b^m$. Therefore all the points of $|z| = 1$ with these arguments are singular points for $f_m(z)$. But $f - f_m$ being regular, any singular point of $f_m(z)$ is also singular for $f(z)$, i.e. all the points of $|z| = 1$ with arguments $h\,2\pi/b^m$, where h and m are any integers, are singular points of $f(z)$. They lie everywhere dense on the circumference, stopping the continuation of $f(z)$ along every radius, for a regular point on the circle would be separated, by a finite arc, from all the singular points on the circle. Thus, *there are Taylor series which cannot be continued beyond the original circle of convergence.* The circle of convergence is a *singular line* of the function.

The simplification of the tests (1) and (2) leads to the determination of quite a large class of Taylor series for which the circle of convergence is a singular line.

For simplicity, we assume that the radius of convergence $R = 1$. As the series on the left-hand side of (1) is convergent, the remainder from a certain term on, varying with r and n, is small. We shall make use of this fact, in order to reduce the infinity of terms to a finite number, in the following way.

If $\overline{\lim}_{n=\infty} |\sqrt[n]{B_n}| < \overline{\lim}_{n=\infty} |\sqrt[n]{A_n}|$, then

(4) $$\overline{\lim}_{n=\infty} |\sqrt[n]{A_n + B_n}| = \overline{\lim}_{n=\infty} |\sqrt[n]{A_n}|.$$

For, by 56. II, since the radius of convergence of $\Sigma A_n z^n$ is less than that of $\Sigma B_n z^n$, the radius of convergence of $\Sigma (A_n + B_n) z^n$ is equal to that of $\Sigma A_n z^n$.

If n and k are positive integers,

(5) $$\frac{(n+k)^{n+k}}{(n+k+1)\,n^n k^k} < C_k^{n+k} < \frac{(n+k)^{n+k}}{n^n k^k}.$$

For, writing

$$(n+k)^{n+k} = \sum_{i=0}^{n+k} C_i^{n+k} n^{n+k-i} k^i = \sum_{i=0}^{n+k} I_i,$$

we have $$\frac{I_i}{I_{i-1}} = \frac{n+k-i+1}{i} \cdot \frac{k}{n} > \text{ or } < 1$$

according as $i \leqslant$ or $> k$. Hence $C_k^{n+k} n^n k^k$ is the greatest of the $(n+k+1)$ terms and (5) follows immediately.

Since the radius of convergence is 1, to every given positive η there corresponds an n_0 such that, for $n > n_0$,

$$|a_n| < (1+\eta)^n.$$

If therefore, for $n > n_0$ and $m \geqslant 0$, we write

$$R_{n+m} = \sum_{k=m}^{\infty} C_k^{n+k} r^k e^{ik\alpha} a_{n+k},$$

we have

(6) $$|R_n| < \sum_{k=0}^{\infty} C_k^{n+k} r^k (1+\eta)^{n+k}.$$

Now, by (5),

(7) $$|\sqrt[n]{C_k^{n+k} r^k (1+\eta)^{n+k}}| < \left(1+\frac{k}{n}\right)^{1+\frac{k}{n}} \left(\frac{rn}{k}\right)^{\frac{k}{n}} (1+\eta)^{1+\frac{k}{n}}$$

and, in (6), the ratio of the $(k+1)$-th term to the k-th is

(8) $$\left(1+\frac{n}{k}\right) r (1+\eta).$$

Let λ be any fixed positive number. Choose (i) $p=p(n)$ so that $p/n\to\lambda$ as $n\to\infty$, (ii) $q\geqslant p$, (iii) $0<l<1$, (iv) $r>0$, but so small that

$$(9)\qquad (1+1/\lambda)^{1+\lambda}(1+\eta)^{1+\lambda}\left(\frac{r}{\lambda}\right)^{\lambda}<\frac{l}{1-r}$$

and

$$(10)\qquad (1+\lambda)(1+\eta)r<l.$$

Then, for $n>N\geqslant n_0$, we have, by (6), (7), (8), (9), and (10),

$$|\sqrt[n]{R_{n+q+1}}|<\left|\sum_{k=q+1}^{\infty}C_k^{n+k}r^k(1+\eta)^{n+k}\right|$$

$$<\left|\sqrt{C_p^{n+p}r^p(1+\eta)^{n+p}\sum_{k=q+1}^{\infty}l^{k-p}}\right|\leqslant\frac{l}{1-r}\left|\sqrt[n]{\frac{1}{1-l}}\right|.$$

Therefore

$$\overline{\lim_{n=\infty}}|\sqrt[n]{R_{n+q+1}}|\leqslant\frac{l}{1-r}<\frac{1}{1-r}.$$

Finally, putting $R_{n,q}=R_n-R_{n+q+1}$ and applying (4), we see that our original test takes the form:

$$(11)\qquad \begin{aligned}&\overline{\lim_{n=\infty}}|\sqrt[n]{R_{n,q}}|<\frac{1}{1-r},\quad \textit{regularity at } e^{i\alpha},\\ &\overline{\lim_{n=\infty}}|\sqrt[n]{R_{n,q}}|=\frac{1}{1-r},\quad \textit{singularity at } e^{i\alpha},\end{aligned}$$

where $\underline{\lim}_{n=\infty}q/n\geqslant\lambda>0$, *i.e. we can neglect* R_{n+q+1} *and replace* R_n *by* $R_{n,q}$.

In order to eliminate r from the right-hand side we must divide R_n by a suitable quantity. We first observe that the greatest of the coefficients $C_k^{n+k}r^k$ in R_n is that for which k is the greatest integer $\leqslant nr/(1-r)$. Let $s=s(n)$ be chosen so that

$$(12)\qquad \lim_{n=\infty}\frac{s}{n}=\frac{r}{1-r}.$$

Then, by (5) and (12),

$$(13)\qquad \lim_{n=\infty}|\sqrt[n]{C_s^{n+s}r^s}|=\frac{1}{1-r}.$$

We now replace $|\sqrt[n]{R_{n,q}}|$ by $|\sqrt[n]{R_{n,s+q}}|$ and divide through by $|\sqrt[n]{C_s^{n+s}r^se^{is\alpha}}|$. Since the latter expression tends to $1/(1-r)$, the right-hand side of (11) becomes 1 and $R_{n,\,s+q}$ is replaced by $H_m(re^{i\alpha})$, where $m = n + s$ and

$$H_m(re^{i\alpha}) = \frac{R_{n,\,s+q}}{C_s^m r^s e^{is\alpha}} = a_m + \frac{m+1}{s+1} re^{i\alpha} a_{m+1} + \dots$$
$$+ \frac{(m+1)(m+2)\dots(m+q)}{(s+1)(s+2)\dots(s+q)} r^q e^{iq\alpha} a_{m+q} + \frac{s}{m} r^{-1} e^{-i\alpha} a_{m-1}$$
$$+ \dots + \frac{s(s-1)\dots 1}{m(m-1)\dots(m-s+1)} r^{-s} e^{-is\alpha} a_{m-s}.$$

This function will be referred to as Hadamard's *test function.*

Finally we can replace the nth root by the mth root. For this purpose we remark that if $\overline{\lim}\, A_n = A$ and $\eta_n \quad \eta$, then $\overline{\lim}\, A_n^{\eta_n} = A^{\eta}$.

[Proof. By hypothesis, $A_n < A + \epsilon$ for every $n > N$ and there are infinitely many values n_i of n for which $A_n > A - \epsilon$. Hence $A_n^{\eta_n} < (A+\epsilon)^{\eta_n}$ for $n > N$ and $A_n^{\eta_n} > (A-\epsilon)^{\eta_n}$ for $n = n_i$. Since $(A+\epsilon)^{\eta_n} \to (A+\epsilon)^{\eta}$, $(A-\epsilon)^{\eta_n} \to (A-\epsilon)^{\eta}$ and, for sufficiently small ϵ, $(A+\epsilon)^{\eta} - A^{\eta}$, $(A-\epsilon)^{\eta} - A^{\eta}$ are as small as we please, the proposition is established.]

In our case

$$\frac{s}{n} = \frac{r}{1-r} + \epsilon_n, \text{ i.e. } \frac{n}{m} = \frac{n}{n+s} = \eta_n,$$

where $\eta_n \to 1 - r$ and the upper limit A in question is 1 or < 1. Thus, if we replace the nth root by the mth root, the upper limit is not altered if it is 1 and it remains less than 1 if it is less than 1. We are thus led to the following test:

III. $e^{i\alpha}$ *is a regular point if and only if, for a sufficiently small* r *and all sufficiently large* m,

$$|H_m(re^{i\alpha})| < (1-\epsilon)^m,$$

i.e. if and only if

$$\overline{\lim_{m=\infty}}\, |\sqrt[m]{H_m(re^{i\alpha})}| < 1.$$

(Fabry, 1896.)

In the above test r is restricted by (9) and (10), s by (12), and q by $\underline{\lim}_{n=\infty}\, q/n \geqslant \lambda > 0$, and the last condition is satisfied if $\underline{\lim}_{m=\infty}\, q/m \geqslant \lambda$. By taking λ and r sufficiently small we may make the limits of q/m and s/m as small as we please. We shall make use of this freedom of choice in proving a beautiful theorem due to Hadamard.

Consider a series $f(z) = \Sigma a_{\lambda_\nu} z^{\lambda_\nu}$ with such *gaps* (i. e. sequences of zero coefficients) that

$$\lambda_{\nu+1} - \lambda_\nu > \theta\lambda_\nu, \quad \theta > 0 \quad \text{(Hadamard gaps).}$$

Taking a surviving coefficient a_m (i. e. $\lambda_\nu = m$) we choose s and q with the additional restrictions

$$s \leqslant \frac{\theta}{1+\theta}\lambda_\nu \text{ and } q \leqslant \theta\lambda_\nu.$$

In this way all the coefficients in $G_m(re^{i\alpha})$, but $a_m\,(= a_{\lambda_\nu})$ itself, are zero, so that

$$|\sqrt[m]{H_m(re^{i\alpha})}| = |\sqrt[m]{a_m}|.$$

On the other hand, if the radius of convergence of $\Sigma a_{\lambda_\nu} z^{\lambda_\nu}$ is 1, there are suffixes $\lambda_{\nu_i} = m_i \to \infty$ such that $|\sqrt[m_i]{a_{m_i}}| \to 1$. Therefore, *for every* α

$$\overline{\lim_{m=\infty}}\, |\sqrt[m]{H_m(re^{i\alpha})}| = 1,$$

and thus every point $e^{i\alpha}$ is a singular point of $f(z)$.

IV. *If* $\overline{\lim}\,|\sqrt[\lambda_\nu]{a_{\lambda_\nu}}| = 1$ *and* $\lambda_{\nu+1} - \lambda_\nu > \theta\lambda_\nu$, $\theta > 0$, *the circle* $|z| = 1$ *is a singular line for* $f(z) = \Sigma a_{\lambda_\nu} z^{\lambda_\nu}$.

(Hadamard, 1892.)

In Chapter XI we shall discuss further properties of gaps in the coefficients.

58. *Essential points.* We notice an important difference between poles and essential points. If a is a pole of $f(z)$, a is a zero of $1/f(z)$, i. e. $\lim_{z\to a} 1/f(z) = 0$. Hence $\lim_{z\to\infty} |f(z)| = \infty$ and thus the only value approached by $f(z)$ as $z \to a$ is infinity.

I. *In the neighbourhood of an essential point $f(z)$ approaches every value,* i. e. if a is an essential point, there is a sequence $z_n \to a$ such that $f(z_n) \to A$ arbitrarily given. (Weierstrass.)

Proof. Suppose that there is a value A not approached by $f(z)$ in the neighbourhood of a. This means that there is a circle about A of sufficiently small radius δ such that for $|z-a| < \epsilon$ (sufficiently small), $f(z)$ does not assume values contained in the circle about A. Hence $g(z) = 1/[f(z) - A]$ is regular and $|g(z)| < 1/\delta$ at every point of $|z-a| < \epsilon$, except possibly at a.

By Laurent's expansion $g(z) = \Sigma A_n (z-a)^n + \Sigma B_n (z-a)^{-n}$ and, as $z \to a$, the first part tends to A_0. Since $\Sigma B_n x^n$ is an integral function, it reduces to a constant, by Liouville's theorem, 40. V, and thus a cannot be an essential singularity of

$$f(z) = A + 1/g(z).$$

This contradiction shows that $1/[f(z)-A]$ is not bounded in $|z-a| < \epsilon$, and there are points $x_n \to \infty$, i.e. $z_n \to a$, for which $1/|f(z_n)-A| \to \infty$, i.e. $f(z_n) \to A$. *$f(z)$ is completely indeterminate in the neighbourhood of an essential point.*

The reasoning is valid also in the case when $f(z)$ has infinitely many poles in the neighbourhood of a. In fact the poles of $f(z)$ are zeros of $1/[f(z)-A]$, i.e. the latter is regular at the poles of $f(z)$, so that the same argument applies.

II. *If a is a regular point of $g(z)$ and a pole (essential point) of $f(z)$, a is a pole (essential point) of $f(z)+g(z)$. If a is a pole of $g(z)$ and an essential point of $f(z)$, a is an essential point of $f(z)+g(z)$.*

Proof. Writing

$$g(z) = \Sigma c_n (z-a)^n, f(z) = \Sigma a_n (z-a)^n + \Sigma b_n (z-a)^{-n},$$

we see that

$$f(z)+g(z) = \Sigma (a_n + c_n)(z-a)^n + \Sigma b_n (z-a)^{-n},$$

i.e. the principal part is the same as in $f(z)$.

If a is a pole of $g(z)$ and an essential point of $f(z)$, only a finite number of terms in the principal part are altered by the addition. Therefore the principal part of $f(z)+g(z)$ has infinitely many non-vanishing coefficients.

Similarly, if a is a pole of order k of $f(z)$ and of order m of $g(z)$, a is a pole of order $k+m$ for $f(z)g(z)$. On the other hand, if a is a zero of order m for $g(z)$, $f(z)g(z) = (z-a)^{k-m} f_1(z)$, where $f_1(z)$ is regular at a, i.e. if $k < m$, a is a pole of fg of order $m-k$ and if $k \geqslant m$, a is a regular point of fg, and a zero of order $k-m$ if $k > m$.

Multiplication may destroy even essential singularities. For example, take $e^{1/z} = \Sigma \frac{1}{n!} \frac{1}{z^n}$ and $e^{-1/z} = \Sigma \frac{(-1)^n}{n!\, z^n}$. Their product is the function 1.

We notice finally that

III. *If a uniform analytic function is regular and bounded in the neighbourhood of a point a, it is regular at a.*

Proof. Laurent's expansion shows that either $f(z)$ is regular also at a or else a is a pole or an essential point. But if $f(z)$ is bounded, $|f(z)| < N$ in a neighbourhood of a, and so this point cannot be a pole nor an essential point, since $f(z)$ does not approach in this neighbourhood any value of A such that $|A| > N$. Hence $f(z)$ is regular also at a.

59. *Residue theorem. Poles are isolated from one another* because they are zeros of $1/f(z)$ and, by 27. VI, zeros are isolated from one another. If k is the degree of the pole at $z = a$, $(z-a)^k f(z)$ is regular at a, (it is differentiable in a neighbourhood of a), and different from 0. Hence $F(z) = 1/(z-a)^k f(z)$ is also regular at a and different from 0, i. e. $(z-a)^k F(z) = 1/f(z)$ is regular at $z = a$ and has a zero at a of order k. We also notice that if $f(z)$ is regular at $z = a$, $1/f(z)$ is either regular at a (when $f(a) \neq 0$) or has a pole at a whose order is that of the zero of $f(z)$ at a.

If $f(z)$ is uniform and has only a finite number of poles in a region R, $f(z)$ is said to be *meromorphic in R*.

Consider now a circle c_a, centre a, containing only one pole $z = a$ of $f(z)$. We are going to calculate $\int_{c_a} f(z)\,dz$.

Since the primitive of $(z-a)^m$, $m \neq -1$, is $(z-a)^{m+1}/(m+1)$ all the terms of Laurent's expansion vanish in the integration except $B_1/(z-a)$. Hence, putting $z-a = re^{i\alpha}$, we find in the usual way

$$\frac{1}{2\pi i}\int_{c_a} f(z)\,dz = B_1. \tag{1}$$

Therefore the coefficient B_1 is called the *residue* of $f(z)$ at a.

I. *Cauchy's residue theorem. If $f(z)$ is uniform and meromorphic inside a simple contour C and continuous on C, we have*

$$\int_C f(z)\,dz = 2\pi i\,\Sigma R_s, \tag{2}$$

where R_s are the residues of the poles inside C. (Cauchy 1831 b.)

Proof. If $a_1, \dots, a_k$ are the poles of $f(z)$ in C, we exclude them by small circles c_s and apply the fundamental theorem to the contour $C - c_1 - \dots - c_k$ and we obtain

$$\int_C f(z)\,dz = \int_{c_1} f(z)\,dz + \dots + \int_{c_k} f(z)\,dz = 2\pi i\,\Sigma R_s. \quad \text{Q. e. d.}$$

In practical applications this is one of the most important formulae of modern analysis.

If $f(z)$ has a zero or a pole at $z = a$, its Taylor expansion about a is of the form $f(z) = (z-a)^k \Sigma b_n (z-a)^n$, $b_0 \neq 0$, where k is a positive or negative integer, giving the order of the zero if $k > 0$ and $-k$ that of the pole if $k < 0$. Since

$$f'(z) = k(z-a)^{k-1} \Sigma b_n (z-a)^n + (z-a)^k \Sigma n b_n (z-a)^{n-1},$$

and

$$\Sigma n b_n (z-a)^n / \Sigma b_n (z-a)^n = \Sigma c_n (z-a)^n \quad (b_0 \neq 0),$$

we have

$$f'(z)/f(z) = k/(z-a) + \Sigma c_n (z-a)^n.$$

Hence, integrating along a circle c_a about a containing no other zero or pole of $f(z)$, we obtain by the residue theorem

$$(3) \qquad \int_{c_a} f'(z)dz/f(z) = 2\pi i k.$$

Thus, if the contour C encloses the zeros and poles $a_1, \dots, a_r$, $b_1, \dots, b_s$, and if $f(z)$ is otherwise regular inside C and continuous (and $\neq 0$) on C, we have

$$(4) \qquad \int_C f'(z)dz/f(z) = 2\pi i (Z-P),$$

where Z is the number of zeros and P the number of poles in C, each counted according to its multiplicity.

If $g(z)$ is uniform and regular inside C and continuous on C, the residue of $g(z)f'(z)/f(z)$ at a is $kg(a)$. Thus (4) is readily generalized for this case, giving

$$(5) \quad \int_C g(z)f'(z)dz/f(z) = 2\pi i \left[\sum_{\rho=1}^{r} g(a_\rho) - \sum_{\sigma=1}^{s} g(b_\sigma) \right],$$

with the convention that $g(a_\rho)$ is repeated as many times as the degree of a_ρ indicates. Formula (5) is very much used in the evaluation of integrals.

Comparing (4) with (55. 4) and noticing that

$$\log f(z) = \log |f(z)| + i \arg f(z),$$

we see that $Z-P$ *is equal to the change in the argument of* $f(z)$ *when* z *describes* C (because $\log |f(z)|$ reassumes its value).

This result is frequently referred to as the *principle of the argument*.

60. *Some theoretical consequences of the residue theorem.* Apply the principle of the argument to two uniform functions $P(z)$ and $Q(z)$, regular in C (no poles), and suppose that, when z describes C, $|P(z)| > |Q(z)|$. Under this condition, as z varies along C, the corresponding value of $1 + Q(z)/P(z)$ describes a curve inside the circle of radius 1 and centre 1, for at the end the argument of $1 + Q/P$ assumes its initial value. Therefore the change in the argument of $P + Q = P(1 + Q/P)$ is due entirely to the change in the argument of P. Hence we have the following result:

I. *If along C, $|P(z)| > |Q(z)|$, the two uniform functions $P(z)$ and $P(z) + Q(z)$ have the same number of zeros in C provided they are both regular in C.* (Rouché.)

Apply this result to the polynomials $P(z) = a_n z^n$ and $Q(z) = a_{n-1} z^{n-1} + \ldots + a_0$. We have obviously, for $|z| = R$,

$$\left|\frac{Q(z)}{P(z)}\right| < \left|\frac{a_{n-1}}{a_n}\right|\frac{1}{R} + \left|\frac{a_{n-2}}{a_n}\right|\frac{1}{R^2} + \ldots + \left|\frac{a_0}{a_n}\right|\frac{1}{R^n},$$

and the right-hand side tends to 0 when R increases indefinitely. Thus, for a sufficiently large R, $|Q(z)/P(z)| < 1$ along $|z| = R$. Hence I applies, and we obtain the result that in a sufficiently large circle the polynomial $a_n z^n + a_{n-1} z^{n-1} + \ldots + a_0$ has just as many zeros (counted according to their multiplicity) as $a_n z^n$, i. e. n. This is apparently a *very short proof of the fundamental theorem of algebra*. But this proof implies all the machinery of complex integration and, in particular, Cauchy's two fundamental results, so that the elegance of this proof is only apparent.

We are going now to establish Jensen's formula, one of the most important consequences of (59. 5).

Consider the integral

$$\text{(1)} \qquad I = \int_c \log f(z) \frac{dz}{z}$$

along the circle c, $|z| = R$. We suppose as usual that $f(z)$ is meromorphic in c and regular and different from 0 on c, and we start the integration from the real axis with the argument of $\log f(z)$ zero or positive and $< 2\pi$. For simplicity we also suppose that the origin is not a zero or a pole of $f(z)$. By partial integration we obtain

$$(2) \qquad I = [\log z \log f(z)]_c - \int_c \log z \frac{f'(z)}{f(z)} dz,$$

where the completely integrated part is the difference between the initial and final values of $\log z \log f(z)$, i. e.

$$(\log R + 2\pi i)[\log f(R) + (r-s)\, 2\pi i] - \log R \log f(R)$$
$$= 2\pi i \log f(R) + 2\pi i (r-s) \log R - 4(r-s)\pi^2,$$

where r and s are respectively the number of zeros and poles of $f(z)$ inside c. The remaining integral is of the form (59. 5), but the conditions of the theorem are not satisfied by $\log z$. Thus we apply the usual artifice of excluding the origin by a small circle of radius ρ, not containing any zero or pole of the function, and join the two circles by a straight segment not meeting any pole or zero. We might suppose this segment to be a part of the positive real axis. Inside the contour C formed by a turn in the positive direction along $|z| = R$, (a, b), a small circle in the negative direction, and (b, a), the function $\log z$ is regular.

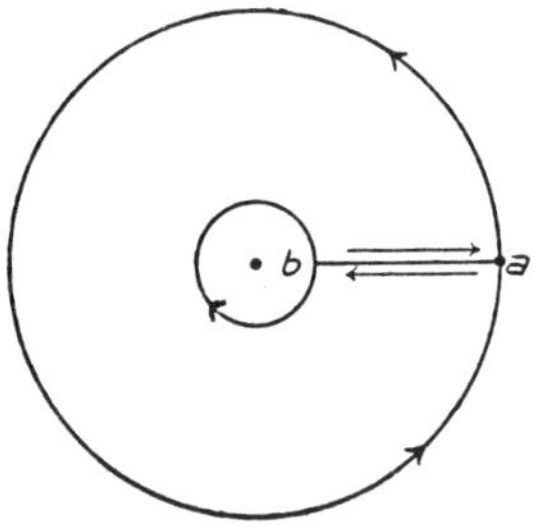

FIG. 40.

Applying (59. 5) to this contour we obtain

$$(3) \qquad \int_C \log z \frac{f'(z)}{f(z)} dz = 2\pi i \Sigma \log a_\rho - 2\pi i \Sigma \log b_\sigma$$
$$= 2\pi i \log \frac{a_1 \dots a_r}{b_1 \dots b_s}.$$

Since in the small circle $|f'(z)/f(z)|$ is bounded ($< M$) and, on the circle $|z| = \rho$, $|\log z| < |\log \rho| + 2\pi$, the integral along $|z| = \rho$ is less in absolute value than $M 2\pi\rho (\log \rho + 2\pi)$ which tends to 0 with ρ.

On the other hand, the difference in the argument of $\log z$ along (a, b) and (b, a) is 2π (after a turn about 0). Thus these two parts yield

$$-\int_a^b 2\pi i \frac{f'(z)}{f(z)} dz = -2\pi i \log f(R) + 2\pi i \log f(\rho),$$

whose limit when $\rho \to 0$ is $-2\pi i \log f(R) + 2\pi i \log f(0)$. Thus we have

$$(4) \qquad \int_c \log z \cdot \frac{f'(z)}{f(z)} dz = 2\pi i \log \frac{a_1 \dots a_r}{b_1 \dots b_s} + 2\pi i \log \frac{f(R)}{f(0)}.$$

Hence, by (2), we obtain the value of I.

Putting $f(z) = |f(z)| e^{i\Phi}$ and $z = Re^{i\phi}$, we have

$$(5) \qquad I = \int_0^{2\pi} [\log |f(z)| + 2\pi i \Phi] i d\phi$$

$$= 2\pi i (r-s) \log R + 2\pi i \log f(0) - 2\pi i \log \frac{a_1 \dots a_r}{b_1 \dots b_s} - 4(r-s)\pi^2.$$

Equating the imaginary parts of the two sides, we obtain *Jensen's formula*:

$$(6) \qquad \int_0^{2\pi} \log |f(Re^{i\phi})| d\phi = 2\pi \log |f(0)| + 2\pi \log \left| R^{r-s} \frac{b_1 \dots b_s}{a_1 \dots a_r} \right|$$

If there are no poles in the circle of radius R, we have to replace $g(b_\sigma)$ in (59. 5) by 0, i.e. in our case we have to replace $\log b_\sigma$ by 0 which amounts to putting $b_\sigma = 1$, and $s = 0$. Similarly for zeros.

The remarkable feature of this formula is that it establishes a relation between the behaviour of the modulus of $f(z)$ along the circumference $|z| = R$ and the number and position of the poles and zeros in $|z| < R$.

As a simple application of Jensen's formula we are going to prove the following theorem.

II. *If $f(z)$ is regular in $|z| < 1$ and its zeros in $|z| < 1$ are z_k (the origin being omitted if it is a zero) and $|z_{k+1}| \geqq |z_k|$, the necessary and sufficient condition that $\prod_{n=1}^{\infty} |z_n|$ be convergent is that the logarithmic mean value $M_\rho = \int_0^{2\pi} \log |f(\rho e^{i\theta})| d\theta < M$ independently of $\rho < 1$.*

Proof. Dividing by cz^k, if necessary, we may suppose that $f(0) = 1$. By Jensen's formula

$$(7) \qquad \log \prod_{|z_n| \leqq \rho} (\rho / |z_n|) = M_\rho(f).$$

The left-hand side, and thus also the right-hand side, is a non-decreasing function of ρ. If there is only a finite number of zeros, the theorem is obviously established by (7). If there are infinitely many zeros in $|z| < 1$, their moduli tend to 1, by 27. VI. Consider values of ρ which are moduli of zeros, and put $\log 1/|z_n| = a_n$, $\sum_1^n a_\nu = s_n$. Then, for $\rho = |z_n|$, the left-hand side of (7) is $s_n - na_n$, and thus, since $a_n \to 0$, 23. VIII proves the statement.

61. *The point at infinity. Definition of a singular point.* In order to examine the behaviour of an analytic function, $f(z)$, at infinity, we put $z = 1/x$, and examine $f(1/x)$ at the origin. (We might similarly put $z = 1/(x-a)$ and examine $f[1/(x-a)]$ at $x = a$.) The neighbourhood of $z = \infty$ is thus, by definition, the neighbourhood of $x = 0$, so that the former is the whole complex plane outside circles whose radii increase to infinity. If $f(1/x)$ is regular at $x = 0$, we have

$$f(1/x) = a_0 + a_1 x + \ldots + a_n x^n + \ldots$$

in a sufficiently small circle of radius r, say, about the origin This means that $f(z) = a_0 + a_1/z + a_2/z^2 + \ldots + a_n/z^n + \ldots$ outside the circle of radius $1/r$. When $a_0 = 0$, we say that ∞ is a zero of $f(z)$. If $a_0 = \ldots = a_{k-1} = 0$, $a_k \neq 0$, ∞ is a zero of order k. If $f(1/x)$ is uniform about the origin and regular everywhere except at $x = 0$, we have, by Laurent's expansion,

$$f(1/x) = \Sigma a_n x^n + \Sigma b_n x^{-n},$$

i. e.

$$f(z) = \Sigma a_n z^{-n} + \Sigma b_n z^n, \tag{1}$$

where now the part with positive indices is the principal part and the other is the regular part.

If the principal part contains only a finite number of terms, k being the greatest index, ∞ is said to be a pole of order k. Otherwise, viz. when the principal part contains infinitely many non-vanishing coefficients, it is an essential point. A polynomial $a_0 + a_1 z + \ldots + a_n z^n$ is regular at every finite point, and thus a polynomial may be considered as the principal part of a Laurent expansion about ∞, the regular part missing. In other words, for a polynomial of the degree k, $z = \infty$ is a pole of order k.

Similarly, an integral function is regular at every finite point, and thus in this case $\Sigma a_n z^n$ can be considered as the principal part at $z = \infty$, i. e. this point is an essential point of the integral function.

The residue at ∞ is defined in the same way, but we must understand that going round ∞ along a circle of radius R means going round the origin in the opposite direction (the enclosed area containing 0 lying on our *right*). Hence, by (1), $-b_1$ is the residue of $f(z)$ at $z = \infty$. If the uniform function $f(z)$ has only a finite number of poles at finite points, then integrating along $|z| = R$, including them all, we obtain the sum of the residues at those finite poles. But the same integration along (R) in the opposite direction gives by definition the residue at $z = \infty$. Hence

I. *If the uniform analytic function $f(z)$ has only a finite number of poles, the sum of its residues including R_∞ is zero.* In particular, if $z = \infty$ is a regular point for $f(z)$ or an isolated singular point with the residue 0, the sum of its residues for finite poles is zero.

II. *A rational fraction $P(z)/Q(z)$ has only a finite number of poles*, viz., the zeros of $Q(z)$, and ∞ if the degree of P is greater than that of Q; *conversely if a uniform function $f(z)$ has only a finite number of poles* [∞ also being either a regular point or a pole of $f(z)$], *$f(z)$ is a rational function.*

Proof. If $a_1, a_2, \ldots, a_r$ are the poles of $f(z)$ with the principal parts

$$(2) \quad P_\rho[1/(z-a_\rho)] = B_{\rho,1}/(z-a_\rho) + \ldots + B_{\rho,k_\rho}/(z-a_\rho)^{k_\rho},$$

the function $F(z) = f(z) - \sum_{\rho=1}^{r} P_\rho$ is regular at every finite point, i. e.

$$(3) \qquad F(z) = \Sigma a_n z^n$$

is an integral function. If (3) contained an infinity of terms, ∞ would be an essential point of $F(z)$ and thus also of $f(z)$. Since, by hypothesis, ∞ is at most a pole of $f(z)$,

$$F(z) = a_0 + a_1 z + \ldots + a_k z^k,$$

and thus $f(z) = \sum_{\rho=1}^{r} P_\rho(z) + F(z)$, which is a rational function of z. Q. e. d.

In some of the results obtained above we omitted the consideration of the point at infinity. Thus, for instance, the first statement of 54. I and 54. VI are each valid for infinite domains, which may be proved by the method of this article. Moreover

III. *Vitali's theorem*, 42. IV, *remains true when* D *is unbounded.*

Proof. If D does not contain $z=\infty$ the result is an immediate consequence of 42. IV itself. If D contains $z=\infty$, suppose D is $|z|>R$. Then by the transformation $z=1/x$ the domain becomes a bounded domain and $z=\infty$ becomes $x=0$. The result then follows from 42. IV, and it may be extended to any domain by combining the two cases.

Singular points. So far we have been chiefly concerned with special singularities like poles and essential points. In the following chapters we shall need a general definition of a singular point applicable to any analytic function, uniform or multiform.

We say that two Taylor series

$$T_a = \Sigma a_n(z-a)^n, \qquad T_b = \Sigma b_n(z-b)^n$$

overlap if (i) their circles of convergence overlap, (ii) at every point of their common part they furnish the same value.

Let an analytic function $f(z)$ be defined by T_a and its continuations and let $C_a^{z_0}$ be any path between a and z_0. If there is a finite chain of overlapping Taylor series along $C_a^{z_0}$ such that the first is T_a and the last T_{z_0}, we say that z_0 is *reached* along $C_a^{z_0}$. If every point 'before' z_0 is reached but z_0 is not, we say that z_0 is *approached* along $C_a^{z_0}$.

Now take any finite ($\neq \infty$) point z_0, and consider the different possibilities.

(a) There is no path between a and z_0 along which z_0 can be reached or approached. If we replace T_a by any other element T_b of $f(z)$, the same will be true for b and z_0. Therefore we say that z_0 is an *external* point of $f(z)$. There may be no such point for a given $f(z)$.

(b) There is a path $C_a^{z_0}$ along which z_0 can be reached or approached. T_a and such a path specify a regular and uniform branch $\phi(z)$ of $f(z)$ in a domain D, limited by a simple contour and containing a simple arc $C_b^{z_0}$ of $C_a^{z_0}$, but not z_0. In fact, every circle of the chain containing $C_b^{z_0}$ can be replaced by a finite number of circles, each containing only one arc of $C_b^{z_0}$, and the inner points of these circles will form such a domain.

(b_1) z_0 is reached along $C_a^{z_0}$. Then z_0 is also reached along *every* path in D between b and z_0, since by adding to D a sufficiently small circle about z_0 we obtain a simply connected D' in which, by 66. III, $\phi(z)$ is regular and uniform. Thus $\phi(z)$ is regular at z_0; z_0 is a *regular point* of $\phi(z)$.

(b_2) z_0 is only approached along $C_a^{z_0}$. Then, by (b_1), it will be only approached along *every* path in D connected to it. We say that z_0 is a *singular point* of $\phi(z)$.

Thus every point z_0 is either an external point, or else it is a regular or a singular point of any given branch of $f(z)$ specified in its neighbourhood by a path.

62. *Analytic functions of two independent variables.* Consider a complex function $u(z, z')$ of the two complex variables $z = x+iy$ and $z' = x'+iy'$ and put

$$u(z, z') = P(x, y, x', y') + iQ(x, y, x', y').$$

When z' (or z) remains constant, u is a function of z (or z') alone, so that, if it is differentiable, u satisfies the four equations

$$(1) \quad \frac{\partial P}{\partial x} = \frac{\partial Q}{\partial y}, \quad \frac{\partial P}{\partial y} = -\frac{\partial Q}{\partial x}; \quad \frac{\partial P}{\partial x'} = \frac{\partial Q}{\partial y'}, \quad \frac{\partial P}{\partial y'} = -\frac{\partial Q}{\partial x'}.$$

A great many properties of $u(z, z')$, like (1), result from the fact that, keeping one of the variables constant, we can apply the whole theory of analytic functions of a single variable. For example, let us suppose that u is differentiable with respect to z and z' in $|z-z_0| \leqslant r$, $|z'-z_0'| \leqslant r'$, and put $z = z_0+ht$, $z' = z_0'+kt$, where $|h| < r$, $|k| < r'$, and t is a complex variable varying in $|t| < 1$. Since the function

$$f(z_0+ht, z'+kt)$$

of the single variable t is differentiable in and on

$$|z-z_0| = h, \quad |z'-z_0'| = k,$$

it can be expanded in a Taylor series

$$f(z_0+ht, z_0'+kt) = \sum_0^\infty \frac{t^n}{n!}\left[\left(h\frac{\partial}{\partial z} + k\frac{\partial}{\partial z'}\right)^{(n)} f\right]_{\substack{z = z \\ z' = z'_0}}$$

convergent in and on $|t| = 1$. For $t = 1$ we obtain

$$(2) \qquad f(z_0+h, z_0'+k) = \sum_0^\infty \frac{1}{n!}\left(h\frac{\partial}{\partial z_0} + k\frac{\partial}{\partial z_0'}\right)^n f,$$

i. e.

I. *If $f(z, z')$ is differentiable in and on*

$$|z-z_0| = r, \quad |z'-z_0'| = r',$$

then $f(z, z')$ can be expanded in a Taylor series (2) *convergent for $|h|<r$, $|k|<r'$.*

We say that $f(z, z')$ is *regular at* $(z = z_0, z' = z_0')$ if $f(z, z')$ can be expanded in a Taylor series like (2) converging for sufficiently small values of h and k.

Cauchy's inequalities are generalized in a similar fashion. Putting for simplicity $z_0 = 0$, $z_0' = 0$, and $h = z$, $k = z'$, we can write (2) in the form

$$(3) \qquad f(z, z') = \sum_0^\infty \frac{1}{n!}\left(z\frac{\partial}{\partial z_0} + z'\frac{\partial}{\partial z_0'}\right)^n f = \Sigma a_{p,q} z^p z'^q,$$

where

$$(4) \qquad a_{p,q} = \frac{1}{p!\,q!}\left(\frac{\partial^{p+q} f}{\partial z^p \partial z'^q}\right)_{\substack{z=z_0\\ z'=z_0'}}.$$

II. *If $f(z, z') = \Sigma a_{p,q} z^p z'^q$ is convergent and $|f(z, z')| \leqslant M$ in $|z|<r, |z'|<r'$, we have*

$$(5) \qquad |a_{p,q}| \leqslant M/r^p r'^q.$$

Proof. For a fixed value of z' we have

$$\frac{\partial^p f(z, z')}{\partial z^p} = \frac{p!}{2\pi i}\int \frac{f(x, z')\,dx}{(x-z)^{p+1}};$$

in particular

$$\left(\frac{\partial^p f}{\partial z^p}\right)_{z=0} = \frac{p!}{2\pi\rho^p}\int_0^{2\pi} f(\rho e^{i\theta}, z')e^{-p\theta i}\,d\theta, \; \rho<r.$$

The same formula applied to the right-hand side as a function of z' gives

$$\left(\frac{\partial^{p+q} f}{\partial z^p \partial z'^q}\right)_{z=0,\, z'=0}$$

$$= \frac{p!\,q!}{2\pi\rho^p . 2\pi\rho'^q}\int_0^{2\pi}\int_0^{2\pi} f(\rho e^{i\theta}, \rho' e^{i\theta'})e^{-p\theta i}e^{-q\theta' i}\,d\theta\,d\theta'.$$

Replacing the integrand by M, we obtain, by (4), the inequality (5) required.

We might formulate our result by saying that

$$G(z, z') = \frac{M}{(1-z/r)(1-z'/r')} = \sum_{p, q=0}^{\infty} M(z/r)^p (z'/r')^q$$

is a *dominant series* for $\Sigma a_{p,q} z^p z'^q$ in the sense (Art. 72) that the coefficients of G are larger than the moduli of the corresponding coefficients in $\Sigma a_{p,q} z^p z'^q$. We notice that $M \Big/ \left(1 - \frac{z}{r} - \frac{z'}{r'}\right)$ is also a dominant series.

63. *Implicit functions.*

I. *Weierstrass's factorization theorem. If $u(z, z')$ is regular at $z = 0$, $z' = 0$, and if $u(0, 0) = 0$, but $u(0, z')$ is not identically zero, then $u(z, z')$ can be written in the form*

$$u(z, z') = p(z, z')\, v(z, z'),$$

where $p(z, z')$ is a polynomial in z' whose coefficients are functions of z, regular at $z = 0$ (the coefficient of the highest power of z' being 1), and $v(z, z')$ is regular in the neighbourhood of $z = 0$, $z' = 0$ and does not vanish when z and z' vary in sufficiently small circles about their respective origins.

(Weierstrass, 1886.)

The theorem displays the vanishing part of $u(z, z')$ as a polynomial in one of the variables. The theorem is generally attributed to Weierstrass as he made use of it in his lectures from 1860 onward. We notice, however, that Cauchy proved a very similar theorem, and that Poincaré published a proof before Weierstrass. The proof here given is due to Simart in Picard (1922), p. 261, and is based on the residue theorem.

Proof. If we put $u = \Sigma A_q(z) z'^q$, the functions $A_q(z)$ are, by hypothesis, regular in $|z| \leqslant r$. Denoting the maximum modulus of u in $|z| \leqslant r$, $|z'| \leqslant r'$ by M, we have for any fixed value of z in $|z| \leqslant r$, $|A_q(z)| \leqslant M/r'^q$. Together with $u(0, 0) = A_0(0)$, some of the $A_q(z)$, $q > 0$, may also vanish for $z = 0$. Suppose that $A_0(0) = 0$, $A_1(0) = 0, \ldots, A_{n-1}(0) = 0$, but $A_n(0) \neq 0$.

We are going to determine the number of roots of the equation in z', $u(z, z') = 0$, for small fixed values of z. Put

$$u(z, z') = A_n z'^n (1 + P + Q),$$

where $$P = \frac{A_0}{A_n z'^n} + \frac{A_1}{A_n z'^{n-1}} + \dots + \frac{A_{n-1}}{A_n z'},$$

$$Q = \frac{A_{n+1} z'}{A_n} + \frac{A_{n+2} z'^2}{A_n} + \dots.$$

Since $A_n(0) \neq 0$, there is a circle $|z| = \rho_0$ in and on which $A_n(z) \neq 0$. We denote the minimum modulus of $A_n(z)$ in $|z| = \rho_0$ by m and the modulus of z' by ρ'. We have

$$|Q| < \frac{M}{m}\left(\frac{\rho'}{r'^{n+1}} + \frac{\rho'^2}{r'^{n+2}} + \dots\right) = \frac{M}{m}\frac{\rho'}{r'^{n+1}}\frac{1}{1-\rho'/r'},$$

i. e. for sufficiently small ρ' we have

(1) $$|Q| < 1/2 \text{ in } |z| \leqslant \rho_0,\ |z'| \leqslant \rho'.$$

On the other hand, if A_ρ denotes the maximum modulus of the functions $A_0(z), A_1(z), \dots, A_{n-1}(z)$ in $|z| \leqslant \rho$, we have

$$|P| < \frac{A_\rho}{m}\left[\frac{1}{\rho'^n} + \frac{1}{\rho'^{n-1}} + \dots + \frac{1}{\rho'}\right].$$

By hypothesis, if ρ be taken sufficiently small, A_ρ can be made as small as we please. It follows that

(2) $|P| < 1/2$ in $|z| \leqslant \rho_1 < \rho_0$, *$z'$ on the circumference $|z'| = \rho'$.*

Now apply Rouché's theorem (60. I) to the two functions $f_1 = A_n z'^n$ and $f_2 = A_n z'^n(P+Q)$. By (1) and (2), $|f_1| > |f_2|$ on $|z'| = \rho$, z being any number in $|z| \leqslant \rho_1$. Hence *the number of roots of $f_1 + f_2 = 0$, i. e. of $u(z, z') = 0$ in $|z'| = \rho'$ is the same as the number of roots of $f_1 = A_n z'^n = 0$, viz. exactly n,* for $A_n \neq 0$, and $z'^n = 0$ has a single root of multiplicity n.

Again, consider the integral

(3) $$I(z, z'') = \frac{1}{2\pi i}\int_{|z'|=\rho'} \frac{\dfrac{\partial u}{\partial z'}\Big/ u}{z' - z''}\, dz',$$

where z'' is any fixed point in $|z'| < \rho'$. Expanding $1/(z'-z'')$ in ascending powers of z'' we have

(4) $$I(z, z'') = \sum_0^\infty G_p(z) z''^p,$$

where the functions $G_p(z)$ are regular in $|z| < \rho_1$. If

$$z'_1, z'_2, \dots, z'_n$$

denote the roots of $u(z, z') = 0$ in $|z'| < \rho'$, the same integral is the sum of the residues of the integrand for the poles $z_1', z_2', \ldots, z_n'$, and z'', i. e.

$$I(z, z'') = \left(\frac{\partial u}{\partial z'}/u\right)_{z'=z''} + \frac{1}{z_1'-z''} + \ldots + \frac{1}{z_n'-z''}.$$

Putting $p(z') = (z'-z_1')(z'-z_2')\ldots(z'-z_n')$, we can write the same equation in the form

$$\Sigma G_p z'^p = \frac{\partial u}{\partial z'}/u - \frac{\partial p}{\partial z'}/p,$$

or

$$(5) \qquad \frac{\partial u}{\partial z'}/u - \frac{\partial p}{\partial z'}/p = H(z, z'),$$

where $H(z, z')$ is regular in $|z| < \rho_1$ and $|z'| < \rho'$.

Moreover, by the residue theorem, it follows from

$$(6) \qquad \frac{1}{2\pi i}\int_{|z'|=\rho'} z'^k\left(\frac{\partial u}{\partial z'}/u\right)dz' = z_1'^k + z_2'^k + \ldots + z_n'^k,$$

where the integral is a regular function of z, that, for every k, the sums on the right-hand side of (6) are regular functions of z and thus the coefficients $a_k(z)$ of the polynomial $p(z') = p(z, z')$ are also regular.

Hence, integrating (5), we obtain the form

$$u(z, z') = p(z, z')\, C(z) e^{H_1(z, z')},$$

where $H_1(z, z')$, like $H(z, z')$, is regular. To determine $C(z)$ we put $z' = z_0'$, where $|z_0'| = \rho'$, i. e. $u(z, z_0') = p(z, z_0')C(z)e^{H_1(z, z_0')}$. Therefore, as neither $u(z, z_0')$ nor $p(z, z_0')$ nor $e^{H_1(z, z_0)}$ vanish, we obtain for $u(z, z')$ the form required by the theorem.

In the particular case when $(\partial u/\partial z')_{z=0, z'=0} \neq 0$, we have $n = 1$, i. e. the root z' of $u(z, z') = 0$ vanishing for $z = 0$, satisfies an equation $z' + a_1(z) = 0$. Hence

II. *Theorem of implicit functions. If $u(z, z')$ is regular at $z = 0$, $z' = 0$, and $(\partial u/\partial z')_{z=0, z'=0} \neq 0$, the equation $u(z, z') = 0$ defines a unique function $z' = f(z)$ regular at $z = 0$ and vanishing for $z = 0$.*

This particular form of Weierstrass's general factorization theorem is of the utmost importance in function theory. For example, when $u = \Sigma a_n z^n$, i. e. $f(u, z) = u - \Sigma a_n z^n = 0$, we can apply II by noticing that u and z play the part of z and z' respectively. Thus, if $a_1 \neq 0$, z is a regular function of $u - a_0$,

i. e. $z = \Sigma b_n(u-a_0)^n$, $(b_1 \neq 0)$ and in this case the inversion of the Taylor series leads to a unique regular function.

More generally, when $u = \Sigma a_n z^n$ and $a_1 = 0, \dots, a_{p-1} = 0$, but $a_p \neq 0$, we have $u - a_0 = z^p(a_p + a_{p+1}z + \dots)$. Thus if we put $z' = z\sqrt[p]{a_p + a_{p+1}z + \dots}$, any definite branch of the p-th root is regular at $z = 0$, so that $u - a_0 = z'\Sigma b_n z'^n$, where $b_0 \neq 0$. Hence this case is reduced to the previous one and we draw the following conclusions.

III. *Inversion of Taylor series. If in* $u = \Sigma a_n z^n$ *the* $p-1$ *coefficients* $a_1, \dots, a_{p-1}$ *all vanish, but* $a_p \neq 0$, z *is a regular function of* $t = \sqrt[p]{u - a_0}$, $z = \Sigma c_n t^n$, *i.e.* z, *as a function of* u, *has a branch-point at* $u = a_0$ *of multiplicity* p. *In particular, when* $a_1 \neq 0$, z *is a regular function of* $u - a_0$.

The coefficients c_n of the inverse series can be obtained by the method of indeterminate coefficients, e.g., if $a_0 = 0$, by putting

$$u = a_1 \sum_1^\infty c_n u^n + a_2\left(\sum_1^\infty c_n u^n\right)^2 + \dots,$$

we obtain $a_1 c_1 = 1$, $a_1 c_2 + a_2 c_1^2 = 0, \dots$ (Ex. IV. 16).

64. *Elliptic and hyper-elliptic integrals.* We are going to examine the different values of the integral

$$\int \frac{P(z)\,dz}{\sqrt{R(z)}}$$

assumed along different paths, where $P(z)$ and $R(z)$ are polynomials. We shall suppose that all the roots $r_1, r_2, \dots, r_k$ of $R(z) = 0$ are distinct. It follows from the last assumption that the integral

$$(1) \qquad I(z) = \int_{z_0}^{z} \frac{P(z)\,dz}{\sqrt{R(z)}}$$

has a definite finite value for every finite z and for every finite path between z_0 and z, for at a root r_σ of $R(z) = 0$ the integrand becomes infinite like $1/\sqrt{z - r_\sigma}$. It follows that, if the integral be taken along the circle $|z - r_\sigma| = \rho$, its value tends to zero with ρ.

Suppose, in addition, that $I(z)$ has a finite value for $z = \infty$. Such an integral is usually referred to as a *hyper-elliptic integral of the first kind.* It means that if $k = 2p+1$ (odd), the degree of $P(z)$ is $\leqslant p-1$. If $k = 2p$, the degree of $P(z)$ is $\leqslant p-2$. It follows that $z = \infty$ is a regular point of $I(z)$.

Hence, every closed path starting and ending at z_0 and containing a single root r_σ is equivalent to an integral from z_0 to r_σ along a path not meeting other roots, followed by another integral along the same path but in the opposite direction. In fact (see fig. 41), C is equivalent to the path from z_0 to $r_\sigma - \epsilon$ followed by a small circle of radius $|c|$ and back to z_0. Since the integrand is not regular between the two paths, the integral along such a 'loop' (lacet) is in general not zero, for in turning about r_σ the sign of the square root changes, as also does that of dz, so that we obtain twice the integral from z_0 to r_σ.

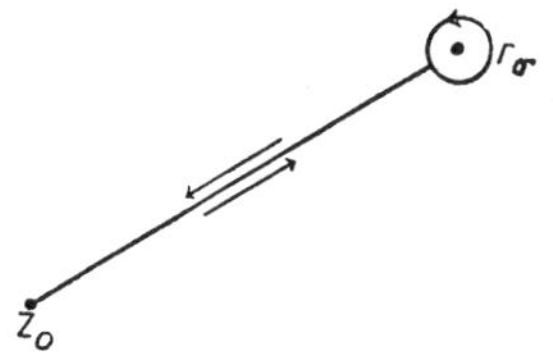

FIG. 41.

Now, every finite path between any two points z_0, z is equivalent to a finite number of loops about some of the roots r_σ starting and ending at z_0, followed by a direct integral from z_0 to z, along a path not meeting any of the roots. In fact (see fig. 42), by inserting the direct path Az_0A we do not change the value of the integral, and the path z_0aAz_0 is equivalent to a loop about r_1. Similarly, the path $ABCDEB$ is equivalent to $ABCEA + AECDB$, both of which can be reduced to loops, and so on. Therefore if we know the integrals

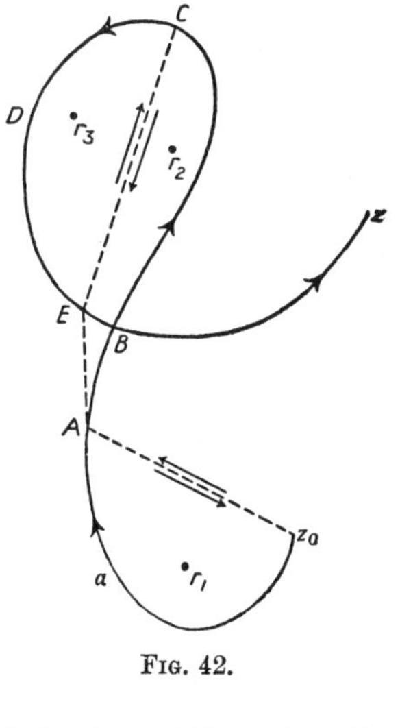

FIG. 42.

$$(2) \quad \int_{l\sigma} \frac{P(z)\,dz}{\sqrt{R(z)}} = 2A_\sigma, \qquad \sigma = 1, 2, \ldots, k,$$

along the loops starting and ending at z_0, then all the different values of $I(z_0)$ along different paths starting and ending at z_0 are of the form

$$(3) \qquad 2A_{\sigma_1} - 2A_{\sigma_2} + 2A_{\sigma_3} - \ldots.$$

The alternations in sign are due to the fact that, starting with one of the two determinations of the radical for the first loop, we come back with the other one and thus start the next loop with the new determination.

Putting

(4) $$\omega_\sigma = A_1 - A_{\sigma+1}$$

we obtain as possible values, for an *even* number of loops taken successively,

(5) $$2m_1\omega_1 + 2m_2\omega_2 + \ldots + 2m_{k-1}\omega_{k-1},$$

where $m_1, m_2, \ldots$ are positive or negative integers (negative when we have to describe a loop in the negative sense); if the number of loops is *odd* we add to (3) $-2A_1 + 2A_1$ and write it in the form

(6) $$2m_1\omega_1 + 2m_2\omega_2 + \ldots + 2m_{k-1}\omega_{k-1} + 2A_1.$$

Adding to (5) or to (6) the value, I, of our integral along a direct path from z_0 to z, we obtain all the possible values of $I(z)$ in the double form

$$2m_1\omega_1 + 2m_2\omega_2 + \ldots + 2m_{k-1}\omega_{k-1} + I \text{ (even number of loops)},$$
$$2m_1\omega_1 + 2m_2\omega_2 + \ldots + 2m_{k-1}\omega_{k-1} + 2A_1 - I$$

(odd number of loops).

The numbers $\omega_1, \ldots, \omega_{k-1}$ are called the periods of the integral (1). We might also say that (1) has only *two* really distinct values, viz. I and $2A_1 - I$, the others being obtained by adding to one of these two values a sum of multiples of some or all the periods.

If $k = 2p$, the number of periods $2p-1$ is reduced by 1 owing to the fact that in integrating along a large circle containing all the roots we obtain zero, i. e.

$$A_1 - A_2 + A_3 - \ldots + (-1)^{k+1} A_k = 0\,;$$
$$\omega_1 - \omega_2 + \ldots + (-1)^k \omega_{k-1} = 0.$$

Thus one of the periods can be expressed as a linear function of the others with integral coefficients. In particular cases, even if k is odd some of the periods may be eliminated in this way. Elementary algebraic considerations on linear systems of equations with integral coefficients show (see Picard's *Traité*, vol. ii,

p. 213) that there is in every case a certain number, m say, of *distinct* periods, not reducible, and such that every period is a linear integral combination of the m distinct periods.

In this respect the most important fact about $I(z)$ is that

I. *$I(z)$ has more than one distinct period.*

Proof. We suppose, to have a concrete case before us, that $k = 2p+1$ (odd). Suppose now that there is only one period, i. e., for every value of z, $I(z)$ assumes values of the types $I+\lambda\omega$ and $2A_1 - I + \mu\omega$ (λ, μ integers). Then it follows that

$$G(z) = e^{2\pi i I(z)/\omega} + e^{[2A_1 - I(z)]2\pi i/\omega}$$

is a uniform function of z. Since $I(z)$ is of the first kind, i. e. remains finite and regular also for $z = \infty$, Liouville's theorem applies and shows that $G(z)$ is a constant. But, putting $e^{2\pi i I(z)/\omega} = v$, we have $G(z) = (v^2+c)/v$ where $c = e^{4A_1\pi i/\omega}$ and the function $(v^2+c)/v$ reduces to a constant only if v is a constant; which is absurd, as $I(z)$ is not a constant.

If the degree of $R(z)$ is $\leqslant 4$, $I(z)$ is called an elliptical integral. We suppose, as before, that the roots of $R(z)$ are distinct. The maximum number of periods for $I(z)$ is in this case 2 and, by I, its minimum number of periods is also 2. But in this particular case we can establish a more specific property of the periods, fundamental in the theory of elliptic integrals and their inversion.

II. *The ratio of the two periods of the integral*

$$\int_{z_0}^{z} \frac{dz}{\sqrt{(z-a)(z-b)(z-c)(z-d)}}$$

is a complex number provided the four roots a, b, c, d are distinct.

We notice that if two roots coincide, $a = b$, say, the corresponding integral has only one distinct period $2(C-D)$. In fact, the quadratic form $(z-c)(z-d)$ under the radical has an even number, 2, of distinct zeros and thus the integral along a circle containing a, c, d is zero, i. e.

$$2A + 2C - 2D = 2A + 2(C-D) = 0,$$

where A, C, D denote the values of the integral along the respective loops. Therefore the condition that a, b, c, d are distinct is essential.

Proof. If the ratio r of the two periods were real, this real number would be an irrational number, for a relation $\omega_2 = \frac{A}{B}\omega_1$ (A and B integers) would eliminate one of the periods. Let a be replaced by a variable t. *The ratio r is then a function of t, $r = r(t)$, regular at $t = a$.* In fact, the two periods $2(B-D)$, $2(C-D)$ are regular functions of t since the loops B, C, D with respect to b, c, d are obviously regular functions of t, t being outside the closed path. This function $r(t)$ defined in the neighbourhood of $t = a$ does not reduce to a constant. For, being regular at $t = a$, $r(t)$ would be a constant throughout, and in particular, for $t = b$, i.e. for $a = b$; but, if this were so, the corresponding integral would have two distinct periods.

Suppose $r(a) = \mu$, a real irrational number. Since the roots of an equation are continuous functions of the coefficients, the equation $r(z) = \mu'$, where μ' is a fraction sufficiently near μ, has at least one root z_0, say, since $r(t) \neq$ const. By taking μ' sufficiently near μ, z_0 is as near a as we please, i.e. *distinct from b, c, d.* Therefore we have an integral of the type considered with the roots z_0, b, c, d, having only one distinct period, which is absurd. Therefore the ratio of the two periods cannot be real.

65. *Applications of the residue theorem.* Consider concentric circles c_ν of radii r_ν ($r_\nu \to \infty$) not passing through any of the poles of a meromorphic function $f(z)$. Denoting the sum of residues in $|z| = r_\nu$ by $\Sigma(c_\nu; f)$, we have, by the residue theorem,

$$(1) \quad \Sigma(c_\nu; f) = \frac{1}{2\pi i}\int_{c_\nu} f(z)dz = \frac{1}{2\pi}\int_0^{2\pi} z_\nu f(z_\nu)\, d\theta,\ z_\nu = r_\nu e^{i\theta}.$$

The limit of $\Sigma(c_\nu; f)$, if it exists, is called the *complete residue* of $f(z)$ with respect to the circles c_ν, and is denoted by $\bar{\Sigma}(c_\nu; f)$.

I. *If* $\lim_{\nu\to\infty} z_\nu f(z_\nu) = A$ *uniformly for* $0 \leqslant \theta < 2\pi$, $\bar{\Sigma}(c_\nu; f) = A$.

(Cauchy, 1827.)

Proof. By (1),

$$\Sigma(c_\nu; f) - A = \frac{1}{2\pi}\int_0^{2\pi}[z_\nu f(z_\nu) - A]\, d\theta,$$

and, by hypothesis, $|z_\nu f(z_\nu) - A| < \epsilon$ for sufficiently large ν. Hence $|\Sigma(c_\nu; f) - A| < \epsilon$. Q. e. d.

We notice that for other sequences of closed curves, e.g. squares extending to ∞, the order of the residues added together may vary, so that, if their sum is only conditionally convergent, its value (if any) may differ from A. Hence the qualifying phrase 'with respect to the circles c_ν'.

Sometimes in order to avoid poles a slight generalization of I is used.

II. *If* $|z_\nu f(z_\nu)| < M$ *and* $\lim_{\nu\to\infty} z_\nu f(z_\nu) = A$ *uniformly for* $0 \leqslant \theta < 2\pi$ *when we exclude a finite number of particular values* $\theta_1, \ldots, \theta_n$ *by arcs subtending arbitrarily small angles, then* $\bar{\Sigma}(c_\nu; f) = A$.

Proof. The arcs excluding the arguments $\theta_1, \ldots, \theta_n$ being $\theta_k - \eta \leqslant \theta \leqslant \theta_k + \eta$, $k = 1, 2, \ldots, n$, on the remaining arcs we have, as before, $|z_\nu f(z_\nu) - A| < \epsilon$. Hence, for sufficiently large ν,

$$|\Sigma(c_\nu; f) - A| < \epsilon + 2n\eta\frac{M + |A|}{2\pi},$$

which proves the statement, since η is arbitrarily small.

The same reasoning leads to

III. *If* $|z_\nu f(z_\nu)| < M$ *and, uniformly for every positive* ϵ,

$$\lim z_\nu f(z_\nu) = A \text{ for } \theta_0 + \epsilon \leqslant \theta \leqslant \theta_0 + \pi - \epsilon,$$
$$\lim z_\nu f(z_\nu) = B \text{ for } \theta_0 + \pi + \epsilon \leqslant \theta \leqslant \theta_0 + 2\pi - \epsilon,$$

then $\bar{\Sigma}(c_\nu; f) = \dfrac{A+B}{2}$.

Consider as an example the function

$$(2) \qquad f(z) = \frac{1}{z^{2k}}\frac{1}{e^z - 1},$$

where k is a positive integer. Its poles are at

$$z = \pm 2\pi i\nu, \; \nu = 0, 1, \ldots,$$

and the corresponding residues, when $\nu \neq 0$, are $(-1)^k (2\pi\nu)^{-2k}$. In order to calculate the residue at $z = 0$, we put

$$(3) \qquad \frac{1}{e^z - 1} = \frac{1}{z} - \frac{1}{2} + \sum_1^\infty (-1)^{\nu-1}\frac{B_\nu z^{2\nu-1}}{(2\nu)!},$$

which gives, by L'Hospital's rule, the residue $\dfrac{(-1)^{k-1}B_k}{(2k)!}$.

We are going to determine B_k by II.

Exclude the poles of $1/(e^z-1)$ by small circles and denote the remaining region by R. Putting $z=x+iy$, we obviously have

$$\left|\frac{1}{e^z-1}\right| < \frac{1}{e^a-1} \quad \text{for } x>a>0,$$

$$\left|\frac{1}{e^z-1}\right| < \frac{1}{1-e^{-a}} \quad \text{for } x<-a.$$

Since $\dfrac{1}{e^z-1}$ has the period $2\pi i$, it is bounded in the part of R which lies in the strip $-a \leqslant x \leqslant a$. If M be larger than the three bounds, we have $1/|e^z-1|<M$ in R. It is so in particular on the circles of radii $r_\nu=(2\nu-1)\pi$, and thus $z_\nu f(z_\nu)\to 0$ uniformly in $0\leqslant\theta<2\pi$ when $\nu\to\infty$, i.e. its complete residue exists and equals zero. Hence

$$(4) \qquad B_k = \frac{2\,(2k)!}{(2\pi)^{2k}} \sum_1^\infty \frac{1}{\nu^{2k}}.$$

The numbers B_k are called *Bernoulli's numbers.*

We might also calculate the number B_k as the coefficient of z^{2k-1} in the Taylor expansion of $1/(e^z-1)-1/z$, and use the formula (4) for the summation of the infinite series on the right-hand side (see Ex. IV. 14).

A very similar argument applies to the more general case

$$f(z) = \frac{1}{z^n}\frac{e^{tz}}{e^z-1}, \quad 0\leqslant t\leqslant 1.$$

If we put

$$(5) \qquad \frac{e^{tz}}{e^z-1} = \frac{1}{z} + \sum_1^\infty \frac{g_\nu(t)z^{\nu-1}}{\nu!},$$

the residue of $f(z)$ at the origin is $g_n(t)/n!$. We have again

$$|e^{tz}/(e^z-1)| < M' = e^a M \quad \text{in } R.$$

In fact, the left-hand side is $<1/(1-e^{-a})$ if $x<-a$ and $<e^a M$ in the band $-a\leqslant x\leqslant a$, and $<1/(1-e^{-a})$ if $x>a$, for

$$e^{tz}/(e^z-1) = e^{-z(1-t)}/(1-e^{-z}).$$

We notice that the *same remark applies to functions like* sec z cosec z, tan z, cot z, $e^{tz}/(e^z+1)$, &c.

Thus, for $n>1$ and $r_\nu = (2\nu-1)\pi$, the product $z_\nu f(z_\nu)\to 0$ uniformly for $0\leqslant\theta<2\pi$, and thus the complete residue of $f(z)$ is 0. Hence we readily obtain for $0\leqslant t\leqslant 1$

$$(6)\qquad \begin{aligned} g_{2k}(t) &= (-1)^{k+1}2\,(2k)!\sum_1^\infty \frac{\cos 2\nu\pi t}{(2\nu\pi)^{2k}},\\ g_{2k+1}(t) &= (-1)^{k+1}2(2k+1)!\sum_1^\infty \frac{\sin 2\nu\pi t}{(2\nu\pi)^{2k+1}}.\end{aligned}$$

For $n=1$, excluding the extremities $t=0$ and $t=1$, we readily verify that $zf(z) = e^{tz}/(e^z-1)$ tends to 0 when $z\to\infty$ in one the two angles

$$-\pi/2+\epsilon\leqslant\theta\leqslant\pi/2-\epsilon,\quad \pi/2+\epsilon\leqslant\theta\leqslant 3\pi/2-\epsilon,$$

for an arbitrarily small ϵ. Hence, by III,

$$(7)\qquad g_1(t) = t-1/2 = -\sum_1^\infty \frac{1}{\nu\pi}\sin 2\nu\pi t.$$

On the other hand, multiplying (3) by the expansion of e^{tz}, we obtain

$$g_\nu(t) = t^\nu - \frac{\nu}{2}t^{\nu-1} + C_1^2 B_1 t^{\nu-2} - C_2^4 B_2 t^{\nu-4} + \dots.$$

The polynomials

$$P_{2k}(t) = g_{2k}(t) + (-1)^k B_k,$$
$$P_{2k+1}(t) = g_{2k+1}(t)$$

are called *Bernoulli's polynomials.* Formulae (6) and (7) are the trigonometrical expansions of these polynomials for $0\leqslant t\leqslant 1$. Since these expansions have the period 1, they reproduce in other intervals the values of the polynomials in the first interval.

We easily verify the following properties of the functions $g_\nu(t)$, (by 6),

$$g'_{\nu+1}(t) = (\nu+1)g_\nu(t),\qquad \nu = 1, 2, \dots$$
$$g_{2k}(1-t) = g_{2k}(t),\qquad g_{2k+1}(1-t) = -g_{2k+1}(t),$$
$$\int_0^1 P_{2k}(t)\,dt = (-1)^k B_k.$$

Changing the sign $-$ into $+$ in the left-hand side of (5) we obtain *Hermite's polynomials*

$$\frac{e^{tz}}{e^z+1} = \sum_0^\infty \frac{h_\nu(t)}{\nu!}z^\nu,\qquad h_0(t) = \tfrac{1}{2},$$

and, following the above reasoning, we obtain, for $0 \leqslant t \leqslant 1$,

$$h_{2k}(t) = (-1)^k 2(2k)! \sum_0^\infty \frac{\sin(2\nu+1)\pi t}{[(2\nu+1)\pi]^{2k+1}}, \; k = 1, 2, \ldots$$

$$h_{2k+1}(t) = (-1)^{k+1} 2(2k+1)! \sum_0^\infty \frac{\cos(2\nu+1)\pi t}{[(2\nu+1)\pi]^{2k+1}}, \; k = 0, 1, 2, \ldots$$

with corresponding properties.

The same method leads to the *decomposition of functions into rational fractions.* Let $z_\nu = r_\nu e^{i\theta}$, and suppose that $|f(z_\nu)| < M$ for every ν and every θ in $(0, 2\pi)$, and also that $\lim f(z_\nu) = A$ uniformly in $0 \leqslant \theta < 2\pi$, with the possible exception of a finite number of arcs subtending arbitrarily small angles excluding $\theta_1, \theta_2, \ldots, \theta_n$. The same is true then of the limit

$$\lim z_\nu f(z_\nu)/(z_\nu - x),$$

for an arbitrary complex x, and thus, by II,

$$\Sigma\,[c_\nu, f(z)/(z-x)] = A.$$

But the residue of $f(z)/(z-x)$ at $z = x$ is $f(x)$. Hence the important formula

$$(8) \qquad f(x) = A + \bar{\Sigma}'\left(c_\nu\,;\; \frac{f(z)}{x-z}\right),$$

where the accent on Σ indicates that the residue at $z = x$ is omitted (it is on the other side).

For example, if $f(z) = \pi \cot \pi z = \dfrac{(\sin \pi z)'}{\sin \pi z}$, the poles (simple) of $f(z)$ are $z = 0, \pm 1, \pm 2, \ldots$ each with the residue 1. From our remark in connexion with $e^{tz}/(e^z - 1)$, its modulus is bounded if $r_\nu = \nu - 1/2$. Hence (8) applies with $A = 0$ and we obtain the well-known formula

$$\pi \cot \pi x = \frac{1}{x} + \sum_1^\infty \left(\frac{1}{x-\nu} + \frac{1}{x+\nu}\right) = \frac{1}{x} + 2x \sum_1^\infty \frac{1}{x^2 - \nu^2}.$$

EXERCISE VII

1. Work out the details of the following remarks:

Putting $z = re^{i\theta}$, we have on the semicircle g_r, $|z| = r$, $0 \leqslant \theta \leqslant \pi$, $\int_{g_r} f(z)dz = \int_0^\pi zf(z)i\,d\theta$ and thus, if $zf(z)$ tends uniformly to 0 when

$r \to \infty$, $\lim \int_{g_r} f(z) dz = 0$. Hence, when the two real integrals $\int_a^\infty f(x)\,dx$ and $\int_{-\infty}^a f(x)\,dx$ exist, the residue theorem gives

$$\int_C f(z)\,dz = 2\pi i \Sigma R_\sigma,$$

where the contour C is formed by the real segment $(-r, r)$ and the upper (or lower) semicircle of radius r. This artifice with a suitable modification of the contour is very much used in the evaluation of integrals. In particular the semicircle may be replaced by a complete circle.

2. Calculate $\int_{-\infty}^{+\infty} \frac{dx}{1+x^4}$. The conditions of Ex. 1 are obviously satisfied and the two poles of the integral in C are $z_1 = e^{\pi i/4}$ and $z_2 = e^{3\pi i/4}$. The corresponding residues are readily calculated by L'Hospital's rule applied to $(z-z_1)/(1+z^4)$ when $z_1 \to z$;

$$R_1 = 1/4z^3 = -z_1/4$$

and $R_2 = -z_2/4$. The value of the integral is $\pi/\sqrt{2}$.

3. Calculate $\int_0^{2\pi} \frac{1+\cos x}{1+\cos^2 x}\,dx$. Transform the integral in Ex. 2.

4. Calculate $\int_0^\infty \frac{x^{a-1}dx}{1+x}$, $0<a<1$. If $f(z)$ is regular along the segment (z_0, z_1), the value of $\int f(z)dz$ on parallel segments sufficiently near (z_0, z_1) differs as little as we like from the value of the same integral along (z_0, z_1). Therefore in our case the contour C_η, $(\epsilon+i\eta, r+i\eta, A, r-i\eta, \epsilon-i\eta, B, \epsilon+i\eta)$ is equivalent to the contour C, $(\epsilon, r, A, r, \epsilon, B, \epsilon)$ in the precise sense that the integrals taken along the two contours have exactly the same value. In fact, when we replace the segment $(\epsilon+i\eta, r+i\eta)$ by $(\epsilon+i\eta', r+i\eta')$, $0<\eta'<\eta$, the parallelogram determined by these segments contains no singular point. On the other hand the only singularity enclosed by C is the pole $z = -1$ with the residue $-e^{a\pi i}$. Since the function is uniform in C_η, the residue theorem applies to C_η, and, by our remark, also to C. Thus we obtain $\int_C \frac{z^a dz}{z(1+z)} = -2\pi i e^{a\pi i}$.

But the part of the integral along is $|z| = r$ is

$$r^a i \int_0^{2\pi} \frac{e^{a\theta i}}{1+re^{\theta i}} d\theta \to 0 \text{ when } r \to \infty \text{ since } a<1;$$

and

$$\left| \epsilon^a i \int_{2\pi}^0 \frac{e^{a\theta i} d\theta}{1+\epsilon e^{\theta i}} \right| < |\epsilon^a| \frac{2\pi}{1-\epsilon} \to 0 \text{ with } \epsilon.$$

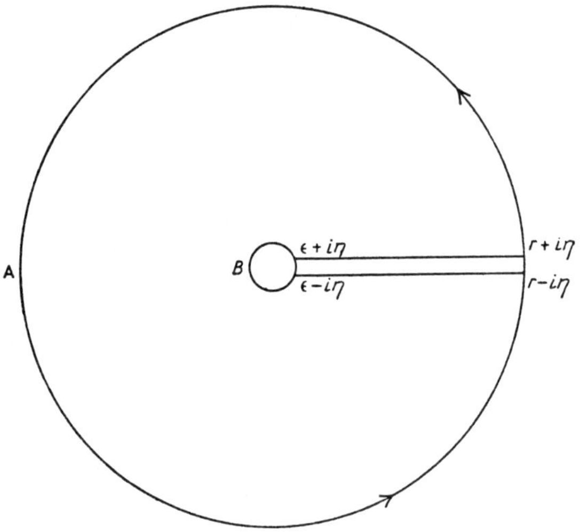

FIG. 43.

After having described the first circle, z becomes $re^{2\pi i}$ and z^a becomes $r^a e^{2\pi a i}$, i.e. passing to the limit $r = \infty$,

$$\int_0^\infty \frac{x^{a-1} dx}{1+x} + \int_\infty^0 \frac{e^{2a\pi i} x^{a-1} dx}{1+x} = -2\pi i e^{a\pi i},$$

$$(e^{-a\pi i} - e^{a\pi i}) \int_0^\infty \frac{x^{a-1} dx}{1+x} = 2\pi i$$

and thus finally $$\int_0^\infty \frac{x^{a-1} dx}{1+x} = \frac{\pi}{\sin a\pi}.$$

5. Calculate $$\int_0^\infty \frac{\sqrt[3]{x} dx}{(x^2+a^2)^2}.$$

6. Calculate $$\int_{|z|=4} \frac{dz}{(z-1)^2 (z-2)^3 \sqrt{z+5}}$$

7. Calculate $$\int_{|z|=2} \frac{z^3 e^{1/z} dz}{z+1}.$$

8. Calculate $$\int_0^{\infty} \frac{x^2 dx}{x^4+x^2+1}.$$

9. Calculate $\int_{|z|=1} \frac{dz}{(z-a)^n(z-b)^n}$, where $|a| < 1 < |b|$, and n is an integer.

10. Putting $J(w,T) = \int_{c-Ti}^{c+Ti} \frac{e^{ws} ds}{s^2}$, $c>0$, w real, show that the limit $J(w) = \lim_{T\to\infty} J(w,T)$ exists and is 0 if $w \leqslant 0$ and is $2\pi i w$ if $w \geqslant 0$.

We put $s = \sigma + it$. From $|e^{ws}/s^2| = e^{cw}/(c^2+t^2)$ and from the fact that $\int_{-\infty}^{+\infty} dt/(c^2+t^2)$ exists, it follows that the limit of $J(w,T)$ exists when $T \to \infty$.

(a) $w \leqslant 0$. Apply the residue theorem to the domain D limited by the segment $(c-Ti, c+Ti)$ and by the semicircle C_T, with the diameter $(c-Ti, c+Ti)$, on the right. Since the integrand is regular in D, we have $$J(w,T) = \int_{C_T} e^{ws} ds / s^2$$ where C_T is the semicircle $s = c + Te^{i\phi}$, $-\pi/2 \leqslant \phi \leqslant \pi/2$. The length of C_T is πT and the modulus of the integrand is, at every point of this path, $\leqslant e^{cw}/T^2$, because $\sigma \geqslant c$, $(w<0)$ and $|s| \geqslant T$, i.e. $|J(w,T)| \leqslant \pi e^{cw}/T \to 0$ with $1/T$.

(b) $w \geqslant 0$. Take $T > c$ and apply the residue theorem to the domain D enclosed by the segment $(c-Ti, c+Ti)$ and by the semicircle $\bar{C}_T$ on the left with the diameter $(c-Ti, c+Ti)$. The integrand has a pole $s=0$ in D with the residue w. Hence, $$J(w,T) - 2\pi i w = \int_{\bar{C}_T} e^{ws} ds / s^2 \text{ with } s = c + Te^{i\phi},\ 3\pi/2 > \phi > \pi/2.$$ The length of the semicircle is πT and the modulus of the integrand along the semicircle is $\leqslant e^{cw}/(T-c)^2$, for $\sigma \leqslant c$ and $|s| \geqslant T-c$. Hence, $|J(w,T) - 2\pi i w| \leqslant \pi e^{cw} T/(T-c)^2 \to 0$. Q. e. d.

11. $f(z)$ is regular and bounded in $|z| < 1$ and, except at a finite number of points on $|z| = 1$, also continuous in $|z| \leqslant 1$. Then $\int_0^{2\pi} f(e^{i\theta}) d\theta = 2\pi f(0)$. Put, for $0 \leqslant r < 1$,

$$I(r) = \int_0^{2\pi} f(e^{i\theta})\,d\theta - 2\pi f(0) = \int_0^{2\pi} [f(e^{i\theta}) - f(re^{i\theta})]\,d\theta,$$

and exclude the points of discontinuity by small arcs c_i of total length σ. Since $|f(z)|$ is bounded, the part of $I(r)$ along the arcs c_i can be made less in absolute value than any ϵ (by taking sufficiently small σ). When σ is fixed, the other parts of $I(r)$ give a sum tending to 0 as $r \to 1$, for $f(z)$ is continuous on these arcs.

12. The domain D is simply connected in the u-plane and is enclosed by a simple contour C; $z = g(u)$ maps D biuniformly upon $|z| < 1$, where $z = 0$ corresponds to $u = v$, say; $u = f(z)$ is the inverse function of $z = g(u)$; $k(u)$ any function regular in D. Putting $k[f(z)] = h(z)$ we have, by Ex. 11,

$$2\pi i h(0) = \int_{|z|=r} h(z)\frac{dz}{z}$$

and from $h[g(u)] = k(u)$ and $g(v) = 0$ we obtain the formula

$$2\pi i k(v) = \int_C \frac{k(u)\,dg(u)}{g(u)}.$$

Use this general remark to prove that

$$f(x+iy) = \int_{-\infty}^{+\infty} f(it)\,d\arctan\frac{t-y}{x}.$$

Take $\mathrm{Rl}\,(u) \geqslant 0$ for D and $\dfrac{v-u}{\bar{v}+u}$ for $g(u)$.

13. *$f(z)$ is meromorphic in $\mathrm{Rl}(z) \geqslant 0$ with the zeros $a_1, \ldots, a_s$ and the poles $b_1, \ldots, b_r$; on the boundary, $f(z)$ is regular (infinity included) and different from 0. Then, for every inner point $z = x + iy$,*

$$\log|f(z)| + \sum_{m=1}^{s} \log\left|\frac{z+\bar{a}_m}{z-a_m}\right| - \sum_{n=1}^{r} \log\left|\frac{z+\bar{b}_n}{z-b_n}\right|$$

$$= \frac{1}{\pi}\int_{-\infty}^{\infty} \log|f(it)|\,d\arctan\frac{t-y}{x}.$$

(F. and R. Nevanlinna, 1922 a.)

Make use of the following general remark. (Notation as in Ex. 12.) $k(u)$ is meromorphic in D, with the zeros $a_1, \ldots, a_s$ and the poles $b_1, \ldots, b_r$, and is different from 0 and ∞ on the boundary and at the inner point z. Then $h(z) = k[f(z)]$ has the zeros $A_m = g(a_m)$ and the poles $B_n = g(b_n)$. Thus, by Jensen's formula (60. 6),

$$\log|h(0)| + \sum \log \frac{1}{|A_m|} - \sum \log \frac{1}{|B_n|} = \int_{|z|=r} \log h(z) \frac{dz}{2\pi i z}.$$

Hence, by a transformation of the variables as in Ex. 12,

$$\sum_{m=1}^{s} \log \frac{1}{|g(a_m)|} - \sum_{n=1}^{r} \log \frac{1}{|g(b_n)|} = \frac{1}{2\pi i}\int_C \log|k(u)| \frac{dg(u)}{g(u)} - \log|k(z)|$$

where $$|g(a_m)| < 1, |g(b_n)| < 1, \frac{dg(u)}{2\pi i\, g(u)} > 0.$$

14. *Suppose $f(z)$ is regular at every finite point and zero for $z = z_1, z_2, \ldots, z_n, \ldots$, where $|z_n| = n$. Then if $|f(z)| < e^{k|z|}$, for $|z| > R$, where $0 < k < 1$, we have $f(z) \equiv 0$.*

If $f(z)$ is not identically zero then, dividing if necessary by Az^p, we may suppose $f(0) = 1$. Then Jensen's formula (60. 6), for $r = n$, gives

$$\log \frac{n^n}{n!} \leqslant \frac{1}{2\pi} \int_0^{2\pi} \log|f(ne^{i\theta})|\, d\theta,$$

i. e. $$n\eta_n \leqslant kn,$$

for sufficiently large n, where by Stirling's formula Ex. IV. 22, $\eta_n \to 1$, which is absurd.

(Estermann. See also Pólya-Szegö, iii. 328.)

CHAPTER VIII

BIUNIFORM MAPPING. PICARD'S THEOREM

66. *Inversion of Taylor series.* In Art. 63 we established a general result on the inversion of Taylor series. We are now going to determine a minimum circle of regularity and a bound for the inverse function.

I. *If* $u = \Sigma a_n z^n = f(z)$ *is regular and* $|u| < M$ *in* $|z| < R$ *and* $a_0 = 0$, $a_1 \neq 0$, *then the inverse function* $z = g(u)$ *is regular and* $|g(u)| < R$ *in* $|u| < \phi(M, R|a_1|)$, *where the function* ϕ *is the same for the whole class of functions satisfying the conditions of the theorem.* (Landau, 1904.)

Proof. To simplify the reasoning we establish the theorem first in the special case when $R = 1$, $a_1 = 1$.

By the principle of the maximum

$$\max_{|z|=r} |a_2 + a_3 z + a_4 z^2 + \ldots| \geqslant |a_2|$$

is a non-decreasing function of r, for $r < 1$. We have

$$\max_{|z|=r} |f(z) - z| = r^2 \max_{|z|=r} |a_2 + a_3 z + \ldots|,$$

so that

$$\frac{1}{r} \max_{|z|=r} |f(z) - z|$$

steadily decreases to 0 with r. Hence there is an R' such that for $0 < r < R'$

$$\phi(r) = r - \max_{|z|=r} |f(z) - z| = r\left(1 - \frac{1}{r} \max_{|z|=r} |f(z) - z|\right) > 0.$$

It follows that for $0 < r < R'$ and $|z| = r$

$$|f(z)| = |z - \{z - f(z)\}| \geqslant |z| - |z - f(z)| \geqslant \phi(r) > 0,$$

and thus, *in* $|z| < R'$, *the origin is the only zero of* $f(z)$.

Consider now the complex variable y varying in the circle $|y| < \phi(r)$, where r is fixed, and form the integral

$$I(y) = \frac{1}{2\pi i} \int_{|z|=r} \frac{f'(z)}{f(z) - y} dz.$$

For $y = 0$, the value of this integral, by (59. 4), is 1, for $Z = 1$ and $P = 0$ (no poles and only one single zero in $|z| \leqslant r$).

On the other hand, by 54. III, $I(y)$ is a continuous (in fact regular) function of y in $|y| < \phi(r)$, since the integrand is a continuous (regular) function of z on $|z| = r$ and is a regular function of y in $|y| < \phi(r)$. But, for a fixed y, $[f(z)-y]' = f'(z)$, i.e. the same integral equals the number of roots of $f(z)-y = 0$ in $|z| < r$. It follows that $I(y)$ has an integral value and, since it is continuous, its value cannot jump from one integer to another. Hence

$$\frac{1}{2\pi i}\int_{|z|=r}\frac{f'(z)}{f(z)-y}\,dz = 1 \text{ in } |y| < \phi(r),$$

and thus, for a fixed $|y| < \phi(r)$, the equation in z, $f(z) = y$, has only one solution in $|z| < r$, i.e. *the inverse function* $z(y)$ is uniform in $|y| < \phi(r)$.

Replacing the function $g(z)$ by z in (59. 5) and $f(z)$ by $f(z)-y$, and noticing that in the present case $f(z)$ has no poles in C and has only one zero denoted by $z(y)$, we obtain

$$z(y) = \frac{1}{2\pi i}\int_{|z|=r} z\,\frac{f'(z)\,dz}{f(z)-y}\,.$$

It follows that $z(y)$ *is a regular function of* y *in* $|y| < \phi(r)$.

We have to find a suitable value of r for which $\phi(r) > 0$. For this purpose we notice first that $M \geqslant 1$ (in the particular case considered). In fact, since $f(z)$ is regular on $|z| = 1$, we have

$$\max_{|z|=1}|f(z)| = \max_{|z|=1}\left|\frac{f(z)}{z}\right| = \max_{|z|=1}|1 + a_2 z + \dots| \geqslant 1.$$

Thus we can propose for r the value $1/4M$. We find, by 41. IV,

$$\phi\left(\frac{1}{4M}\right) \geqslant r - \sum_{2}^{\infty} M r^n = r - \frac{Mr^2}{1-r}$$

and, since

$$\frac{1}{1-r} = \frac{4M}{4M-1} \leqslant \frac{4}{3},$$

we obtain

$$\phi\left(\frac{1}{4M}\right) \geqslant r - \frac{4Mr^2}{3} = \frac{1}{6M}$$

The theorem thus is established for the particular case $R = 1$ and $a_1 = 1$. To prove it in the general case, consider the function

$$F(z) = \frac{f(Rz)}{Ra_1}.$$

We readily verify that $F(0) = 0$, $F'(0) = 1$, and

$$|F(z)| \leqslant \frac{M}{R|a_1|} \quad \text{if} \quad |z| \leqslant 1.$$

Hence $F(z)$ satisfies the conditions of the particular case if we replace M by $M/R|a_1|$, i. e., denoting the inverse function of $v = F(z)$ by $z = g(v)$, we know that $g(v)$ is regular and $|g(v)| < 1$ in $|v| < R|a_1|/6M$.

Putting $Rz = z'$, we have

$$f(z') = Ra_1 F(z'/R),$$

i. e. the inverse function $z'(v)$ of $f(z') = v$ is also the inverse function of

$$f(z'/R) = v/Ra_1.$$

Therefore

$$\frac{z'}{R} = g\left(\frac{v}{Ra_1}\right)$$

and

$$z' = Rg(v/Ra_1).$$

The last equation shows that z' is regular and $|z'| < R$ in

$$\left|\frac{v}{Ra}\right| < \left|\frac{Ra_1}{6M}\right|, \text{ i.e. in } |v| < \frac{R^2|a_1|^2}{6M} \equiv \phi(M, R|a_1|).$$

We notice, suppressing the accent of z' and replacing v by u, that the inverse function $z'(v)$ of $f(z') = v$ is just the inverse function $z = g(u)$ of the theorem.

When $a_0 = f(0) \neq 0$, the theorem is still valid provided we replace u by $u - a_0$. We can similarly replace z by $z - z_0$ provided the conditions are satisfied in $|z - z_0| < R$.

67. *Biuniform mapping.* Suppose that $f'(z) \neq 0$ in the domain D. Then, by 66. I, the inverse function $z = g(u)$ of the uniform function $u = f(z)$ is regular in a sufficiently small circle about every point u in question. Thus, if $f(a) = b$, all the values taken from a small circle about b are assumed near a.

We are going to prove that the *values u corresponding to the points of D form a domain D'.*

Proof. We have just seen that to every value u assumed in D there corresponds a circle of radius r about u, such that all the values taken from the circle are assumed by u, i. e. belong to D'. We have still to show that D' is connex. Since D is, by hypothesis, a domain, we can connect any pair of its points z_1, z_2 by a rectifiable curve (or even by a polygon) $C: z(t)$, such that $z(t_1) = z_1$, $z(t_2) = z_2$. All the points of C are in D, and consequently are inner points. The corresponding curve in the u-plane is $C': u[z(t)]$, reducing to $u_1 = f(z_1)$ and $u_2 = f(z_2)$ for $t = t_1$, $t = t_2$ respectively.

As we have seen, to any point u of the continuous curve C' there corresponds a circle of radius r_u in D'. By Borel's lemma, a finite number of the same circles cover C', i. e. C' lies inside the domain of points belonging to at least one of these finite circles all in D', which shows that D' is connex. As D' has only inner points, it is a domain. Since, by 66. I, $z = g(u)$ is uniform at every point of D' (no branch point in D'), we have proved the following result.

I. *Suppose $u = f(z)$ is uniform and regular in D, $f'(z) \neq 0$ in D. Then the values u corresponding to the points z of D form a one-sheeted domain D'.*

When $f'(a) = 0$, or more generally when

$$f(z) = f(a) + a_k(z-a)^k + \ldots, \quad a_k \neq 0,$$

the inverse function $u = g(z)$ has, by 63. III, a branch-point at a of multiplicity k. Since the zeros of $f'(z)$ are isolated from one another, there are only a finite number of such branch-points in any region R of D. If we mean by neighbourhood of a branch-point b, with a cycle of k branches, the k-fold circle about a of sufficiently small radius r, we see that, even at a branch-point, *neighbourhood corresponds to neighbourhood*, i. e. putting $f(a) = b$, the values of $z(u)$ assumed in an ordinary circle about $u = b$ do not cover a circle about $z = a$, but the values of $z(u)$ assumed in a k-fold circle about $u = b$ do cover a complete circle about $z = a$. Anyhow, points u near $u = b$ correspond to points z near $z = a$. Therefore connexity of the values u assumed at points z of D can be established as before. (We merely consider curves between z_1 and z_2 not passing through branch-points.) Thus D' is a domain.

II. *If* $u = f(z)$ *is uniform and regular in* D, *the values* u *corresponding to the points* z *of* D *form a domain* D'.

Since any region R in D contains only a finite number of branch-points of the inverse function, we can exclude them by small circles, and apply I to the remaining domain. This remark shows that though $f'(z) \neq 0$ in D, the corresponding domain D' may be multiply connected (also D, of course), i.e. *the inverse function may be multiform.* It is, of course, necessarily so when $f'(z)$ vanishes at some point of D.

Suppose now that D is *simply connected* and $f(z)$ regular in D. We are going to prove that $f(z)$ cannot be multiform.

III. (*Theorem of monodromy.*) *If* $f(z)$ *is regular in the simply connected domain* D, $f(z)$ *is uniform in* D. (Weierstrass.)

Proof. To say that $f(z)$ is not uniform in D means that there are two points a and b in D connected by two paths C_1 and C_2 such that, if we start from a with $f(z) = \Sigma a_n (z-a)^n$, the value of $f(z)$ at b arrived at from a along C_1 is different from its value at b obtained in the same way along C_2. Suppose first that the closed curve C formed by C_1 and C_2 is a simple contour with no boundary point of D inside it. Since, by hypothesis, the curves C_1 and C_2 are entirely in D and $f(z)$ is regular in D, there are, by Borel's lemma, a finite number of circles, centres at points of C_1 and C_2, covering C_1 and C_2. Since, in every circle of regular points, $f(z)$ is represented by a Taylor series, $f(z)$ is necessarily uniform in every circle containing only regular points, i.e. the part of C_1 or C_2 inside a circle may be replaced by a chord, and thus the two curves C_1 and C_2 by two simple polygons P_1 and P_2 between a and b. Dividing the closed polygon $P_1 + P_2$ into triangles, we see that if $f(z)$ is multiform inside $P_1 + P_2$, there is a triangle T in $P_1 + P_2$ such that $f(z)$, continued along T, is not uniform. Dividing T into smaller triangles, e.g. by halving the largest side and retaining a triangle along which $f(z)$ is not uniform, T dwindles to a point c of D. By hypothesis, however, $f(z)$ is regular at c, i.e. regular in $|z-c| < \rho$, and thus after a finite number of steps we obtain a triangle lying entirely in this circle, which is absurd.

If C encloses a boundary point of D, it encloses the whole boundary, since, by definition, the boundary of a simply connected domain consists of a single continuum. Therefore every branch of $f(z)$ is regular at $z = \infty$, and thus there is a sufficiently large circle K about the origin containing C and such that every branch of $f(z)$, specified by its expansion at $z = \infty$, is uniform and regular outside and on K. If we join a and b to K by two distinct simple polygons l and l' which do not cross C and meet K at a' and b' respectively, we obtain two closed curves c_1 and c_2 enclosing no boundary point of D. The curve c_1 is formed by the path $a'aC_1bb'K_1a'$ and c_2 by the path $a'aC_2bb'K_2a'$.

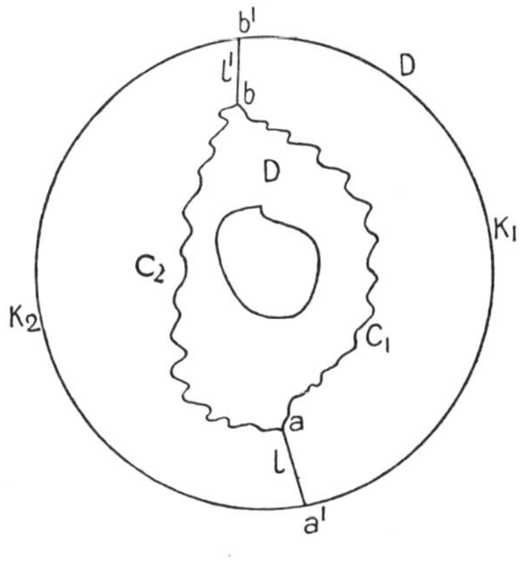

FIG. 43 a.

If z varies from a' to b' along K_1 and K_2, $f(z)$ assumes at b' the same value, provided in each case the initial value at a' is the same; the paths K_1 and K_2 are *equivalent*. But the result just proved applies to both c_1 and c_2 and shows that the path $a'aC_1bb'$ is equivalent to K_1 and the path $a'aC_2bb'$ is equivalent to K_2. Therefore c_1 and c_2 are also equivalent, which proves III, when C is a simple contour. In general we can show that C_1 and C_2 are equivalent by a finite number of applications of the above results, and this completes the proof.

This result states that regularity in a simply connected domain D implies uniformity in D. We shall now show that this implication is a characteristic property of simply connected domains. For this purpose we have to prove that regularity in D does not imply uniformity in D if D is not simply connected. This will prove

IV. *If regularity in D implies uniformity in D, D is simply connected.*

Proof. Suppose that D is not simply connected, i. e. its boundary contains at least two distinct continua C_1 and C_2. If the point at infinity is not an isolated boundary point, take two finite points a and b on C_1 and C_2 respectively, and consider the function

$$\phi(x) = 1/\sqrt{(x-a)(x-b)}.$$

Both branches of $\phi(x)$ are regular at every finite point except a and b. Putting $x = 1/z$ in $\phi(x)$ we obtain the function

$$z/\sqrt{(1-az)(1-bz)},$$

so that both branches are regular at $z = 0$ i. e. at $x = \infty$. Therefore $\phi(x)$ is certainly regular at every point of D.

Now by lemma 1 of Art. 50, there is a finite closed polygon π enclosing C_1 (if C_1 does not contain $x = \infty$) and separating it from C_2. When x describes π, $\phi(x)$ changes its value, since x turns about a but not about b, so that $\phi(x)$ is multiform in D.

If $x = \infty$ is an isolated boundary point of D we can argue in the same way with $\phi(x) = \log(x-a)$, where a is a finite boundary point. This completes the proof.

Apply III to the inverse function $z = g(u)$ of $u = f(z)$, the latter being regular and $f'(z) \neq 0$ in D. By I, $g(u)$ is regular at every point of the domain D' of u. Thus if *D is simply connected, $g(u)$ is uniform in D', by* III. In such a case the uniform function $u = f(z)$ establishes a one-one correspondence, called also a *biuniform mapping*, between D and D'.

V. *If $f(z)$ is uniform and regular and $f'(z) \neq 0$ in a simply connected domain D, the inverse function $u = g(z)$ is regular and uniform in the corresponding domain D'; $u = f(z)$ establishes a biuniform mapping between D and D'.*

68. *Bloch's theorem.* We are going to establish an important property of mapping by Taylor series, i. e. a characteristic property of the inverse function of a Taylor series.

I. *Bloch's theorem. If $u = f(z)$ is regular in $|z| \leqslant 1$ and $f(0) = 0, f'(0) = 1$, then there is in the u-plane a circle of radius B, the same for the whole class of functions satisfying the con-*

ditions, which is the biuniform picture of a domain in $|z|<1$. *B is called the Bloch constant.* (Bloch, 1925.)

Proof. Since, by hypothesis, $f(z) = z + a_2 z^2 + \dots$ is regular in and on $|z| = 1$, $f'(z) = 1 + 2a_2 z + \dots$ is also regular in and on $|z| = 1$ and

$$\max_{|z|=r} |f'(z)| \geqslant 1, \quad r \leqslant 1,$$

while

$$\max_{|z|=0} |f'(z)| = |f'(0)| = 1.$$

Moreover,

$$g(\theta) = \max_{|z|=1-\theta} |f'(z)| \tag{1}$$

is a continuous function of θ in $0 \leqslant \theta \leqslant 1$. Since $\theta g(\theta)$ vanishes at $\theta = 0$ and is 1 at $\theta = 1$ and $\theta g(\theta)$ is a continuous function in $(0, 1)$ there is a least value $\theta = \alpha$ for which $\theta g(\theta) = 1$. Thus

$$g(\alpha) = 1/\alpha \tag{2}$$

$$g(\theta) < 1/\theta \text{ for } \theta < \alpha. \tag{3}$$

We notice also that $g(\theta)$ is a non-increasing function of θ. Hence

$$g(\theta) < 2/\alpha \text{ in } (\alpha/2, \alpha),$$

i. e.

$$\max_{|z|=r} |f'(z)| < 2/\alpha \text{ in the ring } 1-\alpha < r < 1-\alpha/2 \tag{4}$$

and, $g(\theta)$ being a non-increasing function,

$$\max_{|z|=r} |f'(z)| < 1/\alpha \text{ for } r < 1-\alpha.$$

Since the maximum modulus is assumed somewhere on $|z| = r$, there is on $|z| = 1-\alpha$ (inner circle of the ring) a point z_0 such that $|f'(z_0)| = 1/\alpha$. Consider now the circle

$$|z - z_0| \leqslant \alpha/2.$$

By Darboux's mean value theorem (55. IV),

$$f(z) - f(z_0) = \lambda (z - z_0) f'(z'),$$

where $|\lambda| \leqslant 1$ and z' is on the segment between z and z_0.

By (4), z' being in the ring, $|f'(z')| < 2/\alpha$, i. e. when z is in the circle $|z - z_0| < \alpha/2$, we have

$$|f(z) - f(z_0)| < 1.$$

Now apply the inversion theorem 66. I to the function

$$u = f(z) - f(z_0),$$

the point z_0 taking the place of the origin $z = 0$. Since $M \leqslant 1$, we can take 1 for M (it means assigning to the inverse function a smaller circle than is necessary). Moreover $R = \alpha/2$ and

$$|a_1| = |f'(z_0)| = 1/\alpha,$$

i. e. $R|a_1| = 1/2$. Hence theorem 66. I applies with $\phi\,(1, 1/2)$, and thus the inverse function $z(u)$ is regular, and $|z| < 1$ in $|u - f(z_0)| < \phi(1, 1/2) = B$, which proves the theorem, since $\phi(1, 1/2)$ is a number independent of the particular function of the class considered.

69. *Missing values.* Bloch's theorem helps us to prove in a surprisingly simple way some of the most important modern theorems of function theory.

I. *Schottky's theorem. Consider the class K of functions $f(z) = a_0 + a_1 z + a_2 z^2 + \dots$ regular in $|z| \leqslant 1$ and not assuming there the values* 0 *and* 1. *There is a constant S (called the Schottky constant), depending only on $a_0 = f(0)$ and $r = |z|$, such that $|f(z)| < S$ in $|z| < 1$.* (Schottky, 1904.)

Proof. If $f(z)$ is of the class K, then

$$(1)\qquad g(z) = \log\left(\sqrt{\frac{\log f(z)}{2\pi i}} - \sqrt{\frac{[\log f(z) - 1]}{2\pi i}}\right)$$

is regular in $|z| \leqslant 1$.

We choose a branch of $\log f(z)$ by choosing one of the determinations of $\log f(0)$. Similarly, we choose a branch of the square root, and finally a branch of the logarithm of the expression in brackets. Moreover, getting rid of logarithm and square root, we obtain the relation between f and g in the form

$$(2)\qquad f = -e^{\frac{1}{2}\pi i(e^{2g} + e^{-2g})}.$$

It follows from (2) that $g(z)$ does not assume the values

$$(3)\qquad \pm\log(\sqrt{n} + \sqrt{n-1}) + 2m\pi i,\ n \geqslant 1,$$

where n and m are integers, In fact,

$$e^{\log(\sqrt{n}+\sqrt{n-1})^2 + 4m\pi i} = (\sqrt{n} + \sqrt{n-1})^2,$$

$$e^{-\log(\sqrt{n}+\sqrt{n-1})^2 - 4m\pi i} = 1/(\sqrt{n} + \sqrt{n-1})^2$$

and

$$(\sqrt{n}+\sqrt{n-1})^2+1/(\sqrt{n}+\sqrt{n-1})^2 = 4n-2.$$

Hence, if $g(z)$ assumes one of the values (3), $f = -e^{\frac{1}{2}\pi i(4n-2)} = 1$, which is, by hypothesis, impossible.

On the other hand,

$$\log(\sqrt{n+1}+\sqrt{n})-\log(\sqrt{n}+\sqrt{n-1}) = \log\frac{\sqrt{n+1}+\sqrt{n}}{\sqrt{n}+\sqrt{n-1}} \to 0$$

with $1/n$, i. e. the difference between the real parts of the non-assumed values (3), for two consecutive values of n, has a finite greatest value q, and thus the distance between any finite point in the complex plane and the nearest non-assumed value is not greater than $p = \frac{1}{2}\sqrt{q^2+4\pi^2}$. Thus, for the values of the functions $u = g(z)$, there is no circle of radius greater than p covering a complete circle in the u-plane.

For a fixed x, $|x|<r<1$ and for $|z|\leqslant 1$, provided $g'(x)\neq 0$, the function

$$h(z) = \frac{g[x+(1-r)z]-g(x)}{(1-r)g'(x)} = z+\ldots$$

is regular. Moreover, as $u = g(w)$ for $|w|<1$ does not assume all the values in any circle of the u-plane of radius greater than p,

$\dfrac{g(w)}{(1-r)g'(x)}$ does not assume all the values in a circle of radius

$\dfrac{p}{(1-r)\,|g'(x)|}$, and therefore the same is true of $h(z)$ in $|z|<1$.

Hence by Bloch's theorem

$$\frac{p}{(1-r)\,|g'(x)|}\geqslant B,$$

i. e.

$$|g'(x)|\leqslant\frac{p}{B(1-r)}$$

and the same is obviously true when $g'(x) = 0$. Thus, for $|x| = r$,

$$|g(x)|\leqslant|g(0)|+\left|\int_0^x g'(z)dz\right|<|g(0)|+\frac{pr}{B(1-r)}.$$

Since, by (1), $g(0)$ is perfectly determined by $f(0)$, (2) proves the statement.

A function $f(z)$ of the class K, and thus also a_0, being given,

$S(r)$ is a kind of dominant function for $f(z)$ in $|z|<1$. The independence of $S(r)$ of all the coefficients but the very first is a most remarkable fact. $M/(1-r)$ is a dominant function if M is the maximum modulus of $f(z)$ in $|z|<1$. But M depends on all the coefficients.

If $M(R)$ is the maximum modulus of $f(z)$ along $|z|=R$, we have, by Cauchy's inequality, $|a_1| \leqslant M(R)/R$ and by Schottky's theorem,

$$M(R) \leqslant S(a_0, R).$$

Taking $R = 1/2$ we are thus led to

II. *Landau's theorem. For the functions of the class K there is a constant L (the Landau constant), the same for all the functions of the class, depending only on $a_0 = f(0)$ and such that $|f'(0)| < L$ for every function of the class K.* (Landau, 1904.)

III. *Picard's theorem on integral functions. Every non-constant integral function $E(z)$ assumes one of the two values 0 and 1 (or a and b, $a \neq b$), i.e. one of the two equations $E(z) = a$ and $E(z) = b$ has a finite root.* (Picard, 1879.)

Proof. If 0 and 1 are not assumed by $f(z)$, and $f'(0) \neq 0$, $F(z) = f\left(\dfrac{Lz}{f'(0)}\right)$ leads to $L = |F'(0)| < L$, which is obviously impossible. If $f'(0) = 0$ we apply Landau's theorem to the expansion $f(z) = \Sigma b_n (z-a)^n$ in a circle about a. The zeros of $f'(z)$ being isolated we can always find a suitable a as near to zero as we please.

Applying the theorem just proved to $\dfrac{f(z)-a}{b-a}$ we obtain its general form.

IV. *Picard's theorem on essential points. In the neighbourhood of an essential point an analytic function assumes every value, except possibly one.*

Proof. A first approximation to this beautiful theorem is Weierstrass's result 58. I, showing that in the neighbourhood of an essential point every value is approached. We shall make use of the latter result. To simplify writing we suppose that $z = \infty$ is the essential point in question (the transformation $z' = 1/(c-z)$ brings $z = c$ to infinity, and thus any circle about

c into a circle about ∞). Since, by definition, an essential point is an isolated singularity in the neighbourhood of which the function is uniform, we suppose that our function $f(z)$ is regular and uniform in $|z| \geqslant 1/2$ (the transformation $z = 2Rz'$ replaces the circle $|z| = R$ by $|z'| = 1/2$).

Let us suppose now that $f(z)$ does not assume the values 0 and 1 in $|z| \geqslant 1/2$. Then there are points $c_n \to \infty$ such that $|f(c_n)| < 1$. All the functions $f_n(z) = f(c_n z)$ after a suffix N are regular and uniform in $|z| > 1/2$ and $|f_n(1)| < 1$. Applying Schottky's theorem 69. I to the functions $f_n(z)$ in a circle of radius 1/2, centre at $z = 1$, we see that in the concentric inner circle of radius 1/4, say, their moduli are bounded collectively. Covering the circumference of the circle of radius 1, centre at 0, by a finite number of overlapping circles of radius 1/4, centres on $|z| = 1$, we see that the moduli of the functions $f_{N+k}(z)$, ($k = 1, 2, \ldots$), have a common bound B, say, on $|z| = 1$. This means, however, that $|f(z)| < B$ on the circle $|z| = |c_n|$ Since $f(z)$ is regular (and uniform) in the ring between $|z| = 1$ and $|z| = |c_n|$, $|f(z)|$ assumes its maximum on the boundary, i.e. if $B' \geqslant B$ is a bound of $|f(z)|$ on $|z| = 1$, it follows that in that ring $|f(z)| \leqslant B'$. As the same reasoning holds with the same B' for every circle $|z| = |c_n|$ spreading to infinity, $f(z)$ would be bounded in the neighbourhood of $z = \infty$, i.e. $z = \infty$ would not be an essential point, which proves that either 0 or 1 (or both of them) is assumed in $|z| > 1/2$. Applying this result to $\dfrac{f(z)-a}{b-a}$ where $a \neq b$, we obtain the general statement.

We obtain an important consequence of this theorem by applying it to $f(rz)$, $r < 1$. We see, in fact, that $f(z)$ assumes any value in $|z| > 1/2r$, with one possible exception. Denote this exceptional value (if any) by a. If b is any other value, $f(z)$ assumes the value b in $|z| > 1/2r$, at $z = z_1$, say. Repeating the reasoning with an $r > 1/|z_1|$, we see that $f(z)$ assumes b in a circle not containing z_1, i.e. a second time, and so on.

V. *Every value (real or complex) with one possible exception is assumed infinitely many times in the neighbourhood of an essential point.*

70. *Simple properties of biuniform mapping.* By 35. III the

only linear functions mapping the circumference of the unit circle on itself are

$$u = \frac{az-b}{\bar{b}z-\bar{a}},$$

where a and b are arbitrary complex numbers ($a \neq b$) and $\bar{a}$, $\bar{b}$ their conjugates.

If $|b/a| < 1$, the point $z_0 = b/a$ corresponding to $u = 0$, lies in the circle, i.e. the whole circle $|u| < 1$ is biuniformly mapped on $|z| < 1$, inner points corresponding to inner points. In particular, if $z = 0$ and $u = 0$ correspond to one another, we obtain $u = -az/\bar{a}$, i.e., since $|a| = |\bar{a}|$, $u = e^{i\alpha}z$, which is a pure rotation.

As a preliminary to Riemann's theorem, we are going to prove

I. *Only linear functions can establish a biuniform mapping of the unit circle on itself.*

We notice first that, by hypothesis, the inverse function is also regular in $|u| < 1$ and its absolute value is less than 1. Suppose also it vanishes at the origin. Then Schwarz's lemma 42. I applies to both, and we obtain $|z| \leqslant |u|$ and $|u| \leqslant |z|$, i.e. $|u| = |z|$ at every point of the unit circle. Further, by 42. I, $u = e^{i\alpha}z$ and, if we suppose that the positive real axes correspond to one another, we obtain $u = z$.

Now if the function $u = f(z)$ establishes a biuniform mapping of the unit circle on itself, we consider a linear function $v = l(u)$ with the same property, and we suppose moreover $l(u)$ so chosen that in the biuniform mapping $v = l[f(z)]$ the two origins $z = 0$ and $v = 0$, as well as the two positive real axes, correspond to one another. Applying our previous remarks to $v = l[f(z)]$ we see that $v = z$, i.e. $l[f(z)] = z$. Hence $f(z)$ is the inverse function of a linear function, i.e. is itself linear.

The main problem of biuniform mapping is to determine the class of domains that analytic functions can map biuniformly on a circle. Obviously the whole complex plane, even with the exception of one point, e.g. ∞, cannot be biuniformly mapped on a finite circle $|z| < R$ by an analytic function $u = f(z)$, since $z(u)$ would be a uniform function regular at every finite point and its values bounded by R, and thus by Liouville's theorem, 40. V, $z(u)$ would be a constant and would not establish any mapping.

We notice that a linear function maps the whole complex plane on itself, and it is easy to see that *no other analytic function establishes such a mapping*. In fact, if $u = f(z)$ establishes such a mapping, $u = f(z)$ and its inverse function $z = g(u)$ are both uniform functions, and thus $f(z)$ cannot have an essential point (∞ included) since, by Picard's theorem 69. IV, the inverse function would be infinitely multiform and the mapping would not be biuniform. Therefore $f(z)$ is a rational function, $u = P(z)/Q(z)$. Fixing the value of u, the equation $Q(z)u - P(z) = 0$ has as many roots as the higher of the degrees of P and Q. Thus if we suppose that the mapping is biuniform, P and Q are linear. This proves our statement.

We obtain the same result if the mapping leaves out one point on both planes, e.g. $z = \infty$ and an arbitrary $u = a$.

II. *No analytic function $u = f(z)$ maps a multiply connected domain D of the u-plane on a circle of the z-plane.*

Proof. In the proof of 67. IV we showed that there is a function $\phi(u)$ and a finite polygon π such that $\phi(u)$ is regular in D and changes its value when u describes π. On the other hand, $\phi[f(z) - a]$ is regular along any path in the circle k corresponding to D, and in particular when z describes π' corresponding to π. Therefore, by the theorem of monodromy, 67. III, since k is simply connected, $\phi[f(z) - a]$ is uniform in k. This contradiction establishes the theorem.

Therefore we have to restrict ourselves to simply connected domains. The only further restriction will be that *the boundary contains more than one single point.* This restriction is unavoidable, since, in the case of a single boundary point, the inverse mapping function $z = g(u)$ would be bounded and regular everywhere except at one point, and thus, by 58. III, $g(u)$ would be regular also at that point, i. e. regular at every point, which, by Liouville's theorem 40. V, reduces $g(u)$ to a constant, i. e. there is no mapping.

Suppose now that $u = f(z)$ maps the simply connected domain D in the u-plane biuniformly on a circle, whose centre $z = c$ corresponds to $u = a$. We have

$$f(z) = a + \sum_{1}^{\infty} a_n (z-c)^n \quad (a_1 \neq 0).$$

Since the only biuniform mapping of a circle on a concentric circle, centre corresponding to itself, is of the form $z-c = k(z'-c)$, all biuniform mappings of D on circles, whose centres correspond to $u = a$, are of the form

$$u = a + \sum_{1}^{\infty} a_n k^n (z-c)^n.$$

Thus if we 'norm' the mapping with respect to $u = a$ by requiring that $a_1 k = 1$, the radius of the circle is perfectly determinate, as soon as D and a are given. This radius is called the *inner conform radius* $r(a)$ *of* D *with respect to* a.

If $u = \infty$ is in D and it corresponds to $z = c$, we have $u = \Sigma a_n(z-c)^n + b_1/(z-c)$. In fact, the point a cannot be an essential point, for z is also a uniform function of u in D. The same point cannot be a pole of order greater than 1, because, if it is a pole of order k, $1/u$ is a uniform and regular function at $z = a$ and in its neighbourhood, and thus

$(1/u)' =$

$$\frac{-\sum_{1}^{\infty} na_n(z-c)^{n-1} - b_1/(z-c)^2 - \ldots - kb_k/(z-c)^{k+1}}{\left[\sum_{0}^{\infty} a_n(z-c)^n + b_1/(z-c) + \ldots + b_k/(z-c)^k\right]^2} = -u'/u^2$$

tends to a definite limit when $z \to a$ and this limit is not zero, since the mapping is biuniform. Multiplying numerator and denominator by $(z-a)^{2k}$, we see that $k+1 = 2k$, i. e. $k = 1$.

Thus all the mappings of D on circles, whose centres correspond to $u = \infty$, are of the form $u = b_1 k/(z-c) + \Sigma a_n (z-c)^n/k^n$. Therefore, if we norm the mapping with respect to $u = \infty$ by requiring that $b_1 k = 1$, the radius $r(\infty)$ is perfectly determinate.

Finally, if we replace $1/(z-c)$ by $(z-c)$ we obtain $u = b(z-c) + \Sigma a_n/(z-c)^n$, which maps D on the outside of a circle centre c, and $u = \infty$ corresponds to $z = \infty$. The mapping may be normed with respect to $u = \infty$ in the usual way by the transformation $z-c = k(z'-c)$ and the condition $b\,k = 1$, so that the radius of the circle is determinate.

If D is a bounded domain and we map its complementary domain $\overline{D}$ on the outside of a circle $u = \infty$ corresponding to $z = \infty$, and norm the mapping with respect to $u = \infty$, the radius thus determined is called the *outer conform radius* $\bar{r}$ of D. This does not depend on any affix but is defined only for bounded domains.

If A is the area enclosed by a rectifiable curve C in the u-plane, we have by 44. VII,

(1) $$A \geqslant \pi r^2(a),$$

and equality holds only for the circle $|u-a|<r(a)$.

When D is enclosed by a rectifiable curve C and the outside is mapped on the outside of $|z| = \bar{r}$, we have, by 44. V, for the area A enclosed by C and for normed mapping,

$$A = \pi(\bar{r}^2 - |a_1|^2/\bar{r}^2 - 2|a_2|^2/\bar{r}^2 - 3|a_3|^2/\bar{r}^2 - \ldots)$$

i. e.

(2) $$A \leqslant \pi \bar{r}^2,$$

and the equality sign holds only when $u = z$.

On the other hand, by Ex. V. 25, if $f(z)$ is regular in $|z|<R$ and maps the curve C on $|z| = r<R$, the length l of C is given by

$$l = \int_0^{2\pi} |f'(re^{i\theta})| \, r d\theta,$$

and thus, by Hardy's theorem 42. III, the ratio $l(r)/r$ is increasing with r, unless C is a circle, centre the origin.

In particular, if r is the inner radius of D, enclosed by C, with respect to the origin, we have $l(r)/r \to 2\pi$ when $r \to 0$. Hence $l \geqslant 2\pi r(0)$ and, more generally,

(3) $$2\pi r(a) \leqslant l,$$

equality holding only when C is a circle, centre at a.

Similarly for the outer radius,

(4) $$2\pi\bar{r} \leqslant l,$$

i. e.

(5) $$\sqrt{\frac{A}{\pi}} \leqslant \bar{r} \leqslant \frac{l}{2\pi}.$$

The inequalities (1) and (2) show that

(6) $$\bar{r} \geqslant r(a)$$

(equality only when C is a circle centre at a) whatever inner point a may be. The above inequalities are due to Bieberbach, 1916.

Reflecting C in the unit circle, i.e. by the transformation $u'-a = 1/(u-a)$, we obtain a curve C'. Denoting its length, area, and outer conform radius by l', A' and $\bar{r}'$, we see that $\bar{r}' = 1/r(a)$, and hence, by (5),

$$\sqrt{\frac{A'}{\pi}} \leqslant \frac{1}{r(a)} < \frac{l'}{2\pi}. \tag{7}$$

71. *Riemann's theorem on biuniform mapping.*

I. *Every simply connected domain D of the u-plane with at least two boundary points is biuniformly mapped on a circle of the z-plane by a suitable analytic function $u = f(z)$.*

(Riemann.)

Proof. If, for a given D, there is an analytic function $u = f(z)$ mapping D biuniformly on a circle of the z-plane, the inverse function $z = g(u)$ is regular and bounded (and uniform, of course) in D. Consider the class C of analytic functions $g(u)$ which are regular and bounded in D, and map D biuniformly on another domain, and add the two simplifying conditions $g(u_0) = 0$, $g'(u_0) = 1$, where u_0 is an arbitrarily fixed point of D.

There are functions of this description. In fact, if a and b are two boundary points, consider the function

$$v = \sqrt{\frac{u-a}{u-b}}.$$

When u varies in the simply connected domain D, u cannot describe a closed circuit separating a and b, i.e. v (u) is a uniform function in D. Since the radicand is a linear function, it does not assume the same value twice; therefore, if we fix the value of the square root at one point, the same is true of $v(u)$. Thus $v(u)$ maps D on a domain D' of the v-plane. As $v' = (u-a)/(u-b)$ does not map D on the whole of the v'-plane (since D does not cover the whole u-plane), the same holds for $v(u)$. If $v = c$ is an inner point of the non-covered part of the v-plane, the function $w = 1/(v-c)$ is uniform, regular, and bounded in D. Subtracting from it $w(u_0)$ and dividing afterwards by its derivative at $u = u_0$, we have a function satisfying all the conditions required.

If $g(u)$ is a function of C, we denote the upper bound of its maximum modulus in D by $M(g)$ and the lower bound of all the numbers $M(g)$ formed for every function of the class C by ρ.

We are going to show that there is a function $h(u)$ in C for which $M(h) = \rho$. Since ρ is the lower bound of a set of numbers it is either a number of this set or at least a limiting number of it, (9. I). In the first case the statement is proved. In the second case there are functions of C, $g_1, g_2, \ldots$, such that $\lim M(g_n) = \rho$.

In the second case, since after a certain suffix N, $M(g_n) < \rho + \epsilon$, the functions $g_1, g_2, \ldots g_n, \ldots$ are collectively bounded, by B, say. We are going to prove that there is a sub-sequence of g_n tending uniformly to a limit function in every region of D. Consider only the 'rational' points of D, i. e. the points of D whose two coordinates are both rational numbers. As their number is enumerable, imagine these points written in a sequence $p_1, p_2 \ldots, p_n, \ldots$. By Bolzano's theorem 18. I, the bounded sequence of numbers $g_1(p_1), g_2(p_1), \ldots, g_n(p_1), \ldots$ has a limiting number, i. e. there is a sub-sequence

$$(1) \qquad g_{n_1}, g_{n_2}, \ldots, g_{nk}, \ldots$$

such that $g_{nk}(p_1)$ tends to a definite limit when $k \to \infty$.

Every sub-sequence of (1) has, of course, the same property. Thus, (1) has a sub-sequence such that $g_{nk'}(p_2)$ tends to a limit, and the latter has a sub-sequence such that $g_{nk''}(p_3)$ has a limit, and so on. Applying the diagonal process to these sequences, i. e. taking the first function of the first sequence having a limit for $z = p_1$, the second function of the second sequence having a limit for $z = p_1$ and $z = p_2$ and so on, we obtain a sequence of functions tending to a limit for every point $p_1, p_2, \ldots$. It follows from Vitali's theorem, 42. IV and 61, III, that this sequence tends *uniformly* to a limit function in every region of D. We will suppose that $g_1, g_2, \ldots$ is already such a sequence and that $g(u)$ is its limit function and we will show that $g(u)$ belongs to C.

Since $g_n(u)$ is regular in D and $g_n(u_0) = 0$, $g'_n(u_0) = 1$, for every n, we see, by Vitali's theorem, that $g(u)$ is regular in D and $g(u_0) = 0$, $g'(u_0) = 1$. Moreover, $v = g(u)$ maps D biuniformly on a domain D' of v. In fact, if $g(u_1) = v_0$ and $g(u_2) = v_0$, we enclose u_1 and u_2 by two circles, not cutting one another and outside one another, on which $|g(u) - v_0| > 0$. Then there is a number m such that $|g(u) - v_0| > m$ on both circumferences. Now choose an n so large that on both circumferences $|g_n(u)-g(u)|<m$. By Rouché's theorem, 60. I, the functions $g_n(u)-v_0=[g(u)-v_0]+[g_n(u)-g(u)]$ and $g(u)-v_0$ have the same number of zeros in either of the two circles in question. Therefore g_n also assumes the value v_0 at two different points, which is contrary to our hypothesis.

Finally $M(g)\leqslant\rho+\epsilon$ and $M(g)\geqslant\rho$, i.e., ϵ being arbitrary, $M(g)=\rho$. Thus $g(u)$ belongs to the class C with $M(g)=\rho$.

It follows that D' is in $|v|<\rho$. We will prove that D' is the circle $|v|<\rho$, which will establish Riemann's theorem. Suppose that D' has a boundary point v_0 in $|v|<\rho$. We shall see that this supposition leads to the conclusion that the class of functions C contains a function $h(u)$ for which $M(h)<\rho$, and this contradicts the fact that ρ is the lower bound of $M(g)$ for the whole class C.

Both branches of the function

$$v_1(v)=\rho\sqrt{\frac{\rho(v-v_0)}{\rho^2-\bar{v}_0v}},$$

are regular in $|v|<\rho$, and $M(v_1)=\rho$, because every boundary point of D' on $|v|=\rho$ is also on $|v_1|=\rho$. Taking either of the two branches, we construct the function

$$v_2(u)=\frac{\rho^2[v_1-v_1(0)]}{\rho^2-\bar{v}_1(0)v_1}.$$

We have $v_2(u_0)=0$, $M(v_2)=\rho$, and we see also that v_2 is regular in D. Its derivative at $u=u_0$ is $(\rho+|v_0|)/2\sqrt{-v_0\rho}$. Dividing $v_2(u)$ by this number we obtain $v_3(u)$, belonging to the class C, for which

$$M(v_3)=\rho\left|\frac{2\sqrt{-v_0\rho}}{\rho+\sqrt{v\bar{v}_0}}\right|<\rho.$$

This proof is due to Fejér and F. Riesz.

72. *The Taylor coefficients of biuniform functions.* The analytic functions mapping a domain biuniformly on another domain form a special class of functions. If we imagine them as defined by Taylor series, the coefficients of this series will be subject to certain conditions. We are going to establish some

remarkable properties of the Taylor coefficients of biuniform functions.

I. *Area theorem. If* $u = f(z) = z + a_1/z + a_2/z^2 + \dots$ *is convergent for* $|z| > 1$, *and maps the domain* $|z| > 1$ *biuniformly on a domain* D' *of* u, *we have*

$$\sum_1^\infty n\,|a_n|^2 \leqslant 1.$$

Proof. Putting $z = re^{i\theta}$, the circle $|z| = r > 1$ is mapped on the simple closed Jordan curve $u = u(\theta) = f(re^{i\theta})$. The area A enclosed by this curve is (we put $u = u_1 + iu_2$)

$$A = \tfrac{1}{2}\int_0^{2\pi} (u_1 u_2' - u_2 u_1')\,d\theta = \int_0^{2\pi} u_1 u_2'\,d\theta$$

$$= \int_0^{2\pi} \frac{u(\theta) + \bar{u}(\theta)}{2}\;\frac{u'(\theta) - \bar{u}'(\theta)}{2i}\,d\theta$$

$$= \int_0^{2\pi} \left[\frac{re^{i\theta} + re^{-i\theta}}{2} + \sum_1^\infty \frac{a_n e^{-in\theta} + \bar{a}_n e^{in\theta}}{2r^n}\right]$$

$$\times \left[\frac{re^{i\theta} + re^{-i\theta}}{2} - \sum_1^\infty \frac{na_n e^{-in\theta} + n\bar{a}_n e^{in\theta}}{2r^n}\right] d\theta$$

$$= \pi r^2 - \sum_1^\infty \frac{n\,|a_n|^2}{r^{2n}}\,\pi \geqslant 0,$$

since all the terms containing a non-zero power of $e^{i\theta}$ vanish. As the result holds good for every $r > 1$, and the left-hand side cannot be negative, the result holds also for $r = 1$, which proves the statement.

II. *If* $u = f(z) = z + a_2 z^2 + a_3 z^3 + \dots$ *is convergent and biuniform in* $|z| < 1$, *then* $|a_2| \leqslant 2$ *and*

(1) $\quad r/(1+r)^2 \leqslant |f(z)| \leqslant r/(1-r)^2, \quad |z| < r < 1,$

(2) $\quad (1-r)/(1+r)^3 \leqslant |f'(z)| \leqslant (1+r)/(1-r)^3, \quad |z| < r < 1,$

(*distortion formula*). (Koebe, 1910; Bieberbach, 1916.)

We notice that the upper bound for $|a_2|$ is attained by the function $z/(1-z)^2 = \Sigma nz^n$, which is biuniform in $|z| < 1$, as its differential coefficient $(z+1)/(1-z)^3$ does not vanish in this simply connected domain. The bounds in (1) and (2) are attained by the same function.

Proof. Consider the function $F(z) = \sqrt{f(z^2)}$. When the argument of z increases by π, that of z^2 increases by 2π. Hence $f(z^2)$ assumes its initial value, i. e. its argument increases by 2π and that of $F(z)$ by π. Thus $F(-z) = -F(z)$ and we see that $F(z)$ is a *uniform* function. Moreover $F'(z) = zf'(z^2)/\sqrt{f(z^2)}$, and thus $F'(z)$ exists for $z \neq 0$, i. e. $F(z)$ is regular except perhaps at $z = 0$. Hence, as $f(z)$ is bounded in the neighbourhood of $z = 0$, $F(z)$ is also regular at $z = 0$, by 58. III. Its Taylor expansion begins with the terms $z + a_2 z^3/2 + \ldots$. $F(z)$ is biuniform in $|z| < 1$, for if $F(z_1) = F(z_2)$, then also $F^2(z_1) = F^2(z_2)$, i. e. $f(z_1^2) = f(z_2^2)$. Since f is biuniform, $z_1 = \pm z_2$, and hence, $F(z)$ being an odd function, $z_1 = z_2$. It follows that $G(z) = 1/F(1/z)$ maps $|z| > 1$ biuniformly and its Taylor expansion begins with the terms $G(z) = z - a_2/2 \,.\, z + \ldots$. Hence, by I, $|a_2|/2 < 1$.

To prove (1) and (2). It is readily proved that if

$$f(z) = z + a_2 z^2 + \ldots$$

is regular and biuniform in $|z| < 1$, then

$$g(u) = \frac{f\left(\dfrac{u+z}{1+\bar{z}u}\right) - f(z)}{f'(z)(1 - z\bar{z})} = u + b_2 u + \ldots$$

is also regular and biuniform, where

$$b_2 = \frac{f''(z)(1 - z\bar{z})}{2f'(z)} - \bar{z}.$$

Hence, by the first part of our theorem,

$$\left| \frac{f''(z)(1 - z\bar{z})}{f'(z)} - 2\bar{z} \right| \leqslant 4$$

It follows that

$$\left| \frac{zf''(z)}{f'(z)} - \frac{2r^2}{1-r^2} \right| < \frac{4r}{1-r^2}, \quad r = |z| \tag{3}$$

i. e., denoting by $\mathrm{Rl}(z)$ the real part of z,

$$\frac{2r^2 - 4r}{1-r^2} \leqslant \mathrm{Rl}\left(\frac{zf''(z)}{f'(z)}\right) \leqslant \frac{4r + 2r^2}{1-r^2}.$$

But

$$\mathrm{Rl}\left(\frac{zf''(z)}{f'(z)}\right) = \mathrm{Rl}\left(\frac{\partial \log f'(z)}{\partial \log z}\right) = r\frac{\partial}{\partial r}\mathrm{Rl}[\log f'(z)] = r\frac{\partial}{\partial r}\log|f'(z)|.$$

Thus
$$\frac{2r-4}{1-r^2} \leqslant \frac{\partial \log |f'(z)|}{\partial r} \leqslant \frac{4+2r}{1-r^2}$$

and, by integration,

$$\frac{1-r}{(1+r)^3} \leqslant |f'(z)| \leqslant \frac{1+r}{(1-r)^3}.$$

Since $f'(z) \neq 0$ in $|z| < r < 1$, $|f'(z)|$ assumes its minimum as well as its maximum on the circumference $|z| = r$. This proves (2). Integrating along the radius leading to z we obtain

$$|f(z)| = \left|\int_0^z f'(z)\,dz\right| \leqslant \int_0^r |f'(z)|\,dr \leqslant \frac{r}{(1-r)^2},$$

and similarly $|f(z)| \geqslant r/(1+r)^2$, which proves (1).

Formula (1) shows that if $f(z)$ is regular and biuniform in $|z|<1$, its order of infinity when z approaches the boundary is $\leqslant 2$

From (3), denoting by $\mathrm{Im}(z)$ the imaginary part of z, we have

$$\frac{-4r}{1-r^2} \leqslant \mathrm{Im}\left(\frac{zf''(z)}{f'(z)}\right) \leqslant \frac{4r}{1-r^2}.$$

But
$$\mathrm{Im}\left(\frac{zf''(z)}{f'(z)}\right) = r\frac{\partial}{\partial r}\arg f'(z).$$

Hence
$$\frac{-4}{1-r^2} \leqslant \frac{\partial}{\partial r}\arg f'(z) \leqslant \frac{4}{1-r^2}.$$

Therefore, by integration,

$$|\arg f'(z)| \leqslant 2\log\frac{1+r}{1-r}, \qquad \text{(rotation formula)}$$

which limits the rate of change of the direction in uniform mapping for *every* regular and biuniform function $f(z)$.

An interesting consequence of Bieberbach's theorem is the following

III. *If* $u = f(z) = z + a_2 z^2 + \ldots$ *is regular and biuniform in* $|z|<1$, *and maps this circle on the domain* D' *of the* u-*plane, the distance of the nearest boundary point of* D' *from the origin* $u = 0$ *is* $\geqslant 1/4$.

Proof. If $f(z) \neq c$ in $|z|<1$, then necessarily $c \neq 0$, and thus

$$f_1(z) = \frac{cf(c)}{c-f(z)} = z + (a_2 + 1/c)z^2 + \dots$$

is regular and biuniform in $|z|<1$. Consequently, by II,

$$|a_2 + 1/c| \leqslant 2, \text{ i. e. } c \geqslant 1/4.$$

On the other hand

$$u = \frac{(1-1/z)^2}{1/z} = z + 1/z - 2$$

maps $z>1$ on the domain whose complete boundary is the part of the negative real axis between -4 and ∞. Hence $u = z/(1-z)^2$ maps $|z|<1$ on a domain whose complete boundary is the part of the negative real axis between $-1/4$ and ∞. In this mapping the lower bound of the distance is attained, for at $z = -1$, its value is $-1/4$.

Szegö generalized this result by remarking that *if c and c_1, are two values of u on a straight line through $u=0$ and separated by $u=0$ (i. e.* $\arg c - \arg c_1 = \pi$) *and if c and c_1 are not assumed by $u = f(z)$ in $|z|<1$, then either $|c|$ or $|c_1|$ is* $\geqslant 1/2$. In fact, if c_1 is not a value of $f(z)$ in $|z|<1$ then $cc_1/(c-c_1)$ is not a value of $f_1(z)$ in $|z|<1$, i.e. $|cc_1/(c-c_1)| \geqslant 1/4$. Hence,

$$|1/c - 1/c_1| = |1/c| + |1/c_1| \leqslant 4,$$

so that $|1/c|$ and $|1/c_1|$ cannot both be greater than 2.

We now give an important application of II to the determination of a dominant for the mapping function.

We say that

$$F(z) = \Sigma A_n z^n,\ A_n > 0,$$

is a *dominant* of $f(z) = \Sigma a_n z^n$, if $|a_n| \leqslant A_n$ $(n = 1, 2, \dots)$. In symbols

$$f(z) << F(z).$$

If $G(z)$ is a dominant of $g(z)$, we have obviously

$$f(z) + g(z) << F(z) + G(z),$$

$$f(z)\, g(z) << F(z)\, G(z).$$

Moreover, if $f(0) = 1$ and $f(z) << 1/(1-z)$, then

$$1/f(z) << 1/(1-2z).$$

In fact, putting $1/f(z) = \Sigma b_n z^n$, we have, since

$$1\Big/\Big(1+\sum_1^\infty a_n z^n\Big) = 1-\sum_1^\infty a_n z^n + \Big(\sum_1^\infty a_n z^n\Big)^2 - \dots,$$

$$b_n = -a_n + \sum_1^{n-1} a_i a_{n-i} - \sum_{i+j+k=n} a_i a_j a_k + \dots + (-1)^n a_1^n.$$

Hence, since $|a_n| \leqslant 1$, it follows that $|b_n| \leqslant 2^{n-1} < 2^n$.

IV. *If* $u = f(z) = z + a_2 z^2 + a_3 z^3 + \dots$ *is convergent and biuniform in* $|z| < 1$, *then*

$$|a_n| \leqslant 5{\cdot}1\, n^2. \qquad \text{(Bieberbach, 1918.)}$$

Proof. Cauchy's inequalities applied to (1) give, for every $r < 1$,

$$|a_n| \leqslant \frac{1}{r^n}\frac{r}{(1-r)^2}.$$

For a fixed n, choosing r so that the right-hand side is a minimum, we obtain

$$r = \frac{n-1}{n+1}.$$

Hence

$$|a_n| \leqslant \Big(\frac{n+1}{n-1}\Big)^{n-1}\frac{(n+1)^2}{4} = \frac{1}{4}(n^2-1)\Big[\Big(1+\frac{2}{n-1}\Big)^{\frac{n-1}{2}}\Big]^{\frac{2n}{n-1}}.$$

Therefore

$$|a_n| < \frac{n^2}{4} e^{\frac{2n}{n-1}} \leqslant \frac{n^2 e^3}{4} \quad \text{for } n \geqslant 3.$$

Since $e^3/4 < 5{\cdot}1$ and, by II, $|a_2| < 2$, the result follows.

We also remark that, if b is any number $\geqslant 7$,

$$5{\cdot}1\, n^2 < b^{n-1}, \quad \text{for} \quad n \geqslant 3,$$

while $2 < b$ and $1 = b^0$, so that in

$$|f(z)| \leqslant |z| + 2|z|^2 + 5{\cdot}1\,.\,3^2|z|^3 + \dots + 5{\cdot}1\, n^2 |z|^n + \dots$$

$$\leqslant |z| + 2r\frac{|z|^2}{r} + 5{\cdot}1\,.\,3^2 r^2\frac{|z|^3}{r^2} + \dots + 5{\cdot}1\, n^2 r^{n-1}\frac{|z|^n}{r^{n-1}} + \dots, r < 1,$$

we can replace the coefficient of $\dfrac{|z|^n}{r^{n-1}}$ by b^{n-1}.

Therefore
$$\phi(z) = \frac{z}{1-bz/r}$$
is a dominant of $f(z)$.

A further interesting theorem is the following, which we state without proof.

V. *If* $u = f(z) = z + a_2 z^2 + \ldots$ *maps the unit circle biuniformly, then the corresponding domain in the u-plane contains a circle, centre at* $\bar{a}_2/(4-|a_2|^2)$, *radius* $2/(4-|a_2|^2)$.

(Reinhardt, 1928.)

CHAPTER IX

REPRESENTATION OF ANALYTIC FUNCTIONS

73. *The problem of representation.* In the preceding chapters we have got acquainted with two essentially different methods for the investigation of analytic functions, viz. the Taylor series and contour integration. The Taylor series $\Sigma a_n z^n$ is a mathematical formula determined by the enumerable set of its coefficients a_n. It is an explicit formula for, as soon as z is fixed, it supplies a straightforward instrument for calculating, at least approximately, the corresponding value of its sum function. Therefore an analytic function is most conveniently defined by a Taylor series. The drawback of a Taylor series is that it converges only in a circle determined by the singular point nearest to the centre. Consequently the complete definition of an analytic function requires the continuation of the initial function element by an infinite chain of new Taylor series. From the logical point of view this definition of the complete analytic function is flawless and we can replace it by no other method. The only blemish of this definition is the fact that *one function* is defined by *an infinity of concatenated formulae.*

The contour integral

$$\int_C \frac{f(z')\,dz'}{z'-z} = 2\pi i f(z)$$

establishes a relation between the boundary values of $f(z)$ and its inner values, provided $f(z)$ is regular in and on C. If we start with values given only along C, the integral defines the values inside C. But in this way we determine the function by a continuum of values, and we know from the Taylor series that an enumerable set of values is sufficient for this purpose. Thus contour integration is not the most economical way of defining an analytic function.

Moreover, if z is outside C, $f(z')/(z'-z)$ is regular at every point inside C and thus the integral vanishes at z, by Cauchy's fundamental theorem. *The integral is equal to* $f(z)$ *only inside* C *and outside* C *it vanishes identically.* There is a direct discrepancy between function and formula. The analytic function may be defined all over the plane; the integral has a determinate value for all points of the plane except in general on the contour, but the values furnished by the formula, viz. the integral, do not always coincide with those of the function. We say that a mathematical formula 'represents' a function $f(z)$ at a point z if the value furnished by the formula at z is $f(z)$.

A function may be defined without the use of a mathematical formula. For instance, we may assign the value one to points with rational coordinates and zero to the other points. A suitable formula representing such a function for the real variable x is

$$\lim_{n=\infty}\left[\lim_{m=\infty}(\cos n!\,2\pi x)^m\right].$$

Another feature of Taylor series and contour integrals is that they are uniform, i.e. for a given value of z either of them furnishes only one value, if any. But very common analytic functions like $\sqrt{1-z}$, $\log(1+z)$, &c. are multiform.

We are thus led to the two fundamental problems of the representation of analytic functions. (a) A complete uniform analytic function or a uniform branch $f(z)$ of an analytic function being given, find an explicit formula representing $f(z)$. We approach in this way the ideal of one function, one formula. (b) A complete multiform analytic function $f(z)$ being given, find a formula representing $f(z)$. The latter problem is solved by a suitable 'uniformization', one of the most beautiful methods of modern analysis. In this work, however, the only purpose of which is to introduce the reader to a thorough understanding of the fundamentals, we shall restrict ourselves to the first problem. For the second problem, we refer to Osgood's *Lehrbuch der Funktionentheorie* and to Hurwitz-Courant's *Funktionentheorie.*

Order and coefficients of integral functions.

74. *Factorization of integral functions.* The simplest analytic functions after polynomials and their ratios are the *integral*

functions, each of which is defined by a Taylor series convergent at every finite (non-infinite) point of the complex plane

(1) $$f(z) = \Sigma a_n z^n.$$

The condition that the radius of convergence is infinite is equivalent to

(2) $$\overline{\lim_{n=\infty}} |\sqrt[n]{a_n}| = 0, \text{ i.e. } \lim \sqrt[n]{a_n} = 0.$$

Figuratively speaking an integral function is an infinite polynomial. The extension to integral functions of results valid for polynomials is stopped by two specific difficulties. The fundamental properties of a polynomial, $P(z)$, are as follows: (a) $P(z) = a$ has a root, i.e. a polynomial assumes every value. This is a slightly modified form of the fundamental theorem of algebra. (b) A polynomial is a product of linear factors,

$$P(z) = c(z-z_1) \dots (z-z_n).$$

Nearly all the properties of polynomials are more or less remote consequences of these two facts.

Now the integral function e^z does not assume the value 0, which shows that both (a) and (b) may fail for an integral function. As $\Sigma a_n z^n$ is the principal part of Laurent's expansion at $z = \infty$, the latter point is an essential point of $f(z) = \Sigma a_n z^n$, and the complex plane may be considered as its neighbourhood. Thus, by Picard's theorem 69. III, $f(z)$ can miss (not assume) one value only. Thus for example the equation $a = e^z$ has a root for every a but 0, and e^z assumes a at infinitely many different points, by 69. V.

Suppose now that 0 is not an omitted value for $f(z)$, but $f(0) \neq 0$. One condition of the problem of factorization is satisfied, viz. $f(z)$ has a finite or infinite number of zeros, z_1, $z_2, \dots$. Putting $|z_\sigma| = r_\sigma$, we can write the numbers r_σ in a non-decreasing sequence, where a finite number of consecutive terms may be equal. As zeros are isolated, there is only a finite number of them in any finite domain, e.g. in any circle. Hence the condition, if $f(z)$ has infinitely many zeros,

(3) $$\lim_{\sigma=\infty} r_\sigma = \infty$$

If we try to form the product

$$(1-z/z_1)(1-z/z_2)\dots(1-z/z_m)\dots$$

of linear factors, we are stopped by the fact that such an infinite product is absolutely convergent only if

$$\sum_1^\infty |z|/r_m = |z|\sum_1^\infty 1/r_m$$

is convergent. As $\frac{\sin z}{z}$ vanishes at $z_m = m\pi$, m any positive or negative integer, we see that, for this function, $\Sigma\, 1/r_m = \frac{2}{\pi}\Sigma\, 1/m$ is divergent. The simple factorization does not work.

To overcome this difficulty, we notice with Weierstrass that $\Sigma\,(r/r_n)^n$ or $\Sigma\,(r/r_n)^{[\log n]}$ are already convergent ($[x]$ denotes as usual the integral part of x). In fact, r being fixed, there is an N such that for $n \geqslant N$, $r_n > r$, i.e. the n-th root of $(r/r_n)^n$ is less than or equal to $r/r_N < 1$. In the second case,

$$(r/r_n)^{\log n} = e^{(\log r - \log r_n)\log n} = n^{\log r - \log r_n},$$

and there is an N such that for $n \geqslant N$ we have $\log r_n - \log r > 2$, say, i.e. the second series converges like a harmonic series. Imagine therefore that we have chosen a sequence of integers ρ_n such that

$$\sum_1^\infty (r/r_n)^{\rho_n} \tag{4}$$

is convergent. In order to make use of this convergence Weierstrass replaced $1 - z/z_m$ by the *primary factor*, (putting for simplicity $z/z_m = u$)

$$\begin{aligned} E(u\,;k) &= (1-u)e^{\frac{u}{1}+\frac{u^2}{2}+\dots+\frac{u^k}{k}} \\ &= (1-u)e^{-\log(1-u)-\frac{u^{k+1}}{k+1}-\frac{u^{k+2}}{k+2}-\dots} \\ &= 1 + c_1u^{k+1} + c_2u^{k+2} + \dots, \end{aligned} \tag{5}$$

since $1 - u = e^{\log(1-u)}$.

From

$$\begin{aligned} e^{\frac{u}{1}+\frac{u^2}{2}+\dots+\frac{u^k}{k}} &= 1 + \left(\frac{u}{1} + \dots + \frac{u^k}{k}\right) + \frac{1}{2!}\left(\frac{u}{1} + \dots + \frac{u^k}{k}\right)^2 + \dots \\ &= \Sigma\, b_i(k)u^i \end{aligned} \tag{6}$$

we see that $b_i(k)$ is positive and increases with k. But, for $k=\infty$, the left-hand side becomes $e^{\log\frac{1}{1-u}} = 1/(1-u) = \Sigma u^n$, i.e.

$$(7) \qquad 0 < b_i(k) \leqslant 1 \text{ for every } i \text{ and } k.$$

Since every coefficient of $E(u;k)$ is the difference of two consecutive coefficients $b_i(k)$, we have

$$(8) \qquad |c_i| < 1.$$

By (5) and (8),

$$|E(u;k)-1| < |u^{k+1}| + |u^{k+2}| + \ldots = \frac{|u^{k+1}|}{1-|u|}.$$

It follows that the infinite product

$$(9) \qquad \Pi(z) = E\left(\frac{z}{z_1};\rho_1-1\right)E\left(\frac{z}{z_2};\rho_2-1\right)\ldots$$

is, by (4), absolutely convergent for every z, since

$$\left|E\left(\frac{z}{z_n};\rho_n-1\right)-1\right| < \frac{(r/r_n)^{\rho_n}}{1-r/r_n}$$

and the denominator tends to 1.

By 28. I, $\Pi(z)$ vanishes only at the points $z_1, z_2, \ldots$ and, by 42. IV, since its partial products are regular analytic functions uniformly convergent in every finite domain, $\Pi(z)$ is an integral function with the arbitrarily assigned zeros $z_1, z_2, \ldots$

If $\Pi(z)$ has the same zeros as the integral function $f(z)$, repeated according to their multiplicity, $f(z)/\Pi(z)$ is a non-vanishing integral function. In fact, by the third rule of 39. I, if $\Pi(z)$ is regular so is $1/\Pi(z)$, except when $\Pi(z)$ vanishes. But at z_n the vanishing factor $(1-z/z_n)$ of $\Pi(z)$ is cancelled in f/Π by the same factor in $f(z)$. Therefore any fixed branch of $\log(f/\Pi)$ is an integral function, $g(z)$, say, i.e.

$$(10) \qquad f(z) = e^{g(z)}\Pi(z).$$

The exponential factor $e^{g(z)}$ corresponds to the constant factor in the factorization of polynomials.

In the particular case when there is an integer ρ, such that

$$\Sigma(r/r_n)^\rho = r^\rho \Sigma 1/r_n^\rho$$

converges, we can replace $\rho_1, \rho_2, \ldots, \rho_n, \ldots$ by ρ, so that every primary factor used in (9) is of the type

$$E(u\,;\rho-1) = (1-u)e^{\frac{u}{1}+\frac{u^2}{2}+\cdots+\frac{u^{\rho-1}}{\rho-1}}.$$

We notice that, if $\Sigma 1/r_n^\rho$ is convergent for a $\rho > 0$, it is convergent also for $\rho' > \rho$. Thus, since the series certainly diverges for $\rho = 0$, there is a number $p \geqslant 0$ such that $\Sigma 1/r_n^{p+\epsilon}$ converges and $\Sigma 1/r_n^{p-\epsilon}$ diverges for every $\epsilon > 0$. The number p is called *the index of convergence.* The integral part of p can be taken for $\rho - 1$.

The advantage of the representation (10) of an integral function $f(z)$ by the product of an exponential function into an infinite product is that it puts into evidence the zeros of $f(z)$.

If the origin is also a zero of $f(z)$, of degree k, say, we apply (10) to $f(z)/z^k$ and obtain the following theorem.

I. *Every integral function is of the form*

$$f(z) = e^{g(z)} z^k \Pi(z), \tag{11}$$

where $g(z)$ *is an integral function and* $\Pi(z)$ *is given by* (9).

II. *If* $f(z)$ *is meromorphic, i.e. if at finite points* $f(z)$ *has only polar singularities,* $f(z)$ *is the quotient of two integral functions.*

Proof. If the poles of $f(z)$ are $z_1, z_2, \ldots,$ (repeated according to their multiplicity), we form the infinite product $\Pi(z)$ having the same points for zeros, so that $\Pi(z)f(z)$ has no poles. Thus $\Pi(z)f(z) = g(z)$ is an integral function, which proves the theorem.

75. *Integral functions of finite order.* Liouville's theorem, 40. V, shows that the maximum modulus $M(r)$ increases more rapidly than any polynomial. Comparing $M(r)$ with exponential functions, we say that $f(z)$ is of finite order if there is a k such that, for $r > R$,

$$M(r) < e^{r^k}. \tag{1}$$

For brevity's sake we shall denote by $M(r) << g(r)$ the fact that there is an R such that, for $r > R$, we have $M(r) < g(r)$, the individual value of R being irrelevant.

The lower limit of all positive numbers k such that $M(r) << e^{r^k}$

is called the *order* of $f(z)$. It is characterized by the double inequality

$$(2) \qquad \begin{aligned} &M(r) << e^{r^{\rho+\epsilon}} \text{ for every } \epsilon > 0, \\ &M(r) > e^{r^{\rho-\epsilon}} \end{aligned}$$

for every $\epsilon > 0$ and for some sequence $r_k \to \infty$. It follows that

$$(3) \qquad \rho = \overline{\lim_{r\to\infty}} \frac{\log\log M(r)}{\log r}.$$

The order ρ may also be 0. If there is no k satisfying (1), we say that the order of $f(z)$ is ∞.

Suppose now that the order of $f(z)$ is ρ. In certain cases (2) may be replaced by the stricter inequality

$$(4) \qquad M(r) << e^{ar^{\rho}}, \ a > 0.$$

The lower limit σ of numbers a satisfying (4) determines the *type* of $f(z)$ within the order ρ. In particular, if $\sigma = 0$, we say that $f(z)$ is of *minimum type*; if $\sigma > 0$ we say that $f(z)$ is of *normal type*. If no $a > 0$ satisfies (4), we say that $f(z)$ is of *maximum type*.

For example, if $f(z) = e^{\sigma z}$, putting $z = re^{i\alpha}$, we have

$$|e^{\sigma z}| = e^{\sigma r \cos\alpha}, \ (\sigma > 0),$$

i.e. $M(r) = e^{\sigma r}$. The function $e^{\sigma z}, \sigma > 0$, is of normal type of the order 1. Since $|e^{e^z}| = e^{\cos(r\sin\alpha)e^{r\cos\alpha}}$, the maximum modulus of e^{e^z} is $M(r) = e^{e^r}$, i.e. $\rho = \infty$. Similarly, for $\sin z = (e^{iz} - e^{-iz})/2i$ and $\cos z = (e^{iz} + e^{-iz})/2$, we have $M(r) \leqslant (e^r + e^r)/2 = e^r$, while, for $z = iy$, we have $|f(z)| \geqslant (e^r - e^{-r})/2 >> e^{(1-\epsilon)r}$, i.e. $\sin z$ and $\cos z$ are of the order 1, type 1. Finally, if $f(z) = e^{\sqrt{z}} + e^{-\sqrt{z}}$, we have $|f(z)| \leqslant e^{\sqrt{r}} + e^{\sqrt{r}} = 2e^{\sqrt{r}} << e^{(1+\epsilon)\sqrt{r}}$, while, for $z = x$,

$$|f(z)| = e^{\sqrt{r}} + e^{-\sqrt{r}} >> e^{(1-\epsilon)\sqrt{r}},$$

i.e. $e^{\sqrt{z}} + e^{-\sqrt{z}}$ is of the order $1/2$, type 1.

We are going to establish the relation between the order of $f(z)$ and its Taylor coefficients. If $M(r) << e^{ar^k}$, Cauchy's inequality gives $|a_n| << e^{ar^k}/r^n$. Differentiating the right-hand side with respect to r we see that, when r varies, the minimum of the right-hand side is assumed for $r = (n/ak)^{1/k}$. Then we have

$$(5) \qquad |\sqrt[n]{a_n}| < (ake/n)^{1/k}, \text{ for } n \geqslant N, \text{ say.}$$

Conversely, if (5) is satisfied, we have, for a fixed r and for a sufficiently large $n \geqslant N$,

$$(6) \qquad |a_n r^n| \leqslant (ake/n)^{n/k} r^n \leqslant 1/2^n.$$

Thus $\Sigma a_n z^n$ converges for every z, i.e. $f(z)$ is an integral function. We notice that the least suffix N such that (6) is satisfied for $n \geqslant N$ varies with r. Thus we denote it by $N(r)$.

More precisely we have

$$M(r) \leqslant \Sigma |a_n| r^n \leqslant \sum_0^{N(r)-1} |a_n| r^n + 1/(2^{N(r)} - 1),$$

i.e. denoting by $m(r)$ the greatest of the terms

$$|a_0|, |a_1| r, \ldots, |a_n| r^n, \ldots,$$

we have $M(r) \leqslant N(r) m(r) + 1/(2^{N(r)} - 1)$. Since, as $r \to \infty$, $N(r)$ and all the terms $|a_n| r^n$, $n > 0$, tend to infinity, we have

$$(7) \qquad M(r) << N(r) m(r).$$

To find the order of magnitude of $m(r)$ we observe that the suffix of the greatest term, the *central suffix*, tends to infinity with r (see Ex. III. 20), and therefore, for sufficiently large r, by (5), $m(r)$ is not greater than the maximum of $(ake/n)^{n/k} r^n$ when n varies from 1 to ∞. We readily verify that this maximum is attained for $n = akr^k$, i.e.

$$(8) \qquad m(r) \leqslant e^{ar^k}.$$

As for $N(r)$, we see from (6) that, for sufficiently large r, we can take $N(r) = ake(2r)^k$. Thus, *if* (5) *is satisfied, we have*

$$(9) \qquad M(r) << ake(2r)^k e^{ar^k} << e^{(a+\epsilon)r^k}.$$

Now denote by ρ' the lower limit of numbers k for which

$$(10) \qquad |\sqrt[n]{a_n}| << (ek/n)^{1/k}.$$

Since, by hypothesis, (10) is satisfied by $k = \rho' + \epsilon$, we have, by (9), $M(r) << e^{r^{\rho'+\epsilon}}$, i.e. the order of $f(z)$ is at most ρ. But if this order were $<\rho'$, then, by (5), (10) would be satisfied for a number $k<\rho'$. Thus this lower limit $\rho' = \rho$ is the order of $f(z)$. We might sum up these results in the theorem

I. *If $f(z)$ is an integral function of the finite order ρ, we have*

$$\overline{\lim_{r=\infty}} \frac{\log\log M(r)}{\log r} = \overline{\lim_{n=\infty}} \frac{n \log n}{\log \frac{1}{|a_n|}} = \rho.$$

The left-hand term characterizes the maximum order of magnitude of $f(z)$ when $z \to \infty$ and the middle term that of $|a_n|$ when $n \to \infty$.

If we replace $M(r) << e^{ar^k}$ by $M(r) << e^{r^{\rho+\epsilon}}$ (i. e. $a = 1$, $k = \rho+\epsilon$), we find $|\sqrt[n]{a_n}| << [e(\rho+\epsilon)/n]^{1/(\rho+\epsilon)}$. Similarly, starting with $M(r) << e^{(1+\epsilon)\sigma r^\rho}$ (i. e. $a = 1+\epsilon$, $k = \rho$), we find $|\sqrt[n]{a_n}| << [(1+\epsilon)\sigma\rho e/n]^{1/\rho}$.

Therefore we can formulate our results in the following statement

II. (A) *The necessary and sufficient condition that $f(z)$ should belong at most to the minimum type of the order ρ is that*

$$\lim_{n=\infty} n^{1/\rho} |\sqrt[n]{a_n}| = 0.$$

(B) *The necessary and sufficient condition that $f(z)$ should belong to the normal type σ of the order ρ is that*

$$\overline{\lim_{n=\infty}} n^{1/\rho} |\sqrt[n]{a_n}| = (\sigma e \rho)^{1/\rho}.$$

(C) *The necessary and sufficient condition that $f(z)$ should belong to the maximum type of the order ρ is that*

$$\overline{\lim_{n=\infty}} n^{1/\rho} |\sqrt[n]{a_n}| = \infty.$$

In this way the type and order of $f(z)$ are characterized by certain properties of its Taylor coefficients.

Representation of analytic functions by series.

76. *Isolated singular points of uniform functions.* The representation of a meromorphic function as the quotient of two integral functions shows that the affixes and corresponding principal parts of the poles can be arbitrarily assigned, i. e. there

is a meromorphic function with the assigned poles. The same result holds for essential points.

I. *There is a uniform analytic function having no other singularity but the arbitrarily assigned essential points (or poles)* $z_1, z_2, \dots$, $\lim |z_i| = \infty$, *with the arbitrarily assigned principal parts* $g_i\left(\frac{1}{z-z_i}\right)$, *where* $g_i(z)$ *is any integral function (or polynomial).* (Mittag-Leffler, 1884.)

Proof. The expansion

$$g_i\left(\frac{1}{z-z_i}\right) = \sum_{n=0}^{\infty} a_{in} z^n$$

is uniformly convergent in $|z| < \theta |z_i|$, $0 < \theta < 1$, i.e. for sufficiently large ν_i we have

$$(1) \qquad \left| g_i\left(\frac{1}{z-z_i}\right) - \sum_{n=0}^{\nu_i} a_{in} z^n \right| < \epsilon_i,$$

where ν_i depends on the choice of ϵ_i. If we take any convergent series of positive terms $\Sigma \epsilon_i = \epsilon$, the numbers ν_i are determined.

Consider now a circle C of (large) radius R, centre at the origin. The circle C' of radius R/θ contains a finite number of the assigned affixes, $z_1, \dots, z_q$, say. We put

$$(2) \qquad \begin{aligned} f_1(z) &= \sum_{i=1}^{q} \left[g_i\left(\frac{1}{z-z_i}\right) - \sum_{n=0}^{\nu_i} a_{in} z^n \right], \\ f_2(z) &= \sum_{i=q+1}^{\infty} \left[g_i\left(\frac{1}{z-z_i}\right) - \sum_{n=0}^{\nu_i} a_{in} z^n \right]. \end{aligned}$$

If $z = 0$ is among the assigned affixes, incorporate the corresponding $g_0(1/z)$ into $f_1(z)$ without alteration. The second series is absolutely and uniformly convergent in C', i.e. represents a regular function in C'. Adding $f_1(z)$ to $f_2(z)$ the only singularities introduced are at ∞ and $z_1, \dots, z_q$, with the assigned principal parts, because the subtraction of the polynomial

$$\sum_{n=0}^{\nu_i} a_{in} z^n$$

does not alter the principal parts. As the same holds for every

R, the theorem is established if we add an appropriate integral function $g(z)$, and the function required is

$$(3)\quad f(z) = g(z) + f_1 + f_2 = g(z) + \sum_{i=0}^{\infty}\left[g_i\left(\frac{1}{z-z_i}\right) - \sum_{n=0}^{\nu_i} a_{in} z^n\right].$$

The theorem in its general form does not give any indication for the choice of the ν_i. Consider the case of simple poles with the residue 1. Then

$$g_i\left(\frac{1}{z-z_i}\right) = \frac{1}{z-z_i}$$

$$= -\frac{1}{z_i}\left[1 + \frac{z}{z_i} + \left(\frac{z}{z_i}\right)^2 + \dots + \left(\frac{z}{z_i}\right)^{i-1}\right] + \frac{1}{z-z_i}\left(\frac{z}{z_i}\right)^{\nu_i}.$$

We have to choose the indices ν_i in such a way that the series

$$\sum_1^{\infty} \frac{1}{z-z_i}\left(\frac{z}{z_i}\right)^{\nu_i} = -\sum_1^{\infty} \frac{z^{\nu_i}}{1-z/z_i}\frac{1}{z_i^{\nu_i+1}}$$

is convergent. For example, $\nu_i + 1 > \log i$ or $\nu_i = i - 1$ secures the convergence in every case. If $\sum_{i=1}^{\infty} |1/z_i|^p$ is convergent, we can put $\nu_i = p - 1$ as in Weierstrass's factorization theorem.

So far we have supposed that $\lim |z_i| = \infty$, i.e. we have supposed that ∞ is the only limiting point of the isolated singular points. If this is not so these points still form an enumerable set. In fact, by hypothesis, each of the assigned points is the centre of a circle containing no other singular points and not overlapping the circles round other assigned points (e.g. by taking the radius less than half the distance of the nearest other assigned point). Those circles contained in $|z| < n$ can be 'enumerated' in order of magnitude, since only a finite number of them have their radii greater than a given finite magnitude. The same holds for those circles contained in $|z| < n+1$ but not in $|z| < n$, and an enumerable set of enumerable sets is itself enumerable (see 5. II).

Let L denote the set of assigned affixes $z_1, z_2, \dots$ and L' the set composed of their limiting points, and consider a bounded region R containing only a finite number of points of L. Since

L' and R are closed there is a distance $d>0$ between the two sets.

Suppose first that L is bounded, and cover every point z' of L' by a circle C', centre z', radius $<d/2$. Similarly cover every assigned point z_i by a circle C_i, $|z-z_i| = 2\delta_i$, where δ_i is the distance of z_i from L'. If z_i is covered by one of the circles C' its distance from L' is less than $d/2$, so that the corresponding circle C_i does not encroach on R. Then there are only a finite number of points z_i not covered by the circles C', i.e. only a finite number of circles C_i, $i = 1, 2, \ldots, q$, say, encroaching upon R.

Now suppose we choose a set of positive numbers ϵ_i such that $\Sigma\epsilon_i$ is convergent. Then for every $i>q$ we can choose a ν_i such that

$$\left|g_i\left(\frac{1}{z-z_i}\right) - \sum_{n=0}^{\nu_i} a_{in}z^n\right| < \epsilon_i$$

throughout R. Therefore

$$\sum_{i=q+1}^{\infty}\left[g_i\left(\frac{1}{z-z_i}\right) - \sum_{n=0}^{\nu_i} a_{in}z^n\right] \tag{4}$$

is absolutely and uniformly convergent in R, and so the only singularities in R of the function $f(z)$ represented by the series

$$\sum_{i=0}^{\infty}\left[g_i\left(\frac{1}{z-z_i}\right) - \sum_{n=0}^{\nu_i} a_{in}z^n\right], \tag{5}$$

are those assigned for the region, and they have the assigned principal parts.

It should be observed that the series (5) has been so constructed that it may converge only in the region R. However, it is quite easy to modify the above construction so as to define a series which, when added to an appropriate integral function $g(z)$, is convergent throughout the whole domain (or domains) D formed by removing the points of L' from the complex plane, and further, is uniformly convergent throughout any interior bounded region provided an appropriate finite number of terms are omitted. For, in the first place, the domain (or domains) D may be regarded as the limit of a sequence of regions R_k each enclosing the previous ones. For instance, if we surround each point z' of L' by a circle of radius $1/\theta_k$, we may define R_k as the region obtained by removing from the circle $|z| = \theta_k$ the interiors of those circles $|z-z'| = 1/\theta_k$ which encroach on it, where $\theta_k > \theta_{k-1}$ and $\theta_k \to \infty$. Let the circles C_i be defined as before and suppose that those encroaching on R_k are C_1, $C_2, \ldots, C_{i_k}$, so that the circles $C_{i_k+1}, C_{i_k+2}, \ldots, C_{i_{k+1}}$ encroach on R_{k+1} but not on R_k. Then let ν_i be chosen so that

$$\left| g_i\left(\frac{1}{z-z_i}\right) - \sum_{n=0}^{\nu_i} a_{in} z^n \right| < \epsilon_k$$

throughout R_{k+1}, for $i = i_k+1, i_k+2, \ldots, i_{k+1}$. Choosing the series (5) in this manner, we see that

$$\sum_{i=\nu_{i_k}+1}^{\infty} \left[g_i\left(\frac{1}{z-z_i}\right) - \sum_{n=0}^{\nu_i} a_{in} z^n \right]$$

is absolutely and uniformly convergent in R_k, and the series (5) is convergent throughout $\lim R_k = D$, except at the assigned points, where it has the assigned principal parts.

If L is unbounded and ∞ is an assigned point (and so is not a point of L') we modify $g(z)$ to obtain the right principal part at infinity. If ∞ is an isolated point of L' we can combine the above arguments with those of I. Finally, if ∞ is a limiting point of L', we can apply a preliminary transformation

$$z' = \frac{1}{z-v},$$

where v is not a limiting point of L', and argue as before.

The difference between (3) and (5) is that (3) defines a unique analytic function, whereas (5) may represent different analytic functions in different disconnected domains. For example, if we take for $z_1, z_2, \ldots$ the points $(1+1/q)e^{2\pi i p/q}$, where p and q are positive integers, (5) may be shown to converge absolutely and uniformly in any bounded region inside or outside $|z| = 1$, provided in the latter case the region contains no points of z_i, and in these circumstances the series defines one analytic function inside and another outside. These two functions are not the analytic continuation of one another, for every point of $|z| = 1$ is a singular point for each. A series like (5) may define in this way even an infinity of different disconnected analytic functions.

II. *If a set of isolated affixes* z_i *and principal parts* $g_i\left(\frac{1}{z-z_i}\right)$ *be assigned arbitrarily there are series of the type*

$$G(z)+\Sigma\left[g_i\left(\frac{1}{z-z_i}\right)-G_i(z)\right],$$

where $G_i(z)$ *is a rational function and* $G(z)$ *is a uniform analytic function with only one singularity, representing one or more analytic functions having at the points* z_i *the principal parts assigned. Moreover* $G(z)$ *may be so chosen that the only other singularities are the limiting points of the assigned points.*

77. *Representation by rational fractions and polynomials.* If we start with a given uniform analytic function regular in a simply or multiply connected domain D, the fundamental problem of representation is solved by Runge's theorem.

I. *If a uniform function is regular in a domain* D, *it can be represented by a series of rational fractions uniformly and absolutely convergent in every finite inner region.*

(Runge, 1884.)

Proof. By 50. III, D is a limit of polygonal domains limited by the polygons $\pi_1, \pi_2, \dots, \pi_p, \dots$ every one of them consisting, unless D is simply connected, of several closed polygons. These polygons can be so chosen that they do not cut one another. If z is an inner point of π_{p-1}, we have

$$(1) \qquad f(z)=\frac{1}{2\pi i}\int_{\pi_p}\frac{f(u)du}{u-z}.$$

The integral is the limit of sums like

$$(2) \qquad \frac{1}{2\pi i}\sum_{k=1}^{n}\frac{f(u_{pk})\,(u_{pk}-u_{p,\,k-1})}{u_{pk}-z}=g_{pn},$$

where $u_{p0}, u_{p1}, \dots, u_{pn}$ are points of π_p, vertices included. As (2) is a rational fraction, $f(z)$ is represented as the limit of a sequence of rational fractions or as the sum of the infinite series $\sum_n [g_{pn}(z)-g_{p,\,n-1}(z)]$ of rational fractions.

We shall now prove that the series so obtained is uniformly

convergent in π_{p-1}. Let d denote the distance between π_{p-1} and π_p, and δ the length of the longest of the intervals $(u_{p,\,k-1}, u_{pk})$. If u and u' belong to the same interval and z is in the domain π_{p-1}, we have $|u-z| \geqslant d$, $|u'-z| \geqslant d$, $|u'-u| \geqslant \delta$, so that from

$$\frac{f(u')}{u'-z} - \frac{f(u)}{u-z} = \frac{(u-z)\,[f(u')-f(u)] - (u-u')f(u)}{(u'-z)\,(u-z)}$$

we have

$$\left|\frac{f(u')}{u'-z} - \frac{f(u)}{u-z}\right| \leqslant \frac{T\eta + \delta M}{d^2},$$

where T is the diagonal of a square containing the domain π_{p-1} and the polygon π_p, M is the maximum modulus of $f(z)$ on π_p, and η is the maximum oscillation of $f(u)$ in the intervals $(u_{p,\,k-1}, u_{pk})$. Since $f(u)$ is continuous on π_p, η and δ are, for sufficiently large n, as small as we like, so that

$$\left|\frac{f(u')}{u'-z} - \frac{f(u)}{u-z}\right| \leqslant \frac{\epsilon_p\, 2\pi}{L},$$

where L is the length of π_p and ϵ_p is arbitrarily assigned. Therefore, if we split the integral (1) into the sum

$$\sum_{k=1}^{n} \frac{1}{2\pi i}\int_{u_{p,\,k-1}}^{u_{pk}} \frac{f(u)\,du}{u-z}$$

of n integrals, and if we replace each integrand by its value at the first point of the interval of integration, in which way we obtain $g_{pn}(z)$, the modulus of the difference will be less than ϵ_p

$$|f(z) - g_{pn}(z)| < \epsilon_p \quad \text{for } n \geqslant N_p, \text{ say.}$$

This proves that $\lim\limits_{n=\infty} g_{pn}(z) = f(z)$ uniformly in π_{p-1}.

We notice that the finite number of poles of $g_{pn}(z)$ are all on π_p, i.e. inside D, though $f(z)$ is regular in D. Therefore, if we want a unique sequence or series tending uniformly to $f(z)$ in every finite inner region of D, we must get rid of these apparent poles. But, as Runge remarked, a rational function

$$R_a(z) = \sum_{k=1}^{m} \frac{A_k}{(z-a)^k},$$

can be replaced by another,

$$R_b(z) = \sum_{k=1}^{n} \frac{B_k}{(z-b)^k},$$

such that

$$|R_b(z) - R_a(z)| < \epsilon,$$

ϵ and b arbitrarily assigned. In fact

$$\frac{1}{z-a} = \frac{1}{z-b} + \frac{a-b}{(z-b)^2} + \ldots + \frac{(a-b)^{p-1}}{(z-b)^p} + \left(\frac{a-b}{z-b}\right)^p \frac{1}{z-a},$$

i.e. outside the circle $|z-a| = \eta$, where η is any fixed positive number, and for $|a-b| < \theta\eta, \theta < 1$, the sum $s_p(z)$ of the first p terms differs from $1/(z-a)$ by $< \theta^p/\eta$. Similarly, from

$$\frac{1}{(z-a)^k}\left[1 - \left(\frac{a-b}{z-b}\right)^p\right]^k = [s_p(z)]^k,$$

we see that the right-hand side differs from $1/(z-a)^k$, for sufficiently large p, by less than any assigned quantity. Since $R_a(z)$ contains only a finite number of terms and $[s_p(z)]^k$ is a rational function with the single pole $z = b$, the remark is proved, but uniform convergence has been established only for regions outside $|z-a| = \eta$, and for a b sufficiently near a.

Now suppose that D is a definite domain, and join the pole u_{pk} by a polygonal line L to a point b not in D *without crossing* π_{p-1}. In view of the last condition we cannot take the same b for poles lying on different polygons of π_p. Then the distance between L and the region enclosed by π_{p-1} is greater than d. Divide L into a finite number of sections by the points $z_0 = u_{pk}$, $z_1, z_2, \ldots, z_{r-1}, b = z_r$ such that $|z_{i+1} - z_i| < \theta\eta$, $\eta < d$. The remark just proved applies to the successive sections and thus we can replace the term $A_k/(u_{pk} - z)$ of $g_{pn}(z)$ by a conveniently chosen $R_{z_1}(z)$ so that the difference in π_{p-1}, which lies entirely outside $|z - u_{pk}| = \eta$, is $< \epsilon_p/rn$, say. Similarly we replace $R_{z_1}(z)$ by $R_{z_2}(z)$ such that $|R_{z_1}(z) - R_{z_2}(z)| < \epsilon_p/rn$ in π_{p-1}, i.e. $|R_{u_{pk}}(z) - R_{z_2}(z)| < 2\epsilon_p/rn$ in π_{p-1}. Thus after r steps we obtain an $R_b(z)$ such that $|R_b(z) - R_{u_{pk}}(z)| < \epsilon_p/n$ in π_{p-1}. Repeating the same operation for the other terms of $g_{pn}(z)$, we obtain a rational function $h_{pn}(z)$ having its poles outside D and such that

$$|g_{pn}(z) - h_{pn}(z)| < \epsilon_p \text{ in } \pi_{p-1} \text{ for } n \geqslant N_{p-1},$$

and thus

$$|f(z)-h_{pn}(z)|<2\epsilon_p \text{ in } \pi_{p-1} \text{ for } n\geqslant n_p,$$

where n_p is the greater of N_p and N'_p.

If we repeat the same operation for every p, the partial sums $s_p(z) = h_{p, n_p}(z)$ of the series

$$(3) \qquad h_{1, n_1}(z)+\sum_{p=2}^{\infty}[h_{p, n_p}(z)-h_{p-1, n_{p-1}}(z)]$$

satisfy the condition

$$|f(z)-s_p(z)|\leqslant \epsilon_p \text{ in } \pi_{p-1}.$$

But, for a sufficiently large p, any given inner region R of D is within π_{p-1}, which proves that the series (3) converges uniformly to $f(z)$ in R.

If D is unbounded, take consecutive circles C_r whose radii tend to ∞ with r and denote by D_r the points of D in C_r. By our previous result, there is a sequence of rational functions $f_{rp}(z)$ such that if $p\geqslant N_r$, say,

$$|f(z)-f_{rp}(z)|<\epsilon_r$$

in the polygonal domain π_{rp} approaching D_r as $p\rightarrow\infty$. Choose $p=N'_r$ such that π_{rp} tends to D when r tends to ∞, and denote by n_r the greater of N_r and N'_r. The partial sums $S_r(z)=f_{r, n_r}(z)$ of the series

$$(4) \qquad f_{1, n_1}(z)+\sum_{r=2}^{\infty}[f_{r, n_r}(z)-f_{r-1, n_{r-1}}(z)]$$

satisfy the condition

$$|f(z)-S_r(z)|\leqslant\epsilon_r \text{ in } \pi_{r, n_r},$$

and any finite inner region of D is in π_{r, n_r} for a sufficiently large r, which proves that (4) converges uniformly to $f(z)$ in any finite inner region of D.

Finally, we shall show that a suitable bracketing changes (4) into an absolutely convergent series. Suppose that a series

$$(5) \qquad \sum_{n=0}^{\infty} f_n(z)$$

is uniformly convergent in any finite inner region R of a domain D. This means that there is an N_ϵ such that

$$(6) \qquad |s_p-s_q|\leqslant\epsilon \text{ in } R \text{ if } p\geqslant N_\epsilon,\ q\geqslant N_\epsilon,$$

where $s_p = f_0 + f_1 + \dots + f_p$. Now take $\epsilon_k > 0$ such that $\Sigma\epsilon_k$ is convergent and determine the corresponding numbers $N\epsilon_k = n_k$ which we can suppose to form an increasing sequence. Putting $g_k = f_{n_{k-1}} + \dots + f_{n_k - 1}$, we see that $\Sigma f_n = \Sigma g_k$ and thus $\Sigma g_k(z)$ converges uniformly in every inner region of D. Moreover, $g_k = s_{n_k} - s_{n_{k-1}}$ and thus, by (6), $|g_k(z)| \leqslant \epsilon_k$, so that the new series converges *absolutely*. This completes the proof of I.

If D is simply connected, every u_k can be joined to one and the same point b, i.e. *$f(z)$ is a limit of rational functions, all having the same simple pole b.* If $z = \infty$ is not a point of D we can take it for b, for, applying the transformation $z = 1/(v-c)$ we obtain $h_n(v) = g_n\left(\frac{1}{v-c}\right)$ as the sum of rational functions of the type $\sum_{k=1}^{p} \frac{B_k}{(c+1/a-v)^k}$, and approximate to $h_n(v)$ by a rational function having a simple pole at c:

$$\sum_{k=1}^{q} \frac{C_k}{(c-v)^k} = \sum_{k=1}^{q} C_k z^k.$$

In this way we arbitrarily approximate to $f(z)$ in D by a sequence (or series) of polynomials.

II. *If $f(z)$ is regular in a simply connected domain D not containing $z = \infty$, $f(z)$ can be represented in D by a series of polynomials converging absolutely and uniformly in every region of D.* (Runge, 1884.)

Representation of analytic functions by integrals.

78. *Borel's integral and the exponential means.* If $f(z) = \Sigma a_n z^n$ has a finite, non-zero, radius of convergence, the series $\Sigma a_n z^n a^n/n! = F(az)$ defines *an integral function* said to be *associated with $f(z)$*. Let us consider now Borel's integrals

$$(1) \qquad \int_0^\infty e^{-a} F(az)da, \quad \int_0^\infty \frac{e^{-a} d^\lambda F(az)}{da^\lambda} da.$$

I. *If Borel's integrals are absolutely convergent for $z_0 = \rho_0 e^{i\theta_0}$, they are absolutely convergent on the whole segment $(0, z_0)$ and the first of the integrals represents the analytic continuation of $f(z)$ regular in the circle with diameter $(0, z_0)$.* (Borel, 1896 a.)

Proof. Putting $a\rho = b$, $z = \rho e^{i\theta_0}$, $\rho \leqslant \rho_0$ we have

$$\int_0^\infty e^{-a}\left|\frac{d^\lambda}{da^\lambda}F(az)\right|da = |z^\lambda|\int_0^\infty e^{-a}\,|F^{(\lambda)}(az)|\,da$$
$$= \frac{|z^\lambda|}{\rho}\int_0^\infty e^{-b/\rho}\,|F^{(\lambda)}(be^{i\theta_0})|\,db$$

and, by hypothesis, these integrals converge for $\rho = \rho_0$. Therefore, as $e^{-b/\rho} \leqslant e^{-b/\rho_0}$, they converge also for $\rho < \rho_0$. More generally, the integrals

(2) $$\frac{1}{x}\int_0^\infty e^{-b/x}\,|F^{(\lambda)}(be^{i\theta})|\,db$$

are convergent integrals provided $|e^{-b/x}| \leqslant e^{-b/\rho_0}$, i. e. for every x satisfying the condition

$$\mathrm{Rl}\,(b/x) \geqslant b/\rho_0,$$

which is obviously satisfied by the points of the circle whose diameter is $(0, |z_0|)$.

Finally we remark that, if $z = xe^{i\theta_0}$, the expression

$$\frac{1}{x}\int_0^\infty e^{-b/x}\,F(be^{i\theta_0})\,db$$

is obviously a regular function of z in the circle with diameter $(0, z_0)$, and coincides with $f(z)$ along the part of $(0, z_0)$ which is inside the circle of convergence of $f(z)$.

II. *If $f(z)$ is regular in and on the circle C with diameter $(0, z_0)$ Borel's integrals are convergent along $(0, z_0)$, z_0 included.*

(Borel, 1896 a.)

Proof. Consider a circle C' of radius $R' > |z_0/2|$, concentric with C, and such that $f(z)$ is regular in and on C'. We denote by $(0', z_0')$ the diameter of C' containing $(0, z_0)$. By Cauchy's formula $a_n = \frac{1}{2\pi i}\int_{C'}\frac{f(z)dz}{z^{n+1}}$, we have

$$F(az) = \frac{1}{2\pi i}\int_{C'} f(x)\,\Sigma\,\frac{(az)^n}{n!\,x^{n+1}}\,dx = \frac{1}{2\pi i}\int_{C'}\frac{f(x)}{x}\,e^{az/x}\,dx,$$

and

$$e^{-a}F(az) = \frac{1}{2\pi i}\int_{C'}\frac{f(x)}{x}\,e^{a(z/x-1)}\,dx.$$

Suppose that z has such a value that, when x describes the circumference C', we have

$$(3) \qquad \mathrm{Rl}\,(z/x) < 1-\epsilon.$$

If M is the maximum modulus of $f(x)/x$ on C', we have

$$e^{-a}\,|\,F(az)\,| < \frac{M}{2\pi}\int_{C'} e^{-a\epsilon}\,|\,dx\,| = MR'e^{-a\epsilon},$$

and thus

$$\int_0^\infty e^{-a}\,|\,F(az)\,|\,da$$

exists. Similarly for the other integrals.

In order to make explicit the meaning of condition (3), we put $x = \alpha + i\beta$, $z = \xi + i\eta$. The point x being fixed, the equation of the straight line L: $\mathrm{Rl}\,(z/x) = 1$ is $\alpha\xi + \beta\eta - (\alpha^2+\beta^2) = 0$, i. e. it passes through x and is normal to the straight line joining x to the origin. Thus for a fixed x condition (3) is satisfied by all the points of the complex plane z lying on the same side of L as the origin. When x describes C', the envelope

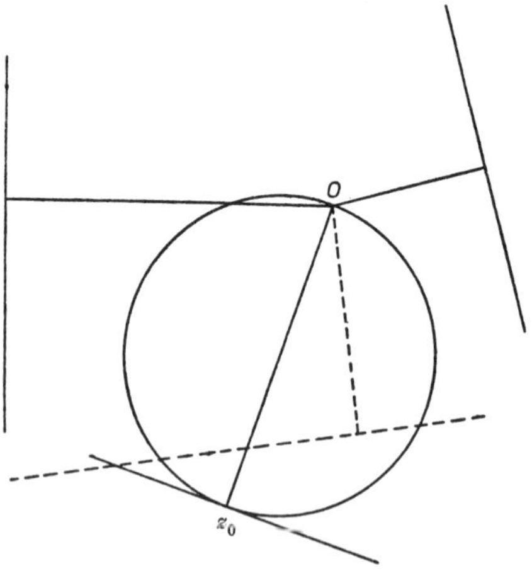

FIG. 44.

of all the corresponding straight lines is an ellipse containing $(0, z_0)$, which proves the theorem.

The two theorems together determine the part of the complex plane z in which Borel's method applies. Take in every direction $(0, z)$ the first singular point of $f(z)$, and trace the normal to $(0, z)$ passing through this first singular point. The domain lying on the same side of these normals as the origin, called the *polygon of summability*, constitutes the part in question. In fact if there is a singular point in the circle with diameter $(0, z_0)$ then z_0 is outside the polygon (see fig. 44). The interest of Borel's integral representation is its simplicity and concreteness. By means of an ingenious use of the exponential function we obtain the analytic continuation of $f(z) = \Sigma a_n z^n$ in the polygon of summability belonging to $f(z)$ as the improper integral of $e^{-a}\Sigma a_n(az)^n/n!$ along $(0, \infty)$.

Borel's integral can be transformed into another, which will lead us to the idea of transformation of infinite sequences. Taking the first of the integrals (1) and integrating by parts, we have

$$(4) \qquad \int_0^a e^{-a} F(az)\,da = -\left[e^{-a} F(az)\right]_0^a + \int_0^a e^{-a} \frac{dF(az)}{da} da.$$

We are going to show that when the integral on the right-hand side has a limit for $a \to \infty$, so also has the integral on the left-hand side, and $\lim e^{-a}F(az) = 0$. We shall thus establish the equation

$$(5) \qquad \int_0^\infty e^{-a} F(az)\,da = a_0 + \int_0^\infty e^{-a} \frac{dF(az)}{da} da,$$

provided the integral on the right-hand side exists.

Put

$$(6) \qquad e^{-a} F(az) = g(a) = g_1(a) + ig_2(a),$$

and suppose that the integral

$$(7) \qquad \int_0^\infty e^{-a} \frac{dF(az)}{da} da,$$

exists, while

$$(8) \qquad \int_0^\infty e^{-a} F(az)\,da = \int_0^\infty g(a)\,da$$

does not exist. We have to show that this assumption leads to an absurdity.

Since

$$e^{-a}\frac{dF(az)}{da} = g(a) + g'(a),$$

it follows that

$$\lim_{a\to\infty}\int_0^a [g(a)+g'(a)]\,da$$

exists, and since, by hypothesis,

$$\lim_{a\to\infty}\int_0^a g(a)\,da,$$

does not exist, the same must hold for

$$\lim_{a\to\infty}\int_0^a g'(a)\,da,$$

i. e. since

$$g(a) = a_0 + \int_0^a g'(a)\,da,$$

$g(a)$ does not tend to a limit when $a \to \infty$.

Suppose that $g_1(a)$ has no limit for $a \to \infty$ and suppose that its greatest limiting number is > 0. Then, since $g(a)$ is continuous, there are two sequences α_n, β_n tending to $+\infty$ in such a way that

$$\lim_{n=\infty} g_1(\alpha_n) = A,\ \lim_{n=\infty} g_1(\beta_n) = B > A \geqslant 0.$$

Denote by H a positive number $< B-A$. We construct by means of α_n and β_n two sequences x_ν and $x_\nu+\delta_\nu$, $x_\nu+\delta_\nu < x_{\nu+1}$ and such that

$$\int_{x_\nu}^{x_\nu+\delta_\nu} g'_1(a)\,da = g_1(x_\nu+\delta_\nu) - g_1(x_\nu) > H.$$

If $g_1(a)$ has only a finite number of zeros in $(0, +\infty)$, we have for sufficiently large a, $g_1(a) > 0$ and thus, for sufficiently large ν,

$$\int_{x_\nu}^{x_\nu+\delta_\nu} [g_1(a) + g'_1(a)]\,da > H,$$

which contradicts the hypothesis that (7) exists. If $g_1(a)$ has an infinity of zeros in $(0, +\infty)$, we take for $x_\nu+\delta_\nu$ the β_ν as before and for x_ν the greatest zero of $g_1(a)$ less than β_ν, and we arrive at the same contradiction. This proves the first part of our remark.

It follows from this result that $e^{-a}F(az)$, the sum of two sequences tending to determinate limits, also tends to a limit when $a \to \infty$. If this were not zero it would follow as above that $\lim_{a\to\infty}\int_0^a g(a)\,da$ and hence $\lim_{a\to\infty}\int_0^a g'(a)\,da$ did not exist— again a contradiction.

Now putting

(9) $$B(az) = e^{-a}\,s(az),$$

where

$$s\,(az) = \sum_0^\infty s_n(z)\,a^n/n!,$$

we have

$$B(az) = a_0 + \int_0^a \frac{d}{da}[e^{-a}s(az)]\,da = a_0 + \int^a e^{-a}\left[\frac{ds(az)}{da} - s(az)\right]da,$$

and

$$\frac{d[s(az)]}{da} - s\,(az) = \sum_0^\infty \frac{s_{n+1}(z) - s_n(z)}{n!}\,a^n = \sum_0^\infty a_{n+1}z^{n+1}\frac{a^n}{n!} = \frac{dF(az)}{da}$$

i. e. $$B(az) = a_0 + \int_0^a e^{-a}\frac{dF(az)}{da}\,da.$$

Finally, by (5),

(10) $$\int_0^\infty e^{-a}F(az)\,da = \lim_{a=\infty} B(az),$$

whenever the limit on the right-hand side exists.

$B(a)$ may be considered as a linear transform of the sequence $s_n(z)$ with the coefficients $e^{-a}a^n/n!$, the general form of a linear transform being

$$\sum_{n=0}^\infty g_n(a)s_n(z) = S(a, z).$$

Thus when $s_n(z)$ is a divergent sequence, e. g. when z is outside the circle of convergence, the limit of the transform for $a \to \infty$ can be interpreted as a generalized or conventional limit of $s_n(z)$. The function $B(a)$ is referred to as the *exponential mean* of $s_n(z)$.

In chapter XII we shall deal with the general properties of transforms and generalized limits.

79. *Mittag-Leffler's integral.* Borel's integral represents the analytic function outside the original circle of convergence in the polygon of summability. We are going to generalize this result in order to obtain the representation in the so-called star domain defined as follows. Consider a straight line $c+re^{i\theta}$ where c is a fixed point of the complex plane, θ is a fixed argument, i. e. a real number such that $0 \leqslant \theta < 2\pi$, and r varies from 0 to $+\infty$. If the analytic continuation of $f(z) = \Sigma a_n (z-c)^n$ has no finite singular point along this line, we retain the whole line. If $c+r_0 e^{i\theta}$ is the first singular point along the line, we retain only the line up to the first singular point excluding that point. With the same construction for every θ, the portion of the plane obtained (∞ omitted) is the *star domain* of $f(z)$ with respect to the point c. When we have also introduced curvilinear star domains, we shall refer to the one just defined as the *principal star domain* with respect to c.

Consider the integral

$$(1) \qquad I(z,a) = \frac{1}{2\pi i}\int_S \frac{f(zy)}{y-1} E\left(\frac{a}{y}\right) dy,$$

where $E(z)$ is an integral function, $E(0)=1$ and S, described in the positive sense, is a simple contour, containing $y=1$ and $y=0$, inside and on the boundary of which, $f(zy)$ is regular (for a given z). Under these conditions the only singular points of the integrand in S are $y=0$ and $y=1$, and thus $I(a) = I_{(0)}(a) + I_{(1)}(a)$ where $I_{(b)}$ is the same integral taken along a small circle about $y=b$ in the positive sense. Also, at $y=1$, the residue of the integrand is $f(z)E(a)$.

On the other hand, putting

$$E(z) = \sum_0^\infty c_n z^n,$$

we have

$$E\left(\frac{a}{y}\right) = \Sigma \frac{c_n a^n}{y^n}$$

and, since this series converges on the circumference of the small circle about the origin, we can multiply it by $f(zy)/(1-y)$ and integrate it term by term. Therefore

$$I_{(0)} = -\frac{1}{2\pi i}\int_{(0)} \left[\sum_{n=0}^\infty \frac{c_n a^n}{y^n} \cdot \sum_{\nu=0}^\infty s_\nu(z) y \right] dy$$

where $s_\nu(z) = a_0 + a_1 z + \ldots + a_\nu z^\nu$. Therefore, by the residue theorem, 59. I,

$$I_{(0)} = -\sum_{n=0}^{\infty} s_n(z) c_{n+1} a^{n+1},$$

and

$$\text{(2)}\quad f(z) = \frac{\Sigma s_n c_{n+1} a^{n+1}}{E(a)} + \frac{1}{2\pi i E(a)} \int_S \frac{f(zy)}{1-y} E\left(\frac{a}{y}\right) dy.$$

Consequently, if for a convenient $E(z)$ the integral on the right-hand side tends to 0 when $a \to \infty$, we obtain a representation of the character of Borel's exponential means, where the exponential function is replaced by the integral function $E(a)$. We have to choose $E(a)$ such that

$$\text{(3)}\qquad \lim_{a \to \infty} \frac{1}{E(a)} \int_S \frac{f(zy)}{1-y} E\left(\frac{a}{y}\right) dy = 0,$$

where z is any point of the star domain of $f(z)$ with respect to the origin (for simplicity). A general sufficient condition to this effect is given by the following theorem.

I. *If for every positive* ϵ *and* $r \to \infty$, $E(re^{i\theta}) = \Sigma c_n z^n$ $(c_n \geqslant 0)$, *tends uniformly to* 0 *in the region* $\epsilon \leqslant \theta \leqslant 2\pi - \epsilon$, *then* (3) *is satisfied for any region* R *lying in the star domain of* $f(z)$ *and for some* S *containing* 0 *and* 1. (Dienes, 1913.)

Proof. It is sufficient to prove that, when $a \to \infty$, then $E(az)/E(a)$ tends uniformly to 0 in every finite region outside the segment $(1, +\infty)$ of the real axis. In fact, when y describes a contour S containing $(0, 1)$, $1/y$ describes a contour outside $(1, +\infty)$. On the other hand, when R is fixed, we can take S so near the segment $(0, 1)$ that zy is in the star domain when, z being a fixed point of R, y moves along S. Thus

$$|f(zy)/(1-y)| < M,$$

in and on S, and

$$\frac{1}{E(a)} \left| \int_S \frac{f(zy)}{1-y} E\left(\frac{a}{y}\right) dy \right| < \frac{ML \max \left| E\left(\frac{a}{y}\right) \right|}{E(a)},$$

where L is a length of S. Therefore it is sufficient to prove that

$$\text{(4)}\qquad \lim_{a \to \infty} \frac{E(az)}{E(a)} = 0,$$

uniformly in z for every finite region E outside $(1, \infty)$.

For this purpose take a large circle containing E and a strip containing $(1, +\infty)$ so small that E is outside this strip. Denote by A_1 the part of E outside the angle AOB, and by A_2 the

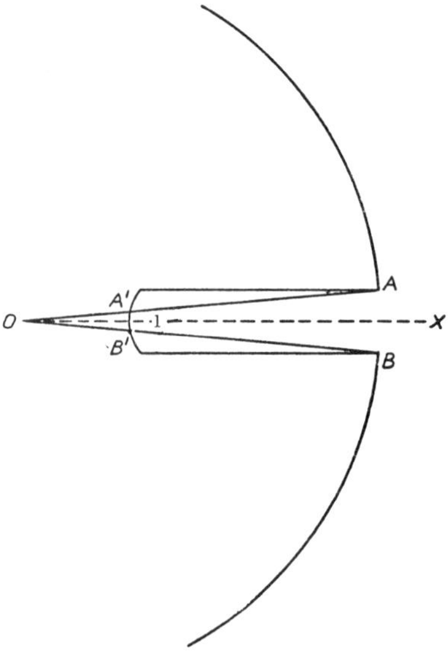

FIG. 45.

remaining part which is, by construction, inside or on the boundary of $A'OB'$.

Taking ϵ less than the angle AOX, we have, by hypothesis, $\lim_{a\to\infty} E(az) = 0$ uniformly in A_1, for if z is outside AOB so also is az. *A fortiori* $E(az)/E(a) \to 0$, uniformly in every finite region outside AOB, in particular in A_1.

On the other hand the largest modulus of z in A_2 is that of A' (and of B') so that $|z| < \overline{OA'} = b < 1$ in A_2. Hence $|E(az)| < E(ab)$, since all the coefficients of $E(z)$ are positive. Thus

$$\frac{|E(az)|}{E(a)} < \frac{E(ab)}{E(a)},$$

and so, by Appell's comparison theorem, Ex. III. 13,

$$\lim_{a\to\infty} \frac{E(ab)}{E(a)} = \lim_{n=\infty} \frac{c_n b^n}{c_n} = 0.$$

Thus (4) exists uniformly in $A'OB'$, i. e. in A_2, which proves the theorem. From (2) we obtain *Mittag-Leffler's representation*

$$(5) \qquad f(z) = \lim_{a \to \infty} \frac{\Sigma s_n(z) c_{n+1} a^{n+1}}{\Sigma c_n a^n},$$

valid in the star domain provided the summatory function $E(a) = \Sigma c_n a^n$ *satisfies the conditions of* I.

We shall see in the next chapter that Lindelöf's integral function

$$L(a) = \sum_0^\infty \frac{a^n}{[\log(n+\beta)]}, \; \beta > 1,$$

satisfies the requirements.

The function $\Sigma s_n(z) c_{n+1} a^{n+1}/E(a)$ may be called Mittag-Leffler's mean of the type $E(a)$. Mittag-Leffler first constructed a representation in the star domain directly from the Taylor series. We owe to him a good many representations of this kind.

Representation and conformal mapping.

80. *Painlevé's expansions.* Painlevé's idea of making use of conformal mapping is as follows:—A closed Jordan curve

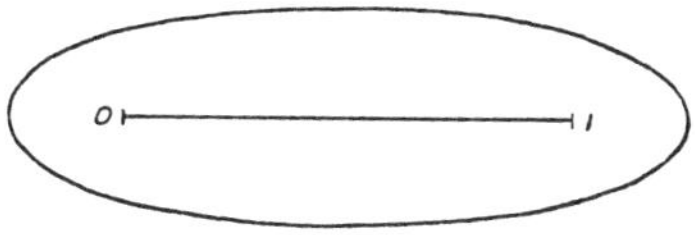

Fig. 46.

C containing the segment $(0, 1)$ in its interior being given in the z-plane, there is a conformal mapping $z = g(u)$ of the inner domain on a circle of radius $r > 1$ in the u-plane such that $u = 0$ and $u = 1$ correspond to the points $z = 0$ and $z = 1$ respectively. Since $z(u)$ is regular at the origin and vanishes there, we have, for sufficiently small $|u|$, $|g(u)| < \epsilon$ so small that we can substitute $z = g(u)$ in the Taylor series $f(z) = \Sigma a_n z^n$,

$$(1) \qquad f[g(u)] = \Sigma a_n [g(u)]^n.$$

Moreover,

$$(2)\qquad g(u) = \sum_{1}^{\infty} c_n u^n,$$

and

$$(3)\qquad f[g(u)] = \sum_{0}^{\infty} Q_n(a_n) u^n,$$

where $Q_n(a_n)$ is a homogeneous linear expression in $a_0, a_1, \ldots, a_n$ with coefficients determined by $c_1, c_2, \ldots, c_n$. If $f(z)$ is regular in C, $f[g(u)]$ is regular in and on $|u| = 1$, i.e. the radius of convergence of (3) is >1. Putting $u = 1$ we obtain

$$(4)\qquad f(1) = \sum_{0}^{\infty} Q_n(a_n),$$

valid for *every* function $f(z)$ regular inside C. We can apply the same argument to $F(z) = \Sigma a_n z_0^n z^n$, if $f(z)$ is regular in and on C^{z_0}, where C^{z_0} is the contour described by $z_0 g(e^{i\theta})$ when θ varies from 0 to 2π. Under these conditions

$$(5)\qquad F(1) = f(z_0) = \sum_{0}^{\infty} Q_n(a_n z_0^n).$$

Let us examine the domain A in which (5) applies, for in that domain $f(z)$ is represented by a series of polynomials easy to construct. The boundary points of A are the points x such that $f(z)$ is regular in C^x and has one or more singular points on the boundary of C^x. Denoting by ζ any of these singular points, we see that for every boundary point x there is a ζ such that $\zeta = xz$ for a value of z on C. Fixing ζ we consider $C_1{}^\zeta$ described by $x = \zeta/z$ when z describes C. In particular, for $\zeta = 1$, we obtain $C_1 \equiv C_1^1$ by the inversion of degree 1, pole at the origin, of the symmetric of C with respect to the real axis. The contour of A is formed by arcs of the curves $C_1{}^\zeta$, i.e. by arcs similar to C_1 or parts of C_1.

The chief property of A is, however, that it varies with C in such a way that if, for $\alpha \to 0$, the maximum distance of C_α from the segment $(0, 1)$ tends to zero, then A_α, for $\alpha \to 0$, tends to the star domain of $f(z)$ with respect to the origin. In fact, if z is any point of the star domain, we can take α so small that $f(z)$ is regular in and on zC_α and thus we can repeat the reasoning leading to (5).

Thus we obtain *the remarkable formula*

(6) $$f(z) = \sum_0^\infty Q_n(a_n z^n, \alpha),$$

valid in A_α *tending for* $\alpha \to 0$ *to the star domain.*

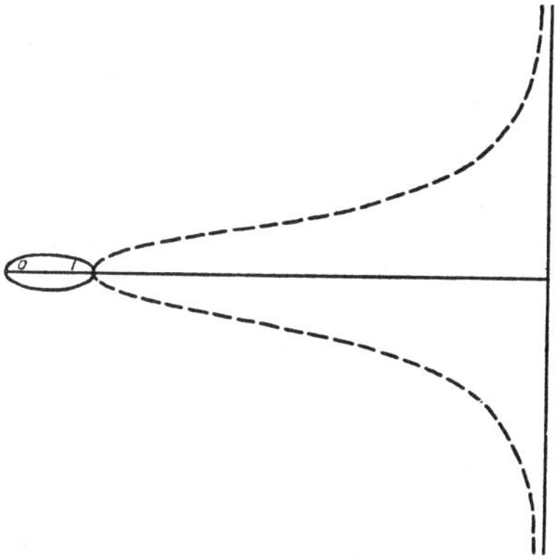

FIG. 47.

More precisely, denoting by $g(u, \alpha)$ the conformal mapping of C_α on a circle of radius $r > 1$, where

$$g(0, \alpha) = 0, \; g(1, \alpha) = 1,$$

we have

(7) $$f[zg(u, \alpha)] = \Sigma Q_n(a_n z^n, \alpha) u^n,$$

valid for $|u| \leqslant 1$ when z is any inner point of A_α.

All these considerations extend without modification to *curvilinear star domains* defined as follows:—We replace the segment (0, 1) by an open Jordan curve L joining 0 and 1 and we replace the contours C_α by simple contours γ_α reducing to L when $\alpha \to 0$. The conformal mapping of the inner domain of γ_α on $|z| < r$, $(r > 1)$, may be again denoted by $g(u, \alpha)$, where $g(0, \alpha) = 0$, $g(1, \alpha) = 1$. Now if z is any finite point of the complex plane, we consider the curve L^z formed by taking the homothetic of L with respect to the origin, with the homothetic ratio $|z|$, and turning it through an angle arg z. If $f(z)$ is regular along L^z, z included, z is a point of the curvilinear star domain $S(L)$. We obtain in this way the general formulae

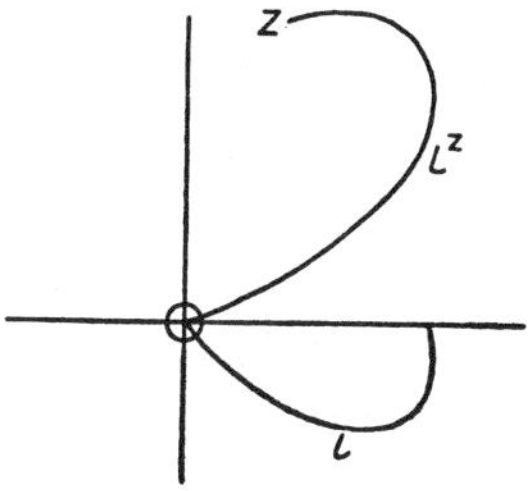

FIG. 48.

(8) $$f(z) = \Sigma G_n(a_n z^n, \alpha),$$

(9) $$f[zg(u, \alpha)] = \Sigma G_n(a_n z^n, \alpha) u^n, \; |u| \leqslant 1,$$

valid in a domain B_α tending for $\alpha \to 0$ to the curvilinear star domain $S(L)$.

To establish the absolute and uniform convergence of (6) or of (8) in every region R inside A_α or B_α respectively, we notice first that the radius of convergence of (7) and (9) being >1, the series converge absolutely for $u=1$, i. e. (6) and (8) converge absolutely: $\Sigma\,|\,G_n(a_n z^n,\alpha)\,|$ is convergent for any point of B_α. On the other hand if the radius of convergence of $\Sigma\, b_n z^n$ is $r>1$, we have, by Cauchy's inequalities (40. 3)

$$(10)\quad |\,b_{n+1}+b_{n+2}+\,\dots\,|<M\Big(\frac{1}{\rho^n}+\frac{1}{\rho^{n+1}}+\,\cdots\Big)=\frac{M}{\rho^n}\,\frac{1}{\rho-1},$$

where $1<\rho<r$ and M is the maximum modulus of $\Sigma b_n z^n$ in $|\,z\,|\leqslant\rho$. In order to apply this remark to (9), we have to show that, the region R being given, (9) is bounded in $|\,u\,|\leqslant\rho$, $(\rho>1)$ independently of z taken from R.

Consider for this purpose the contours $\gamma_\alpha^{\,z}$ defined by the equation $v=zg(e^{i\theta},\alpha)$ when θ varies from 0 to 2π and z is a fixed point of R. Denote by d the points lying inside at least one of the contours $\gamma_\alpha^{\,z}$. By hypothesis $f(z)$ is regular in d as well as on its boundary. Now replace $\gamma_\alpha^{\,z}$ by the contour $\delta_\alpha^{\,z}$ defined by the equations $v=zg(\rho e^{i\theta},\alpha)$, $(\rho>1)$. The set of points d_ρ corresponding to d contains d and for $\rho=1$ coincides with d. Moreover d_ρ varies continuously with ρ, so that we can take ρ so near 1 that $f(z)$ is regular in d_ρ and on its boundary. But then $f[zg(u,\alpha)]$ is a regular function of u (when z is any point of D) at least in and on the circle $|\,u\,|\leqslant\rho$. Finally all the functions of u, when z varies in R, are composed of values $f(z)$ assumed in d_ρ. Hence they have a common maximum M and (10) can be applied to (9):

$$|\,G_{n+1}(a_{n+1}z^{n+1},\alpha)+G_{n+2}(a_{n+2}z^{n+2},\alpha)+\dots\,|<\frac{M}{\rho^n(\rho-1)},$$

independently of z in R. Thus the convergence is uniform.

The only defect of all the representations of this type is that none of them converges in the whole star domain, but only in domains tending to the star domain. If a region R in the star domain is given we have to take α so small that A_α or B_α contains R.

We can, however, construct a representation of $f(z)$ in the complete star domain, independently of α, in the following way. Let us choose three positive zero sequences α_i, ϵ_i and $\rho_i - 1$ such that $\Sigma\epsilon_i$ is convergent. Determine afterwards the sequence n_i such that $1/\rho_i^{n_i}(r_i - 1) < \epsilon_i$ and denote by $H_k(z)$ the sum of the first $n_k + 1$ terms of the expression

$$(11) \qquad a_0 + \sum_1^\infty G_n(a_n z^n, \alpha_k).$$

The series of polynomials

$$(12) \qquad a_0 + \sum_1^\infty [H_k(z) - H_{k-1}(z)],$$

converges in the whole star domain $S(L)$. In fact the k-th partial sum of this series is $a_0 + H_k(z)$, i. e. the k-th partial sum S_k of the Taylor series

$$a_0 + \sum_1^\infty G_n(a_n z^n, \alpha_k) u^n,$$

for $u = 1$, i. e.

$$|f(z) - S_k| < \frac{M}{r_k^{n_k}(r_k - 1)} < M\epsilon_k,$$

since for large k, ρ_k is so near 1 that the values of $f(z)$ figuring in the function $f[zg(u, \alpha)]$ are all in d_{ρ_k} and thus have a common maximum modulus. We prove in the same way that (12) is *absolutely convergent.*

81. *Examples.* We know that the branch of $v = \log u$ vanishing for $u = 1$ maps the half-plane of u on the right of the imaginary axis upon the strip of the v-plane parallel to the real axis and symmetrical with respect to it, of width π. Thus $v = \alpha \log u$, α real, very small, maps the same half-plane upon similar narrow strips of width $|\alpha|\pi$ having the real axis for their diameter. Finally,

$$v = -\alpha \log(1 - \beta u), \text{ with } \beta = 1 - e^{-1/\alpha},$$

maps the half-plane Π of u of abscissae $> -1/\beta$ on a similar strip of the v-plane with the supplementary conditions that

$v = 0$ and $v = 1$, correspond to $u = 0$ and $u = 1$ and that the circle $\gamma, |v| \leqslant 1$, is included in Π.

We are going to determine first the domain c of u corresponding to the circle γ. This domain c is symmetrical with respect to the real axis and is very flat, for it is contained in the narrow strip of width $|\alpha|\pi$. To determine its maximum and minimum abscissae we have to determine the maximum and minimum of the real part of

$$-\alpha \log(1-\beta u)$$
$$= -\alpha[\log\beta + \log(1/\beta - u)],$$

i. e. the maximum and minimum moduli of $1/\beta - u$ when u varies in γ. In Fig. 49 the affix of M is ζ and that of Q is $1/\beta$ so that $|1/\beta - \zeta| = QM$.

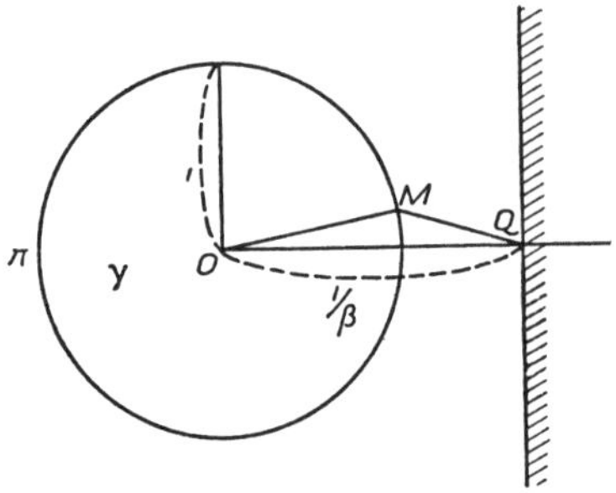

FIG. 49.

Thus the extreme values are assumed at

$$u = -1 \text{ and } u = +1,$$

i. e. the maximum abscissa is $-\alpha \log(1-\beta) = 1$ and the minimum abscissa is $-\alpha \log(1+\beta) = -\alpha \log(2-\epsilon^{-1/\alpha}) \to 0$ with α. Hence the domain c reduces to $(0, 1)$ when $\alpha \to 0$.

Now replace γ by a larger concentric circle Γ of radius ρ inside Π. Then, by hypothesis, $\rho = 1 + \lambda e^{-1/\alpha}$, with $0 < \lambda < 1$. The domain C of v corresponding to Γ is in the strip B and its extreme abscissae correspond to $u = \pm\rho$ and are equal to $-\alpha \log(1 \mp \beta\rho)$. As $\rho < 1/\beta$, we have $\log(1+\beta\rho) < \log 2$, i. e. the minimum abscissa is $> -\alpha \log 2$.

On the other hand,

$$\log(1-\beta\rho) = \log(1-\beta-\beta\lambda e^{-1/\alpha})$$
$$= \log[e^{-1/\alpha}(1-\beta\lambda)] = -1/\alpha + \log(1-\beta\lambda),$$

i. e. the maximum abscissa is equal to

$$1 - \alpha \log(1-\beta\lambda) < 1 - \alpha \log(1-\lambda),$$

since $0 < \beta < 1$. Taking $\lambda = 1/2$, the domain C is between the abscissae $-\alpha \log 2$ and $1 + \alpha \log 2$, i. e. between $-\alpha$ and $1+\alpha$ and between the ordinates $\pm\alpha\pi/2$. Hence C reduces to $(0, 1)$ when $\alpha \to 0$.

Take now a function $f(z) = \Sigma a_n z^n$ which is regular and $|f(z)| < H$ in C. The function $f[-\alpha \log(1-\beta u)] = F(u)$ is regular in the circle Γ and thus $F(u) = \Sigma A_n u^n$. In particular $f(1) = F(1) = \Sigma A_n$ and

$$\left|\sum_0^n A_i - f(1)\right| < \frac{H}{(1+e^{-1/\alpha}/2)^n e^{-1/\alpha}/2} = \frac{2He^{1/\alpha}}{(1+e^{-1/\alpha}/2)^n}.$$

We have to calculate A_n in terms of $a_0, a_1, a_2, \ldots$, i. e. to arrange

$$F(u) = a_0 - a_1 \alpha \log(1-\beta u) + \ldots + (-1)^k a_k \alpha^k [\log(1-\beta u)]^k + \ldots$$

according to the powers of u. Putting

$$(-1)^k [\log(1-u)]^k = u^k (1 + E_{k+1}^k u + E_{k+2}^k u^2 + \ldots)$$

we have

$$F(u) = a_0 + a_1 \alpha\beta u + \ldots$$
$$+ \beta^n u^n [\alpha^n a_n + \alpha^{n-1} a_{n-1} E_n^{n-1} + \ldots + \alpha a_1 E_n^1] + \ldots$$

Therefore putting

$$\bar{E}_n^{n-j} = n(n-1)\ldots(n-j+1) E_n^{n-j},$$

we obtain

$$A_n = \frac{\beta^n}{n!}[\alpha^n f^{(n)}(0) + \alpha^{n-1} \bar{E}_n^{n-1} f^{(n-1)}(0) + \ldots + \alpha \bar{E}_n^1 f'(0)].$$

To determine the constants $\bar{E}_n^{n-j}$ we take $1/(1-z)$ for $f(z)$ and obtain for sufficiently small $|u|$

$$1/[1+\alpha\log(1-u)] = 1 + \alpha u + \ldots$$
$$+ u^n [n!\alpha^n + (n-1)!\bar{E}_n^{n-1}\alpha^{n-1} + \ldots + \bar{E}_n^1 \alpha]/n! + \ldots$$

Noticing that the coefficient of $u^n/n!$ is $[dg(u)/du]_{u=0}$ with $g(u) = 1/[1+\alpha\log(1-u)]$ we have only to put

$$G(u) = 1 + \alpha \log(1-u),$$

$$\frac{d^n g(u)}{du^n} = \frac{1}{(1-u)^n} \sum_{i=1}^n \frac{\lambda_i^n \alpha^i}{G^{i+1}},$$

(by induction) and to notice that for $u = 0$,

$$\sum_{i=1}^n \lambda_i^n \alpha^i = n!\,\alpha^n + (n-1)!\,\bar{E}_n^{n-1}\alpha^{n-1} + \ldots + \bar{E}_n^1 \alpha,$$

for every α. Hence

$$\frac{d^n g(u)}{du^n} = \frac{1}{(1-u)^n}\sum_{i=1}^{n} i!\,\bar{E}_n^i \frac{\alpha^i}{G^{i+1}},\ \bar{E}_n^n = 1.$$

Differentiating and putting $u = 0$, we obtain

$$\left[\frac{d^{n+1}g}{du^{n+1}}\right]_{u=0} = n\sum_{i=1}^{n} i!\,\bar{E}_n^i\alpha^i + \sum_{i=1}^{n} i!\,\bar{E}_n^i(i+1)\alpha^{i+1},$$

where the left-hand side is, by definition,

$$\sum_{i=1}^{n+1} i!\,\bar{E}_{n+1}^i\alpha^i.$$

Equating the coefficients we obtain the formulae

$$\bar{E}_{n+1}^i = n\bar{E}_n^i + \bar{E}_n^{i-1},\quad 1 < i < n+1,$$

with $\bar{E}_n^n = 1$, $\bar{E}_n^1 = n!$. These formulae determine the constants E_n^{n-j} and thus the representation in question.

We can simplify the expressions giving $\bar{E}_n^{n-j}$ by introducing the polynomial $K_n(u) = u(u+1)\dots(u+n-1)$. We are going to prove, namely, that $K_n(u) = u^n + \bar{E}_n^{n-1}u^{n-1} + \dots + \bar{E}_n^1 u$. This equation is obvious for $n = 1$. Suppose that it is true for n. Then it is true also for $n+1$ since

$$\begin{aligned} K_{n+1}(u) &= (u+n)K_n \\ &= u^{n+1} + u^n(n+\bar{E}_n^{n-1}) + \dots + u^i(n\bar{E}_n^i + \bar{E}_n^{i-1}) + \dots + un!. \end{aligned}$$

Hence

$$A_n = \frac{\beta^n}{n!}[\alpha^n f^{(n)}(0) + \alpha^{n-1}\bar{E}_n^{n-1}f^{(n-1)}(0) + \dots + \alpha\bar{E}_n^1 f'(0)],$$

where $\bar{E}_n^i$ is a positive integer, viz. the coefficient of u in $K_n(u)$.

In a symbolic form

$$A_n = \frac{\beta^n}{n!}K_n(\alpha f_0') \equiv \frac{\beta^n}{n!}\alpha f_0'(1+\alpha f_0')(2+\alpha f_0')\dots(n-1+\alpha f_0')$$

provided after multiplication we replace $(f_0')^i$ by $(f^{(i)})_0$.

If we want to construct a representation valid in the star domain, we have to take values of α tending to 0, e.g. $\alpha = 2/\log j$, j being an integer. Then $\beta = 1 - 1/\sqrt{j}$ and there is a k such that for $j>k$ the function $f(z)$ is regular in C_j and $|f(z)|<H$. Hence for $j>k$,

$$|A_0+A_1+\ldots+A_j-f(1)|<\frac{2H\sqrt{j}}{\left(1+\frac{1}{2\sqrt{j}}\right)^{2\sqrt{j}\frac{\sqrt{}}{2}}}<M$$

In fact

$$(1+h)^{1/h}=e^{\frac{\log(1+h)}{h}}=e^{\frac{1}{h}(h-h^2/2+\ldots)}>e^{1-h/2}>e^{1/2},$$

for $0<h<1$. Hence

$$\frac{2H\sqrt{j}}{\left(1+\frac{1}{2\sqrt{j}}\right)^{j}}<\frac{2H\sqrt{j}}{e^{\sqrt{j}/4}}.$$

Putting

$$\pi_0=f(0),\quad \pi_n=f(0)+\sum_{i=1}^{n}\frac{\beta^i}{i!}K_i(\alpha z f_0'),$$

and
$$\phi_0=\pi_0,\ \phi_1=\pi_1-\pi_0,\ \ldots,\ \phi_n=\pi_n-\pi_{n-1},\ \ldots$$
$$\alpha=2/\log n,\quad \beta=1-1/\sqrt{n},$$

we see that $\phi_0+\phi_1+\ldots+\phi_n+\ldots$ represents $f(z)$ in the star domain.

CHAPTER X

SINGULARITIES OF ANALYTIC FUNCTIONS

Determination of polar singularities.

82. *Taylor coefficients of rational functions.* In the previous chapter we dealt with the problem of representation by appropriate formulae of the values of an analytic function assumed at regular points outside the original circle of convergence. The singular points, however, characterize the function more intimately than its values at regular points. For example, an integral function is characterized by the fact that its only singular point is ∞; meromorphic functions have only poles in the finite part of the complex plane, &c. Therefore, the determination of the affixes of singular points and that of the behaviour of the function in their neighbourhood is of paramount importance in function theory.

The complete analytic function is fully determined by its Taylor expansion $f(z) = \Sigma a_n z^n$, about the origin for simplicity. Therefore we ought to be able *to detect every property of $f(z)$ by means of the properties of the given coefficients a_n and by the formal properties of power series. This is the central problem of Taylor series.* It was also the point of view of Weierstrass in his treatment of analytic functions.

The results of the previous chapter give a very incomplete answer to one of the questions raised by our problem, viz. how to represent by a single formula a more or less extended portion (branch) of an analytic function given by a Taylor series. The problem of singularities involves new difficulties. First of all, since the singular points may form an infinite set or even a continuum, the calculation of the position (affix) of all singular points of a given analytic function is plainly impossible. Moreover the irregular behaviour of an analytic function near its singular points is so varied in character that it defies exhaustive classification, though a relation between some properties of the Taylor coefficients and some properties of the function in the neighbourhood of a singular point logically implies at least a partial description of the latter.

A complete answer to the first question—where are the singular points?—has been given by Hadamard for polar singularities lying in a *circle of meromorphy*, i.e. in the largest circle about a regular point containing only poles.

There are very few results which go beyond this theorem in the effective determination of the affixes of singular points. In the general case we have to content ourselves with finding more or less general relations between properties of coefficients and properties of the corresponding function.

The simplest case is when the function has only a finite number of poles and zeros, i.e. when the function in question is the quotient of two polynomials: $\Sigma a_n z^n = P(z)/Q(z)$, and the corresponding problem is to find the necessary and sufficient conditions on the coefficients a_n in order that $\Sigma a_n z^n$ should represent such a function.

I. *If*

$$D_\lambda^{(\mu)} = \begin{vmatrix} a_\lambda, & a_{\lambda+1}, & \ldots, & a_{\lambda+\mu} \\ a_{\lambda+1}, & a_{\lambda+2}, & \ldots, & a_{\lambda+\mu+1} \\ \cdot & \cdot & \cdot & \cdot \\ a_{\lambda+\mu}, & a_{\lambda+\mu+1}, & \ldots, & a_{\lambda+2\mu} \end{vmatrix}, \tag{1}$$

the necessary and sufficient condition that $\Sigma a_n z^n$ should represent a rational function is that $D_0^{(n)} = 0$ for $n \geqslant N$.

(Kronecker, 1881.)

Proof. The condition is necessary. In fact if

$$\Sigma a_n z^n = (c_0 + c_1 z + \ldots + c_m z^m)/(b_0 + b_1 z + \ldots + b_p z^p),$$

the coefficients a_n satisfy the conditions

$$\begin{aligned} c_0 &= b_0 a_0 \\ c_1 &= b_1 a_0 + b_0 a_1 \\ &\cdot\ \cdot\ \cdot\ \cdot\ \cdot\ \cdot \\ c_m &= b_m a_0 + b_{m-1} a_1 + \ldots + b_0 a_m \\ 0 &= b_{m+1} a_0 + b_m a_1 + \ldots + b_0 a_{m+1} \\ &\cdot\ \cdot\ \cdot\ \cdot\ \cdot\ \cdot\ \cdot\ \cdot\ \cdot\ \cdot\ \cdot\ \cdot \end{aligned} \tag{2}$$

where $b_{p+i} = 0$, $i = 1, 2, \ldots$. It follows that all the $D_0^{(n)}$ vanish after a suffix N. In fact, suppose $m \leqslant p-1$, and insert zero coefficients; then from

$$(3)\qquad \begin{aligned} 0 &= a_0 b_p + a_1 b_{p-1} + \dots + a_p b_0 \\ &\cdots\cdots\cdots \\ 0 &= a_p b_p + a_{p+1} b_{p-1} + \dots + a_{2p} b_0 \end{aligned}$$

we see that $D_0^{(p)} = 0$, and from

$$\begin{aligned} 0 &= a_0 0 + a_1 b_p + a_2 b_{p-1} + \dots + a_{p+1} b_0 \\ &\cdots\cdots\cdots \\ 0 &= a_{p+1} 0 + a_{p+2} b_p + a_{p+3} b_{p-1} + \dots + a_{2p+2} b_0, \end{aligned}$$

that $D_0^{(p+1)} = 0$, &c.

If $m > p-1$, the left-hand side is permanently 0 after the m-th equation, and thus the equations

$$\begin{aligned} 0 &= a_0 0 + a_1 0 + \dots + a_{m+1-p} b_p + \dots + a_{m+1} b_0 \\ 0 &= a_1 0 + a_2 0 + \dots + a_{m+2-p} b_p + \dots + a_{m+2} b_0 \\ &\cdots\cdots\cdots \\ 0 &= a_{m+1} 0 + a_{m+2} 0 + \dots + a_{2m+2-p} b_p + \dots + a_{2m+2} b_0 \end{aligned}$$

lead to $D_0^{(m+1)} = 0$, $D_0^{(m+2)} = 0$, &c.

The condition is sufficient. It follows from the identity

$$(4)\qquad D_\lambda^{(\mu)} D_{\lambda+2}^{(\mu)} - D_\lambda^{(\mu+1)} D_{\lambda+2}^{(\mu-1)} = [D_{\lambda+1}^{(\mu)}]^2$$

that if, for a fixed λ, $D_\lambda^{(r+i)} = 0$, $i = 0, 1, 2, \dots$, we have also $D_{\lambda+1}^{(r+i)} = 0$ and thus also $D_{\lambda+2}^{(r+i)} = 0$, &c. Therefore, if $D_0^{(r+i)} = 0$, we have also $D_\lambda^{(r+i)} = 0$, $\lambda = 1, 2, \dots$. Now let p be the least number such that $D_\lambda^{(p)} = 0$ for all sufficiently large λ, and suppose $D_{\nu+i}^{(p)} = 0$, $i = 0, 1, 2, \dots$. Then $D_{\nu+i}^{(p-1)} \neq 0$, $i = 0, 1, 2, \dots$ for, since $D^{(p)} = 0$, $D_\nu^{(p-1)} = 0$ would imply $D_{\nu+1}^{(p-1)} = 0$, by (4), and so on. It follows that the equations

$$\begin{aligned} 0 &= a_\nu b_p + a_{\nu+1} b_{p-1} + \dots + a_{\nu+p} b_0 \\ 0 &= a_{\nu+1} b_p + a_{\nu+2} b_{p-1} + \dots + a_{\nu+p+1} b_0 \\ &\cdots\cdots\cdots \\ 0 &= a_{\nu+p-1} b_p + a_{\nu+p} b_{p-1} + \dots + a_{\nu+2p-1} b_0 \end{aligned}$$

determine $b_0 = 1, b_1, b_2, \dots b_p$ uniquely, where $b_p \neq 0$. Then the first $\nu+p$ equations of (2) determine $c_0, c_1, \dots, c_m$, where $m \leqslant \nu+p-1$. Finally the condition $D_{\nu+i}^{(p)} = 0$ shows that all the following equations are satisfied with $b_{p+1} = 0$, $i = 1, 2, \dots$.

This result can also be formulated as follows:

II. *The necessary and sufficient condition that* $\Sigma a_n z^n$ *should be a rational function is that there be a number* p *such that* $\Sigma D_\lambda^{(p)} z^\lambda = P(z)$ *is a polynomial. Then the least value of* p *is the degree of the denominator, and the degree of* $P(z)$ *is not less than* $m-p$, m *being the degree of the numerator.*

83. *Integral coefficients. Finite number of different coefficients.*

I. *If all the coefficients of* $f(z) = \Sigma a_n z^n$ *are integers and if* $f(z)$ *is regular in a domain* D *whose inner conform-radius with respect to* $z = 0$ *is* >1, $f(z)$ *is rational.* (Pólya, 1922.)

This result is the generalization of simpler theorems due to Borel (1894), Pólya (1916 b), Carlson (1921).

Proof. Put

$L_k a_m = a_m + t_1^{(k)} a_{m-1} + \ldots + t_k^{(k)} a_{m-k}$, $L_0 a_m = a_m$, $a_{-\nu} = 0$, $(\nu > 0)$, where the coefficients $t_i^{(k)}$ will be determined later on. By elementary transformations of determinants

$$D_0^{(n)} = \begin{vmatrix} a_0, a_1, & \ldots a_n \\ a_1, a_2, & \ldots a_{n+1} \\ \cdot & \cdot \\ a_n, a_{n+1}, & \ldots a_{2n} \end{vmatrix} = \begin{vmatrix} a_0, & L_1 a_1, & \ldots L_n a_n \\ L_1 a_1, & L_1 L_1 a_2, & \ldots L_1 L_n a_{n+1} \\ \cdot & \cdot & \cdot \\ L_n a_n, & L_n L_1 a_{n+1}, & \ldots L_n L_n a_{2n} \end{vmatrix}$$

Putting $Q_k^*(z) = t_k^{(k)} z^k + t_{k-1}^{(k)} z^{k-1} + \ldots + t_1^{(k)} z + 1$, we have

$$Q_k^*(z) f(z) = \Sigma L_k a_i z^i, \quad Q_l^*(z) Q_k^*(z) f(z) = \Sigma L_l L_k a_i z^i.$$

It follows that $L_l L_k a_m = L_k L_l a_m$, and that

$$L_l L_k a_{l+k} = \frac{1}{2\pi i} \int_C \frac{f(z) Q_l^* Q_k^* dz}{z^{l+k+1}},$$

where C is a contour in D enclosing $z = 0$. Therefore, putting $Q_n^*(z)/z^n = Q_n(1/z)$, we have

$$L_l L_k a_{l+k} = \frac{1}{2\pi i} \int_C \frac{f(z) Q_l(1/z) Q_k(1/z)}{z}$$

For the next step we want a lemma by Faber:

Lemma 1. Suppose $u = g(z)$ *maps* D *containing* $z = 0$ *biuniformly upon the circle* $|u| < \rho$, where $g(0) = 0$, $g'(0 = 1$. *Put*

$$1/g(z) = \frac{1}{z} + \lambda_0 + \lambda_1 z + \ldots, \quad [1/g(z)]^m = \frac{1}{z^m} + \frac{l_1^{(m)}}{z^{m-1}} + \ldots$$
$$+ l_m^{(m)} + P_m^*(z) = P_m(1/z) + P_m^*(z),$$

where $P_m^*(0) = 0$. *Then, in every region of* D,

(1) $$[g(z)]^m P_m(1/z) \to 1.$$ (Faber, 1920 a.)

Proof of the lemma. By the residue theorem

$$P_m(1/z) = \frac{1}{2\pi i}\int_\Gamma \left(\frac{1}{g(x)}\right)^m \left[\left(\frac{x}{z}\right)^m + \left(\frac{x}{z}\right)^{m-1} + \ldots + 1\right]\frac{dx}{x},$$

where Γ is the picture of a circle $|u| = r < \rho$ by $u = g(x)$, and z is inside Γ.

We have

$$P_m(1/z) = \frac{1}{2\pi i}\int_\Gamma \frac{1}{z^m}\left(\frac{x}{g(x)}\right)^m \frac{dx}{x-z} - \frac{1}{2\pi i}\int_\Gamma \frac{z}{x-z}\left(\frac{1}{g(x)}\right)^m \frac{dx}{x}.$$

Thus, $x/g(x)$ being regular in D, we obtain by calculating the residue for $x = z$,

$$P_m(1/z) - \left(\frac{1}{g(z)}\right)^m = -\frac{1}{2\pi i}\int_\Gamma \frac{z}{x-z}\left(\frac{1}{g(x)}\right)^m \frac{dx}{x}.$$

On the other hand, since $|g(x)| = r$ along Γ,

$$|[g(z)]^m P_m(1/z) - 1| < \frac{|g(z)|^m}{r^m}\frac{1}{2\pi}\int_\Gamma \left|\frac{z}{x-z}\right|\left|\frac{dx}{x}\right|.$$

Since the integral is independent of m and $|g(z)| < r$, equation (1) is established.

Returning now to the proof of I, $f(z)$ is by hypothesis regular in D, whose inner conform radius with respect to $z = 0$ is $\rho > 1$. Put $1 < R < r < \rho$ and choose for $Q_m(1/z)$ the function $P_m(1/z)$. Then

$$\left|\frac{1}{2\pi i}\int_\Gamma f(z) P_k(1/z) P_l(1/z)\frac{dz}{z}\right| < \frac{M}{r^k r^l},$$

where M does not depend on k and l. For, by lemma 1,

$$|P_k(1/z)| < c/|g(z)|^k = c/r^k,$$

where c is independent of k, since (1) is valid for $|g(z)| \leqslant r$. Thus

$$|D_0^{(n)}| < \frac{M^{n+1}(n+1)!}{(r^{1+2+\cdots+n})^2} < \left[\frac{(n+1)M}{r^n}\right]^{n+1} \to 0,$$

since $r > 1$. Since the determinants $D_0^{(n)}$ are integers, $D_0^{(n)} = 0$ for sufficiently large n and thus, by 82. I, $f(z)$ is a rational function.

II. *If among the coefficients a_n of a Taylor series $f(z) = \Sigma a_n z^n$ there are only a finite number of different numbers, then either $f(z) = P(z)/(1-z^m)$, where $P(z)$ is a polynomial and m a positive integer, or else $f(z)$ is not continued beyond the circle of convergence of $\Sigma a_n z^n$.* (Szegö, 1922 a.)

Proof. It follows from our hypothesis that the radius of convergence is 1. If $f(z)$ is continued outside $|z| = 1$, there is a domain of the form indicated in fig. 50, and enclosed by the curve Γ, inside and on which, $f(z)$ is regular. We are going to prove first that there is an M such that

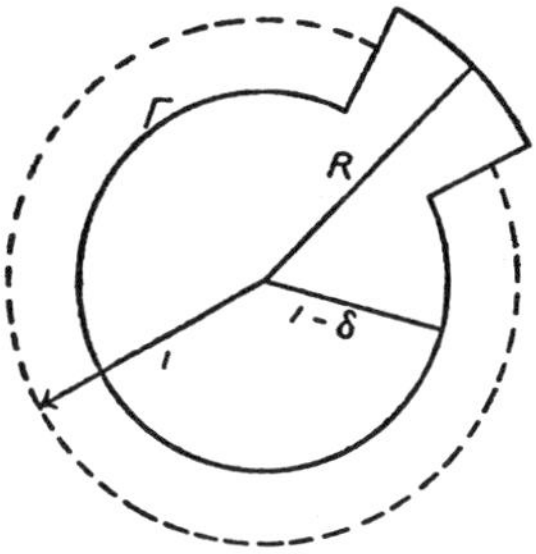

FIG. 50.

(2) $|[f(z)-s_{n-1}(z)]/z^{n+1}| < M$ on Γ.
For this purpose we consider a curve Γ' similar to Γ containing the latter and so near to it that $f(z)$ is regular in and on Γ'. If z_1 and z_2 denote the two points at which Γ' cuts $|z| = 1$, it is sufficient to prove the existence of an M_1 such that

$$(3) \quad |\Delta_n(z)| \equiv \left|\frac{f(z)-s_{n-1}(z)}{z^n}(z-z_1)(z-z_2)\right| < M_1 \text{ on } \Gamma'.$$

For if (3) is satisfied on Γ' it is also satisfied on Γ, from which (2) follows.

If $A \geqslant |a_n|$ for every n, and $1-\delta'$ is the inner radius of Γ', we have

$$|\Delta_n(z)| = |(a_n + a_{n+1}z + \ldots)(z-z_1)(z-z_2)|$$
$$< A\,|z-z_1|\,|z-z_2|/(1-|z|) < 4A/\delta'$$

on the inner circle of Γ'. On the straight sections of Γ' inside $|z| = 1$, we obtain similarly

$$|\Delta_n(z)| < A\,|z-z_1|\,|z-z_2|/(1-|z|),$$

and $|z-z_1| = 1-|z|$ on one and $|z-z_2| \leqslant z+|z_2|$ on the other, so that $|\Delta_n(z)| < 2A$ on the straight section inside $|z| = 1$.

Outside $|z| = 1$ along Γ' there is an S such that $|f(z)| < S$, and thus $|f(z)-s_{n-1}(z)| < S + A\,|z|^n/(|z|-1)$. Hence on the straight sections outside $|z| = 1$,

$$|\Delta_n(z)| < S(|z|-1)2|z|/|z|^n + A(|z|-1)2|z|/(|z|-1)$$
$$< S2R'(R'-1) + A\,2R',$$

where R' is the outer radius of Γ'.

Finally, on $|z| = R'$ along Γ',

$$|\Delta_n(z)| < 4R'^2[S/R'^n + A/(R'-1)] < 4R'^2[S + A/(R'-1)],$$

which proves (3) and hence (2).

Now vary the *inner* radius $1-\delta$ and denote the corresponding curves by $\Gamma(\delta)$. We are going to prove that for every given $\eta>0$ there is a polynomial in $1/z$:

$$Q(1/z) = c_0 + c_1/z + \ldots + 1/z^q,$$

such that

(4) $$|Q(1/z)| < 1/2 \text{ on } \Gamma(\delta) \text{ for } \delta < \eta.$$

The degree q depends on the given η. We prove this proposition by showing that there is a polynomial Q satisfying (3) even for the limiting case $\Gamma(0)$. For this purpose consider a ring domain containing the arc of $|z| = 1$ belonging to $\Gamma(0)$, and approximate to -1 in this domain by polynomials (e.g. by Runge's method 77. II). Thus we obtain a

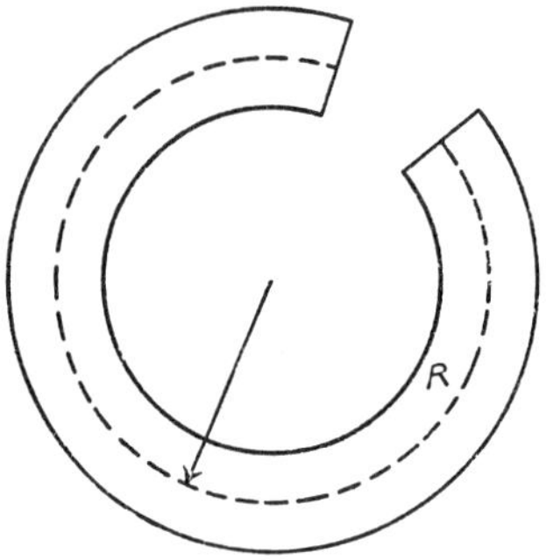

Fig. 51.

$$P(z) = c_0 z^p + c_1 z^{p-1} + \ldots + c_{p-1} z$$

such that

$$|c_0 z^p + c_1 z^{p-1} + \ldots + c_{p-1} z - (-1)| < 1/2 \text{ in } R,$$

i.e. $$|c_0 + c_1/z + \ldots + 1/z^p| < 1/(2|z|^p) \text{ in } R.$$

Hence on the arc of $|z| = 1$ in R,

(5) $$|c_0 + c_1/z + \ldots + 1/z^p| < 1/2.$$

On the other part of $\Gamma(0)$, there is an N such that

$$|c_0 + c_1/z + \ldots + 1/z^p| < N.$$

Since (5) is valid also in certain neighbourhoods of the end points of the arc of $\Gamma(0)$ on $|z| = 1$, we can determine p_1 such that $N/|z|^{p_1} < 1/2$ on the remaining part of $\Gamma(0)$ outside these neighbourhoods. This proves (4), where $Q(1/z) = P(z)/z^{p+p_1}$.

Suppose now that $d_1, d_2, \ldots, d_k$ are the numbers out of which all the coefficients a_n are taken, and let

(6) $$|d_\lambda - d_\mu| \geqslant d > 0 \text{ for } \lambda \neq \mu.$$

Choose δ so small that $Q(1/z)$ is $< 1/2$ on $\Gamma(\delta)$ and $f(z)$ is regular in $\Gamma(\delta)$. Raise $Q(1/z)$ to a sufficiently high power in order that for the polynomial obtained, $R(1/z) = \alpha_0 + \alpha_1/z + \ldots + 1/z^r$, we have

$$\frac{1}{2\pi}\int_{\Gamma(\delta)} |R(1/z)|\,|dz| < \frac{d}{2M},$$

where M is the number on the right-hand side of (2). By Cauchy's theorem

$$|\alpha_0 a_n + \alpha_1 a_{n+1} + \ldots + \alpha_{r-1} a_{n+r-1} + a_{n+r}|$$

$$= \frac{1}{2\pi}\left|\int_{\Gamma(\delta)} \frac{f(z)}{z^{n+1}} R(1/z)\,dz\right| = \frac{1}{2\pi}\left|\int_{\Gamma(\delta)} \frac{f(z) - s_{n-1}(z)}{z^{n+1}} R(1/z)\,dz\right|$$

$$< \frac{M}{2\pi}\int_{\Gamma(\delta)} |R(1/z)|\,|dz| < \frac{d}{2}.$$

Consider now the group of coefficients

$$a_n, a_{n+1}, \ldots, a_{n+r-1}, \quad (n = 0, 1, \ldots).$$

From the k different numbers $d_1, \ldots, d_k$ we can form only k^r different groups, so that there are infinitely many identical groups. Suppose that

$$(a_\mu, a_{\mu+1}, \ldots, a_{\mu+r-1}) \equiv (a_\nu, a_{\nu+1}, \ldots, a_{\nu+r-1}), \quad \mu < \nu.$$

Then

$$|a_{\mu+r} - a_{\nu+r}| \leqslant |a_{\mu+r} + \alpha_{r-1} a_{\mu+r-1} + \ldots + \alpha_0 a_\mu|$$
$$+ |a_{\nu+r} + \alpha_{r-1} a_{\nu+r-1} + \ldots + \alpha_0 a_\nu| < d/2 + d/2 = d.$$

Therefore, by (5) $a_{\mu+r} = a_{\nu+r}$, and hence, $a_{\mu+\sigma} = a_{\nu+\sigma}, \sigma \geqslant 0$. It follows that

$$f(z) = \sum_0^{\mu-1} a_n z^n + \sum_{n=\mu}^{\nu-1} a_n z^n/(1 - z^{\nu-\mu}). \qquad \text{Q. e. d.}$$

84. *Taylor coefficients of algebraic functions.*

I. *If the power series $u = \Sigma a_n z^n$ with rational coefficients represents an algebraic function, there is an integer k such that all the numbers $k^n a_n$, $n \geqslant 1$ are integers.* (Eisenstein, 1852.)

Proof. (Heine, 1854.) By hypothesis, u satisfies an algebraic equation

(1) $$f(z, u) = 0,$$

where $f(z, u)$ is a polynomial in z and u. If it contains some irrational coefficients $\alpha_1, \alpha_2, \ldots$ we write

$$f(z, u) = f_0(z, u) + \alpha_1 f_1(z, u) + \ldots,$$

where all the coefficients of $f_0, f_1 \ldots$ are rational, and if there are linear relations $\beta_0+\beta_1\alpha_1+\ldots=0$, with rational coefficients β_i, we eliminate as many irrational coefficients as we can. Thus we may suppose that there is no linear relation with rational coefficients between the irrational coefficients of (1). If we subtitute $u = \Sigma a_n z^n$ in (1), all the coefficients must vanish, and this condition leads to equations of the type $C_0+C_1\alpha_1+\ldots=0$, where C_i comes from f_i and is a rational combination of the a_n and the coefficients of f_i, i. e. C_i is rational. Thus, by our last hypothesis, all the coefficients C_i vanish, i. e. u satisfies all the equations $f_i = 0$ separately. Thus we shall suppose that *all the coefficients of the original equation* (1) *are already rational.*

We may, of course, suppose also that $f(z, u)$ is irreducible, i. e. that it is not a product of two or more factors with rational coefficients. Moreover we might assume that $f(0, u)$ is linear in u. In fact, putting $u = a_0+a_1 z+\ldots+a_{p-1}z^{p-1}+z^p v$, and substituting in (1), we obtain an algebraic equation in z and v: $F_p(z, v) = 0$. We are going to show that, for sufficiently large p, $F_p(0, v)$ is linear. If this were not so, $v(z)$ would have several branches with a finite value at $z = 0$. Hence u would have several branches whose Taylor series begin with

$$a_0+a_1 z+\ldots+a_{p-1}z^{p-1}.$$

But u has only a finite number of branches about $z = 0$, and all these branches have different Taylor series at $z = 0$. Hence the number of identical initial coefficients for two different branches is limited. This proves that there is a p such that $F_p(0, v)$ is linear.

Suppose now that we prove the theorem for the function $v = a_p+a_{p+1}z+\ldots$. This means that there is an integer k_1 such that $a_{p+\nu}k_1^\nu$, $\nu>0$, are integers. But there certainly is an integer k_2 such that $k_2 a_1, \ldots, k_2^p a_p$ are integers. Thus the integer $k_1 k_2$ satisfies the theorem.

Finally, we may suppose that the coefficients of (1) are all integers with no common factor and that a_0 is an integer. The last assumption is possible, for if $k' a_0$ is an integer, $v = k' u$ satisfies an algebraic equation with integral coefficients. If we prove the theorem for v, i. e. if $k' k_1^\nu a_\nu$ $(\nu>0)$ are integers, then also $(k' k_1)^\nu a_\nu$, $(\nu>0)$ are integers, i. e. $k' k_1$ satisfies the theorem.

To sum up, we suppose that $f(z, u)$ is irreducible, its coefficients are integers without a common factor, $f(0, u)$ is linear and a_0 is an integer. Now put

$$(2) \qquad f(z,u) = \Sigma A_\lambda(z) u^\lambda, \quad A_\lambda(z) = \sum_\mu c_{\lambda\mu} z^\mu,$$

where the $c_{\lambda\mu}$ are integers and

$$c_{\lambda\mu} = 0 \quad (\lambda > m), \quad c_{\lambda 0} = 0 \quad (\lambda > 1), \quad c_{10} \neq 0,$$

since $f(0, u)$ is linear. Replacing $u = \Sigma a_n z^n$ in (2), and equating the coefficients of z^n to 0, we obtain first, for $n = 1$,

$$c_{m1} a_0^m + c_{m-1,1} a_0^{m-1} + \dots + c_{11} a_0 + c_{10} a_1 + c_{01} = 0,$$

i. e. $c_{10} a_1$ is an integer. Suppose now that

$$c_{10} a_1, (c_{10})^2 a_2, \dots, (c_{10})^n a_n$$

are integers. We are going to show that $(c_{10})^{n+1} a_{n+1}$ is also an integer. For this purpose consider the coefficient of z^{n+1} in $f(z, \Sigma a_n z^n)$. Since for $\lambda > 1$, $A_\lambda(z)$ has no constant term, the contribution of $A_\lambda(z) u^\lambda$ to the coefficient of z^{n+1}, for $\lambda > 1$ contains only $a_0, a_1, \dots, a_n$ and is a polynomial in the latter coefficients with integral coefficients. Hence the contribution in question is a sum of terms like $A_{\lambda_0, \lambda_1, \dots, \lambda_n} a_0^{\lambda_0} a_1^{\lambda_1} \dots a_n^{\lambda_n}$ where the coefficients $A_{\lambda_0, \lambda_1, \dots, \lambda_n}$ are integers and $\lambda_1 + 2\lambda_2 + \dots + n\lambda_n \leqslant n$. Thus the product of this contribution into $(c_{10})^n$ is an integer.

The remaining part of the coefficient of z^{n+1} in $f(z, \Sigma a_n z^n)$ comes from $A_0(z) + A_1(z) u$, i. e. equals

$$c_{0,n+1} + c_{10} a_{n+1} + c_{11} a_n + \dots + c_{1,n+1} a_0$$

Equating the complete coefficient to 0, we obtain

$$r(a_0, a_1, \dots, a_n) + c_{10} a_{n+1} = 0,$$

where $(c_{10})^n r(a_0, a_1, \dots, a_n)$ is an integer. Hence also

$$(c_{10})^{n+1} a_{n+1}$$

is an integer. Q. e. d.

85. *Hadamard's results on polar singularities.* We are now going to determine the position of the poles in the circle of meromorphy centre at origin (for simplicity). By definition

$$l_0 \equiv \overline{\lim} \, |\sqrt[n]{a_n}| = 1/r,$$

where r is the radius of convergence of $\Sigma a_n z^n = f(z)$. It follows that

$$l_1 \equiv \overline{\lim} \mid \sqrt[n]{a_n a_{n+2} - a_{n+1}^2} \mid \leqslant 1/r^2.$$

More generally

$$l_p \equiv \overline{\lim} \mid \sqrt[n]{D_n^{(p)}} \mid \leqslant 1/r^{p+1},$$

since every term of the determinant $D_n^{(p)}$ satisfies this condition and there is only a finite number of terms.

Lemma 1. *If* $l_i = 1/r^{i+1}$ *for* $i = 0, 1, \ldots, p-1$ *and* $l_p < 1/r^{p+1}$, *then*

$$\lim \mid \sqrt[n]{D_n^{(p-1)}} \mid = 1/r^p,$$

i.e. for $i = p-1$ *the upper limit is replaced by an ordinary limit.* (Hadamard, 1892.)

Proof. We first establish this rather delicate limit relation for $p = 1$ by proving

Lemma 2. *If* (a) $\mid a_{\nu-1} a_{\nu+1} - a_\nu^2 \mid \leqslant \theta^{6\nu}$ *for* $\nu > N$, $\theta < 1$,

(b) $\overline{\lim} \mid \sqrt[\nu]{a_\nu} \mid = 1$, *then there are two numbers* c *and* α, $\mid \alpha \mid = 1$, *such that* $a_\nu = c\alpha^\nu + O(\theta^\nu)$.

The form of a_ν readily shows that $\mid \sqrt[\nu]{a_\nu} \mid$ tends regularly to 1 i.e. lemma 1 is proved for $p = 1$ and for $r = 1$.

Proof of lemma 2 (Ostrowski, 1926 c).

Take $N > 0$ so large that, for $\nu > N$,

(c) $$1 - \theta^\nu > 1 - \frac{\theta^{\nu-1}}{1-\theta} > \theta, \quad \frac{\theta^\nu}{1-\theta} < 1/2.$$

Putting, for $a_{\nu-1} \neq 0$, $a_\nu / a_{\nu-1} = q_\nu$ we are going to prove that from a ν on, $a_\nu \neq 0$ and

(1) $$\mid q_{\nu+1} - q_\nu \mid < \theta^\nu.$$

If $\mid \sqrt[\nu]{a_\nu} \mid$ steadily decreases from a ν on, then by (b), $\mid a_\nu \mid \geqslant 1$ from a ν on and thus, by (a), dividing by $\mid a_\nu a_{\nu-1} \mid$ we obtain (1). In every other case there is an $n > N$ such that

(d) $\mid \sqrt[n-1]{a_{n-1}} \mid \leqslant \mid \sqrt[n]{a_n} \mid$, $\mid \sqrt[n]{a_n} \mid > \theta$, $\mid \sqrt[\nu]{a_\nu} \mid < 1/\theta$ for $\nu > n$.

Thus, by (a), (c), and (d),

$$\mid a_{n+1} a_{n-1} \mid > \theta^{2n} - \theta^{6n} = \theta^{2n}(1 - \theta^{4n}) > \theta^{2n}(1 - \theta^n) > \theta^{2n+1},$$

and, by (d),

(2) $$\mid a_{n-1} \mid > \frac{\theta^{2n+1}}{(1/\theta)^{n+1}} = \theta^{3n+2}.$$

Dividing $|a_{n-1}a_{n+1}-a_n^2|$ by $|a_n a_{n-1}|$, we have, by (a), (d), and (2), $|q_{n+1}-q_n|<\theta^{6n}/\theta^{4n+2}<\theta^n$, since $n\geqslant 2$, which establishes (1) for $\nu = n$.

On the other hand, by (d), as $a_{n-1}\neq 0$,

$$(3)\ |q_n| = |a_n/a_{n-1}| = \left[\frac{|\sqrt[n]{a_n}|}{|\sqrt[n-1]{a_{n-1}}|}\right]^{n-1} |\sqrt[n]{a_n}| \geqslant |\sqrt[n]{a_n}| > \theta.$$

Suppose now that (1) is verified for $\nu = n,\dots, m$ (and thus also $a_{n-1},\dots, a_m \neq 0$). We are going to show that (1) is verified also for $\nu = m+1$. In fact, by (1),

$$|q_\mu - q_n| \leqslant |q_\mu - q_{\mu-1}| + \dots + |q_{n+1}-q_n| < \theta^n + \theta^{n+1} + \dots + \theta^\mu$$
$$< \theta^n/(1-\theta),\ n<\mu\leqslant m+1,$$

and thus by (3), (c), and (d),

$$|q_\mu| > |q_n| - \theta^n/(1-\theta) > \theta - \theta^n/(1-\theta) = \theta[1-\theta^{n-1}/(1-\theta)] > \theta^2$$

for $n<\mu\leqslant m+1$ and

$$|a_\mu/a_n| = |q_{n+1}||q_{n+2}|\cdots|q_\mu| > \theta^{2(\mu-n)},\ |a_\mu| > \theta^{2(\mu-n)}\theta^n > \theta^{2\mu}.$$

Applying this result for the cases $\mu = m, m+1$ and dividing (a) in the case $\nu = m+1$ by $|a_m a_{m+1}|$ we obtain

$$|q_{m+2}-q_{m+1}| < \theta^{6m+6}/\theta^{4m+2} < \theta^{m+1},$$

i. e. (1) is valid for $\nu = m+1$ and thus for all $\nu\geqslant n$.

Hence the series $q_n + (q_{n+1}-q_n) + \dots$ is convergent i. e.

$$(4)\qquad a_\nu/a_{\nu-1} \to \alpha,$$

when $\nu\to\infty$, where

$$(5)\qquad |\alpha - q_\nu| \leqslant \theta^\nu + \theta^{\nu+1} + \dots = \theta^\nu/(1-\theta),\quad \nu\geqslant n.$$

It follows by (4) and (b) that

$$|\sqrt[\nu]{a_\nu}| \to |\alpha| = 1.$$

To prove the last part of the statement we put

$$(6)\qquad q_k/\alpha = 1 + \gamma_k\theta^k/(1-\theta),\ k\geqslant n,$$

where from $|\alpha| = 1$, by (5), we have $|\gamma_k|\leqslant 1$.

Thus
$$\prod_{k=n}^{\infty}[1+\gamma_k\theta^k/(1-\theta)] = P$$
is convergent and, by (6), putting $a_{n-1}P/\alpha^{n-1} = c$,

$$(7) \qquad \frac{a_\nu}{\alpha^\nu} = \frac{a_{n-1}}{\alpha^{n-1}}\prod_{k=n}^{\nu}\left(1+\frac{\gamma_k\theta^k}{1-\theta}\right) = \frac{c}{\prod\limits_{k>\nu}\left(1+\frac{\gamma_k\theta^k}{1-\theta}\right)}.$$

On the other hand for $|x| \leqslant 1/2$ we have $e^{-2|x|} \leqslant |1+x| \leqslant e^{|x|}$. Hence by (c)

$$e^{-\frac{2}{1-\theta}\sum\limits_{k>\nu}\theta^k} \leqslant \prod_{k>\nu}\left|1+\frac{\gamma_k\theta}{1-\theta}\right| \leqslant e^{\frac{1}{1-\theta}\sum\limits_{k>\nu}\theta^k}$$

i. e.
$$\prod_{k>\nu}\left|1+\frac{\gamma_k\theta^k}{1-\theta}\right| = 1+O(\theta^\nu),$$

and hence, by (7),
$$a_\nu = c\alpha^\nu + O(\theta^\nu). \qquad \text{Q. e. d.}$$

Proof of lemma 1. It follows as a simple corollary of lemma 2 that lemma 1 is true for $p=1$. To prove it for $p>1$, suppose that p is the first suffix such that the inequality holds, i. e.
$$l_0 = 1/r,\, l_1 = 1/r^2, \dots, l_{p-1} = 1/r^p,$$
but $l_p < 1/r^{p+1}$. Then, by hypothesis, $\overline{\lim}\,|\sqrt[n]{D_n^{(p-1)}}| = 1/r^p$. But from
$$|\sqrt[n]{D_{n-1}^{(p-1)}D_{n+1}^{(p-1)} - [D_n^{(p-1)}]^2}| = |\sqrt[n]{D_{n-1}^{(p)}D_{n+1}^{(p-2)}}|,$$
since
$$\overline{\lim}\,|A_nB_n| \leqslant \overline{\lim}\,|A_n|\,\overline{\lim}\,|B_n|$$
and
$$\overline{\lim}\,|\sqrt[n]{D_{n-1}^{(p)}}| < 1/r^{p+1},\quad \overline{\lim}\,|\sqrt[n]{D_{n+1}^{(p-2)}}| = 1/r^{p-1},$$
we have also
$$\overline{\lim}\,|\sqrt[n]{D_{n-1}^{(p-1)}D_{n+1}^{(p-1)} - [D_n^{(p-1)}]^2}| < 1/r^{2p},$$
i. e. the conditions for the case $p=1$ are satisfied, with a_n replaced by $D_n^{(p-1)}$ and r by r^p, and we draw the conclusion that $\lim|\sqrt[n]{D_n^{(p-1)}}| = 1/r^p$.

We are now going to prove Hadamard's general result on polar singularities.

I. *The necessary and sufficient condition that* $f(z) = \Sigma a_n z^n$ *should have at most* p *poles and no other singularities on the circumference of its circle of convergence is that* $l_i = 1/r^{i+1}$ *for* $i = 0, 1, \ldots, p-1$ *and* $l_p < 1/r^{p+1}$. (Hadamard, 1892.)

Proof. The condition is necessary. Suppose that $f(z) = \Sigma a_n z^n$ has k poles and no other singularities in and on $|z| = r$ and denote by $r(z) = \Sigma r_\nu z^\nu$ the sum of the principal parts pertaining to these poles. We write $f(z) = r(z) + R(z)$ where the radius of convergence of $R(z) = \Sigma R_\nu z^\nu$ is $r' > r$. Since $a_\nu = r_\nu + R_\nu$, we have

$$(8)\quad D_\lambda^{(k)}(a_\nu) = \begin{vmatrix} r_\lambda + R_\lambda, & r_{\lambda+1} + R_{\lambda+1}, & \ldots, & r_{\lambda+k} + R_{\lambda+k} \\ \cdot & \cdot & \cdot & \cdot \\ r_{\lambda+k} + R_{\lambda+k}, & r_{\lambda+k+1} + R_{\lambda+k+1}, & \ldots, & r_{\lambda+2k} + R_{\lambda+2k} \end{vmatrix}$$

Since $r(z)$ is a rational function with k poles (counted according to their multiplicity) the determinants $D_\lambda^{(k)}(r_\nu)$ all vanish for $\lambda > \mu$, and we know also that this is not true if the suffix k be replaced by a smaller number.

Thus we can determine $k+1$ numbers $c_0 = 1, c_1, \ldots, c_k$ satisfying for $\lambda > \mu$ all the equations

$$(9)\quad \begin{array}{l} c_0 r_\lambda \;\;\; + c_1 r_{\lambda+1} \;\;\; + \ldots + c_k r_{\lambda+k} \;\;\; = 0 \\ \cdot \quad \cdot \quad \cdot \quad \cdot \quad \cdot \quad \cdot \quad \cdot \quad \cdot \\ c_0 r_{\lambda+\nu} + c_1 r_{\lambda+\nu+1} + \ldots + c_k r_{\lambda+k+\nu} = 0 \\ \cdot \quad \cdot \quad \cdot \quad \cdot \quad \cdot \quad \cdot \quad \cdot \quad \cdot \end{array}$$

($c_0 = 0$ would mean that the $D^{(k-1)}(r_\nu)$ vanish after a suitable suffix λ).

Having determined the coefficients c_i in this way we use them to reduce (8) by multiplying the $(i+1)$-th column by c_i $(i = 0, 1, \ldots, k)$ and adding all to the first. We obtain in the first column linear expressions of the R's alone. If we now decompose the determinant we see that we can express the series $\Sigma D_\lambda^{(k)}(a_\nu) z^\lambda$ as the sum of $(k+1)!$ series, in which every coefficient contains at least one R factor, i.e. the radius of convergence of every one of these series is $\geqslant r' r^k$. Thus the radius of convergence of $\Sigma D_\lambda^{(k)} z^\lambda$ is $\geqslant r' r^k > r^{k+1}$. This shows that Hadamard's condition is necessary.

The condition is sufficient. We will show that under the

conditions in question it is possible to determine a polynomial $P(z) = 1 + c_1 z + \dots + c_p z^p$, such that the radius of convergence of

$$P(z) f(z) = \Sigma A_{m+p} z^{m+p} \equiv \Sigma (a_{m+p} + c_1 a_{m+p-1} + \dots + c_p a_m) z^{m+p}$$

is $> r$.

It follows from the hypotheses, by lemma 1, that

$$\lim | \sqrt{D_m^{(p-1)}} | = 1/r^p \quad \textit{(regular limit)}.$$

Therefore, for $m > M$, $D_m^{(p-1)} \neq 0$. We can therefore determine $c_1^{(m)}, c_2^{(m)}, \dots, c_p^{(m)}$, for $m > M$, by the equations

$$(10) \qquad \begin{array}{llll} a_{m+p} & + c_1^{(m)} a_{m+p-1} & + \dots + c_p^{(m)} a_m & = 0 \\ a_{m+p+1} & + c_1^{(m)} a_{m+p} & + \dots + c_p^{(m)} a_{m+1} & = 0 \\ \cdot & \cdot & \cdot & \cdot \\ a_{m+2p-1} & + c_1^{(m)} a_{m+2p-2} & + \dots + c_p^{(m)} a_{m+p-1} & = 0. \end{array}$$

From $c_i^{(m)} = D_{m,i}^{(p-1)} / D_m^{(p-1)}$, where $D_{m,i}^{(p-1)}$ is $D_m^{(p-1)}$ with the $(p+1-i)$-th column replaced by $a_{m+p}, \dots, a_{m+2p-1}$, we obtain

$$c_i^{(m+1)} - c_i^{(m)} = [D_{m+1,i}^{(p-1)} D_m^{(p-1)} - D_{m,i}^{(p-1)} D_{m+1}^{(p-1)}] / D_{m+1}^{(p-1)} D_m^{(p-1)}$$

$$= \frac{D_m^{(p)} D'_m}{D_m^{(p-1)} D_{m+1}^{(p-1)}},$$

(by Sylvester's theorem) where D'_m is a $(p-1)$ rowed determinant of the a's and thus

$$\overline{\lim} | \sqrt[m]{D'_m} | \leqslant 1/r^{p-1}.$$

Now $\overline{\lim} | \sqrt[m]{D_m^{(p)}} | < 1/r^{p+1}$ and $\lim | \sqrt[m]{D_m^{(p-1)}} | = 1/r^p$. It follows that $\Sigma | c_i^{(m+1)} - c_i^{(m)} |$ converges like a geometrical progression. *Hence the p limits* $\lim\limits_{m=\infty} c_i^{(m)} = c_i$ *exist and*

$$c_i = c_i^{(m)} + \gamma_{i,m} \theta_i^m, \quad | \gamma_{i,m} | \leqslant 1, \ 0 < \theta_i < 1.$$

By (10), $A_{m+p} = \gamma_{1,m+p-1} \theta_1^m a_{m+p-1} + \dots + \gamma_{p,m} \theta_p^m$, i. e.

$$\overline{\lim_{m=\infty}} | \sqrt[m]{A_{m+p}} | < \theta/r < 1/r.$$

Thus the radius of convergence of $P(z) f(z)$ is $> r$. Q. e. d.

The affixes of the poles on the circle of radius r are the roots $\alpha_1, \alpha_2, \dots, \alpha_p$ of $P(z) = 0$. For the product of the roots is $(-1)^p / c_p = (-1)^p / \lim\limits_{m=\infty} c_p^{(m)}$, i. e. by (10),

$$\alpha_1 \alpha_2 \dots \alpha_p = \lim_{m=\infty} \frac{D_m^{(p-1)}}{D_{m+1}^{(p-1)}},$$

and thus $1/|\alpha_1\alpha_2\ldots\alpha_p| = l_{p-1} = 1/r^p$. But $|\alpha_i| \geqslant r, (i = 1, 2, \ldots, p)$, and hence $|\alpha_i| = r$. Applying the theorem to $P(z)f(z)$, we determine the poles on the next circle of convergence, and so on.

The consequences of Hadamard's result may be summed up as follows. Consider the sequence $l_0, l_1, \ldots$. Then $l_0 = 1/r$, where r is the original radius of convergence. In general, for a certain number of successive suffixes we have $l_i = 1/r^{i+1}$; denote by p the first suffix such that $l_p < 1/r^{p+1}$: then $l_i/l_{i-1} = 1/r$ for $i = 1, 2, \ldots, p-1$ and $l_p/l_{p-1} = 1/r_1 < 1/r$, where r_1 is the distance from the origin of the second set of singularities. Then again, for some suffixes

$$i = 1, 2, \ldots,\ l_{p+1}/l_{p+i-1} = 1/r_1$$

and so on. In any case l_i/l_{i-1} *is not increasing*. There are various possibilities.

(a) There is a q such that $l_q/l_{q-1} = 0$. The function $f(z)$ has q poles in the whole plane. $f(z)$ is an integral function divided by a polynomial.

(b) $l_i/l_{i-1} \to 0$. The function $f(z)$ is meromorphic in every finite region.

(c) $l_i/l_{i-1} \to 1/R$. The function $f(z)$ is meromorphic in every circle $|z| \leqslant \rho, < R$ but has infinitely many poles in the neighbourhood of the circle $|z| = R$, i. e. $f(z)$ has a non-polar singularity on $|z| = R$.

(d) l_i/l_{i-1} has the same value $1/R$ after a suffix $i \geqslant 1$. There is a non-polar singularity on $|z| = R$, but only a finite number of poles inside the circle.

86. *The coefficients as functions of the suffix. Unique finite singular point.* The coefficients a_n of a Taylor series can be considered as values of a function $g(z)$ assumed at $z = 0, 1, 2, \ldots$. In particular there is an *integral function* $g(z)$ such that $g(n) = a_n$. But there are infinitely many functions satisfying the same condition, i. e. we may complete (extrapolate) the given coefficients into an analytic function in infinitely many ways. For instance, when $\Sigma|a_n/n|$ is convergent, we may put $g(z) = \sin \pi z \Sigma(-1)^n a_n/(z-n)\pi$. In this section we are going to examine the relation between the function $g(z)$ determining the coefficients and the function $f(z) = \Sigma g(n)z^n$.

I. *If, for* $\nu \geqslant \mu$,

(1) $$a_\nu = P(1/\nu),$$

where

(2) $$P(z) = \Sigma c_\lambda z^\lambda$$

is convergent for $|z| \leqslant 1/\mu$, *then the first branch of the function* $f(z)$, *defined by* $\Sigma a_n z^n$ *and its analytic continuation, is regular in the domain outside* $(1, +\infty)$. (Leau, 1899.)

Proof. Instead of $f(z)$ we may consider

$$a_m + a_{m+1}z + \ldots = [f(z) - \sum_{\nu=0}^{m-1} a_\nu z^\nu]/z^m \quad (a_m \neq 0),$$

so that we shall denote the latter also by $f(z)$. Consider the functions

$$f_0(z) = \frac{1}{1-z}, \quad f_1(z) = \frac{1}{z^m}\int_0^z f_0(z) z^{m-1} dz, \ldots$$
$$f_k(z) = \frac{1}{z^m}\int_0^z f_{k-1}(z) z^{m-1} dz, \ldots,$$

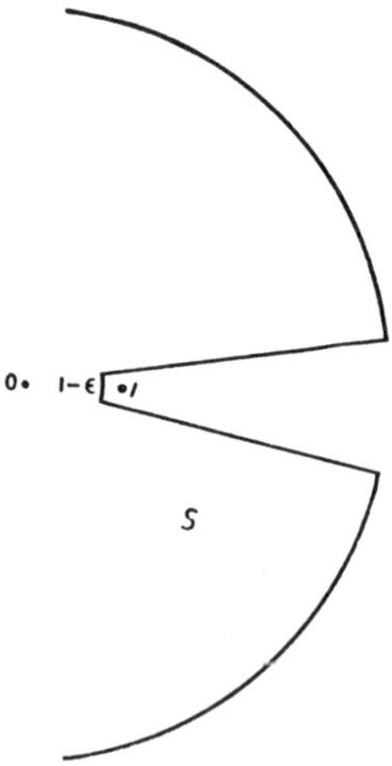

Fig. 52.

the integrations being carried out along straight lines outside $(1, +\infty)$. Then round the origin

(3) $$f_k(z) = 1/m^k + z/(m+1)^k + z^2/(m+2)^k \ldots.$$

Consider the domain S and let G be the maximum of $|1/(1-z)|$ in S. Thus, putting $z = re^{i\theta}$, we have in S

(4) $$|f_1(z)| < Gr^{-m}\int_0^{|z|} |z^{m-1}|\,|dz| = Gr^{-m}\int_0^r r^{m-1} dr = G/m.$$

If we assume generally that

$$|f_{k-1}(z)| < G/m^{k-1}$$

in S, it follows that in S

(5) $$|f_k(z)| < \frac{G}{m^{k-1} r^m}\int_0^r r^{m-1} dr = G/m^k,$$

which justifies our assumption.

Since $\overline{\lim_{\nu=\infty}} | \sqrt[\nu]{c_\nu} | \leqslant \mu$, it follows that

$$(6) \qquad \Phi(z) = \Sigma c_\nu f_\nu(z) = \sum_{\nu=0}^{l} c_\nu f_\nu(z) + R_l(z)$$

is uniformly convergent in S, since

$$(7) \qquad | R_l(z) | < G \sum_{\nu=l+1}^{\infty} \frac{|c_\nu|}{m^\nu} < \epsilon,$$

for sufficiently large l. About the origin, however,

$$(8) \qquad f(z) = \sum_{\nu=0}^{\infty} \frac{c_\nu}{m^\nu} + z \sum_{\nu=0}^{\infty} \frac{c_\nu}{(m+1)^\nu} + z^2 \sum_{\nu=0}^{\infty} \frac{c_\nu}{(m+2)^\nu} + \dots$$
$$= \sum_{\nu=0}^{\infty} c_\nu f_\nu(z).$$

Thus $\Phi(z)$ is the analytic continuation of $f(z)$ in S, and since S may be chosen to include any given point outside $(1, +\infty)$, the result follows.

It may be remarked that if S be replaced by a simply connected domain, which may cross the line $(1, +\infty)$ but does not contain the point 1, it may be shown that no branch of $f(z)$ has a singular point between 1 and $+\infty$. The origin, however, may be singular for some branches.

II. *If* $g(z)$ *is an integral function such that* $| g(re^{i\theta}) | < e^{\epsilon r}$ *for an arbitrary positive* ϵ *and* $r > r'$, *the function* $f(z)$, *defined by* $\Sigma g(n) z^n$ *and its analytic continuation, has the point* 1 *as its only singular point. If* $g(z)$ *is a polynomial of degree* m *then* 1 *is a pole of order* $m+1$. (Leau 1899, Faber 1903.)

Proof. If we put $g(z) = \Sigma c_\nu z^\nu$, it follows from the hypotheses, by (75. 5) and by Stirling's formula Ex. IV. 22, that

$$(9) \qquad \lim_{n=\infty} | \sqrt[n]{c_n n!} | = 0.$$

Consider the functions

$$f_0(z) = z/(1-z),\ f_1(z) = z f_0'(z), \dots,\ f_k(z) = z f_{k-1}'(z), \dots.$$

Then round the origin $f_k(z) = \Sigma n^k z^n$. Also $f_k(z)$, for $k \geqslant 1$, can be written in the form

$$(10) \qquad f_k(z) = \sum_{n=1}^{k} b_n^{(k)} z^n \frac{d^n f_0(z)}{dz^n}.$$

This is plainly true for $k = 1$ and, if we suppose it to be true for $k-1$, we obtain, for $k>1$,

$$f_k(z) = zf'_{k-1}(z) = \sum_{n=1}^{k} (nb_n^{(k-1)} + b_{n-1}^{(k-1)}) z^n \frac{d^n f_0(z)}{dz^n},$$

where $b_0^{(k-1)} = 0$ and $b_k^{(k-1)} = 0$, i. e.

(11) $$b_n^{(k)} = nb_n^{(k-1)} + b_{n-1}^{(k-1)}.$$

Since $b_k^{(k-1)} = 0$, we have, by (11),

(12) $$b_k^{(k)} = b_{k-1}^{(k-1)} = \ldots = b_1^{(1)} = 1.$$

Furthermore

(13) $$b_n^{(k)} < 2^k(k-1)\,!/n\,!$$

for $n \leqslant k$. For, by (12), this is true for $k = 1$ (since $0\,! = 1$) and, if we assume it for $k-1$, we have, by (11),

$$b_n^{(k)} < n\,2^{k-1}(k-2)\,!/n\,! + 2^{k-1}(k-2)\,!/(n-1)\,!$$
$$= 2^k(k-2)\,!/(n-1)\,! < 2^k(k-1)\,!/n\,!$$

for $n \leqslant k-1$ and, by (12), for $n = k$ also. Thus (13) is valid in every case. Therefore

(14) $$|f_k(z)| < 2^k(k-1)\,! \sum_{n=1}^{k} \frac{1}{n\,!} \left| z^n \frac{d^n f_0(z)}{dz^n} \right|$$
$$< 2^k(k-1)\,! \sum_{n=1}^{k} \frac{|z^n|}{|1-z|^{n+1}}.$$

If we exclude 1 by a small circle c, $|z/(1-z)| < G$ outside c, i. e.

$$\sum_1^k |z|^n/|1-z|^{n+1} < kG^k/|1-z|.$$

Putting $2^kG^k/|1-z| = H'^k$, we have $H' < H$ for all k and all z outside c, i. e. $|f_k(z)| < H^k k\,!$. Hence $\Phi(z) = \Sigma c_n f_n(z)$ is uniformly convergent outside c, and about the origin

$$f(z) - c_0 = z\Sigma c_n + z^2 \Sigma c_n 2^n + z^3 \Sigma c_n 3^n + \ldots = \Sigma c_n f_n(z).$$

Thus $\Phi(z)$ is the analytic continuation of $f(z)$ and 1 is the only singular point. Since $f_k(z)$ has a pole of order $k+1$ at 1, the second statement also follows.

III. (Converse of II.) *If the uniform function* $f(z) = \Sigma a_n z^n$ *has the unique singular point* 1 (*necessarily a pole or an essential point), then there is a unique integral function* $g(z)$, *such that* $g(n) = a_n$ *and* $|g(re^{i\theta})| < e^{\epsilon r}$, *for an arbitrary positive* ϵ *and* $r > r'$. *If* 1 *is a pole of order* m, $g(n)$ *reduces to a polynomial of degree* $m-1$. (Wigert 1900, Faber 1903.)

Proof. $f(z)$ is, by hypothesis, an integral function of $1/(1-z)$, but we imagine it as an integral function of

$$z/(1-z) = 1/(1-z) - 1.$$

Then $f(z) = \Sigma e_n z^n/(1-z)^n$, where $\lim |\sqrt[n]{e_n}| = 0$, and we have

$$a_n = e_1 + C_1^{n-1} e_2 + C_2^{n-1} e_3 + \ldots + C_{n-1}^{n-1} e_n. \tag{15}$$

Consider now the expression

$$\Phi(z) = e_1 + (z-1)e_2 + (z-1)(z-2)e_3/2! + (z-1)(z-2)(z-3)e_4/3! + \ldots. \tag{16}$$

We shall prove that (16) is the required integral function. For this purpose we have to prove that (a) $\Phi(z)$ is an integral function $= g(z)$, (b) $g(n) = a_n$, (c) $|g(re^{i\theta})| < e^{\epsilon r}$ for $r > r'$.

(a) We shall show that $\Phi(z)$ is uniformly convergent for $|z| < R$ (arbitrary). Write

$$\Phi(z) = e_1 + \frac{z-1}{1} e_2 + \ldots + \frac{(z-1)(z-2)\ldots(z-n+1)}{(n-1)!} e_n + \Phi_n(z).$$

Now determine m' such that, for $m > m'$ and ϵ given between 0 and 1, we have $|e_m| < \epsilon^m$. Then, for $n > m'$,

$$|\Phi_n(z)| < \frac{(R+1)(R+2)\ldots(R+n)}{n!}\epsilon^n + \frac{(R+1)(R+2)\ldots(R+n+1)}{(n+1)!}\epsilon^{n+1} + \ldots,$$

and the right-hand side is the remainder after n terms of $[1/(1-\epsilon)]^{R+1}$ when expanded in powers of ϵ, which establishes the first point.

(b) is obvious by (15) and (16).

(c) Since $|e_m| < \epsilon^m$ for $m > m'$, we have

$$|\Phi(re^{i\theta})| < |e_1| + \frac{r+1}{1!}|e_2| + \frac{(r+1)(r+2)}{2!}|e_3| + \ldots$$

$$< |e_1| + \frac{r+1}{1!}|e_2| + \dots + \frac{(r+1)\dots(r+m-1)}{(m-1)!}|e_m|$$
$$+ \frac{(r+1)\dots(r+m)}{m!}\epsilon^m + \frac{(r+1)\dots(r+m+1)}{(m+1)!}\epsilon^{m+1} + \dots$$
$$< 1/(1-\epsilon)^{r+1} + P(r),$$

where $P(r)$ is a polynomial of degree m, i. e.

$$|\Phi(re^{i\theta})| < e^{-(r+1)\log(1-\epsilon)} + P(r) < e^{(r+1)\epsilon'} + P(r) < e^{\epsilon'' r}.$$

Moreover $\Phi(z)$ is the only function satisfying the conditions for, by Ex. VII. 14, if there were two, their difference would be identically zero.

Finally, if $f(z) = A/(1-z)^m = \Sigma e_n z^n/(1-z)^n$, $e_n = 0$ for $n > m$, but $e_m = 1$. Thus $\Phi(z)$ is a polynomial of degree $m-A$ Q. e. d.

87. *A theorem of Le Roy and Lindelöf.*

I. *Suppose* (a) $g(x+iy)$ *is regular in the semiplane* $x \geqslant \alpha$, (b) *there is a* $\theta < \pi$ *such that for every arbitrarily small positive* ϵ *and for sufficiently large* ρ,

$$|g(\alpha + \rho e^{i\psi})| < e^{(\theta+\epsilon)\rho}, \quad -\pi/2 \leqslant \psi \leqslant \pi/2.$$

Then

$$(1) \qquad f(z) = \sum_{n=0} g(n) z^n, \; z = re^{i\phi},$$

is regular in the angle

$$\theta < \phi < 2\pi - \theta.$$

In particular if (b) *is satisfied for* $\theta = 0$, $f(z)$ *is regular everywhere except maybe at the points of the positive real axis between* 1 *and* ∞. (Le Roy 1902, 1903, Lindelöf 1900 a.)

Proof. It follows from (b) that the radius of convergence of (1) is at least $e^{-\theta}$. We might suppose that α is not an integer, for if (b) is satisfied for an α, it is satisfied for any number greater than α. Thus we put $m-1 < \alpha < m$.

If n is an integer, from $\sin \pi z = \sin \pi (z-n) \cos \pi n$ we see that $\lim_{z \to n} (z-n)/\sin \pi z = (-1)^n/\pi$, i. e. the residue of $1/(e^{2\pi iz} - 1) = \frac{1}{2i}\cot \pi z - 1/2$, at $z = n$, is $\frac{1}{2\pi i}$. Thus the residue of $G(x, z) = g(z) x^z/(e^{2\pi iz} - 1)$, at $z = n$, is $\frac{1}{2\pi i} g(n) x^n$. Therefore, by the residue theorem 59. I,

$$(2) \qquad \sum_{n=m}^{p} g(n)x^n = \int_S G(x, z)\, dz,$$

where S is a contour enclosing the integers $m, m+1, \dots, p$ and no others. For example, we may take for S the half of the circumference of the circle of radius $R = p + 1/2 - \alpha$, centre at α, which lies in $x \geqslant \alpha$ and the diameter of this circle.

We shall prove that for $p = \infty$, i.e. $R = \infty$, the integral along the semi-circumference C_R tends to 0, i.e. that

$$(3) \qquad \sum_{n=m}^{\infty} g(r)x^n = -\int_{\alpha - i\infty}^{\alpha + i\infty} \frac{g(z)x^z dz}{e^{2\pi i z} - 1}.$$

We suppose first that x is real and negative. Putting

$$z = \alpha + Re^{i\psi}, \quad x = re^{i\pi} = -r,$$

we have

$$(4) \qquad G(x, z) = \frac{g(\alpha + Re^{i\psi})\, r^z}{e^{\pi i z} - e^{-\pi i z}}.$$

Also, by (b), for sufficiently large R,

$$|g(\alpha + Re^{i\psi})\, r^z| < r^{\alpha} e^{-R(\log \frac{1}{r} \cos\psi - \theta - \epsilon)}.$$

On the other hand, excluding the poles $z = 2k\pi i$, $k = 0, \pm 1, \dots$ of $h(z) = 1/(e^z - 1)$ by small circles, we have, in the remaining region, $|h(z)| < N$. In fact, if a is a positive number and $z = \tau + it$, we have for $\tau > a : |h(z)| < 1/(e^a - 1)$ and for $\tau < -a$, $|h(z)| < 1/(1 - e^{-a})$. In the band $-a \leqslant \tau \leqslant a$, $h(z)$ is bounded for it is continuous and a periodic function of t.

Applying this remark to the semicircle C_R we obtain *on* C_R, $1/|e^{\pi i z} - e^{-\pi i z}| < k'$ for $|\psi| \leqslant \frac{\pi}{2}$ and $1/|e^{\pi i z} - e^{-\pi i z}| < k'' e^{-\pi |\sin\psi|}$

for $\psi_0 \leqslant |\psi| \leqslant \frac{\pi}{2}$, where ψ_0 is an angle between 0 and $\pi/2$ and k', k'' are independent of R. Thus, for $r \leqslant 1$,

$$(5) \qquad \left.\begin{aligned} |G(x,z)| &< k' r^{\alpha} e^{-R(\log \frac{1}{r} \cos\psi_0 - \theta - \epsilon)} \text{ for } |\psi| \leqslant \psi_0 \\ |G(x,z)| &< k'' r^{\alpha} e^{-R(\pi \sin\psi_0 - \theta - \epsilon)} \text{ for } \psi_0 \leqslant |\psi| \leqslant \frac{\pi}{2} \end{aligned}\right\} \text{on } C_R.$$

Fixing ψ_0 by the condition $\pi \sin \psi_0 = \theta'$, $\theta < \theta' < \pi$ and determining r_0 such that $\log \frac{1}{r_0} \cos \psi_0 = \theta'$, we have, on C_R and for $r \leqslant r_0 < 1$, $|G(x, z)| < kr^{\alpha} e^{-(\theta' - \theta - \epsilon)R}$, where k denotes the greater of k' and k''. Thus, when $-r_0 < x < 0$ and $R \to \infty$, the integral along C_R tends to 0 and (3) is established.

To prove that the function represented by this formula is regular in $\theta < \phi < 2\pi - \theta$ we put $z = \alpha + it$, $x = re^{i(\phi' \pm \pi)}$, where the upper (lower) sign is taken if t is positive (negative), i.e. $\phi' = \phi \mp \pi$ is the argument of x measured from the *negative* real axis. Therefore we have

$$|G(x, z)| = r^{\alpha} e^{-(\pi \pm \phi')|t|} \left| \frac{g(\alpha + it)}{e^{\pi i \alpha - \pi t} - e^{-\pi i \alpha + \pi t}} \right| < r^{\alpha} e^{-[\pi - \theta \pm \phi' + \epsilon(t)]|t|}.$$

Now, if x is a point of the domain

$$(6) \qquad r > 0,\ \theta + \sigma < \phi < 2\pi - \theta - \sigma, \text{ i.e. } |\phi'| < \pi - \theta - \sigma,$$

where σ is an arbitrarily small positive number, we have, for $0 < \eta < \sigma$ and for all sufficiently large $|t|$, $\pi - \theta \pm \phi' + \epsilon(t) > \eta$, i.e.

$$(7) \qquad |G(x, z)| < r^{\alpha} e^{-\eta |t|} \text{ for } |t| > T, \text{ say.}$$

Now write

$$-\int_{\alpha - i\infty}^{\alpha + i\infty} G(x, z) dz = -\sum_{-\infty}^{+\infty} \int_{\alpha + i\nu}^{\alpha + i(\nu + 1)} G(x, z) dz,$$

and notice that every term of the right-hand side is regular in the domain (6), since every term is an integral function of $\log x$ (by expanding $x^z = e^{z \log x}$ in series). Formula (7) proves the uniform convergence in any finite region of (6), and this proves the proposition.

Since the segment $-r_0 < x < 0$ is in $\theta < \phi < 2\pi - \theta$, the right-hand side of (3) certainly equals the left-hand side on this segment and thus the right-hand side is the analytic continuation of the left-hand side.

By (3), if m is positive

$$(8) \quad f(x) = \sum_{0}^{m-1} g(n) x^n - \int_{\alpha - i\infty}^{\alpha + i\infty} \frac{g(z) x^z}{e^{2\pi i z} - 1} dz, \qquad m - 1 < \alpha < m.$$

If $m = -k$ is negative, we have

$$(9)\quad f(x) = -\sum_1^k \frac{g(-n)}{x^n} - \int_{\alpha-i\infty}^{\alpha+i\infty} \frac{g(z)\,x^z dz}{e^{2\pi iz}-1},\quad -(k+1) < \alpha < -k.$$

If $m = 0$,

$$f(x) = -\int_{\alpha-i\infty}^{\alpha+i\infty} \frac{g(z)\,x^z dz}{e^{2\pi iz}-1}.$$

Thus the theorem is completely established.

We complete this result by proving

II. *Under the conditions of theorem* I,

$$(10)\qquad f(x) = x^\alpha \epsilon(x),\quad \textit{if } \alpha > -1,$$

$$(11)\quad f(x) = -\sum_1^k g(-n)/x^n + x^\alpha \epsilon(x),\qquad \textit{if } -(k+1) < \alpha \leqslant -k,$$

where $\epsilon(x)$ *tends uniformly to* 0 *when* $x \to \infty$ *in*

$$(12)\qquad \theta + \sigma \leqslant \phi \leqslant 2\pi - \theta - \sigma,$$

for an arbitrarily small positive σ. (Lindelöf, 1902, 1903.)

Proof. (a) Suppose α is not an integer. By (7), there is a t' such that $r^{-\alpha}\left| \int_{\alpha-i\infty}^{\alpha-it'} G(x,z)dz + \int_{\alpha+it'}^{\alpha+i\infty} G(x,z)dz \right| < \epsilon/2$ in (12).

We have still to prove the existence of an R such that

$$(13)\qquad \left| x^{-\alpha} \int_{\alpha-it'}^{\alpha+it} G(x,z)dz \right| < \epsilon/2 \text{ in}$$

$$(14)\qquad \theta + \sigma \leqslant \phi \leqslant 2\pi - \theta - \sigma,\qquad r > R.$$

Putting $z = \alpha + it$, $x = re^{i\phi}$, we have, since α is not an integer,

$$(15)\quad x^{-\alpha} G(x,z) = e^{-\phi t}[A(t) + iB(t)][\cos(t \log r) + i \sin(t \log r)]$$

where $A(t)$ and $B(t)$ are real functions, regular for real values of t.

We prove first that the number of the alternating intervals of increase and decrease of $|e^{-\phi t}A(t)|$ (or of $|e^{-\phi t}B(t)|$) between $-t'$ and t' is $< N$ *independently of* ϕ. In fact the extremities of such intervals are either zeros of $A(t)$ or of $[e^{-\phi t}A(t)]'$, i.e. roots of $A'(t) - \phi A(t) = 0$. This may be satisfied by common roots of $A(t) = 0$ and $A'(t) = 0$, finite in number since $A(t)$ and

$A'(t)$ are regular in $(-t', t')$, or else the roots correspond to the intersection of $y = A'(t)/A(t)$ and $y = \phi$. In the latter case, between two consecutive intersections there is either an infinity of $A'(t)/A(t)$, i. e. a zero of $A(t)$, or a zero of its derivative and thus a root of $A(t)A''(t) - [A'(t)]^2 = 0$. The number of these is, however, finite since the left-hand side is regular in $(-t', t')$.

Having established this point, we shall show that if M is the maximum of $|e^{-\phi t}A(t)|$ in $(-t', t')$, $\theta + \sigma \leqslant \phi \leqslant 2\pi - \theta - \sigma$, then

$$\left| \int_a^b e^{-\phi t} A(t) \sin(t \log r)\, dt \right| < 2M/\log r$$

for any interval of monotony (a, b). Denote by $t_1, \ldots, t_\mu$ the successive multiples of $\pi/\log r$ in (a, b). The integrals $\int_{t_1}^{t_2}, \ldots, \int_{t_\mu}^{b}$ are of alternating sign and their absolute value is constantly decreasing (or constantly increasing). Their sum in absolute value is thus less than the absolute value of the first (last) integral. Moreover the integrals $\int_a^{t_1}$ and $\int_{t_1}^{t_2}$ have opposite signs and are both, in absolute value, less than $M \int_0^{\pi/\log r} \sin(t \log r)\, dt = 2M/\log r$, which proves our remark. Therefore

$$\left| \int_{-t'}^{t'} e^{-\phi t} A(t) \sin(t \log r)\, dt \right| < 2MN/\log r$$

in $\theta + \sigma \leqslant \phi \leqslant 2\pi - \theta - \sigma$ and, the same being true also for the other three integrals making up (15), we see that the left-hand side of (13) tends to 0 when $r \to \infty$, which proves the theorem for a non-integral α.

(b) Suppose α is an integer. Formulae (8) and (9) do not apply. For simplicity's sake we take $\alpha = 0$. Put $m = 1$ in the right-hand side of (8) and exclude $z = 0$ by a small circle. When α tends to 0, we readily see that

$$f(x) = g(0)/2 - \int_{-i\infty}^{+i\infty} \frac{g(z) x^z dz}{e^{2\pi i z} - 1} \quad \text{in (12).} \tag{16}$$

Putting, for symmetry, $x = e^{i\pi} x_1$, $x_1 = re^{i\phi_1}$

and $\qquad z = it$, $g(\pm it) = p(t) \pm iq(t)$,

we have

$$(17) \qquad f(x) = g(0)/2 + \int_0^\infty P(t, x_1)\,dt + \int_0^\infty Q(t, x_1)\,dt,$$

where

$$P(t, x) = -2p(t) \sin(t \log x_1)/(e^{\pi t} - e^{-\pi t}),$$
$$Q(t, x) = -2q(t) \cos(t \log x_1)/(e^{\pi t} - e^{-\pi t}).$$

We prove first that the second integral in (17) tends to 0 when x tends to 0 or to ∞ in the angle (12). In fact,

$$\cos(t \log x_1) = \tfrac{1}{2}(e^{\phi_1 t} + e^{-\phi_1 t}) \cos(t \log r) + \tfrac{1}{2}(e^{\phi_1 t} - e^{-\phi_1 t}) \sin(t \log r),$$

and $g(z)$ being, by hypothesis, regular at $z = 0$,

$$2q(t) = [g(it) - g(-it)]/i = tA(t),$$

where $A(t)$ is regular for $t = 0$, i.e. $Q(t, x_1)$ is regular for $t = 0$. Hence there is a t_0 such that

$$(18) \qquad \left| \int_0^{t_0} Q(t, x_1)dt \right| < \epsilon/3 \qquad \text{when } x \text{ is in (12).}$$

On the other hand, in (12) we have $|\phi_1| \leqslant \pi - \theta - \sigma$, i.e. $Q(t, x_1)$ decreases more rapidly than an exponential function of the type $e^{-\eta t}$, $\eta > 0$ and thus we can choose a T such that

$$\left| \int_T^\infty Q(t, x_1)dt \right| < \epsilon/3 \qquad \text{in (12).}$$

We complete the reasoning by proving as before that there is an R such that $\left| \int_{t_0}^T Q(t, x_1)dt \right| < \epsilon/3$ in (12) for $|\log r| > R$. If we change x into $1/x$ or x_1 into $1/x_1$, the integral in question changes only in sign, which proves our first remark.

Next, when in (17) $x \to 0$ in (12), we have from $f(0) = g(0)$,

$$\lim_{x_1 \to 0} \int_0^\infty P(t, x_1)dt \to g(0)/2.$$

Thus, when $x \to \infty$ in (12), the same integral tends to $-g(0)/2$, i.e. $f(x) \to 0$ when $x \to \infty$ in (12). Q. e. d.

We notice that the reasoning also holds good when $g(z)$ is not regular at $z = 0$ but has there a determinate limiting value and $\int_0^t |q(t)|\,dt/t$ has a meaning.

As an application of the above results, take

$$g(z) = [\log(z+\beta)]^{-z}, \ \beta > 1.$$

This function is regular for $x \geqslant 0$ and

$$|g(\rho e^{i\psi})| = e^{\rho\left[\frac{\psi \sin\psi + \epsilon(\rho)}{\log\rho} - \log\log\rho\cos\psi\right]},$$

i. e. $|g(\rho e^{i\psi})| < e^{\epsilon\rho}$ for $-\pi/2 \leqslant \psi \leqslant \pi/2$ and ρ sufficiently large. The conditions of our theorem are satisfied for $\alpha = 0$, $\theta = 0$ and thus we obtain the remarkable result that *the integral function*

$$(19) \qquad L_\beta(z) = \sum_0^\infty [z/\log(n+\beta)]^n, \qquad \beta > 1,$$

tends to 0 *along every radius vector but the positive real axis.*

If $\beta > 2$, the conditions of the theorem are satisfied for $\theta = 0$ and $-2 < \alpha < -1$. Hence

$$L_\beta(z) = -[\log(\beta-1) + \epsilon(z)]/z,$$

where $\lim_{z\to\infty} \epsilon(z) = 0$ uniformly in the angle $\epsilon \leqslant \theta \leqslant 2\pi - \epsilon$ for arbitrarily small ϵ.

The integral functions $e^{-L_\beta(z)}$ tends to 0 along the positive real axis and to 1 along the other radii, and thus the integral function $e^{-L_\beta(z)} - e^{-L_{\beta'}(z)}$, $\beta' \neq \beta$, $\beta' > 1$, $\beta > 1$, tends to 0 along every radius vector (but not uniformly!).

88. *Multiplication of singularities.* We close this chapter by discussing a beautiful theorem of Hadamard's, which displays a surprisingly simple connexion between coefficients and singularities.

I. *If* α *and* β *denote the vertices of the star domains, with respect to the origin, of* $a(z) = \Sigma a_n z^n$ *and* $b(z) = \Sigma b_n z^n$ *respectively, then* $f(z) = \Sigma a_n b_n z^n$ *is regular in the star domain whose vertices are the points* $\alpha\beta$. (Hadamard, 1898.)

Proof. (Borel 1898 a.) If the radii of convergence of $a(z)$, $b(z)$ and $f(z)$ are R, R' and R'' respectively, then from

$$\overline{\lim}\, p_n \, \overline{\lim}\, q_n \geqslant \overline{\lim}\, p_n q_n,$$

where $p_n \geqslant 0$, $q_n \geqslant 0$, we have

$$(1) \qquad R'' \geqslant RR'.$$

In particular, if $a(z)$ or $b(z)$ is an integral function, so is $f(z)$.

Suppose that $|z| \leqslant \eta RR'$, $\eta < 1$, and consider the integral

(2) $$H(z) = \frac{1}{2\pi i}\int_C a(zx)\, b\left(\frac{1}{x}\right)\frac{dx}{x},$$

where C is $|x| = \theta/R'$ and $1 < \theta < 1/\eta$. The function $a(zx)$ is regular in $|x| \leqslant \theta/R'$, since

$$|zx| \leqslant \eta RR'.\ \theta/R' < R.$$

Moreover, all the lines $(0, 1/\beta)$, which contain the singularities of the first branch of $b(1/x)$, are in $|x| \leqslant 1/R'$. Therefore the integrand of (2) is uniform and regular in $1/R' < |x| < \theta/R'$, and is thus expansible in a Laurent series about $x = 0$, convergent throughout this domain. The coefficient B_1 of $1/x$ in this expansion is equal to the integral (2). Moreover, for a fixed z, $|z| \leqslant \eta RR'$, the series $\Sigma a_n z^n x^n$ and $\Sigma b_n/x^n$ are absolutely convergent in the ring $1/R' < x < \theta/R'$, so that we can rearrange the product $\frac{1}{x}\Sigma a_n z^n x^n \Sigma b^n/x^n$ in descending and ascending powers of x. Since the coefficient of $1/x$ will be $\Sigma a_n b_n z^n$, we see that

(3) $$H(z) = f(z), \text{ if } |z| < RR'.$$

Now if, for a fixed z, we deform the contour of integration C in such a way that the area swept over contains no singular points of the integrand, the value of the integral will remain the same. Moreover, if z varies, the singular points $1/\beta$ of $b(1/x)$ will remain the same (imagine red pins fixed at them), while the singular points of $a(zx)$ (white pins) will move, i.e. $|\alpha/z|$ decreases as $|z|$ increases. Imagine now that, as z moves, C recedes, if necessary, before the singular points of $a(zx)$, avoiding the red pins, which form a closed set, so that C separates the two systems of pins. This is possible so long as these two closed sets have no point in common. But if $zx = \alpha$ and $1/x = \beta$, then $z = \alpha\beta$. Thus, if z varies in the star domain whose vertices are $\alpha\beta$, we can modify C in the required manner. In this way the singular points of the integrand never cross C and the above argument applies to the integral H along C. We also remark that, by 54. III, the integral $H(z)$ is a regular function of z in a domain D provided that the integrand is regular in z and continuous (for example regular) in x, as z varies in D and x varies along C. For a closed contour C, (2) may represent different functions in different domains, which are not the analytic continuation of one another. We obtain, however the analytic continuation of $f(z)$ if D contains the origin. This condition is satisfied in particular if D is the star domain whose vertices are $\alpha\beta$, which proves the theorem.

The example $a(z) = \Sigma z^{2n}$, $b(z) = \Sigma z^{2n+1}$, for which $f(z) \equiv 0$, shows that the star domain of $f(z)$ may extend beyond the star formed by all the products $\alpha\beta$.

Precisely the same argument proves Faber's extension (Faber, 1907), that if α and β denote the affixes of the *singular and external points* of $a(z)$ and $b(z)$ respectively, then $H(z)$ *furnishes the analytic continuation of* $f(z)$ *along any finite path which does not pass through any point* $\alpha\beta$ *and does not return to the origin.* Thus all the singular points of $f(z)$ are of the form $\alpha\beta$, except possibly the origin, which may be an extra singularity for $f(z)$.

Borel (1898) showed by means of the example

$$a(z) = b(z) = \log(1-z) = \Sigma(-1)^{n+1}z^n/n,$$

for which $f(z) = \Sigma z^n/n^2$, that $z = 0$ may in fact be a singular point for every branch except the initial one.

Faber's result is further illustrated by the following example. Let $a_n = 2$ when $n = 2^\mu$, and $a_n = 1$ when $n \neq 2^\mu$, $b_n = (1/2^n + 1/3^n)/a_n$. Then the only singularities of $a(z)$ and $b(z)$ are of the form $\alpha = e^{2\pi i\theta_1}$, and $\beta = 2e^{2\pi i\theta_2}$ respectively, with arbitrary θ_1 and θ_2, i.e. the products of singularities cover $|z| = 2$. On the other hand,

$$f(z) = \Sigma a_n b_n z^n = \Sigma z^n/2^n + \Sigma z^n/3^n = 1/(1-z/2) + 1/(1-z/3),$$

i.e. $z = 3$ is a singular point of $f(z)$ and 3 is *not* of the form $\alpha\beta$. But the external points consist of the domains $|z|>1$ and $|z|>2$, and so 3 may be obtained in infinitely many ways by multiplying an external point of one function by a singularity or external point of the other.

Hadamard's and Faber's results suggest the problem of determining the conditions under which $\alpha\beta$ is effectively a singular point of $f(z)$. The first result in this direction is due to Borel.

II. *If* α *and* β *are poles of the order* p *and* q *of* $a(z) = \Sigma a_n z^n$ *and* $b(z) = \Sigma b_n z^n$ *respectively, and if* $\alpha\beta \neq \alpha'\beta'$, *where* α' *and* β'

are any other singular or external points of $a(z)$ *and* $b(z)$ *respectively, then* $\alpha\beta$ *is a pole of* $f(z) = \Sigma a_n b_n z^n$ *of order* $p+q-1$.

(Borel, 1898.)

Proof. By hypothesis

$$a(z) = a'(z) + \sum_{i=1}^{p} A_i/(1-z/\alpha)^i,$$

$$b(z) = b'(z) + \sum_{i=1}^{q} B_i/(1-z/\beta)^i,$$

where $a'(z) = \Sigma a'_n z^n$ and $b'(z) = \Sigma b'_n z^n$ are regular at α and β respectively. Hence, putting

$$a_n = a'_n + a''_n, \; b_n = b'_n + b''_n$$

we see, by I, that $\Sigma (a'_n b'_n + a'_n b''_n + a''_n b'_n) z^n$ is regular at $\alpha\beta$, since its possible singular points are of the form $\alpha'\beta'$, $\alpha\beta'$, $\alpha'\beta$.

On the other hand, by 86. III, $a''_n = g(n)/\alpha^n$ and $b''_n = h(n)/\beta^n$ where $g(n)$ and $h(n)$ are polynomials in n of degree $p-1$ and $q-1$ respectively. Therefore,

$$a''_n b''_n = g(n)h(n)/(\alpha\beta)^n = H(n)/(\alpha\beta)^n$$

where $H(n)$ is a polynomial in n of degree $p+q-2$ and thus, by 86. II, $\Sigma a''_n b''_n z^n$ has the unique pole $z = \alpha\beta$ of the order $p+q-1$. Q. e. d.

Faber extended this result to essential points.

III. *If* $a(z) = \Sigma a_n z^n$ *and* $b(z) = \Sigma b_n z^n$ *are uniform in the neighbourhood of the isolated singular points* α *and* β *respectively, one of the two or both being essential points, and if* $\alpha\beta \neq \alpha'\beta'$, *where* α' *and* β' *are any other singular or external points of* $a(z)$ *and* $b(z)$ *respectively, then* $\alpha\beta$ *is an essential point of* $f(z) = \Sigma a_n b_n z^n$. (Faber, 1907.)

Proof. By hypothesis

$$a(z) = \Sigma a'_n z^n + \Sigma a''_n z^n, \; b(z) = \Sigma b'_n z^n + \Sigma b''_n z^n,$$

where $\Sigma a''_n z^n$ and $\Sigma b''_n z^n$ have the singular points α and β respectively and no others. Hence,

$$f(z) = \Sigma (a'_n b'_n + a'_n b''_n + a''_n b'_n) z^n + \Sigma a''_n b''_n z^n$$

and by I, the first term represents a function regular at $\alpha\beta$ since its singular points are all of the form $\alpha'\beta'$, $\alpha'\beta$, $\alpha\beta'$. Thus the singularity of $f(z)$ in the neighbourhood of $\alpha\beta$ depends exclusively on the behaviour of $\Sigma a''_n b''_n z^n$. But, by 86. III, $a''_n = g_1(n)/\alpha^n$, $b''_n = g_2(n)/\beta^n$, where $g_i(z)$ is an integral function and

(4) $\lim\limits_{z\to\infty} |g_i(z)e^{-\epsilon|z|}| = 0$ for every positive ϵ, $i = 1, 2$.

Hence $a''_n b''_n = g_3(n)/(\alpha\beta)^n$ where $g_3(n) = g_1(n)g_2(n)$ satisfies the same condition (4), and thus, by 86. II, the unique singular point of $\Sigma a''_n b''_n z$ is $\alpha\beta$, and this is an essential point provided $g_3(n)$ does not reduce to a polynomial. This is only possible if $g_1(n)$ and $g_2(n)$ are polynomials, which case we have excluded. In fact, if $g_1(z)\, g_2(z)$ is a polynomial, then $g_1(z) = P_1(z)\, h_1(z)$ and $g_2(z) = P_2(z)\, h_2(z)$, where $P_1(z)$ and $P_2(z)$ are polynomials and $h_1(z)$ and $h_2(z)$ are integral functions, with no zeros, and such that $\lim\limits_{|z|\to\infty} |h_i(z)\, e^{-\epsilon|z|}| = 0$, $i = 1, 2$. But this is impossible, by (40. 10), unless $h_i(z)$ $(i = 1, 2)$ reduces to a constant, since $\log|h_i(z)|$ is the real part of the integral function $\log h_i(z)$ and $\log|h_i(z)| < \epsilon|z|$ for sufficiently large $|z|$.

For further extensions of the above results see Faber, 1907, and Pólya, 1927.

CHAPTER XI

OVERCONVERGENCE AND GAP THEOREMS

89. *Zeros of sections.* Let us consider a sequence of functions $f_n(z)$, uniform and regular in a region R and tending uniformly to $f(z)$ in R. We say that a point c belongs to the set Z if c is a zero of one of the functions $f_n(z)$. As usual, the set of the limiting points will be denoted by Z'. If necessary, we shall also write $Z[f_n(z)]$.

I. *If all the functions $f_n(z)$ are uniform and regular in the region R and if $f_n(z) \to f(z)$ uniformly in R, the set of the zeros of $f(z)$ in R is identical with the points of Z' in R.*

(Hurwitz, 1889.)

Proof. Since the zeros of analytic functions are isolated, for every point c in R there is a circle $|z-c| < d_0$ in which $f(z) \neq 0$, except perhaps at c. Therefore, for every positive $d < d_0$, the integral

$$\frac{1}{2\pi i}\int_{|z-c|=d} \frac{f'(z)\,dz}{f(z)}$$

is equal to the degree of the zero at c, i.e. is an integer $k \geqslant 0$.

Moreover, since, on $|z-c| = d$, $f_n(z)$ and $f_n'(z)$ tend uniformly to $f(z)$ and $f'(z)$ respectively, we have

$$\frac{f_n'(z)}{f_n(z)} \to \frac{f'(z)}{f(z)} \qquad \text{uniformly on } |z-c| = d.$$

Hence

$$(1) \qquad \frac{1}{2\pi i}\int_{|z-c|=d} \frac{f_n'(z)\,dz}{f_n(z)} \to \frac{1}{2\pi i}\int_{|z-c|=d} \frac{f'(z)\,dz}{f(z)},$$

and thus, after a certain suffix $n = N$, the left-hand side is the integer $k \geqslant 0$. But the right-hand side of (1) equals the number of zeros of $f(z)$ in $|z-c| = d$. Therefore, if $k = 0$, $f_n(z)$, for a sufficiently large n, has no root in $|z-c| = d$. If, on the other hand, $k > 0$, all the functions $f_n(z)$, for a sufficiently large n, have exactly k roots (counted according to their multiplicity) in $|z-c| = d$, which proves the theorem, since d is arbitrarily small.

Now consider a Taylor series $\Sigma a_n z^n = f(z)$ convergent in $|z| < r$, and put

$$s_n(z) = a_0 + a_1 z + \dots + a_n z^n$$

(partial sums or *sections*). Jentzsch discovered an important fact about the condensation of the zeros of the sections along the circumference $|z| = r$.

II. *There are infinitely many sections* $s_n(z)$ *having at least one zero in the circle* $|z - z_0| < \epsilon$ *for every* ϵ *and about every point* $z_0 = re^{i\theta_0}$, *regular or not, of the circle of convergence* $|z| = r$.

(Jentzsch, 1917 a.)

Proof. We begin with some general remarks on the n-th root of $s_n(z)$. Dividing, if necessary, by a convenient power of z we may suppose that $a_0 \neq 0$. Denote the zeros of $s_n(z) = 0$ by $z_{1n}, z_{2n}, \dots, z_{nn}$. If the degree of $s_n(z)$ is $k < n$, infinity is counted as a simple or multiple zero. Hence

$$s_n(z) = a_0\left(1 - \frac{z}{z_{1n}}\right)\left(1 - \frac{z}{z_{2n}}\right)\cdots\left(1 - \frac{z}{z_{nn}}\right),$$

i. e.

$$|s_n(z)| \leqslant |a_0| \left(1 + \left|\frac{z}{z_{1n}}\right|\right)\left(1 + \left|\frac{z}{z_{2n}}\right|\right)\cdots\left(1 + \left|\frac{z}{z_{nn}}\right|\right).$$

Since the origin is not a zero of the limit function $f(z)$ and, for every n, $s_n(0) = a_0 \neq 0$, all the zeros z_{kn} of the sections are at a finite distance σ from the origin (by I), i. e. $|z_{kn}| \geqslant \sigma > 0$, and thus

$$|s_n(z)| \leqslant |a_0| \left(1 + \left|\frac{z}{\sigma}\right|\right)^n.$$

It follows that, if z is restricted to a finite region R in which $|z| < d$, then

$$(2) \qquad |\sqrt[n]{s_n(z)}| < |\sqrt[n]{a_0}| \left(1 + \frac{d}{\sigma}\right) \qquad \text{in } R.$$

Therefore *the sequence of functions* $\sqrt[n]{s_n(z)}$, whatever branch we select for the n-th root, *is collectively bounded in every finite region.*

If the region R lies entirely in the circle of convergence, the sections $s_n(z)$ tend uniformly to their limit function $f(z)$. Putting

$$s_n(z) = r_n e^{i\phi_n}, \quad \sqrt[n]{s_n(z)} = |\sqrt[n]{r_n}|\, e^{i\phi_n/n}, \quad -\pi < \phi_n \leqslant \pi,$$

we see that $\sqrt[n]{s_n(z)} \to 1$ at every point of R, *provided* r_n *does not tend to* 0 *in* R, i. e. provided $f(z)$ has no zero in R. Moreover there is a domain D containing R in which all the conditions of Vitali's theorem, 42. IV, are satisfied, for the selected branch of the n-th root is uniform in R, and hence in some D. Thus we conclude

$$\sqrt[n]{s_n(z)} \to 1 \quad \text{uniformly in } R. \tag{3}$$

Now consider a point z outside the circle of convergence. We shall show that

$$\overline{\lim_{n=\infty}} \left| \sqrt[n]{s_n(z)} \right| > 1 \quad \text{if} \quad |z| > r. \tag{4}$$

Suppose if possible that $\overline{\lim\limits_{n=\infty}} \left| \sqrt[n]{s_n(z)} \right| \leqslant 1$. Then, for every given σ, there is an $n(\sigma)$ such that, for $n > n(\sigma)$,

$$|s_n(z)| \leqslant (1+\sigma)^n, \quad |s_{n+1}(z)| \leqslant (1+\sigma)^{n+1},$$

i. e.

$$|a_{n+1} z^{n+1}| = |s_{n+1}(z) - s_n(z)| \leqslant 2(1+\sigma)^{n+1}.$$

Now put $z = r + \epsilon$ and take $\sigma = \epsilon/2r$. Then

$$|a_{n+1}|(r+\epsilon)^{n+1} \leqslant 2\left(1+\frac{\epsilon}{2r}\right)^{n+1},$$

i. e.

$$\overline{\lim_{n=\infty}} \left| \sqrt[n+1]{a_{n+1}} \right| \leqslant \frac{1+\dfrac{\epsilon}{2r}}{r+\epsilon}, \qquad \frac{1}{r} \leqslant \frac{1+\dfrac{\epsilon}{2r}}{r+\epsilon}, \qquad r+\epsilon \leqslant r+\epsilon/2.$$

The last contradiction establishes (4).

Let us now suppose that II is not true, i. e. that there is a point z_0 on the circle of convergence such that, for a sufficiently large n, the functions $s_n(z)$ have no zero in $|z-z_0| < \epsilon$. It follows, by I, that the limit function $f(z)$ is different from 0 in every region R' lying within this circle as well as within $|z| = r$. On the other hand, (3) applies in R' and thus, as the functions $\sqrt[n]{s_n(z)}$ (with the specified branches) are uniform and collectively bounded in $|z-z_0| < \epsilon$, the uniform convergence in R' extends, by Vitali's theorem, to any region R within this circle. The limit function so defined is $\equiv 1$ throughout R, for it is 1 in R'. However, the circle $|z-z_0| < \epsilon$ contains points outside $|z| = r$ and, for those points, our result contradicts (4). Thus II is established.

It follows from I and II that the circle $|z| \leqslant r-\epsilon$ contains only a finite number of points of Z', and that every point of the circumference $|z| = r$ is contained in Z' and so also in Z''.

Denoting by $\phi_\epsilon(n)$ the number of zeros of $s_n(z)$ in $|z| \leqslant r+\epsilon$, we prove next that

III. *There are infinitely many $s_n(z)$ having more than $n(1-\delta)$ of their n zeros in $|z| < r+\epsilon$ where δ and ϵ are arbitrarily small, i.e.*

(5) $$\overline{\lim_{n=\infty}}\, \phi_\epsilon(n)/n = 1 \textit{ for every fixed } \epsilon.$$

(Jentzsch, 1917 a.)

Proof. $f(z)$ has only a finite number of zeros in $|z| < r-\epsilon_0$, $z_1, \ldots, z_\nu$, say $(0 < |z_1| \leqslant \ldots \leqslant |z_\nu|)$. Since, in $|z| \leqslant r-\epsilon_0$, $s_n(z)$ converges uniformly to $f(z)$, we see, as in the proof of I, that there is an $n(\delta)$ such that, for $n > n(\delta)$, ν of the zeros $z_{1n} \ldots, z_{nn}$ of $s_n(z)$ differ by less than δ from $z_1, \ldots, z_\nu$ respectively and, for the remaining zeros, $|z_{\lambda n}| > r-\epsilon_0-\delta$. Hence

$$|a_0/a_n| = |z_{1n} \ldots z_{nn}| > ||z_1|-\delta|^\nu (r-\epsilon_0-\delta)^{\phi(n)-\nu}(r+\epsilon)^{n-\phi(n)}.$$

Thus, taking $\delta < |z_1|/2$, we have

$$|a_0/a_n| > |z_1/2|^\nu (r-\epsilon_0-\delta)^{\phi(n)-\nu}(r+\epsilon)^{n-\phi(n)},$$

$$|\sqrt[n]{a_n}| < |\sqrt[n]{a_0}|\, |2/z_1|^{\nu/n} \frac{(r+\epsilon)^{\phi(n)/n\,-1}}{(r-\epsilon_0-\delta)^{\phi(n)/n\,-\nu/n}}.$$

Since, for every fixed ϵ_0, ν is finite, we have

$$\overline{\lim_{n=\infty}} |\sqrt{a_n}| \leqslant \frac{1}{r+\epsilon} \overline{\lim_{n=\infty}} \left(\frac{r+\epsilon}{r-\epsilon_0-\delta}\right)^{\phi(n)/n}.$$

Putting $\epsilon_0+\delta = \delta_1$ (arbitrarily small) we have

$$\overline{\lim_{n=\infty}} |\sqrt[n]{a_n}| \leqslant \frac{1}{r+\epsilon} \left(\frac{r+\epsilon}{r-\delta_1}\right)^{\overline{\lim} \frac{\phi(n)}{n}}.$$

Hence, if $\overline{\lim}\, \phi(n)/n = \alpha$, we have

$$\overline{\lim} |\sqrt[n]{a_n}| = 1/r \leqslant \frac{1}{r+\epsilon}\left(\frac{r+\epsilon}{r-\delta_1}\right)^\alpha.$$

Thus, as the left-hand side is independent of δ_1,

$$1/r \leqslant \frac{1}{r+\epsilon}\left(\frac{r+\epsilon}{r}\right)^\alpha$$

i.e. $1/r^{1-\alpha} \leqslant 1/(r+\epsilon)^{1-\alpha}$, which is absurd unless $\alpha = 1$. Q.e.d.

We can deal in the same way with the zeros of $s_n(z)-a$ or with those of $s_n'(z)$, &c. We notice that for $\Sigma z^{\nu!}$ the sections $s_n(z) = 1+z+z^2+z^6+\ldots+z^{\nu!}$, where $\nu! \leqslant n < (\nu+1)!$, have $\nu!$ zeros, so that for $s_{\nu!-1}(z)$, we have $\phi(n) \leqslant (\nu-1)!$, i.e.

$$\underline{\lim}\, \phi(n)/n = \lim \frac{(\nu-1)!}{\nu!-1} = 0.$$

If, from a certain n on, all the zeros of $s_n(z)$ are real or in a half plane (or in an angle $<2\pi$), the Taylor series either converges nowhere ($z=0$ excepted) or everywhere, because the set Z' does not fill the circumference of a circle $|z| = r$.

If $\Sigma_\mu |1/z_{\mu n}|^p < M$, $p>0$, the same conclusion can be drawn, because in $|z| \leqslant r$, $s_n(z)$ has at most $\nu = Mr^p$ zeros, and thus

$$\lim \phi(n)/n = 0$$

for $|z| = r$, where r is arbitrarily large.

IV. *If the only singularity of $f(z)$ on $|z| = r$ is a simple pole, all the zeros of the sections from a certain n on lie inside the circle $|z| = r+\epsilon$, where ϵ is arbitrary.* (Jentzsch, 1917 a.)

Proof. Let $f(z) = \Sigma b_n z^n + \alpha \Sigma (z/z_1)^n$, so that

$$\begin{aligned} s_n(z) &= b_0 + b_1 z + \ldots + b_n z^n + \alpha(1 + z/z_1 + \ldots + z^n/z_1^n) \\ &= Q_n(z) + R_n(z) = b_0 + \ldots + b_n z^n + \alpha \frac{1-(z/z_1)^{n+1}}{1-z/z_1}, \end{aligned}$$

where $z = z_1$ is the pole in question. Let $r+\epsilon \leqslant \rho < r_1$, where $\Sigma b_\nu z^\nu$ is regular in $|z| < r_1$. Then $\left|\sum_{\nu=0}^{n} b_\nu z^\nu\right| \leqslant M$ for $|z| \leqslant r+\epsilon$.

On the other hand, for $|z| = r+\epsilon$,

$$\left|\frac{(z/z_1)^{n+1}-1}{z/z_1-1}\right| \geqslant \frac{[(r+\epsilon)/r]^{n+1}-1}{(r+\epsilon)/r+1} = \frac{[(r+\epsilon)/r]^{n+1}-1}{2+\epsilon/r} \to \infty \text{ with } n,$$

so that, from a certain n on, $M < |\alpha| \left|\dfrac{(z/z_1)^{n+1}-1}{z/z_1-1}\right|$, and thus

$|Q_n(z)| = \left|\sum_{\nu=0}^{n} b_\nu z^\nu\right| < |R_n(z)|$ for $|z| = r+\epsilon$. Hence by Rouché's theorem, 60. I, $Q_n(z)+R_n(z)$ has in $|z| < r+\epsilon$ just as many zeros as $R_n(z)$. But $R_n(z)$ has n zeros so that, from a certain n on, $\phi(n) = n$ for $|z| < r+\epsilon$. Q.e.d.

The example

$$\frac{1}{2}\left(\frac{1}{1+z}+\frac{1}{1-z}\right)=1/(1-z^2)=\Sigma z^{2\nu}$$

gives $\phi(2n)=2n$ and $\phi(2n-1)=2n-2$, so that in general there may be roots outside $|z|=r+\epsilon$.

90. *Overconvergence.* The Taylor series may converge at points on its circle of convergence, but it certainly diverges at every point outside this circle. Porter (1906–7) discovered the fact that conveniently chosen sub-sequences of partial sums may sometimes be found which converge outside the circle of convergence. In such a case we say that the sub-sequence *overconverges.*

Porter's example is as follows. Consider a series

(1) $$\Sigma a_{n_i} z^{n_i}, \quad n_{i+1}>2n_i,$$

with the circle of convergence $|z|=r$. The series of polynomials

(2) $$F(x)=\Sigma a_{n_i} k^{n_i} x^{n_i}(1+x)^{n_i}, \quad k>0$$

converges absolutely and uniformly in every region within

(3) $$|kx(1+x)|=r \qquad \text{(Cassinian)}$$

and diverges at every point outside (3).

If in (2) we replace $x(1+x)$ by $|x|(1+|x|)$, the new series will be absolutely convergent for $|kx|(1+|x|)<r$, so that, if we rearrange the series in powers of x, the sum of the Taylor series $\Sigma c_n x^n$ so constructed is again $F(x)$. Moreover, it follows from $n_{i+1}>2n_i$ that the least power of x in $x^{n_{i+1}}(1+x)^{n_{i+1}}$ is greater than the greatest power of x in $x^{n_i}(1+x)^{n_i}$, so that the partial sum of $\Sigma c_n x^n$ corresponding to the suffix $2n_i$ is the sum of the first i terms of (2). *The partial sums of* (2) *form a sub-sequence of those of* $\Sigma c_n x^n$.

On the other hand, since $F(x)$ is regular within the Cassinian (3), the circle of convergence of $\Sigma c_n x^n$ is the largest circle in (3) about the origin. Since the Cassinian is not a circle, there are points inside (3) and outside the circle of convergence of $\Sigma c_n x^n$. At those points (2) converges, i.e. a conveniently chosen sub-sequence of partial sums pertaining to $\Sigma c_n x^n$ overconverges (to the right value).

We notice that, if we take $n_{i+1} = 2n_i + 1$, the series is complete in the sense that no coefficient is zero.

The important fact of overconvergence was rediscovered by Jentzsch. His example is as follows:

Consider the integral functions $f_\nu(z) = z^\nu e^{-\nu(1+z)}$ in the domain D_1, of fig. 53. Putting

$z = x + iy$, we see that

$$|f_1(z)| < (1+x)\,e^{-(1+x)} < 1 \text{ for } x > 0$$

and

$$|f_1(z)| \leqslant |z|\,e^{-(1+x)} \leqslant |z| < 1 \text{ in } |z| < 1.$$

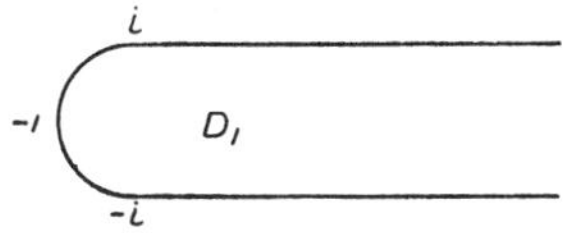

FIG. 53.

Hence $|f_1(z)| < 1$ in D_1 and, as $f_\nu(z) = [f_1(z)]^\nu$, we have in general

$$|f_n(z)| < 1 \text{ in } D_1.$$

Therefore, by Cauchy's inequalities, (40. 3), the coefficients in the expansion of $f_\nu(z) = e^{-\nu} z^\nu + \ldots$ are all less in absolute value than 1.

Consider the part D of D_1 characterized by the condition $\mathrm{Rl}(z) < 3$, and take a partial sum $\varDelta_1$ of f_1 such that

$$|f_1 - \varDelta_1| < (1/2)^2 \text{ in } D,$$

i.e.
$$|\varDelta_1| < 1 + (1/2)^2 \text{ in } D.$$

Now take an integer ν_1, greater than the degree of the polynomial $\varDelta_1$, and choose a partial sum $\varDelta_2$ of $(1/\nu_1)^2 f_{\nu_1+1}$ such that

$$|(1/\nu_1)^2 f_{\nu_1+1} - \varDelta_2| < (1/3)^2 \quad \text{in } D,$$

i.e.
$$|\varDelta_2| < (1/3)^2 + (1/\nu_1)^2 \quad \text{in } D.$$

Continue the construction in this way by choosing a partial sum $\varDelta_{k+1}$ of $(1/\nu_k)^2 f_{\nu_k+1}$ such that

$$|(1/\nu_k)^2 f_{\nu_k+1} - \varDelta_{k+1}| < [1/(k+2)]^2 \quad \text{in } D,$$

i. e.
$$|\varDelta_{k+1}| < (1/\nu_k)^2 + [1/(k+2)]^2,$$

where ν_k is an integer greater than the degree of $\varDelta_k$. By construction

(4)
$$\Sigma \varDelta_k = \Sigma b_\nu z^\nu$$

is a power series and, as all its coefficients are < 1 in absolute value, its radius of convergence is $\geqslant 1$. Moreover $b_{\nu_k+1} = e^{-(\nu_k+1)}/\nu_k^2$ i.e.

$$\lim_{k=\infty} |\sqrt[\nu_k+1]{b_{\nu_k+1}}| = \frac{1}{e} \lim_{k=\infty} (1/\nu_k^2)^{1/(\nu_k+1)} = 1/e.$$

Therefore $\overline{\lim} | \sqrt[\nu]{b_\nu} | \geqslant 1/e$, i.e. the radius of convergence is $\leqslant e$, and thus the domain D reaches outside the circle of convergence.

But
$$|\Delta_1| < 1 + (1/2)^2,$$
$$|\Delta_1 + \Delta_2| < 1 + (1/2)^2 + (1/3)^2 + (1/\nu_1)^2, \ldots,$$
$$|\Delta_1 + \Delta_2 + \ldots + \Delta_k| < 2\,[1 + (1/2)^2 + (1/3)^2 + \ldots] = \pi^2/3,$$

i.e. the partial sums of the series of polynomials $\Sigma \Delta_k$ are collectively bounded in D. As this series converges in $|z| < 1$, Vitali's theorem, 42. IV, shows that it converges uniformly in every region of D. Since the series of polynomials is at the same time a Taylor series, we see that the sequence of partial sums $\Delta_1, \Delta_2, \ldots, \Delta_k, \ldots$ of $\Sigma b_\nu z^\nu$ converges outside the circle of convergence of the same series.

The nature of overconvergence and, in particular, its connexion with gaps (groups of consecutive zero coefficients) in the Taylor series has been examined and cleared up by Ostrowski.

Weierstrass's example, in Art. 57, suggests a connexion between infinitely enlarging gaps and the fact that the function is not continued beyond the circle of convergence. Ostrowski's results establish with rather unexpected precision the link between the three phenomena of (a) gaps in the Taylor coefficients, (b) overconvergence, (c) the circle of convergence as a cut.

I. *If in* $f(z) = \Sigma a_\mu z^{\lambda_\mu}$ *there are infinitely many suffixes such that* $\lambda_{\mu_k+1} - \lambda_{\mu_k} > \theta \lambda_{\mu_k}$, $\theta > 0$, *then the series* $\sum_{k=0}^{\infty} \Delta_k(z)$ *where*

$$\Delta_0(z) = a_0 + \ldots + a_{\mu_1} z^{\lambda_{\mu_1}}, \ldots,$$
$$\Delta_k(z) = a_{\mu_k+1} z^{\lambda_{\mu_k+1}} + \ldots + a_{\mu_{k+1}} z^{\lambda_{\mu_{k+1}}}$$

converges uniformly in the neighbourhood of every regular point on the circle of convergence. (Ostrowski, 1921.)

Proof. Taking $|z| = 1$ for the circle of convergence, we assume that $z = 1$ is a regular point and apply Hadamard's three circles theorem, 42. II, to the three circles with centres at $z = 1/2$, and radii r_1, r_2, r_3 such that $1/2 + r_1 < 1 < 1/2 + r_2 < 1/2 + r_3$, and to the function

$$R_n(z) = f(z) - \sum_{0}^{n-1} \Delta_k(z).$$

We can choose r_2, r_3 such that $f(z)$ is regular in and on these circles.

If we put

$$M_k^{(n)} = \max_{|z-\frac{1}{2}| = r_k} |R_n(z)|, \quad k = 1, 2, 3,$$

the three circles theorem gives

$$\log \frac{r_3}{r_1} \log M_2^{(n)} \leqslant \log \frac{r_3}{r_2} \log M_1^{(n)} + \log \frac{r_2}{r_1} \log M_3^{(n)}.$$

Since the first circle is in the original circle of convergence, $M_1^{(n)} \to 0$. We will show that r_2, r_3 can be so chosen that on the right-hand side the first term dominates, i.e. the right-hand side tends to $-\infty$. Thus also the left-hand side tends to $-\infty$, i.e. $M_2^{(n)} \to 0$, and so in the second circle

$$\sum_{0}^{n-1} \Delta_k(z) \to f(z)$$

uniformly. As $z = 1$ is in the second circle, we thus prove the theorem for $z = 1$. Since a rotation, i.e. the substitution of $ze^{i\phi}$ in the place of z, does not change the gaps, the theorem extends to every regular point of the circle.

We introduce another circle centre at $1/2$, of radius r_1' such that $1/2 + r_1 < 1/2 + r_1' < 1 < 1/2 + r_2 < 1/2 + r_3$. By Cauchy's inequalities (40. 3), applied to the circle $|z| \leqslant 1/2 + r_1'$ we have $|a_\mu| \leqslant S/(1/2 + r_1')^{\lambda_\mu}$, where $S = \max_{|z| = \frac{1}{2} + r_1'} |f(z)|$. Furthermore we put

$$1/2 + r_1 = 1 - \delta\rho, \quad 1/2 + r_1' = 1 - \delta^2, \quad 1/2 + r_2 = 1 + \delta^2,$$
$$1/2 + r_3 = 1 + \delta\rho, \quad 0 < \delta < \rho,$$

where ρ is any fixed positive number. We will show that if δ

be chosen sufficiently small, the argument sketched above holds good. For the first circle we have

$$M_1^{(n)} \leqslant \sum_{\mu=\mu_n+1}^{\infty} |a_\mu||z|^{\lambda_\mu} \leqslant S \sum_{\mu=\mu_n+1}^{\infty} \left(\frac{1-\delta\rho}{1-\delta^2}\right)^{\lambda_\mu}$$

$$< S \sum_{\lambda=\lambda_{\mu_n+1}}^{\infty} \left(\frac{1-\delta\rho}{1-\delta^2}\right)^{\lambda} = \left(\frac{1-\delta\rho}{1-\delta^2}\right)^{\lambda_{\mu_n+1}} \cdot \frac{S}{1-\dfrac{1-\delta\rho}{1-\delta^2}}$$

$$= \left(\frac{1-\delta\rho}{1-\delta^2}\right)^{\lambda_{\mu_n+1}} S_1,$$

where S_1 depends only on δ.

If M is the maximum of $|f(z)|$ on the third circle, we have, since $R_n = f - \sum_0^{n-1} \Delta_k$,

$$M_3^n \leqslant M + \sum_{\mu=0}^{\mu_n} |a_\mu||z|^{\lambda_\mu} \leqslant M + S \sum_{\mu=0}^{\mu_n} \left(\frac{1+\delta\rho}{1-\delta^2}\right)^{\lambda_\mu}$$

$$< M + S \sum_{\lambda=0}^{\lambda_{u_n}} \left(\frac{1+\delta\rho}{1-\delta^2}\right)^{\lambda} < M + \left(\frac{1+\delta\rho}{1-\delta^2}\right)^{\lambda_{\mu_n}} \cdot \frac{S}{1-\dfrac{1-\delta^2}{1+\delta\rho}}$$

$$\leqslant \left(\frac{1+\delta\rho}{1-\delta^2}\right)^{\lambda_{\mu_n}} S_2,$$

where S_2 depends only on δ. Hence,

$$\log\frac{r_3}{r_1}\log M_2^{(n)} < \log\frac{1/2+\delta\rho}{1/2+\delta^2}\log\left(\frac{1-\delta\rho}{1-\delta^2}\right)^{\lambda_{\mu_n+1}}$$

$$+\log\frac{1/2+\delta^2}{1/2-\delta\rho}\log\left(\frac{1+\delta\rho}{1-\delta^2}\right)^{\lambda_{\mu_n}} + S_3,$$

where S_3 depends only on δ.

Now since the first term on the right-hand side is negative and $\lambda_{\mu_k+1}-\lambda_{\mu_k} > \theta\lambda_{\mu_k}$, we have

$$\log\frac{r_3}{r_1}\log M_2^{(n)} < \lambda_{\mu_n}\log\frac{1/2+\delta\rho}{1/2+\delta^2}\log\frac{1-\delta\rho}{1-\delta^2}$$

$$\times\left\{1+\theta+\frac{\log\dfrac{1/2+\delta^2}{1/2-\delta\rho}\log\dfrac{1+\delta\rho}{1-\delta^2}}{\log\dfrac{1/2+\delta\rho}{1/2+\delta^2}\log\dfrac{1-\delta\rho}{1-\delta^2}}\right\}+S_3.$$

The factor before the bracket is negative. The third term of the bracket $\to -1$ if $\delta \to 0$. If, therefore, δ be chosen sufficiently small, we have

$$\log \frac{r_3}{r_1} \log M_2^{(n)} \leqslant -\lambda_{\mu_n} S_4 + S_3,$$

where S_4 is positive and S_3 and S_4 depend only on δ. Hence when n tends to infinity the right-hand side tends to $-\infty$.

Q. e. d.

If there are only single surviving terms in each group, i. e. if $a_\mu = 0$ for $\mu_k < \mu < \mu_{k+1}$, $\Sigma \Delta_k$ is identical with the original Taylor series and thus the sequence Δ_k is the complete sequence of the different partial sums. Consequently, the sequence Δ_k cannot converge outside the circle of convergence. But, by Ostrowski's theorem, it does so long as $f(z)$ is regular at a single point on $|z| = 1$. Hence $f(z)$ is regular at no point of $|z| = 1$. Thus Hadamard's theorem 57. IV is a consequence of I.

When the Taylor coefficients satisfy the first condition of I, i. e. when in the Taylor series $\Sigma a_\mu z^{\lambda_\mu}$ there are infinitely many suffixes μ_k such that $\lambda_{\mu_k+1} - \lambda_{\mu_k} > \theta \lambda_{\mu_k}$, $\theta > 0$, we say that there are *Hadamard gaps* in the succession of Taylor coefficients.

91. *Complete domains of uniform convergence.* The two examples and Ostrowski's first theorem show that overconvergence is in fact an extension of *uniform* convergence beyond the original circle of convergence. For the complete sequence of partial sums the latter circle is the *complete* domain of uniform convergence in the sense that no *inner* points can be added to it. Ostrowski introduced the general idea of a complete domain for a sequence of functions.

The domain $D_u(f_n)$ is a complete domain of uniform convergence for the sequence of analytic functions $f_n(z)$ if (a) in every region of D_u all the functions $f_n(z)$ are regular and converge uniformly, (b) the point P belongs to D_u provided there is a connex region containing P and inner points of D_u in which all the functions $f_n(z)$ are regular and converge uniformly.

Condition (b) makes D_u *complete.* It follows from uniform convergence (by 89. I) that unless the limit function is identically zero, D_u contains only isolated limiting points of zeros of $f_n(z)$, and these limiting points are zeros of the limit function. The object of this article is to establish important connexions between overconvergence and the condensation of zeros of sequences of partial sums. The chief instrument used for this purpose is the idea of the complete domain of uniform convergence.

We begin with a very interesting remark of Ostrowski's on the rapidity of uniform convergence in D_u, which establishes a close similarity between the rates of approximation of the sequence to the limit function in the different regions of D_u.

The natural measure of the rapidity of (uniform) convergence in a region R is the maximum of $|f(z)-f_n(z)|$ in R, or, what comes to the same thing, at the boundary points of R. Take a circle k in D_u and put

$$(1) \qquad m_n(k) = \max_{z \text{ in } k} |f(z)-f_n(z)|.$$

Consider *any* region R in D_u (containing or not containing k or part of k). Ostrowski's problem is to determine an upper bound for the rapidity of uniform convergence in R in terms of m_n.

Lemma 1. *Suppose $f_n(z) \to f(z)$ in $D_u(f_n)$ and that the circle k and the region R are entirely in D_u. Then there are two positive constants C and σ, independent of n and depending only on k and the geometrical configuration of D_u and R, such that, for every z in R,*

$$(2) \qquad |f(z)-f_n(z)| \leqslant C(m_n)^\sigma.$$

(Ostrowski, 1922 a.)

Proof. We shall first prove that to every point P of D_u corresponds a circle centre at P in which $|f(z)-f_n(z)| \leqslant C(m_n)^\sigma$, $\sigma > 0$. For this purpose connect P to the circle k by a chain of overlapping circles, as in analytic continuation, $k_0 = k, k_1, \ldots, k_m$ with radii $r_0, r_1, \ldots, r_m$ and centres at $Q_0, Q_1, \ldots, Q_m = P$, such that, if k_i' and k_i'' are two circles of radii $r_i/2$ and $2r_i$ respectively with centres at Q_i, k_i' is in k_{i-1} and k_i'' is in D_u. By inserting new points Q the last two conditions can always be satisfied.

Denote by $m_n(r_i)$ the maximum modulus of $f(z)-f_n(z)$ in k_i and by c the maximum modulus of $f(z)-f_n(z)$ in the domain formed by $k_0'', k_1'', \ldots, k_m''$, and apply the three circles theorem, 42. II, to the function $f(z)-f_n(z)$ in the circles k_1', k_1, k_1''. We obtain

$$[m_n(r_1)]^{\log 4} \leqslant (m_n)^{\log 2} c^{\log 2},$$

i. e.

$$m_n(r_1) \leqslant c_1 (m_n)^{1/2}.$$

Applying the same theorem in the circles k_2', k_2, k_2'' and noticing that k_2' is in k_1, we obtain

$$m_n(r_2) \leqslant c_1[m_n(r_1)]^{1/2} \leqslant c_2 m_n^{1/4}.$$

After a finite number of steps our first statement is established: to every point P of R belongs a circle k_P in which

$$m_n(k_P) \leqslant C m_n^{\sigma}, \quad \sigma > 0.$$

Since a region is a closed set, a finite number of these circles, belonging to $P_1, P_2, \ldots, P_s$, say, cover R (by Borel's lemma, 11. III). If we take the greatest of the constants C and the least of the corresponding σ's the lemma is established for the arbitrary region R.

Now consider the boundary of D_u. No boundary point P at which the $f_n(z)$ are all regular is isolated from the other boundary points because from the uniform convergence of $f_n(z)$ on the circumference of a circle centre at P together with the regularity of all the functions $f_n(z)$ throughout the circle, uniform convergence follows in the whole circle, by 54. V. If $f(z)$ is regular at a boundary point P, so that there is a circle K in and on which $f(z)$ is regular, the corresponding $m_n(K)$ does not tend to 0 because if it did, the convergence would be uniform in K, and thus the whole circle K would belong to D_u and P would not be a boundary point. If, at the boundary point P, $f(z)$ has a singularity, e. g. a pole, $f(z)$ is not defined at P and thus $m_n(K)$ has no definite meaning. Suppose however that, as in the case of sections of Taylor series, the functions $f_n(z)$ are all regular in and on a circle K centre at P. The maximum modulus M_n of $f_n(z)$ tends, in general, to infinity with n.

We have seen that, for the complete sequence of sections of a Taylor series, D_u coincides with the circle of convergence, and in this case every boundary point of D_u is a limit point of zeros of sections. For the boundary points of D_u corresponding to a subsequence of sections, as well as for those of a general complete domain of uniform convergence D_u, Ostrowski established two results which, when applied to a sub-sequence of sections of a Taylor series, lead to a simple and important theorem (IV).

To understand the nature of the conditions in these two results consider circles K_n, or other regions, inside D_u but also inside smaller and smaller circles about P. When we apply lemma 1 to the successive circles, the constants $C(k_n)$ may tend to infinity and the indices σ_n to 0. Hence, in the first theorem, condition (3) restricts the increase of m_n corresponding to regions near P. Similarly, condition (4) of the first theorem restricts the increase of M_n as compared with the decrease of $m_n(k)$ where k is an arbitrarily fixed circle in D_u. The second result seems to show that the latter condition is more essential than the former.

I. *Let P be a boundary point of $D_u(f_n)$, in which domain the limit function $f(z) \neq 0$, and suppose that*

(a) *there is a circle K centre at P in which all the functions $f_n(z)$ are regular and $|f_n(z)| \leqslant M_n$;*

(b) *for every region R inside the common part of K and D_u*

$$(3) \qquad |f(z)-f_n(z)| < C(R) m_n(k),$$

where k is a fixed circle in D_u;

(c) *there is a positive ϵ such that*

$$(4) \qquad [m_n(k)]^\epsilon \log M_n \to 0.$$

Then P is either a singular point of $f(z)$ or a point of Z'' (or both). (Ostrowski, 1922 a.)

Proof. We shall prove that there are boundary points $P_i' \to P$ such that every P_i' is either a zero or a singular point of $f(z)$ or a point of Z'. Then P is certainly either a singular point of $f(z)$ (having near P an infinity of zeros or singular points or both), or a point of Z'' (a limiting point of points of Z'), or both.

We first notice that if the conditions of the theorem are satisfied in the circle K about the boundary point P, the same conditions are satisfied, without the slightest change, in every circle completely within K, with centre at any boundary point contained in K.

Now take inner points $P_i \to P$ and the largest circle k_i in D_u centre at P_i. By construction, there is at least one boundary point P_i' of D_u on the circumference of k_i. Replacing P_i, if necessary, by a suitable point on the segment $P_i P'_i$, we may suppose that P'_i is the only boundary point of D_u on k_i. Discarding, if necessary, a finite number of points P_i, we may also suppose that all the points P'_i are within K, so that the conditions of the theorem are satisfied for every P'_i in a conveniently small circle about P.

We are now going to prove that P'_i is either a zero or a singular point of $f(z)$ or a point of Z'. Suppose that this is not

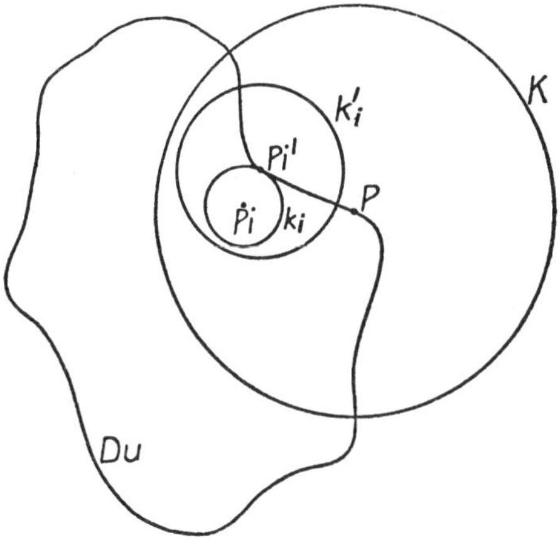

FIG. 54.

true. Then, by our assumption, $f(z)$ is regular at the only possible singular point P'_i on k_i, i.e. $f(z)$ is regular in a circle larger than k_i. Also, by (a), all the functions $f_n(z)$ are regular in the circle K about P containing k_i. Again, by our assumption, P'_i is not a zero of $f(z)$, i.e. there is a small circle k'_i about P'_i in which $f(z) \neq 0$, and P'_i is not a limit point of zeros of $f_n(z)$, i.e. there is a small circle k''_i about P'_i in which, neglecting if necessary a finite number of $f_n(z)$, no $f_n(z)$ vanishes. Therefore, taking P_i, if necessary, sufficiently near to P'_i on the segment $P_i P'_i$, in order that k_i should be contained in k'_i and k''_i, a suitable transformation $z' = az+b$ transforms k_i into the unit circle about the origin, and all the functions $f_n(z)$ and $f(z)$ are regular and different from 0 in a circle which, if $P_i P'_i$ be taken small enough, may be transformed into $|z'| \leqslant 2e$, say.

Replacing z' by z and denoting the transformed functions again by $f_n(z)$, $f(z)$, we shall now prove that under these conditions no point on the circumference of the unit circle is a boundary point of D_u by showing that $f_n(z)$ converges uniformly in a circle of radius > 1 and centre the origin. This contradiction will establish theorem I.

Replacing $f_n(z)$ by $f_n(z)/f(z)$ we may assume that $f(z) \equiv 1$, for $f(z)$ does not vanish in the circle in question. Choose for q the lesser of the two numbers $1/5$ and $1/5\epsilon$, where ϵ has been taken from (4). By (b), there is a number c_3 such that

$$(5) \qquad |1-f_n(z)| < c_3 m_n \qquad \text{in } |z| \leqslant 1-q.$$

Since $m_n \to 0$, suppressing, if necessary, a finite number of $f_n(z)$, we may assume that

$$(6) \qquad c_3 m_n < 1/2 \qquad \text{in } |z| \leqslant 1-q, \text{ for every } n.$$

Thus the series

$$\log f_n(z) = \log[1-(1-f_n)]$$
$$= -\frac{1-f_n(z)}{1} - \frac{[1-f_n(z)]^2}{2} - \dots$$

determines a branch $G_n(z)$ of $\log f_n(z)$ in $|z| \leqslant 1-q$ which can be analytically continued in $|z| \leqslant 2e$, as $f_n(z)$ does not vanish in this circle.

From the inequality

$$\left|\frac{a}{1} + \frac{a^2}{2} + \dots\right| \leqslant \frac{|a|}{1} + \frac{|a|^2}{2} + \dots < |a| + |a|^2 + \dots$$

we obtain

$$(7) \qquad |\log(1-a)| < 2|a| \quad \text{if} \quad |a| < 1/2.$$

Applied to $G_n(z)$ in $|z| \leqslant 1-q$, this inequality leads to

$$|G_n(z)| \leqslant 2c_3 m_n.$$

On the other hand, the real part of $G_n(z)$ is $\log|f_n(z)|$, and so, if we apply Borel's inequality (40. 11) to $G_n(z)$, with $r = 2e$ and $\rho = e$, and denote by M_n the maximum modulus of $f_n(z)$ on $|z| = 2e$, $C(r)$ is $\log M_n$ if $M_n \geqslant 1$ and zero otherwise. Thus, noticing that

$$C(r) \leqslant \log M_n \leqslant c_4 m_n^{-\epsilon},$$

and that $G_n(0)$ tends to a limit, we have, by (40. 11), for every n,

$$|G_n(z)| \leqslant c_5 m_n^{-\epsilon} \text{ in } |z| \leqslant e.$$

We now apply the three circles theorem, 42. II, to $G_n(z)$ for the circles of radii $1-q$, $1+q$, and e. We obtain for $|z|\leqslant 1+q$

$$|G_n(z)| < (2c_3 m_n)^{\gamma_1}(cm_n^{-\epsilon})^{\gamma_2},$$

where

$$\gamma_1 = \frac{1-\log(1+q)}{1-\log(1-q)} > \frac{1-q}{1+q+q^2+\ldots} > 1-2q,$$

$$\gamma_2 = \frac{\log(1+q)-\log(1-q)}{1-\log(1-q)} = 2q\,\frac{1+\frac{q^2}{3}+\frac{q^4}{5}+\ldots}{1+q+\frac{q^2}{2}+\ldots} < 2q.$$

Since $2q\epsilon \leqslant 2/5$ and, for a sufficiently large n, $m_n < 1$, it follows that, for $|z|\leqslant 1+q$,

$$|G_n(z)| < c_6 m_n{}^{1-2q-\epsilon 2q} \leqslant c_6 m_n{}^{3/5-2q^\epsilon} \leqslant c_6 m_n{}^{1/5} \to 0.$$

Therefore, $f_n(z) \to 1$ uniformly in $|z|\leqslant 1+q$ as was to be proved.

In Ostrowski's second theorem condition (b) is dropped and (c) is replaced by a stronger one of the same nature. The conclusion is the same.

II. *Let P be a boundary point of $D_u(f_n)$ in which domain the limit function $f(z)\not\equiv 0$, and suppose*

(a) *there is a circle K about P in which all the functions $f_n(z)$ are regular and $|f_n(z)|\leqslant M_n$;*

(c′) *for every positive ϵ,*

$$[m_n(k)]^\epsilon\,|\log M_n| \to 0. \tag{8}$$

Then P is either a singular point of $f(z)$ or a point of Z''.

(Ostrowski, 1922 a.)

Proof. We shall make use of condition (c′) in the following way. If the positive numbers $g_n \to 0$ and the positive numbers $a_n \to \infty$ in such a way that, for every positive ϵ,

$$g_n^\epsilon a_n \to 0, \text{ then } \frac{\log a_n}{\log g_n} \to 0. \tag{9}$$

To prove this statement we have only to notice that for every $\epsilon > 0$ there is a $c(\epsilon) > 1$ such that $a_n < c(\epsilon)/g^n$, and thus

$$\frac{\log a_n}{|\log g_n|} < \frac{\log c(\epsilon)}{|\log g_n|} + \epsilon.$$

It follows that, as $n \to \infty$, all the limiting numbers of the left-hand side are between 0 and ϵ. Since ϵ is, by hypothesis, arbitrary, the limit is 0.

By lemma 1, for any given region R of D_u, there is a $\sigma > 0$ such that

(10) $$|f(z) - f_n(z)| < c_1(R)[m_n(k)]^\sigma ;$$

and, replacing the M_n if necessary by larger numbers, we may suppose that $M_n > 3e$, say. Thus, from (8) and (9),

$$\frac{\log\log M_n}{\log m_n} \to 0, \qquad \frac{\sqrt{\log\log M_n}}{\sqrt{|\log m_n|}} \to 0.$$

We write the last limit equation in the form

$$\log\log M_n = o(\sqrt{|\log m_n| \log\log M_n}).$$

Finally, putting

$$m_n' = e^{-\sqrt{|\log m_n| \log\log M_n}},$$

the equation becomes

$$\log\log M_n = o(\log m_n'),$$

where

$$\log m_n' = -\sqrt{|\log m_n| \log\log M_n} = o(\log m_n).$$

Hence

$$\log M_n = e^{\epsilon_n \log m_n'} \text{ where } \epsilon_n \to 0,$$

i. e. $$(m_n')^\sigma \log M_n = e^{(\sigma+\epsilon_n) \log m_n'}.$$

Since, for a sufficiently large n, $\sigma + \epsilon_n > 0$ and $m_n' \to 0$, i. e. $\log m_n' \to -\infty$, we see that, for the specified σ,

(11) $$(m_n')^\sigma \log M_n \to 0.$$

In order to replace m_n by m_n' in I we notice that

(12) $$\log m_n' = \delta_n \log m_n, \text{ where } \delta_n \to 0,$$

and that, for a sufficiently large n, $m_n' < 1$ and $\sigma/\delta_n > 1$. Therefore

(13) $$(m_n)^\sigma = (m_n')^{\sigma/\delta_n} < c_2 m_n'.$$

Thus, from (10) and (13),

(14) $$|f(z) - f_n(z)| < c_1 c_2 m_n'.$$

It follows from (11) and (14) that conditions (b) and (c) of theorem I are satisfied with m_n' in place of m_n and $\epsilon = \sigma$, and in this way I establishes II.

We are now going to apply these results to a Taylor series $\Sigma a_n z^n$ convergent in $|z|<1$. Take $|z|<r<1$ as the circle k. To evaluate the corresponding m_n, we notice that, by Cauchy's inequalities,

$$|a_n| \leqslant M/(r+\epsilon)^n, \text{ where } M = \max|f(z)| \text{ in } |z| \leqslant r+\epsilon<1.$$

Therefore

$$|a_n z^n + \dots| \leqslant M\left(\frac{r}{r+\epsilon}\right)^n \frac{r+\epsilon}{\epsilon} \text{ in } |z| \leqslant r,$$

i. e.

$$m_n = \max_{|z| \leqslant r} |f(z) - s_n(z)| < c\rho^n, \text{ where } \rho<1.$$

The same obviously holds for every sub-sequence of partial sums.

As to condition (c′) of II, putting

$$1/(r+\epsilon) = g > 1,$$

we have, for every polynomial of degree n,

$$|s_n(z)| \leqslant M(1+g+ \dots +g^n) \leqslant M(n+1)g^n \text{ in } |z| \leqslant 1/g,$$

where in our case M is the same for all the functions $f_n(z)$, since it is the maximum modulus of $f(z)$ in $|z|<1/g$. Hence $\log M_n = o(n)$, and thus

$$(m_n)^\epsilon |\log M_n| \leqslant \rho^{n\epsilon} cn \to 0,$$

i. e. condition (c′) of II is satisfied for every $\epsilon>0$ in every finite domain and for every sub-sequence of partial sums. Hence the following result.

III. *Every boundary point of $D_u(s_n)$ belonging to any sub-sequence of partial sums s_{nk} is either a singular point of $f(z)$ or a point of $Z''(s_{n_k})$.* (Ostrowski, 1922 a.)

We deduce from this result the following final statement.

IV. *If the regular point z_0 is on the circle of convergence $|z|=1$, the necessary and sufficient condition that $s_{n_k}(z)$ shall overconverge uniformly at z_0 is that z_0 shall not be a point of $Z''(s_{n_k})$.* (Ostrowski, 1922 a.)

Proof. Since z_0 is either an inner or a boundary point of $D_u(S_{n_k})$, the necessary and sufficient condition for overconvergence at z_0 is that z_0 shall be an inner point. As Z'' contains no inner point, by 89. I, and by the hypothesis that z_0 is not a singular point, IV follows.

92. *Overconvergence and Hadamard gaps.* We shall now establish Ostrowski's main result connecting the occurrence of overconvergence with that of gaps in the Taylor coefficients. It consists of a converse to his first theorem, 90. I.

I. *If* $f(z) = \Sigma a_n z^n$ *has a sub-sequence of partial sums* $s_{n_k}(z)$ *overconverging uniformly in the neighbourhood of a regular point of the circle of convergence* $|z| = 1$, $\Sigma a_n z^n$ *is the sum of two Taylor series, the first of which has a radius of convergence* >1, *and the coefficients of the second possess Hadamard gaps.*

(Ostrowski, 1923 a.)

Proof. We are going to show that certain coefficients a_n, together with groups of coefficients preceding and following them, have such small moduli that they can be separated from the others to form a Taylor series with a radius of convergence >1, and that the gaps so created in the sequence of a_n are of the Hadamard type, i. e. I is a consequence of the following result.

II. *If* $f(z) = \Sigma a_n z^n$ *has a sub-sequence of partial sums* $s_{n_k}(z)$ *overconverging uniformly in the neighbourhood of a regular point of the circle of convergence* $|z| = 1$, *there is a* $\theta > 0$ *and a positive* $\rho < 1$ *such that for sufficiently large* k

$$(1)\quad \begin{aligned} &\text{a.} \quad |a_n| < \rho^n \quad \textit{for} \quad (1-\theta)n_k < n < n_k, \\ &\text{b.} \quad |a_n| < \rho^n \quad \textit{for} \quad n_k \leqslant n < (1+\theta)n_k. \end{aligned}$$

(Ostrowski, 1923 a.)

Proof of II. We prove only (1) b; (1) a is established in a similar way, and either of them is sufficient to prove I. We first establish some general remarks on mapping. Suppose the function $u = z + c_2 z^2 + \dots$ maps the simply connected domain D (containing $z = 0$) upon $|u| < r$. Then, by our remark after 72. IV,

$$(2)\qquad u(z) \ll \frac{z}{1-\dfrac{bz}{r}},$$

where b is any positive number $\geqslant 7$.

Now consider a function $\phi(z) = a_n z^n + \dots$, regular and such that $|\phi(z)| \leqslant 1$ in D. If we map D on $|u| < r$, $\phi(z)$ is transformed into

$$\bar{\phi}(u) = b_n u^n + \dots.$$

From the condition $|\bar{\phi}(u)| \leqslant 1$, for $|u| < r$, it follows by Cauchy's inequalities (40. 3) that $|b_m| \leqslant r^{-m}$, i. e.

$$\bar{\phi}(u) << \frac{u^n}{r^n\left(1-\frac{u}{r}\right)}.$$

Therefore, by (2),

$$\phi(z) = \bar{\phi}(u) << \frac{z^n}{r^n} \frac{1}{\left(1-\frac{bz}{r}\right)^n} \cdot \frac{1}{1-\frac{z}{r(1-bz/r)}},$$

and thus

$$\phi(z) << \frac{z^n}{r^n} \cdot \frac{1}{\left(1-\frac{bz}{r}\right)^{n-1}} \cdot \frac{1}{1-\frac{(b+1)z}{r}} << \frac{z^n}{r^n} \cdot \frac{1}{\left(1-\frac{2bz}{r}\right)^n}$$

Hence, by the binomial formula for the index $-n$,

$$(3) \qquad |a_{n+p}| \leqslant 2^p b^p C_p^{n+p}/r^{n+p}.$$

We next consider the $(n+p)$-th root of this expression in terms of $\sigma = p/n$ when $n+p$ tends to infinity in such a way that σ remains $< \theta$, where θ is a conveniently chosen small positive number *independent of n and p.*

Since $p/(n+p) = \sigma/(1+\sigma) \leqslant \sigma$, we have

$$\sqrt[n+p]{|a_{n+p}|} \leqslant \frac{2^\sigma b^\sigma}{r} [C_p^{n+p}]^{1/(n+p)}.$$

For $p = 0$ the right-hand side plainly tends to $1/r$.

For $p \geqslant 1$, by (57. 5), we have

$$C_p^{n+p} < \frac{\left(1+\frac{p}{n}\right)^{n+p}}{\left(\frac{p}{n}\right)^p},$$

i. e.

$$[C_p^{n+p}]^{\frac{1}{n+p}} < \frac{1+\frac{p}{n}}{\left(\frac{p}{n}\right)^{\frac{p}{n+p}}} = \frac{1+\sigma}{\sigma^{\frac{\sigma}{1+\sigma}}}.$$

Also, when $\sigma \to 0$,

$$\sigma^{\frac{\sigma}{1+\sigma}} = e^{\frac{\sigma}{1+\sigma}\log\sigma} \to 1.$$

Therefore, for $p \geqslant 0$, we have

$$|\sqrt[n+p]{a_{n+p}}| \leqslant g(\sigma)/r,$$

where $g(\sigma) \to 1$, when $\sigma \to 0$, independently of n and p, and $g(0) = 1$. In particular, if $r > 1$, there is a $\theta > 0$ and a positive $\rho < 1$ such that $g(\sigma)/r < \rho < 1$ for $0 \leqslant \sigma < \theta$.

Returning now to the proof of II, we consider the sequence of power series

$$r_k(z) = f(z) - s_{n_k}(z).$$

It follows from the hypothesis of overconvergence that there is a rectifiable curve C (containing $z = 0$) inside which $r_k(z) \to 0$ uniformly and the inner conform radius of which with respect to the origin is > 1. In fact, by (70. 7), the latter condition is satisfied if the length of the inverse curve with respect to the origin is $< 2\pi$, and C can always be chosen so that its inverse has this property. It follows from the uniform convergence of $r_k(z)$ that from a certain k onwards $|r_k(z)| \leqslant 1$ in and on C. If then we take the interior of C for the domain D and choose θ and ρ as above, (2) a is established and hence I follows.

The connexion between overconvergence and zeros of partial sums is given by the following theorem.

III. *If $f(z) = \Sigma a_n z^n$ has a sequence $s_{n_k}(z)$ overconverging uniformly in the neighbourhood of a regular point z_0 of the circle of convergence $|z| = 1$ and if z_0 is not a point of $z''(n_k)$, then* (1) *is satisfied for a convenient $\theta > 0$ and $\rho < 1$.*

(Ostrowski, 1923 a.)

93. *Non-continued Taylor series.* Hadamard's theorem, 57. IV, is the first to point out a class of Taylor series which are not continued beyond the circle of convergence. This property is due in that case to the large and regularly distributed gaps in the succession of the coefficients of $\Sigma a_n z^{\lambda_n}$. The lengths of the successive gaps increase indefinitely and satisfy the condition $\lambda_{n+1} > (1+\theta)\lambda_n$, $\theta > 0$ and the only surviving terms are the extremities of the gaps.

Wider classes of non-continued Taylor series have been obtained by Fabry, including, in particular, the class of Taylor series with gaps satisfying the relation

(1) $$\lambda_{n+1} - \lambda_n \to \infty,$$

or, more generally,

$$(2) \qquad \lambda_n / n \to \infty .$$

The latter condition includes the first. In fact it follows from (1), for an arbitrarily large M, that $\lambda_{n+1} - \lambda_n > M$ provided $n > N$, i.e. $\lambda_{n+p} - \lambda_n > pM$ and $\lambda_{n+p}/(n+p) > \lambda_n/(n+p) + pM/(n+p)$ Therefore, letting p tend to infinity, $\underline{\lim}\, \lambda_n/n \geqslant M$ and, as M is arbitrarily large, $\lambda_n/n \to \infty$. Thus the class (2) includes the class (1), and the example $\lambda_{2n} = n^2, \lambda_{2n+1} = n^2 + 1$ shows that (2) may be verified and (1) not.

Fabry's general result also includes cases where the surviving terms are sufficiently thinly distributed in intervals about certain suffixes.

I. *If* $f(z) = \Sigma a_n z^n$ *contains infinitely many suffixes* m_i *such that* (a) $\lim\limits_{i=\infty} |\sqrt[m_i]{a_{m_i}}| = 1$, (b) $\lim\limits_{i=\infty} s_i/m_i = 0$, *where* s_i *is the number of non-vanishing coefficients in the interval* I_i: $m_i(1-\theta) < n < m_i(1+\theta)$, $n \neq m_i$, $0 < \theta < 1$, *then* $f(z)$ *is not continued beyond the unit circle.* (Fabry, 1896.)

Proof. (Faber, 1904.) By choosing a sub-sequence of m_i, we may suppose that

$$(3) \qquad m_{i+1} > 2m_i(1+\theta)/(1-\theta),$$

$$(4) \qquad \prod_{\nu=0}^{\infty} \left[1 - \frac{m_i^2}{\{m_{i+1}(1-\theta)+\nu\}^2}\right] > (1-\epsilon_i)^{m_i},$$

where $\epsilon_i \to 0$. By (b), for an arbitrarily given ϵ, we can fix an n such that $s_{n+r} < \frac{\epsilon}{4} m_{n+r}$, $r \geqslant 0$, i.e. by (3),

$$s_n + \ldots + s_{n+l} < \frac{\epsilon}{4}(m_{n+l} + \ldots + m_n)$$
$$< \frac{\epsilon}{4}\left(m_{n+l} + \frac{m_{n+l}}{2} + \ldots + \frac{m_{n+l}}{2^l}\right) < \frac{\epsilon}{2} m_{n+l}.$$

Thus, taking l so large that $s_1 + s_2 + \ldots + s_{n+l} < \frac{\epsilon}{2} m_{n+l}$, we have

$$(5) \qquad (s_1 + \ldots + s_k)/m_k < \epsilon, \text{ for } k \geqslant n+l.$$

We now form an integral function $G(z)$ having for zeros the *suffixes* of the non-vanishing coefficients in the intervals I_i, except the m_i themselves, and the negative values of the same suffixes (to ensure convergence). Denote the positive zeros of $G(z)$ arranged in increasing order of moduli by r_ν. Then

$$(6) \qquad G(z) = \prod_{\nu=1}^{\infty} (1 - z^2/r_\nu^2)$$

and

$$(7) \qquad \nu/r_\nu \to 0, \text{ i.e. } r_\nu/\nu \to \infty.$$

In fact, by (5), if r_ν is in the m_k group, its index

$$\nu = s_1 + s_2 + \ldots + s_{k-1} + s_k' \quad \text{with } s_k' \leqslant s_k.$$

Hence

$$\nu/r_\nu < (s_1 + \ldots + s_k)/m_k(1-\theta) < \epsilon/(1-\theta).$$

The number ϵ being arbitrary, (7) follows.

We are going to show that in virtue of (7) the integral function $G(z)$ is of the minimum type of the order 1, i.e. for an arbitrarily given ϵ there is an R such that

$$(8) \qquad |G(z)| < e^{\epsilon|z|} \text{ when } |z| > R.$$

In fact

$$|G(z)| < \prod_1^n (1 + |z|^2/|r_\nu|^2) \prod_{n+1}^{\infty} (1 + |z|^2/|r_\nu|^2)$$

$$< e^{n \log\left(1 + \frac{|z|^2}{|r_1|^2}\right)} \prod_{n+1}^{\infty} \left(1 + \frac{|z|^2}{|r_\nu|^2}\right).$$

Now choose n such that $1/|r_\nu| < \epsilon/2\pi\nu$ for $\nu > n$, where ϵ is arbitrarily given. Then

$$\prod_{n+1}^{\infty} (1 + |z|^2/|r_\nu|^2) < \prod_1^{\infty} \left(1 + \frac{\epsilon^2 |z|^2}{4\pi^2\nu^2}\right) = \frac{2}{i\epsilon|z|} \sin\left(\frac{i\epsilon|z|}{2}\right) < e^{\frac{1}{2}\epsilon|z|}$$

provided $\epsilon|z| > 1$. By taking $|z|$ large enough to satisfy the inequality $n \log(1 + |z|^2/|r_1|^2) < \frac{1}{2}\epsilon|z|$, (8) is proved. It follows from (8), by 86. II, that the *only singular point of* $L(z) = \Sigma G(n) z^n$ *is* $z = 1$.

The last step in the proof consists in showing that $|z| = 1$ is a singular line for $F(z) = \Sigma a_n G(n) z^n$. For in this case, by Hadamard's multiplication theorem, 88. I, the affixes of all the singular points of $F(z)$ are products of 1 and the affixes of the singular points of $\Sigma a_n z^n$, and so it follows that every point on $|z| = 1$ is singular for $f(z) = \Sigma a_n z^n$.

To prove that $|z| = 1$ is a singular line for $F(z)$ we shall make use of Hadamard's simplified test for singularities (57. III). For this purpose we first prove that

$$\lim_{i=\infty} |\sqrt[m_i]{G(m_i)}| = 1. \tag{9}$$

We see from (8) that

$$\overline{\lim_{i=\infty}} |\sqrt[m_i]{G(m_i)}| \leqslant e^{\epsilon},$$

i. e., ϵ being arbitrary,

$$\overline{\lim_{i=\infty}} |\sqrt[m_i]{G(m_i)}| \leqslant 1.$$

Thus we have only to show that

$$\underline{\lim_{i=\infty}} |\sqrt[m_i]{G(m_i)}| \geqslant 1. \tag{10}$$

Let $G(z) = P_1(z)\, P_2(z)\, P_3(z)$, where the positive zeros of $P_1(z)$ are in the intervals $I_1, I_2, \dots I_{i-1}$, those of $P_2(z)$ are in I_i and those of $P_3(z)$ are in $I_{i+1}, \dots$. Then, by (3), $m_i > 2r_\nu$ in $P_1(z)$ and so $\left|1 - \frac{m_i^2}{r_\nu^2}\right| > 3$. Thus $\underline{\lim_{i=}} |\sqrt[m_i]{P_1(m_i)}| \geqslant 1$.

Now $P_3(m_i)$ is greater than the left-hand side of (4), and hence

$$\underline{\lim_{i=\infty}} |\sqrt[m_i]{P_3(m_i)}| \geqslant 1.$$

Next we have

$$|P_2(m_i)| = \prod_{r_\nu \text{ in } I_i} \frac{r_\nu + m_i}{r_\nu} \cdot \frac{|r_\nu - m_i|}{r_\nu} > \prod_{r_\nu \text{ in } I_i} \frac{|r_\nu - m_i|}{r_\nu}.$$

Let s_i' of the r_ν in I_i be $> m_i$ and s_i'' of them $< m_i$, so that $s_i' + s_i'' = s_i$. Then, since the difference between two consecutive r_ν is $\geqslant 1$, and they are all $< m_i(1+\theta)$, we have

$$|P_2(m_i)| > \frac{s_i'!\, s_i''!}{m_i^{s_i}(1+\theta)^{s_i}}.$$

Now $n! > (n/e)^n$, since $e^n = \Sigma n^\nu/\nu! > n^n/n!$, and thus

$$|\sqrt[m_i]{P_2(m_i)}| > \frac{1}{e^{\frac{s_i}{m_i}}(1+\theta)^{\frac{s_i}{m_i}}} \cdot \left(\frac{s_i'}{m_i}\right)^{\frac{s_i'}{m_i}} \left(\frac{s_i''}{m_i}\right)^{\frac{s_i''}{m_i}},$$

where, by (b), the factors all tend to 1 (since $x^x \to 1$ when $x \to 0$, $x > 0$). This proves (10) and thus (9).

Now consider the series $\Sigma G(\nu) a_\nu z^\nu$. When ν is in I_i, the only non-vanishing coefficient is $a_{m_i} G(m_i)$, and thus H_{m_i} in Hadamard's test, 57. III, can be chosen so that it reduces to a single term $a_{m_i} G(m_i)$. By (a) and (9), we see that

$$\overline{\lim_{i=\infty}} \left| \sqrt[m_i]{a_{m_i} G(m_i)} \right| = \overline{\lim_{i=\infty}} \left| \sqrt[m_i]{a_{m_i}} \right| \lim_{i=\infty} \left| \sqrt[m_i]{G(m_i)} \right| = 1.$$

Since the condition for singularity is satisfied for every $z = e^{i\theta}$ it follows that $F(z)$ is singular all along $|z| = 1$. This completes the proof of Fabry's theorem.

Particular cases. Consider now a series $\Sigma a_n z^{\lambda_n}$ where $\lambda_{n+1} - \lambda_n \to \infty$ or, more generally, $\lambda_n / n = M_n \to \infty$. An *Hadamard interval* about λ_n is formed by all the terms corresponding to indices λ_k satisfying the condition

$$\lambda_n - \theta\lambda_n < \lambda_k < \lambda_n + \theta\lambda_n.$$

For, in the first place, if $(n+\nu) M_{n+\nu} < \lambda_n (1+\theta)$, it follows that

$$(11) \qquad 1/M_n + \nu/\lambda_n < (1+\theta)/M_{n+\nu}.$$

Now let i'_n be the number of existing suffixes between λ_n and $\lambda_n + \theta\lambda_n$, and i''_n the number between $\lambda_n - \theta\lambda_n$ and λ_n. Then it follows from (11) that $i'_n/\lambda_n \to 0$. Similarly $i''_n/\lambda_n \to 0$. Thus condition (b) of Fabry's theorem is satisfied. Since, by hypothesis, the radius of convergence is 1, we have

$$\overline{\lim_{n=\infty}} \left| \sqrt[\lambda_n]{a_n} \right| = 1,$$

i. e. there is a sub-sequence of λ_n such that

$$\lim_{\nu=\infty} \left| \sqrt[\lambda_{n_\nu}]{a_{n_\nu}} \right| = 1,$$

which is condition (a). Hence

II. *If $\lambda_n / n \to \infty$ and the radius of convergence of*

$$f(z) = \Sigma a_n z^{\lambda_n}$$

is 1, $f(z)$ is not continued beyond $|z| = 1$. (Fabry, 1896.)

94. The reasoning leading to Fabry's theorem 93. I, can also be used, in a slightly modified form, for detecting singular points. 93. I is in fact included in the following general theorem, also due to Fabry.

I. *Suppose the radius of convergence of* $\Sigma a_n z^n$ *is* 1; *let* σ_n *denote the number of changes of sign of* Rl $[a_{m_n+\nu} e^{(\nu\alpha-\gamma_n)i}]$ *where* ν *runs through the integer values between* $-\theta m_n$ *and* θm_n, $0<\theta<1$. *If there exist real numbers* γ_n *such that*

$$\text{(a)} \qquad \lim_{n=\infty} [\text{Rl}\,(a_{m_n} e^{-\gamma_n i})]^{1/m_n} = 1,$$

$$\text{(b)} \qquad \lim_{n=\infty} \sigma_n / m_n = 0,$$

then $e^{i\alpha}$ *is a singular point of* $\Sigma a_n z^n$. (Fabry, 1896.)

Proof. (Faber, 1904). By choosing a sub-sequence of m_n we can suppose that the m_n satisfy the inequalities (3) and (4) of 93. I and also that Rl $(a_{m_n} e^{-\gamma_n i})>0$. As in 93. I, we construct an integral function with pairs of positive and negative zeros, whose moduli are of the form $m_n+\nu+\frac{1}{2}$, where $m_n+\nu$ is a suffix after which Rl $[a_{m_n+\nu} e^{(\nu\alpha-\gamma_n)i}]$ changes sign, when ν runs through the integer values between $-\theta m_n$ and θm_n. Then as in 93. I, it may be shown that $G(z)$ is of the minimum type of the order 1, so that $L(z)=\Sigma G(\nu) z^\nu$ has 1 for its only singularity, and also that $\lim_{n=\infty} |\sqrt[m_n]{G(m_n)}|=1$. Moreover $Hm_n(e^{i\alpha})$, Hadamard's test function for $F(z)=\Sigma a_\nu G(\nu) z^\nu$, can be chosen so that the real parts of all the terms of $e^{-\gamma_n i} H_{m_n}(e^{i\alpha})$ have the same sign, since $G(z)$ has been chosen so that

$$G(m_n+\nu)\,\text{Rl}\,[a_{m_n+\nu}\, e^{(\nu\alpha-\gamma_n)i}]$$

has no changes of sign in the interval corresponding to m_n; and thus

$$\text{Rl}\,[e^{-\gamma_n i} H_{m_n}(e^{i\alpha})] \geqslant \text{Rl}\,[G(m_n) a_{m_n} e^{-\gamma_n i}].$$

Therefore

$$\varlimsup_{n=\infty} |\sqrt[m_n]{H_{m_n}(e^{i\alpha})}| \geqslant \lim_{n=\infty} |\sqrt[m_n]{G(m_n)}| \lim_{n=\infty} |\sqrt[m_n]{\text{Rl}\,(a_{m_n} e^{-\gamma_n i})}| = 1,$$

and so $e^{i\alpha}$ is a singularity for $F(z)$. The theorem follows by Hadamard's multiplication theorem.

The most interesting application of the last result is the following theorem.

II. *If* $\lim a_n/a_{n+1}=e^{i\alpha}$ *exists,* $e^{i\alpha}$ *is a singular point of* $\Sigma a_n z^n$. (Fabry, 1896.)

Proof. For simplicity we suppose that $\alpha=0$. By the Ratio

Test, 24. IV, we see that the radius of convergence is 1. Moreover if $a_n = \rho_n e^{i\omega_n}$, we have by hypothesis $\omega_{n+1} - \omega_n \to 0$. Thus also the maximum δ_n of the differences $|\omega_{k+1} - \omega_k|$, for k lying in the interval I_n: $(1-\theta)\, m_n < k < (1+\theta) m_n$, $0 < \theta < 1$, tends to 0, and

$$\sum_{k \text{ in } I_n} |\omega_{k+1} - \omega_k| < 2\theta m_n \delta_n,$$

i. e.

$$(1) \qquad \Big(\sum_{k \text{ in } I_n} |\omega_{k+1} - \omega_k|\Big) / m_n \to 0.$$

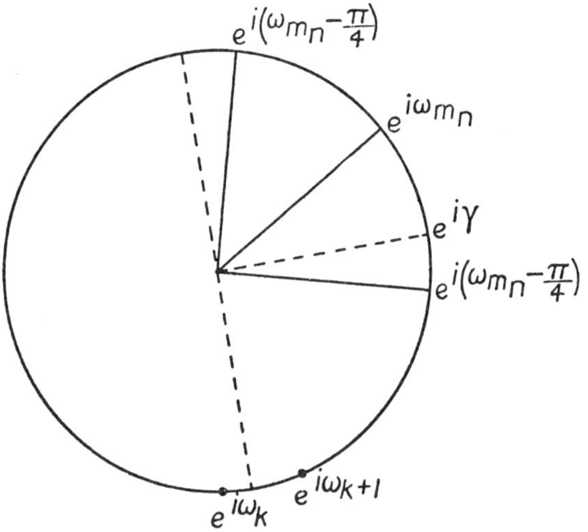

FIG. 55.

Now joining the points $e^{i\omega_k}$ and $e^{i\omega_{k+1}}$ by the lesser arc on $|z| = 1$, and putting

$$a_k e^{-\gamma i} = \rho_k e^{(\omega_k - \gamma)i} = a_k' + i a_k'',$$

where $a_{m_n} - \pi/4 \leqslant \gamma \leqslant a_{m_n} + \pi/4$, we see that the sign of

$$a_k' = \rho_k \cos(\omega_k - \gamma)$$

changes, as k runs through the interval I_n, when k changes to $k+1$ and the arc (ω_k, ω_{k+1}) passes through one of the two points $e^{(\gamma \pm \frac{1}{2}\pi)i}$. Let q_n be the minimum number of changes as

γ varies. Then there are at least q_n arcs passing through one or other of the two points $e^{(\gamma \pm \frac{1}{4}\pi)i}$ for all possible values of γ, i.e. there are at least q_n sets of arcs each covering altogether more than one-quarter of the circumference. Therefore

$$(2) \qquad \sum_{k \text{ in } I_n} |\omega_{k+1} - \omega_k| > \frac{\pi}{2} q_n,$$

and hence it follows from (1) and (2) that $q_n/m_n \to 0$.

Now let γ_n be a value of γ for which the number of changes of sign is a minimum. Then condition (b) of I is satisfied. Again, since $|\omega_{m_n} - \gamma_n| \leqslant \pi/4$ it follows that

$$\text{Rl}\,(a_{m_n} e^{-\gamma_n i}) \geqslant |a_{m_n}| \cos\frac{\pi}{4} = |a_{m_n}|/\sqrt{2}.$$

Therefore

$$\overline{\lim_{n=\infty}} \left| \sqrt[m_n]{\text{Rl}\,(a_{m_n} e^{-\gamma_n i})} \right| = \overline{\lim_{n=\infty}} \left| \sqrt[m_n]{a_{m_n}} \right| = 1,$$

and so condition (a) is satisfied. The theorem then follows from I.

We finish these particular cases by discussing an ingenious use of gaps to produce series not continued beyond their circle of convergence. It was suggested by Fatou (1906) and established by Pólya (Hurwitz and Pólya, 1916).

III. *If the radius of convergence of* $\Sigma a_n z^n$ *is* 1, *there are real numbers* ϵ_n, $\epsilon_n^2 = 1$, *such that* $\Sigma \epsilon_n a_n z^n$ *is not continued beyond* $|z| = 1$.

Proof. From $\Sigma a_n z^n$ form a series $H(z) = \Sigma a_{n_k} z^{n_k}$, where $\overline{\lim_{k=\infty}} \left| \sqrt[n_k]{a_{n_k}} \right| = 1$, and $n_{k+1} > 2n_k$, so that $H(z)$ is not continued beyond $|z| = 1$. Put $f(z) = H(z) + f_0(z)$ and decompose the power series $H(z)$ into a sum of infinite power series $f_1(z) + f_2(z) + \ldots$ such that the same power of z occurs in no two of the component series. Now consider the whole class of series

$$(3) \qquad f_0(z) + \epsilon_1 f_1(z) + \epsilon_2 f_2(z) + \ldots,$$

where ϵ_i is either 1 or -1.

There are as many different distributions of the signs ± 1 as there are numbers in the scale of two, of the type $\cdot a_1 a_2 \ldots$, where every digit is 0 or 1. Since every decimal number between 0 and 1 can be written as a number in the scale of two and vice versa, their number has the cardinal number c of the continuum. Suppose now that for every distribution of ± 1, (3) is continued beyond $|z|=1$. Since the roots of unity $\sqrt{1}, \sqrt[3]{1}, \ldots, \sqrt[n]{1}, \ldots$ form an everywhere dense but enumerable sequence of points on $|z|=1$, and the number of possible series (3) has the cardinal number of the continuum, if the theorem were not true for a $\Sigma a_n z^n$, there would be two different series of the class continued beyond $|z|=1$ in the direction of some root of unity. Thus their difference would also be continued in the same direction. But in the difference $f_0(z)$ is cancelled, i. e. the difference of the two series is formed from the terms of $H(z)$, apart from changes of sign, and thus cannot be continued beyond $|z|=1$. This proves the absurdity of the hypothesis that all the series of the class (3) are continued beyond $|z|=1$.

The result can be interpreted by saying that series not continued beyond their circle of convergence occur more frequently than series continued in some directions. In fact, by IV, to every continued series corresponds one (indeed infinitely many) non-continued series, and non-continued series with Hadamard gaps and isolated terms cannot be turned into continued series by altering only the argument of the coefficients, because the gaps survive.

For further discussion of this interpretation see Hadamard 1926, Chapter IV.

Recently Mandelbrojt obtained some remarkably precise results *in the detection of singularities by gaps in the coefficients.* His proofs have been simplified and some of his results extended by Ostrowski. We follow the latter.

$f(z)=\Sigma a_n z^n$ is meromorphic on its circle of convergence of radius 1. What can we state about the possible gaps? Let the principal part of a pole on the circle of convergence be

$$T_\alpha(z) = b_0(\alpha - z)^{-m} + b_1(\alpha - z)^{-m+1} + \ldots,$$

$b_0 \neq 0$, where $|\alpha|=1$. This part contributes to the coefficient a_n the expression

$$\frac{b_0 n^{m-1} \alpha^{-n}}{(m-1)!\,\alpha^m} + O(n^{m-2}).$$

Suppose there are k poles of order m on the circle and none of higher order. Then

$$(4) \quad a_n = (c_1\alpha_1^{-n} + \ldots + c_k\alpha_k^{-n})n^{m-1} + O(n^{m-2}),\ c_i \neq 0.$$

We are going to prove that there is a $\gamma > 0$ such that, for every $n \geqslant 0$, at least one of the k numbers

$$c_1\alpha_1^{-n-\nu} + \ldots + c_k\alpha_k^{-n-\nu}, \quad \nu = 0, 1, 2, \ldots, k-1$$

is $>\gamma$. Suppose that it is not so, i.e. that to every $\gamma > 0$ there corresponds at least one $n \geqslant 0$ such that

$$(5) \quad \sum_{\lambda=1}^{k} \frac{c_\lambda}{\alpha_\lambda^{\,n}} \alpha_\lambda^{-\nu} = \beta_\nu \gamma, \quad |\beta_\nu| \leqslant 1, \quad \nu = 0, 1, \ldots, k-1.$$

Since the α_λ are, by hypothesis, all different, the determinant $\|\alpha_\lambda^{-k}\|$ is different from 0, i.e.

$$(6) \qquad c_\lambda / \alpha_\lambda^{n} = \gamma \sum_{i=0}^{k-1} \delta_{\lambda, i}\beta_i.$$

Since not every $\delta_{\lambda, i}$ is 0, putting

$$\gamma_0 = \min(|c_\lambda|) \text{ and } \gamma_1 = \sum_{\lambda, i} |\delta_{\lambda, i}| > 0,$$

we have $|c_\lambda| \leqslant \gamma_1\gamma$, $\gamma_0 \leqslant \gamma_1\gamma$, $\gamma \geqslant \gamma_0/\gamma_1$. Thus for $\gamma < \gamma_0/\gamma_1$, (5) is impossible. Hence we see that there is a sequence of suffixes $n_1, n_2, \ldots$ with $0 < n_{i+1} - n_i \leqslant k$ such that the order of infinity of the first term in (4) is effectively greater than that of the second, i.e. for which $\lim_{i=\infty} |\sqrt[n_i]{a_{n_i}}| = 1$. Thus

IV. *If $f(z) = \Sigma a_n z^n$ is meromorphic on its circle of convergence $|z| = 1$, and there are k poles of the highest order on $|z| = 1$, then, from and after a sufficiently large n, there are not k consecutive coefficients $a_n, a_{n+1}, \ldots, a_{n+k-1}$ which all vanish, i.e. there is no k-gap.* (Mandelbrojt, 1923.)

V. *If $f(z) = \Sigma a_n z^{\lambda_n}$, $\lambda_0 < \lambda_1 < \ldots$, and for a partial sequence λ_{n_i} of λ_n we have $\lim(\lambda_{n_i+1} - k\lambda_{n_i}) = \infty$, where k is a positive integer, then $f(z)$ is not of the form $f_1(z)/[P(z)]^{1/k}$, where $f_1(z)$ is regular on the circle of convergence and $P(z)$ is a polynomial.* (Mandelbrojt, 1924.)

Proof. The power series for $[f(z)]^k$ has gaps between the suffixes $k\lambda_{n_i}$ and λ_{n_i+1} whose lengths tend to infinity. In fact

$$[\Sigma a_n z^{\lambda_n}]^k = \lim_{m=\infty} \sum_{m_1,\ldots,m_k=0}^{m} c_{m_1,\ldots,m_k} z^{\lambda_{m_1}+\cdots+\lambda_{m_k}}.$$

and, for $\lambda_{n_i} \leqslant m < \lambda_{n_i+1}$, the largest index is $k\lambda_{n_i}$. The next index is $(k-1)\lambda_0 + \lambda_{n_i+1} \geqslant \lambda_{n_i+1}$, and hence, by IV, the result follows.

VI. *If* $a_n = 0$ *for* $n \equiv r \pmod q$ *and* ζ *is a primitive* q*-th root of unity, then* $f(z) = \Sigma a_n z^n$ *has necessarily at least two singular points on its circle of convergence, viz. at* α *and at one of the points* $\alpha\zeta^{-\nu}$ $(\nu = 1, 2, \ldots, q-1)$. (Mandelbrojt, 1923.)

Proof. We have

$$(7) \qquad f(z) + \zeta^{-r} f(\zeta z) + \zeta^{-2r} f(\zeta^2 z) + \ldots + \zeta^{-(q-1)r} f(\zeta^{q-1} z)$$
$$= \Sigma a_n [1 + \zeta^{n-r} + \ldots + \zeta^{(q-1)(n-r)}] z^n = 0.$$

We suppose as usual that the radius of convergence is 1. If α is a singular point of $f(z)$ ($|\alpha| = 1$), then another term in (7) also has a singularity at $z = \alpha$, for the right-hand side is the regular zero function, so that the singularity at α must be destroyed. But if $z = \alpha$ is a singular point for $f(\zeta^\nu z)$, say, then $\alpha\zeta^{-\nu}$ is a singular point for $f(z)$. The example $1/(1-z) - 1/(1-\zeta z) = \Sigma(1-\zeta^n)z$ shows that the minimum number is actually 2. More generally

VII. *If* $q_1, \ldots, q_m$ *are relative prime integers and* $a_n = 0$ *for at least one residue class to every modulus* $q_1, q_2, \ldots$ *and* q_m, $f(z) = \Sigma a_n z^n$ *has at least* 2^m *singular points, and if* α *is one of them, there are* $2^m - 1$ *singular points at* $z = \epsilon_i \alpha$, *where* ϵ_i *is a suitable* $q_1 q_2 \ldots q_m$*-th root of unity.*

(Mandelbrojt 1923, Ostrowski 1926.)

Proof. By the previous proposition for $q = q_1$, if α is a singular point, so also is $\alpha\epsilon_{q_1}$, where ϵ_{q_1} is a primitive q_1-th root of unity. Applied to α and then to $\alpha\epsilon_{q_1}$ for $q = q_2$, we establish the existence of further singular points $\alpha\epsilon_{q_2}, \alpha\epsilon_{q_1}\epsilon'_{q_2}$ (where ϵ_{q_2} and ϵ'_{q_2} are the same or different primitive q_2-th roots of unity) &c. All the points so obtained are different because

$$\epsilon_{q_1}\epsilon_{q_2}\cdots\epsilon_{q_m} = \epsilon'_{q_1}\epsilon'_{q_2}\cdots\epsilon'_{q_m} \text{ implies } \epsilon_{q_i} = \epsilon'_{q_i}.$$

(Mandelbrojt proved the existence of $m+1$ points only).

The example

$$\frac{1}{1-z}-\frac{1}{1-\zeta_1 z}-\frac{1}{1-\zeta_2 z}+\frac{1}{1-\zeta_1\zeta_2 z}$$
$$=\Sigma[1-\zeta_1^n-\zeta_2^n(1-\zeta_1^n)]z^n=\Sigma[1-\zeta_2^n-\zeta_1^n(1-\zeta_2^n)]z^n$$

shows that the minimum 2^m is attainable.

CHAPTER XII

DIVERGENT SERIES

95. *Transformation of sequences.* The reason for rejecting divergent sequences as useless is that such a sequence does not naturally lead to a well-defined number. It is possible, of course, to assign conventionally a number to any divergent sequence z_n, e.g. $\overline{\lim}\,|z_n|$ if this number is finite. But such a definition is useful only if it satisfies certain requirements, first of all, the requirement of *consistency* with ordinary convergence, i.e. when the definition is applied to a convergent sequence, the convergence should not be destroyed and the value of the limit should not be altered. Or, if the value of the limit is altered, we require at least a known relation between the conventional and ordinary limit.

Nearly all the methods used so far in generalizing the idea of limit are particular cases of the linear transformation of sequences by a two-fold table of given, real or complex, numbers a_{nk} referred to as the matrix A. Thus $z_n' = \sum\limits_k a_{nk} z_k$ is the *transform* of z_n by A, provided, for a sufficiently large n, all the series on the right-hand side converge, in which case we say that the transformation A *applies* to the sequence z_k. If $z_n' \to z$ whenever $z_n \to z$, and if the transformed sequence also converges for some divergent sequence z_n, we may assign the limit of z_n' to the divergent sequence z_n as its *generalized limit by A* or briefly as its *A-limit.*

For example, the sequence of arithmetical means

$$(z_1 + z_2 + \dots + z_n)/n$$

of 1, 0, 1, 0, ... (the partial sums of $1-1+1-1+1 \dots$) tends to $1/2$, and the sequence of arithmetic means of *any* convergent sequence converges to the limit of the sequence. Hence, denoting by M the matrix $a_{11} = 1$, $a_{1k} = 0$ for $k > 1$; $a_{21} = 1/2$, $a_{22} = 1/2$, $a_{2k} = 0$ for $k > 2$, &c.; $a_{n1} = 1/n, \dots, a_{nn} = 1/n$,

$a_{nr} = 0$ for $r > n$; ... (also referred to as the *semi-matrix M*), we say that the M-limit of 1, 0, 1, 0, ... is 1/2. In symbols

$$M\text{-}\lim_{n=\infty} z_n \equiv \lim_{n=\infty} \frac{z_1 + z_2 + \dots + z_n}{n}$$

whenever the limit on the right-hand side exists.

Our first problem is to determine the family K of matrices such that convergence is not destroyed by the corresponding transformations. The second step will be the determination of that section of K for which the value of the limit of any convergent sequence is invariant. Both problems will be solved by the following two theorems.

I. *The necessary and sufficient conditions that* $z'_n = \sum_{k=1}^{\infty} a_{nk} z_k$ *should be convergent whenever* z_k *is convergent are*

(a) $$\sum_{k=1}^{\infty} |a_{nk}| \leqslant M \qquad \textit{independently of } n;$$

(b) $$\lim_{n=\infty} a_{nk} = \alpha_k,$$

i.e. the limit of a_{nk} *exists when* k *is fixed and* $n \to \infty$;

(c) $\sum_{k=1}^{\infty} a_{nk} = A_n$ *tends to a limit* α *when* $n \to \infty$.

Moreover if $z_k \to z$ *we have*

(d) $$z' = \lim_{n=\infty} z'_n = \alpha z + \sum_{k=1}^{\infty} \alpha_k (z_k - z).$$

(Kojima, 1917, for semi-matrices; independently for complete matrices, Schur, 1920 (written in 1918).)

Replacing n by a continuous real positive variable a we obtain a slightly more general result.

I′. *The necessary and sufficient conditions that*

$$z'(a) = \sum_{k=1}^{\infty} f_k(a) z_k$$

should tend to a finite limit as $a \to \infty$ *whenever the sequence* z_k *is convergent are:*

(a′) $$\sum_{k=1}^{\infty} |f_k(a)| \leqslant M \qquad \textit{independently of } a > a';$$

(b′) $$\lim_{a\to\infty} f_k(a) = \alpha_k \qquad \textit{for every fixed } k;$$

(c′) $$\sum_{k=1}^{\infty} f_k(a) = f(a) \to \alpha \qquad \textit{as } a \to \infty.$$

Moreover if $z_k \to z$,

(d′) $$\lim_{a\to\infty} z'(a) = \alpha z + \sum_{k=1}^{\infty} \alpha_k (z_k - z).$$

Proof of I′. The conditions are sufficient. By (a′) and (b′), $\sum_{k=1}^{p} |f_k(a)| \leqslant M$ for every a and thus also $\sum_{k=1}^{p} |\alpha_k| \leqslant M$, i.e. $\Sigma\alpha_k$ is an absolutely convergent series. Putting $z_k = z + \epsilon_k$ we shall prove that $\lim_{a\to\infty} \sum_{k=1}^{\infty} f_k(a)\epsilon_k = \sum_{k=1}^{\infty} \alpha_k \epsilon_k$. In fact, for every given $\epsilon > 0$, there is a p such that $|\epsilon_k| < \frac{\epsilon}{3M}$ for $k > p$ and a q such that, when $a > q$, $\left|\sum_{k=1}^{p} (f_k(a) - \alpha_k)\epsilon_k\right| < \epsilon/3$. Thus

$$\left|\sum_{k=1}^{\infty} (f_k(a) - \alpha_k)\epsilon_k\right| \leqslant \left|\sum_{k=1}^{p} (f_k(a) - \alpha_k)\epsilon_k\right|$$
$$+ \sum_{k=p+1}^{\infty} (|f_k(a)| + |\alpha_k|)\,|\epsilon_k| < \epsilon/3 + 2M\epsilon/3M = \epsilon,$$

which proves our remark.

Finally, as $z'(a) = \sum_{k=1}^{\infty} f_k(a) z_k = f(a)z + \sum_{k=1}^{\infty} f_k(a)\epsilon_k$, we have, by (c′), $\lim_{a\to\infty} z'(a) = \alpha z + \sum_{k=1}^{\infty} \alpha_k (z_k - z)$, which completes the first part.

The conditions are necessary. Putting $z_p = 1$ and every other $z_k = 0$, we have $z_k \to 0$. In this case, however, $z'(a) = f_p(a)$. Hence, in order that $z'(a)$ should tend to a limit when $a \to \infty$, (b′) must be satisfied.

Similarly putting $z_k = 1$ for every k, we have $z_k \to 1$ and $z'(a) = \sum_{k=1}^{\infty} f_k(a) = f(a)$. Therefore $f(a)$ must tend to a limit, i. e. (c′) is a necessary condition.

It is more difficult to prove that (a′) is a necessary condition. We first notice that if $\Sigma |a_k|$ is divergent, there is a sequence $z_k \to 0$ such that $\left|\sum_{k=1}^{n} a_k z_k\right| \to \infty$. In fact, putting $a_k = |a_k| e^{i\phi k}$ and choosing $\alpha > 1$, we first determine p_0 by the condition that $\sum_{k=1}^{p_0} |a_k| > \alpha$, then p_1 by the condition that $\sum_{k=p_0+1}^{p_1} |a_k| > \alpha^2$, &c., and put $z_k = e^{-i\phi k}$ for $1 \leqslant k \leqslant p_0$, $z_k = e^{-i\phi k}/\alpha$ for $p_0 < k \leqslant p_1$, &c. Thus

$$\Sigma a_n z_k = \sum_{1}^{p_0} |a_k| + \frac{1}{\alpha^2}\sum_{p_0+1}^{p_1} |a_k| + \frac{1}{\alpha^2}\sum_{p_1+1}^{p_2} |a_k| + \ldots > \alpha + \alpha + \ldots = \infty,$$

though $z_k \to 0$.

Therefore $\sum_{k=1}^{\infty} |f_k(a)| = B(a)$ must be convergent for every fixed a. If (a′) is not satisfied, $\overline{\lim}_{a \to \infty} B(a) = \infty$ and, if we put

$$f_k(a) = \phi_k(a) + i\psi_k(a),$$

there is a sequence a_n for which $\sum_k |\phi_k(a_n)|$ or $\sum_k |\psi_k(a_n)|$ (or both) tends to ∞. Putting $\phi_k(a_n) = \alpha_{nk}$, we shall suppose that

$$(1) \qquad \sum_{k=1}^{\infty} |\alpha_{nk}| = G_n \to \infty,$$

and we shall construct a real sequence $x_k \to 0$, with the supplementary condition $|x_k| \leqslant 1$ for every k, and such that $x_n' = \sum_{k=1}^{\infty} \alpha_{nk} x_k$ has a sub-sequence tending to ∞. This will prove that (a′) is a necessary condition.

By (b′), p being fixed, the sequence $\sum_{k=1}^{p} |\alpha_{nk}|$, $n = 1, 2, \ldots,$ has a maximum term (dependent upon p). We denote the maximum sum of the first p terms by C_p. By (1), for conveniently chosen n and p, n_1 and p_1', say, $\sum_{k=1}^{p_1} |\alpha_{n_1 k}| > \alpha^2$, where

$\alpha > 1$ is fixed. When n_1 is already fixed, there is a $p_1 \geqslant p_1'$ such that $\sum_{p_1+1}^{\infty} |\alpha_{n_1 k}| \leqslant \epsilon$.

Putting now $\operatorname{sign}(x) = +1$ if x is positive and $= -1$ if x is negative and

$$x_k = \frac{1}{\alpha} \operatorname{sign}(\alpha_{n_1 k}), \qquad 1 \leqslant k \leqslant p_1,$$

we have

$$x'_{n_1} = \frac{1}{\alpha} \sum_{k=1}^{p_1} |\alpha_{n_1 k}| + \sum_{k=p_1+1}^{\infty} \alpha_{n_1 k} x_k,$$

i.e.

(2) $$|x'_{n_1}| > \alpha - \epsilon.$$

In order to continue the construction of the sequence x_k we determine an $n_2 > n_1$ and a $p_2' > p_1$ such that

(3) $$\frac{1}{\alpha^2} \sum_{k=p_1+1}^{p_2} |\alpha_{n_2 k}| > C_{p_1} + \alpha^2,$$

and, n_2 being fixed, we determine a $p_2 \geqslant p_2'$ such that

(4) $$\sum_{k=p_2+1}^{\infty} |\alpha_{n_2 k}| < \epsilon.$$

Then we put $x_k = \frac{1}{\alpha^2} \operatorname{sign}(\alpha_{n_2 k})$ for $p_1 < k \leqslant p_2$ and have

$$x'_{n_2} = \frac{1}{\alpha} \sum_{1}^{p_1} \alpha_{n_2 k} \operatorname{sign}(\alpha_{n_1 k}) + \frac{1}{\alpha^2} \sum_{p_1+1}^{p_2} |\alpha_{n_2 k}| + \sum_{k=p_2+1}^{\infty} \alpha_{n_2 k} z_k,$$

i.e. by (3) and (4)

(5) $$|x'_{n_2}| > \alpha^2 - \epsilon.$$

Continuing in this way we determine a sequence $x_k \to 0$ such that, for certain values of n, x'_n tends to ∞. Thus (a′) is necessary. Q. e. d.

A matrix or transformation satisfying conditions (a), (b), (c) or (a′), (b′), (c′) will be referred to as a *Kojima matrix* or *transformation* or briefly as a *K-matrix* or *K-transformation*, with α_k, α for its *characteristic numbers*. A matrix satisfying condition (a) will be referred to as *a* K_a*-matrix*.

An important special case of I is

II. *Toeplitz's theorem. The necessary and sufficient conditions that* $z'_n = \Sigma a_{nk} z_k$ *should converge to* z *whenever* $z_k \to z$ *are:*

$$(\alpha) \equiv (\mathrm{a}) \qquad \sum_{k=1}^{\infty} |a_{nk}| \leqslant M \qquad \textit{independently of } n;$$

$$(\beta) \qquad \lim_{n=\infty} a_{nk} = 0 \qquad \textit{for every fixed } k;$$

$$(\gamma) \qquad \sum_{k=1}^{\infty} a_{nk} = A_n \to 1.$$

(Toeplitz, 1911, for row-finite matrices; Schur, 1920, for complete matrices; sufficiency for semi-matrices Silverman (1910), published 1913.)

The corresponding more general case of II is

II′. *The necessary and sufficient conditions that*

$$z'(a) = \sum_{k=1}^{\infty} f_k(a) z_k$$

should tend to a finite limit z *as* $a \to \infty$ *are*

$$(\alpha') \equiv (\mathrm{a}') \qquad \sum_{k=1}^{\infty} |f_k(a)| \leqslant M \qquad \textit{independently of } a > a';$$

$$(\beta') \qquad \lim_{a \to \infty} f_k(a) = 0 \qquad \textit{for every fixed } k;$$

$$(\gamma') \qquad \sum_{k=1}^{\infty} f_k(a) = f(a) \to 1 \qquad \textit{as } a \to \infty.$$

Since II is included in II′ we prove the latter. By I′ and (d′) and by the supplementary conditions $\alpha_k = 0$, $\alpha = 1$, conditions (α'), (β'), (γ') are sufficient.

They are also necessary. In fact, if $\alpha_k \neq 0$ for a particular k, the sequence $z_i = 0$ if $i \neq k$, $z_k = 1$, which tends to 0, reduces the right-hand side of (d′) to $\alpha_k \neq 0$, so that the limit would be altered. Moreover, since now the right-hand side of (d′) reduces to αz, α must be 1.

A matrix or transformation satisfying conditions (α), (β), (γ) or (α'), (β'), (γ') will be referred to as a *Toeplitz matrix* or *transformation* or briefly a *T-matrix* or *T-transformation.*

For the case of an infinite limit we have the following theorem:

III. *Suppose the numbers* $z_k = x_k + iy_k$ *are, for* $k > l$, *in an angle* $\alpha < \pi$ *of the complex plane, vertex at the origin, and* $\lim\limits_{k=\infty} |z_k| = \infty$. *If the positive T-transformation* $f_k(a) \geqslant 0$ *transforms* $\dot{z}_k$ *into* $z'(a)$, *then* $\lim\limits_{a\to\infty} |z'(a)| = \infty$.

(Schur, 1920, for real sequences.)

Proof. Suppose first that the numbers $z_k = x_k$ are real and that $x_k \geqslant 0$ for $k > l$. By hypothesis,

$$f(a) = \sum_{k=1}^{\infty} f_k(a) \to 1 \qquad \text{as } a \to \infty,$$

so that for $a > a'$, say, $f(a) > \theta$, where θ is any positive number less than 1. Moreover, to every given large positive number n there corresponds a p such that, for $k > p$, $x_k > n/\theta$. Putting $x_k = n/\theta + \eta_k$, we have $\eta_k > 0$ for $k > p$ and

$$x'(a) = f(a)\, n/\theta + \sum_{k=1}^{p} f_k(a)\, \eta_k + \sum_{k=p+1}^{\infty} f_k(a)\, \eta_k.$$

All the terms of the last sum are positive, $\lim\limits_{a\to\infty} f_k(a) = 0$, and $f(a) > \theta$ for $a > a'$. Therefore all the limiting numbers of $x'(a)$ as $a \to \infty$ are greater than n. Since n is arbitrarily large, $+\infty$ is the only limiting number.

In the general case, multiplying the sequence by a conveniently chosen number $e^{\phi i}$, we may suppose that the angle α is bisected by the positive real axis, so that, for $k > l$, $x_k \geqslant 0$, and $x_k \to \infty$. Now it follows from the above argument that $x'(a) = \Sigma f_k(a) x_k \to \infty$ and thus also $|z'(a)| \to \infty$ with a.

We notice that the result does not hold for some K-transformations, e.g. the positive K-matrix $a_{nk} = 1/k^3$, where all the rows are identical, transforms $z_k = k$ into a convergent sequence. We also remark that if, besides ∞, z_k has also a finite limiting number z, there is a positive T-transformation leading to the limit z. More generally we have the following result:

IV. *Every finite or infinite limiting number of a sequence is the generalized limit of that sequence for some positive T-matrix.*

Proof. If every row contains only one non-zero element, whose value is 1, and if every column contains only a finite number of non-zero elements, the matrix is a T-matrix. If z is a finite limiting number of z_k, there is a sub-sequence $z_{m_k} \to z$, and the positive T-matrix $z_{nk} = 1$, if $m_k \leqslant n < m_{k+1}$, $z_{nk} = 0$ otherwise, transforms z_k into $z_n' = z_{m_k}$ for $m_k \leqslant n < m_{k+1}$, so that $z_n' \to z$. If $\overline{\lim_{k=\infty}} |z_k| = \infty$, the numbers z_k possess at least one direction of density, ϕ, say (see p. 83), i. e. we may choose a sub-sequence z_{m_k} such that $|z_{m_k}| \to \infty$ and $\arg z_{m_k} \to \phi$. Complete this sub-sequence into a sequence ζ_k such that $|\zeta_k| \to \infty$ and $\arg \zeta_k \to \phi$. Then the above matrix transforms both z_k and ζ_k into z_n' such that $|z_n'| \to \infty$, by III.

For real sequences we have the following result, analogous to a result concerning series due to Perron (see 96. V).

V. *Every number x between the upper and lower bounds U and L of a real sequence x_k is the generalized limit of this sequence for some positive T-matrix.*

Proof. Suppose first that both U and L are finite, and take two sub-sequences $a_k \to U$, $b_k \to L$ of the sequence x_k, such that $\Sigma |U - a_k| = a$ and $\Sigma |L - b_k| = b$ are convergent. Putting $a_k = U + \epsilon_k$, $b_k = L + \eta_k$, $U - x = p$, $x - L = q$, we have

$$(6) \qquad \frac{\sum_{k=1}^{n} q a_k + \sum_{k=1}^{n} p b_k}{n(p+q)} = x + \frac{\sum_{k=1}^{n} q \epsilon_k + \sum_{k=1}^{n} p \eta_k}{n(p+q)} \to x.$$

For

$$\left| \sum_{k=1}^{n} q \epsilon_k + \sum_{k=1}^{n} p \eta_k \right| \leqslant aq + bp,$$

and $\dfrac{q}{n(p+q)}$ and $\dfrac{p}{n(p+q)}$ tend to 0 as $n \to \infty$.

Now construct the n-th row of the matrix a_{nk} by letting $a_{nk} = 0$ if k is the suffix of a number x_k not occurring in $a_1, a_2, \ldots, a_n$ or $b_1, b_2, \ldots, b_n$, and taking $\dfrac{q}{n(p+q)}$ or $\dfrac{p}{n(p+q)}$ for a_{nk} if x_k is an a_ν or a b_ν respectively, $\nu \leqslant n$. Noticing that $\sum_k a_{nk} = 1$ for all $n > 0$, and that each row contains only a finite number of non-zero terms, we see that the positive matrix so constructed is a T-matrix. Hence (b) proves the theorem for finite U and L.

Suppose now that $U = +\infty$ and L is finite. Given any real number $x \geqslant L$, we take numbers $B_m > x$ of the sequence x_k tending to infinity with m. We now construct a T-matrix corresponding to the numbers x_k between L and B_m, the numbers $x_k < B_m$ being excluded by zero terms, and transform x_k into a sequence $x_k^{(m)} \to x$ as $n \to \infty$. All the matrices $a_{nk}^{(m)}$ so obtained are positive T-matrices for which $\sum_k a_{nk}^{(m)} = 1$. Now construct a matrix α_{mk} by selecting a row from each of these matrices subject to the conditions

$$\text{(a)} \qquad \alpha_{mk} = a_{n_m k}^{(m)} \leqslant a_{n_{m-1} k}^{(m-1)} \text{ if } a_{n_{m-1}}^{(m-1)} \neq 0,$$

$$\text{(b)} \qquad |x_{n_m}^{(m)} - x| < \epsilon_m, \text{ where } \epsilon_m \to 0.$$

This is possible since each row contains only a finite number of terms. The positive T-matrix so obtained leads to the generalized limit x. The case $x = +\infty$ is covered by IV. The cases U finite, $L = -\infty$, and $U = +\infty$, $L = -\infty$ can be dealt with on similar lines.

In a paper in course of publication Mr. H. L. Heuss has proved that any finite number can be made the generalized limit of any divergent sequence for some T-matrix, not in general positive. These somewhat puzzling results raise the question of how we are to choose one generalization of limit rather than another. This problem will be discussed in Art. 100.

The following result is also of interest.

VI. *Given any T-matrix, there is always a bounded sequence which has no generalized T-limit.* (Steinhaus, 1911.)

Proof. (For real matrices.) Suppose the real matrix a_{nk} satisfies conditions (α), (β), (γ) of II and let the sequence z_k satisfy the condition $0 \leqslant z_k \leqslant 1$. First choose n_1, by (γ), such that

$$\sum_{k=1}^{\infty} a_{n_1 k} > \frac{3}{4},$$

and then m_1, by (α), such that

$$\sum_{k=m_1+1}^{\infty} |a_{n_1 k}| < \frac{1}{12}.$$

Then if $z_k = 1$, $1 \leqslant k \leqslant m_1$, we have

$$z'_{n_1} = \sum_{k=1}^{\infty} a_{n_1 k} z_k \geqslant \sum_{k=1}^{\infty} a_{nk} - \sum_{k=m_1+1}^{\infty} |a_{n_1 k}| > \frac{2}{3}.$$

Next choose $n_2 < n_1$, by (β), such that

$$\sum_{k=1}^{m_1} |a_{n_2 k}| < \frac{1}{6},$$

and then $m_2 > m_1$, by (α), such that

$$\sum_{k=m_2+1}^{\infty} |a_{n_2 k}| < \frac{1}{6}.$$

Then if $z_k = 0$, $m_1 < k \leqslant m_2$, we have

$$z'_{n_2} = \sum_{k=1}^{\infty} a_{n_2 k} z_k \leqslant \sum_{k=1}^{m_1} |a_{n_2 k}| + \sum_{k=m_2+1}^{\infty} |a_{n_2 k}| < \frac{1}{3}.$$

Next choose $n_3 > n_2$, by (γ), such that

$$\sum_{k=1}^{\infty} a_{n_3 k} > \frac{3}{4}$$

and also, by (β), such that

$$\sum_{k=1}^{m_2} |a_{n_3 k}| < \frac{1}{24},$$

and then $m_3 > m_2$, by (α), such that

$$\sum_{k=m_3+1}^{\infty} |a_{n_3 k}| < \frac{1}{24}.$$

Then if $z_k = 1$, $m_2 < k \leqslant m_3$, we have

$$z'_{n_3} = \sum_{k=1}^{\infty} a_{n_3 k} z_k \geqslant \sum_{k=1}^{\infty} a_{n_3 k} - \sum_{k=m_1+1}^{m_2} |a_{n_3 k}| - \sum_{k=m_3+1}^{\infty} |a_{n_3 k}| > \frac{2}{3}.$$

By continuing in this way we can choose the sequence z_k so that its terms are all either 0 or 1 and z'_n does not tend to a limit.

96. *Transformation of series.* The transformation

$$\gamma(a) = \sum_{k=1}^{\infty} g_k(a) c_k$$

of the series $\sum_{k=1}^{\infty} c_k$ leads to various generalizations of the sum of a divergent series. Here also our first requirements are that the convergence of a series should not be destroyed and that its sum should either be unaltered or at least altered by a known relation.

I. *The necessary and sufficient conditions that*

$$\gamma(a) = \sum_{k=1}^{\infty} g_k(a) c_k$$

should tend to a finite limit as $a \to \infty$ *whenever* $\sum_{k=1}^{\infty} c_k = s$ *is convergent are*

(A) $$\sum_{k=1}^{\infty} |g_k(a) - g_{k+1}(a)| \leqslant M \text{ independently of } a > a';$$

(B) $$\lim_{a\to\infty} g_k(a) = \beta_k \qquad \text{for every fixed } k.$$

Moreover

(D) $$\lim_{a\to\infty} \gamma(a) = \beta_1 s + \sum_{k=1}^{\infty} (\beta_k - \beta_{k+1})(s_k - s),$$

where $s_k = c_1 + c_2 + \ldots + c_k$, *and the existence of either side of* (D) *implies the other provided* Σc_k *is convergent and its sum is* s.

(Bosanquet, 1931.)

The proof is based on the following lemma due to Abel and Hadamard (1903).

Lemma. *The necessary and sufficient condition that* $\Sigma b_k c_k$ *should converge whenever* $\Sigma c_k = s$ *converges is that* $\Sigma |b_k - b_{k+1}|$ *should converge.*

Proof of the Lemma (Kojima, 1917, and Schur, 1920). We have

(1) $$\sum_{k=1}^{n} b_k c_k = \sum_{k=1}^{n-1} (b_k - b_{k+1}) s_k + b_n s_n,$$

where the right-hand side may be considered as the transform of the sequence $s_k = c_1 + c_2 + \ldots + c_k$ by the semi-matrix: $a_{nk} = b_k - b_{k+1}$ if $k < n$, $a_{nn} = b_n$, $a_{nk} = 0$ if $k > n$. We shall prove that, for this transformation, condition (a) of 95. I, which in our case reduces to

(2) $$\sum_{k=1}^{n-1} |b_k - b_{k+1}| + |b_n| \leqslant M \qquad \text{independently of } n,$$

is equivalent to the condition

(3) $$\sum_{k=1}^{\infty} |b_k - b_{k+1}| \quad \text{is convergent.}$$

If (3) is satisfied, we put $\epsilon_k = b_k - b_{k+1}$, $\sum_{k=1}^{\infty} |\epsilon_k| = E$, and thus we have $b_n = b_1 - \sum_{k=1}^{n-1} \epsilon_k$. Therefore $|b_n| \leqslant |b_1| + E$ and (2) is satisfied. Conversely, (2) obviously implies (3).

Our matrix satisfies condition (b) of I since, for a fixed k, the terms are independent of n, for $n > k$; $\alpha_k = b_k - b_{k+1}$. Finally

$$(4) \qquad A_n = \sum_{k=1}^{\infty} a_{nk} = \sum_{k=1}^{n-1} (b_k - b_{k+1}) + b_n = b_1$$

independently of n, so that (c) is satisfied and $\alpha = b_1$. Therefore I applies and, from (d),

$$(5) \qquad \sum_{k=1}^{\infty} b_k c_k = b_1 s + \sum_{k=1}^{\infty} (b_k - b_{k+1})(s_k - s),$$

where the existence of one side implies that of the other, provided s_k tends to a limit, which proves the lemma.

Proof of I. The conditions are sufficient. It follows from (A) and from $s_k \to s$ that the right-hand side of

$$(6) \qquad \sum_{k=1}^{\infty} g_k(a) c_k = s g_1(a) + \sum_{k=1}^{\infty} [g_k(a) - g_{k+1}(a)].(s_k - s)$$

exists, and thus the lemma establishes (6) for every particular value of a. Now let p be chosen so that $|s_k - s| < \epsilon/M$ for $k > p$, and write (6) in the form

$$\sum_{k=1}^{\infty} g_k(a) = s g_1(a) + \sum_{k=1}^{p} + \sum_{k=p+1}^{\infty}.$$

As $a \to \infty$, $\sum_{k=1}^{p}$ tends to $\sum_{k=1}^{p} (\beta_k - \beta_{k+1})(s_k - s)$, and $\left|\sum_{k=p+1}^{\infty}\right| < \epsilon$ for all a. Since, by hypothesis, $g_1(a) \to \beta_1$, we have

$$(7) \qquad \lim_{a \to \infty} \sum_{k=1}^{\infty} g_k(a) c_k = \beta_1 s + \sum_{k=1}^{\infty} (\beta_k - \beta_{k+1})(s_k - s).$$

The conditions are necessary. For suppose $\gamma(a)$ tends to a limit whenever Σc_k is convergent. Then, taking $c_q = 1$ for a fixed q and $c_k = 0$ for $k \neq q$, we have $\gamma(a) = g_q(a)$, i. e. (B) is necessary. Moreover, since the number $\gamma(a)$ exists, at least for $a > a'$,

$\Sigma \,|\, g_k(a)-g_{k+1}(a) \,|$ is convergent for $a>a'$, by the lemma. We have to prove that these sums are bounded. But it follows from

$$g_k(a) = g_1(a) - \sum_{i=1}^{k-1} [g_i(a) - g_{i+1}(a)]$$

that $g_k(a)$ tends to a limit as $k \to \infty$. Moreover, by hypothesis, so does the left-hand side of (6), and by (B), already established, $\lim\limits_{a\to\infty} g_1(a) = \beta_1$. Therefore the sum on the right-hand side tends to a limit as $a \to \infty$. But this sum may be considered as the the transform of the zero sequence $s_k - s$ by $g_k(a) - g_{k+1}(a)$ and, in the proof of 95. I′, we have seen that if the upper bound of

$B(a) = \sum\limits_{k=1}^{\infty} |\, f_k(a) \,|$ is ∞ [in our case $f_k(a) = g_k(a) - g_{k+1}(a)$],

is a sequence $x_k \to 0$ whose $f_k(a)$-transform does not tend to a limit. Taking $c_1 = s + x_1$, $c_k = x_k - x_{k-1}$ for $k>1$, we see that (A) is a necessary condition.

II. *The necessary and sufficient conditions that*

$$\gamma(a) = \sum_{k=1}^{\infty} g_k(a) c_k$$

should tend to the finite limit s *as* $a \to \infty$ *whenever* $\sum\limits_{k=1}^{\infty} c_k = s$ *are*

(A′) ≡ (A) $\quad \sum\limits_{k=1}^{\infty} |\, g_k(a) - g_{k+1}(a) \,| \leqslant M$ *independently of* $a > a'$,

(B′) $\quad \lim\limits_{a\to\infty} g_k(a) = 1.$

(Sufficiency Carmichael, 1918, Perron, 1920; necessity Bosanquet, 1931.)

We remark also (Perron, 1920) that *condition* (A) ≡ (A′) *is satisfied if*

(A″) $\quad 0 \leqslant g_{k+1}(a) \leqslant g_k(a) \leqslant 1.$

Proof of II. By I the conditions are sufficient. They are also necessary, for if $\beta_k - \beta_{k+1} \neq 0$ for a particular k, the numbers $c_i = 0$ if $i<k$, $c_k = e$, $c_{k+1} = -e$, $c_{k+i} = 0$ if $i>k$ form a series whose sum is 0 and $\lim g(a) = e(\beta_k - \beta_{k+1}) \neq 0$

It also follows from $\lim_{a\to\infty}\gamma(a)=\beta_1 s$ that $\beta_1=1$ is a necessary condition.

If a assumes integral values n only, we put $g_k(n)=b_{nk}$, and I and II reduce to two theorems on the transformation of series corresponding to theorems 95. I and II on the transformation of sequences. A matrix $g_k(a)$ satisfying (A) and (B) will be referred to as a *β-matrix*. A matrix $g_k(a)$ satisfying (A′) and (B′) will be referred to as a *γ-matrix*.

III. *Suppose the numbers $c_k=a_k+ib_k$ are, for $k>l$, in an angle $\alpha<\pi$ of the complex plane, vertex at the origin, and $\lim_{k=\infty}|c_1+c_2+\dots+c_k|=\infty$. If the γ-matrix $g_k(a)\geqslant 0$ transforms Σc_k into $\gamma(a)$, then $\lim_{a\to\infty}|\gamma(a)|=\infty$.*

Proof. If the c_k are real and $\geqslant 0$ for $k>l$, then for $p\geqslant l$ the second term of

$$\sum_{k=1}^{\infty} g_k(a)c_k=\sum_{k=1}^{p} g_k(a)c_k+\sum_{k=p+1}^{\infty} g_k(a)c_k$$

is $\geqslant 0$, and the limit of the first term, as $a\to\infty$, is

$$c_1+c_2+\dots+c_p=s_p.$$

Thus all the limiting numbers of the left-hand side are $\geqslant s_p$, and since, by hypothesis, $\lim s_k=+\infty$ (not only $\overline{\lim}\, s_k=+\infty$) the result follows.

In the general case, multiplying all the terms by a suitable number $e^{i\phi}$, we may suppose that the angle α is bisected by the positive real axis, so that $a_k\geqslant 0$ for $k>l$, and, as in the proof of 57. II, $\lim_{k=\infty}(a_1+a_2+\dots+a_k)=+\infty$. Hence, by the above argument, $\Sigma g_k(a)a_k\to+\infty$, and thus also

$$|\Sigma g_k(a)a_k+i\Sigma g_k(a)b_k|\to\infty$$

with a.

IV. *Every finite or infinite limiting number of the partial sums of a series Σc_k is the generalized sum of this series for some positive γ-matrix.* (Bosanquet, 1931.)

Proof. If s is a finite limiting number of $s_n=c_1+c_2+\dots+c_n$, there is a sub-sequence $s_{m_k}\to s$, and if $\overline{\lim}_{k=\infty}|s_k|=\infty$ there is a sub-sequence $|s_{m_k}|\to\infty$ and $\arg s_{m_k}\to\phi$, for some ϕ. In both cases the corresponding γ-matrix, $b_{nk}=1$ if $k \leqslant m_n$, $b_{nk}=0$ if $k > m_n$, transforms $\sum c_k$ into $\sum_k b_{nk}c_k = s_{m_n}$. Hence the result.

V. *Every number s between the upper and lower bounds U and L of the partial sums s_k of a real series Σc_k is the generalized sum of this series for some positive γ-matrix.*

(Perron, 1920, for bounded series.)

Proof. Suppose L and U finite. Take suffixes k_n', $k_n'' > k_n'$ such that $s_{k_n'} \to L$, $s_{k_n''} \to U$, and determine the γ-matrix by putting $b_{nk}=1$ if $k \leqslant k_n'$, $b_{nk}=0$ if $k > k_n''$, $b_{nk}=p/(p+q)$ if $k_n' < k \leqslant k_n''$, where $q = U-s$, $p = s-L$. Then

$$(8) \qquad \sum_k b_{nk}c_k = s_{k_n'} + \frac{p}{p+q}(s_{k_n''} - s_{k_n'})$$
$$= \frac{qs_{k_n'} + ps_{k_n''}}{p+q} \to \frac{qL+pU}{p+q} = s.$$

The case U or L (or both) infinite can be dealt with as in 95. V.

Since the sum of an infinite series Σc_k is, by definition, the limit s of the sequence $s_k = c_1 + c_2 + \dots + c_k$ of its partial sums, the question arises if there is a relation between the generalized sums $\lim_{a\to\infty} \sum_{k=1}^{\infty} g_k(a)c_k$ of $\sum c_k$ and the generalized limits

$$\lim_{a\to\infty} \sum_{k=1} f_k(a)s_k$$

of its partial sums.

Let $f_k(a)$ be a K-transformation which applies to s_k and consider the series transformation

$$(9) \qquad g_k(a) = f_k(a) + f_{k+1}(a) + \dots.$$

Writing $s_0 = 0$, we have

$$\sum_{k=1}^{\infty} f_k(a)s_k = \lim_{p=\infty} \sum_{k=1}^{p} f_k(a)s_k = \lim_{p=\infty} \sum_{k=1}^{p} \{g_k(a) - g_{k+1}(a)\} s_k$$
$$= \lim_{p=\infty} \left[\sum_{k=1}^{p-1} g_k(a)\,(s_k - s_{k-1}) - g_p(a)s_p \right] = \sum_{k=1}^{\infty} g_k(a)\,c_k,$$

provided $\lim_{k=\infty} g_k(a)s_k = 0$. But from the convergence of

$$f(a) = \sum_{k=1}^{\infty} f_k(a)$$

it follows that $g_k(a) \to 0$ when $k \to \infty$. Hence the argument is justified if s_k is bounded. Moreover $g_k(a) - g_{k+1}(a) = f_k(a)$ so that (A) follows from (a′), and

$$\text{(10)} \qquad \lim_{a\to\infty} g_k(a) = \lim_{a\to\infty} [f(a) - f_1(a) - \dots - f_{k-1}(a)]$$
$$= \alpha - \alpha_1 - \dots - \alpha_{k-1},$$

so that (B) is also satisfied and thus (9) is a β-matrix. Thus we have

VI. *To every K-matrix $f_k(a)$ corresponds the β-matrix* (9) *so that the K-limit of $s_k = c_1 + \dots + c_k$ is equal to the β-sum of Σc_k, provided the partial sums are bounded. If $f_k(a)$ is a T-matrix,* (9) *is a γ-matrix.*

Conversely, from

$$\text{(11)} \qquad f_k(a) = g_k(a) - g_{k+1}(a)$$

the sequence transformation (11) seems to correspond to the given series transformation $g_k(a)$. Conditions (a′) and (b′) follow from (11) and (A) and (B) respectively, with $\alpha_k = \beta_k - \beta_{k+1}$. Moreover it follows from the convergence of

$$\sum_{k=1}^{\infty} [g_k(a) - g_{k+1}(a)] = \lim_{k=\infty} [g_1(a) - g_k(a)]$$

that the limit

$$\text{(12)} \qquad \lim_{k=\infty} g_k(a) = g(a)$$

exists, and thus

$$f(a) = \Sigma f_k(a) = \Sigma[g_k(a) - g_{k+1}(a)] = g_1(a) - g(a).$$

But $f(a)$ does not necessarily tend to a limit as $a \to \infty$, for all that follows from conditions (A) and (B) is that $g(a)$ is bounded for $a > a'$. Thus we have

VII. *The necessary and sufficient condition that the K-limit* (11) *of the partial sums $s_k = c_1 + \dots + c_k$ should be equal to the β-sum of Σc_k is that $g(a)$ should tend to a limit.*

Thus, in a sense, generalized sums are more general than generalized limits. To every sequence transformation K corresponds a series transformation β, but there are series transformations β possessing no corresponding sequence transformation K.

96 a. *Examples. Arithmetic and exponential means.*

1. The arithmetic means correspond to the semi-matrix

$$(M) \qquad \begin{array}{l} 1 \\ 1/2,\ 1/2 \\ 1/3,\ 1/3,\ 1/3 \\ \cdot\ \cdot\ \cdot\ \cdot\ \cdot\ \cdot \\ 1/n,\ 1/n, \ldots,\ 1/n \\ \cdot\ \cdot\ \cdot\ \cdot\ \cdot\ \cdot\ \cdot \end{array}$$

Here, obviously, conditions (α), (β), (γ) are satisfied.

2. The arithmetic means of any real order r ($\neq$ negative integer) are defined by the semi-matrix

$$(M^r) \qquad a_{nk} = A_{n-k}^{r-1}/A_n^r,$$

where

$$(1) \qquad A_n^r = (r+1)(r+2)\ldots(r+n)/n!.$$

We also write $$s_n^{(r)} = \sum_{k=0}^{n} A_{n-k}^{r-1} s_k/A_n^r.$$

It follows from

$$(2) \qquad \sum_{k=0}^{n} A_{n-k}^{r-p-1} A_k^p = A_n^r \qquad \text{and } A_k^0 = 1,$$

if we put $p = 0$, that $\sum_k a_{nk} = \Sigma|a_{nk}| = 1$, i.e. ($\alpha$) and ($\gamma$) are satisfied.

Similarly, by

$$(3) \qquad A_n^r \sim n^r/\Gamma(r+1),$$

(β) is satisfied.

3. We obtain a large class of sequence transformations by taking any integral function $E(a) = \Sigma e_k a^k$, where $e_k \geqslant 0$, and putting

$$(4) \qquad z'(a) = \sum_k e_k a^k z_k/E(a),$$

i.e. by considering the matrices

$$(5) \qquad f_k(a) = e_k a^k/\sum_{k=0}^{\infty} e_k a^k,$$

where a assumes either all positive real values or only positive integral values, both processes leading to the same limit. Conditions (α') and (γ') are obviously satisfied for every integral function $E(a)$. To satisfy (β') we must have

$$\lim_{a \to \infty} a^k/E(a) = 0.$$

This condition is certainly satisfied if all the coefficients from a k onward are positive or zero for, if there are no negative coefficients,

$$a^k/E(a) < a^k/(e_0 + e_1 a + \dots + e_m a^m), \quad m > k,$$

and the right-hand side obviously tends to 0 when $a \to \infty$.

Taking e^a for $E(a)$ we obtain Borel's exponential limit, B-lim z_k. (Similarly e^{a^r} leads to Borel's generalized exponential limit.)

The exponential method can also be applied to the transformation of series. We put

$$(6) \qquad g_k(a) = \frac{1}{k!}\int_0^a e^{-t}t^k\,dt.$$

By partial integration

$$g_k(a) = e^{-a}a^{k+1}/(k+1)! + g_{k+1}(a),$$

which shows that (A$'$) is satisfied. On the other hand the properties of the Γ function in the form of an integral, (33. 8), show, by Stirling's formula Ex. IV. 22, that (B) is also satisfied.

Moreover in the series

$$(7) \qquad \Sigma \frac{c_k}{k!}\int_0^a e^{-t}t^k dt$$

we can interchange Σ and $\int$ whenever $\Sigma c_k a^k/k!$ is an integral function. In fact

$$\int_0^a e^{-t}t^k dt < \int_0^a t^k dt = \frac{a^{k+1}}{k+1}$$

and $\lim\limits_{k=\infty} \sqrt[k]{\dfrac{c_k}{k!}\cdot\dfrac{a^{k+1}}{k+1}} = 0$ for every fixed a. Therefore (7) is uniformly convergent in any finite region, and thus the Borel sum of Σc_k can be written in the form

$$\lim_{a \to \infty}\int_0^a e^{-t}\,\Sigma \frac{c_k}{k!} t^k dt = \int_0^\infty e^{-t}\Sigma \frac{c^k}{k!} t^\kappa dt$$

whenever the limit in question exists.

The summation of a series Σc_k by (6), called *exponential summation,* is not fully equivalent to the exponential limit of $s_k = c_0 + c_1 + \dots + c_k$.

The exponential limit can be put into the concise form of an integral. Putting

$$s(a) = \sum_0^\infty s_n a^n/n!$$

$$B(a) = e^{-a} s(a)$$

$$u(a) = \sum_0^\infty c_n a^n/n!$$

we see that

$$B(a) - c_0 = \int_0^a \frac{d}{da}[e^{-a} s(a)]da = \int_0^a e^{-a}[s'(a) - s(a)]da.$$

Moreover,

$$s'(a) - s(a) = \sum_0^\infty (s_{n+1} - s_n)a^n/n! = \Sigma c_{n+1} a^n/n! = u'(a).$$

i. e.

(8) $$B(a) - c_0 = \int_0^a e^{-a} u'(a) da.$$

A further simplification consists of replacing $u'(a)$ by $u(a)$. (Proof by Perron, 1920.)

Integrating by parts, we find

(9) $$\int_0^a e^{-a} u'(a) da = [e^{-a} u(a)]_0^a + \int_0^a e^{-a} u(a) da,$$

and we are going to prove that *if the left-hand side has a limit for $a \to \infty$, then also the integral on the right-hand side tends to a limit when $a \to \infty$ and at the same time*

$$\lim_{a \to \infty} e^{-a} u(a) = 0.$$

We shall establish in this way the relation

(10) $$\int_0^\infty e^{-a} u'(a) da = -c_0 + \int_0^\infty e^{-a} u(a) da,$$

provided the left-hand side exists.

The proof is based on the following

Lemma (Perron, 1920).

(11) $$\lim_{a \to \infty} f(a) = \lim_{a \to \infty} [f(a) + f'(a)],$$

provided the limit on the right-hand side exists.

This lemma is established by Stolz's extension (1893) of L'Hospital's rule.

$$\text{(12)} \qquad \lim_{a\to\infty} \frac{g(a)}{h(a)} = \lim_{a\to\infty} \frac{g'(a)}{h'(a)},$$

i. e. the limit on the left-hand side exists and is equal to that on the right-hand side, provided the latter exists and $h(a) \to \infty$ with a (nothing further is supposed about $g(a)$ itself). If we put $f(a)+f'(a) = \phi(a)$, the solution $f(a)$ of this linear differential equation is

$$f(a) = e^{-a}\int_{a_0}^{a} e^{a}\phi(a)\,da.$$

Applying (12) to

$$g(a) = \int_{a_0}^{a} e^{a}\phi(a)da,\; h(a) = e^{a},$$

and noticing that

$$\frac{g'(a)}{h'(a)} = \phi(a) = f(a)+f'(a),$$

we prove (11).

In our case

$$f(a) = \int_0^a e^{-a}u(a)\,da,\; f'(a) = e^{-a}u(a),$$

so that
$$f(a)+f'(a) = c_0 + \int_0^a e^{-a}u'(a)\,da,$$

by (9), and thus the lemma proves (10).

In this way we obtain Borel's final formula

$$\text{(13)} \qquad \lim_{a\to\infty} B(a) = \int_0^\infty e^{-a}u(a)da.$$

We remark, however, that the integral on the right-hand side may have a sense when $B(a)$ does not tend to a definite limit.

For example, if $u(a) = e^{a}\cos(a^2)$, the integral

$$\int_0 e^{-a}u(a)da = \int_0^\infty \cos(a^2)\,da$$

exists, and

$$B(a) = f(a)+f'(a) = \int_0^a \cos(a^2)dt + \cos(a^2)$$

does not tend to a limit as $a \to \infty$. The summation by Borel's integral is more general than the summation by his exponential means. We say that Σc_k is summable (B) to s if Borel's integral tends to s.

To avoid certain difficulties met with in the application of exponential means and B-summability, Borel introduced a third type of summability which is a special case of the exponential means and of the B-summation. We say that Σc_k is *absolutely summable* (B) if all the integrals

$$(14) \qquad \int^{\infty} e^{-a} \left| \frac{d^r u(a)}{da^r} \right| da, \qquad r = 0, 1, 2, \ldots,$$

exist. Condition (14) for $r = 0$ shows that a series absolutely summable (B) is summable (B); the case $r = 1$ shows that a series absolutely summable (B) is summable by the exponential means.

96 b. *Further examples.*

4. Consider an increasing real function $g(a)$ such that the two limits

$$(1) \qquad \lim_{a \to 0} g(a) = A \quad \text{and} \quad \lim_{a \to \infty} g(a) = A + 1$$

exist, and form the functions

$$(2) \qquad f_k(a) = g(\theta_k a) - g(\theta_{k+1} a),$$

where the sequence of positive numbers θ_k is steadily decreasing to 0. We have $f_k(a) > 0$ and

$$\Sigma | f_k(a) | = \Sigma f_k(a) = \lim_{k = \infty} [g(\theta_0 a) - g(\theta_k a)] = g(\theta_0 a) - A.$$

Therefore (α') and (γ') are satisfied. By (1) and (2), condition (β') is also satisfied.

5. Take $$g_k(a) = [a/(a+1)]^k$$

which obviously satisfies (A″) and (B′) and leads to

$$\sum_k c_k [a/(a+1)]^k,$$

i.e. if we put $a/(a+1) = t$, to the power series $\Sigma c_k t^k$. When $a \to \infty$, $t \to 1$. Thus the value of this generalized limit is

$\lim_{t\to 1} \Sigma c_k t^k$ for $0 < t < 1$. Therefore this generalized limit exists whenever the function $f(z) = \Sigma c_k z^k$ has a limiting value as $z \to 1$ along the real axis. If Σc_k is convergent, 96. II, applied to this particular case, reduces to Abel's well-known result on power series. Therefore this transformation of series is called an *Abel transformation* and the corresponding sum, if it exists, the Abel sum of the series.

6. Le Roy takes

$$g_k(a) = \Gamma(kt+1)/\Gamma(k+1) \quad \text{where} \quad t = a/(a+1).$$

From

$$g_k(a) - g_{k+1}(a) = \frac{\Gamma(kt+1)}{\Gamma(k+1)} - \frac{\Gamma(kt+2)}{\Gamma(k+2)}$$
$$= \frac{\Gamma(kt+1)}{\Gamma(k+1)}\left(1 - \frac{kt+1}{k+1}\right) \geqslant 0$$

we see that (A″) is verified. Condition (B′) obviously is.

7. $$g_0(a) = 1,$$
$$g_k(a) = \frac{a}{a+r}\,\frac{a+1}{a+r+1} \cdots \frac{a+k+1}{a+r+k+1}, \quad r > 0.$$

Conditions (A″) and (B′) are readily verified.

8. If $g_k(a)$ satisfies (A″) and (B′), then $[g_k(a)]^r$, $r > 0$, also satisfies the same conditions. This remark applied to ordinary arithmetic means (Ex. 1) leads to Riesz summation, very important in the theory of Dirichlet series. Applied with $r = 2$ to Borel's exponential summation we obtain

$$g_k(a) = \frac{1}{[k!]^2}\int_0^a e^{-t} t^k dt \int_0^a e^{-u} u^k du = \frac{1}{[k!]^2}\int_0^a\int_0^a e^{-t-u}(tu)^k dt\, du$$

and

$$\sum_k g_k(a) c_k = \int_0^a\int_0^a e^{-t-u}\left[\sum_k \frac{c_k}{[k!]^2}(tu)^k\right] dt du.$$

The interchange of Σ and $\iint$ is justified as in the case of exponential summation.

This summation applies in particular to $c_k = (-1)^k k!z^k$, $\mathrm{Rl}(z) \geqslant 0$, and we obtain by integrating with respect to t

$$\lim_{a\to\infty} \sum_k g_k(a) c_k = \int_0^\infty \frac{e^{-u} du}{1+zu},$$

i.e. the summation in view assigns a value to a power series divergent for every value of z except $z = 0$.

97. *General properties of K- and T-matrices and transformations.*

I. *The sum and product of two K-matrices exist and are K-matrices. K-matrices form the elements of an algebra, in which addition is associative and commutative, and multiplication is distributive and associative but not necessarily commutative.*

II. *If, for every r, $a_{nk}^{(r)}$ is a $K(K_a)$ matrix with the bound M_r and the characteristic numbers $\alpha_k^{(r)}$, $\alpha^{(r)}$, and if $\sum_{r=1}^{\infty} |c_r| M_r = b$ is convergent, $C = \sum_{r=1}^{\infty} c_r a_{nk}^{(r)}$ is a $K(K_a)$ matrix, with the characteristic numbers $\sum_r c_r \alpha_k^{(r)}$, $\Sigma a_r \alpha^{(r)}$ and its bound does not exceed b.*

III. *The product of two T-matrices exists and is a T-matrix and their multiplication is associative, but T-matrices do not form an algebra.*

IV. *If, for every r, $a_{nk}^{(r)}$ is a T-matrix with the bound M_r, and if $\sum_{r=1}^{\infty} |c_r| M_r = b$ is convergent and $\sum_{r=1}^{\infty} c_r = 1$, then $\sum_{r=1}^{\infty} c_r a_{nk}^{(r)}$ is a T-matrix and its bound does not exceed b.*

Proof of I–IV. The sum $a_{nk} + b_{nk}$ of any two matrices exists, and addition is obviously associative and commutative. As for the product, if M and N are bounds of a_{nk} and b_{nk}, we have

$$\sum_{i=1}^{\infty} \sum_{k=1}^{\infty} |b_{ni} a_{ik}| \leqslant \sum_{i=1}^{\infty} |b_{ni}| M \leqslant NM,$$

so that the product of any two K_a-matrices exists and is a K_a-matrix. Moreover, from

$$\sum_{i=1}^{\infty} b_{ni} c_{ik} + \sum_{i=1}^{\infty} a_{ni} c_{ik} = \sum_{i=1}^{\infty} (b_{ni} + a_{ni}) c_{ik},$$

we see that multiplication is distributive. To prove that the product of two K-matrices is a K-matrix, we notice that if z_k is a regular sequence, i.e. if z_k tends to a limit $z, z'_i = \sum_k a_{ik} z_k$ and thus also $z''_n = \sum_i b_{ni} z'_i$, are regular sequences. Moreover

$$|z''_n| \leqslant \sum_i |b_{ni}| \sum_k |a_{ik}| |z_k| \leqslant NM\omega,$$

where ω is any number greater than all the numbers $|z_i|$. Therefore we can rearrange the double sum $\sum_i b_{ni} \sum_k a_{ik} z_k$ at will without destroying its convergence or altering its sum. Thus $\sum_k \left(\sum_i b_{ni} a_{ik}\right) z_k$ tends to the limit of z''_n. Since this is true for *every* regular sequence, the matrix $c_{nk} = \sum_i b_{ni} a_{ik}$ transforms every regular sequence into a regular sequence. Hence, by 95. I, c_{nk} is a K-matrix and its bound does not exceed MN.

If both a_{nk} and b_{nk} are T-matrices, $z''_n \to z$, which proves that c_{nk} is also a T-matrix. On the other hand the sum of two T-matrices is not a T-matrix.

To prove that multiplication is associative we have to show that

$$\sum_j \left(\sum_i a_{ni} b_{ij}\right) c_{jk} = \sum_i a_{ni} \sum_j b_{ij} c_{jk},$$

i.e. that the inversion of the order of the two summations is legitimate. But

$$\sum_{ij} |a_{ni}| |b_{ij}| |c_{jk}| \leqslant M_1 \sum_{ij} |b_{ij}| |c_{jk}| \leqslant M_1 M_2 \sum_j |c_{jk}| \leqslant M_1 M_2 M_3,$$

where M_1, M_2, M_3 are the bounds of the three arbitrarily given K-matrices a_{nk}, b_{nk}, c_{nk}.

To prove II, we put

$$(1) \qquad A_n^{(r)} = \sum_k a_{nk}^{(r)}, \quad \lim_{n=\infty} A_n^{(r)} = \alpha^{(r)}, \quad \lim_{n=\infty} a_{nk}^{(r)} = \alpha_k^{(r)}.$$

Since $|a_{nk}^{(r)}| \leqslant M_r$ and $\sum_r |c_r| M_r = b$ is convergent, the series

$$(2) \qquad \sum_r c_r a_{nk}^{(r)} = a_{nk},$$

converges for every n, so that the matrix a_{nk} exists.

Moreover, from

$$\sum_r \sum_k |c_r|\,|a_{nk}^{(r)}| \leqslant \sum_r |c_r| M_r = b$$

we see that

$$(3) \qquad A_n = \sum_k a_{nk} = \sum_r c_r A_n^{(r)}.$$

We have to prove that A_n and a_{nk} tend to definite limits as $n \to \infty$. To every positive ϵ there corresponds a p such that

$$(4) \qquad \sum_{r=p+1}^{\infty} |c_r| M_r < \frac{\epsilon}{2}.$$

Therefore it follows from

$$(5) \qquad |A_n^{(r)}| \leqslant \sum_k |a_{nk}^{(r)}| \leqslant M_r,$$

that

$$(6) \qquad \left| \sum_{r=p+1}^{\infty} c_r A_n^{(r)} \right| \leqslant \sum_{r=p+1}^{\infty} |c_r| M_r < \frac{\epsilon}{2},$$

for every n, and that

$$(7) \qquad |\alpha^{(r)}| \leqslant M_r,$$

so that

$$(8) \qquad \left| \sum_{r=p+1}^{\infty} c_r \alpha^{(r)} \right| < \frac{\epsilon}{2}.$$

Now $\sum_r c_r \alpha^{(r)}$ is a determinate number, and

$$\sum_r c_r A_n^{(r)} - \sum_r c_r \alpha^{(r)}$$
$$= \sum_{r=1}^{p} c_r (A_n^{(r)} - \alpha^{(r)}) + \sum_{r=p+1}^{\infty} c_r A_n^{(r)} - \sum_{r=p+1}^{\infty} c_r \alpha^{(r)},$$

while, by (6) and (8),

$$\left| \sum_r c_r A_n^{(r)} - \sum_r c_r \alpha^{(r)} \right| < \left| \sum_{r=1}^{p} c_r A_n^{(r)} - \alpha^{(r)} \right| + \epsilon.$$

As $n \to \infty$ the first term on the right-hand side tends to 0, so that all the limiting numbers of the left-hand side are less than ϵ. Since ϵ is arbitrary

$$(9) \qquad \lim_{n=\infty} \sum_r c_r A_n^{(r)} = \sum_r c_r \alpha^{(r)}.$$

In a similar way we prove that

$$(10)\qquad \lim_{n=\infty} \sum_r c_r a_{nk}^{(r)} = \sum_{r=1}^{\infty} c_r \alpha_k^{(r)}.$$

In fact, $|a_{nk}^{(r)}| \leqslant M_r$, so that the proof applies without any modification.

In theorem IV we have to add the condition $\sum_{r=1}^{\infty} c_r = 1$, in order that the limit of A_n as $n \to \infty$ should be 1.

Our results readily extend to the case when n is replaced by a continuous variable a.

We shall now establish some general properties of K- and T-matrices when applied to the transformation of sequences.

If every row of a matrix contains only a finite number of non-zero numbers, we say that the matrix or the corresponding transformation is *row-finite* (' Zeilen-finite '), e. g. semi-matrices, $a_{nk} = 0$ if $k > n$, and, in particular, *diagonal* matrices, $a_{nk} = 0$ if $n \neq k$, are row-finite. If a_{nk} is row-finite, $z'_n = \sum_k a_{nk} z_k$ reduces to a finite sum, so that *a row-finite transformation applies to every sequence* but may transform a convergent one into a divergent one. However, if there is an l such that, in every row of a K-matrix, $a_{nk} = 0$ if $k > l$ (row-bounded) every sequence z_k, however divergent it may be, is transformed into a convergent sequence z'_n whose limit is $\sum_{k=1}^{l} \alpha_k z_k$, which has no connexion whatsoever with the eventual, finite or infinite, limit of z_k. We see thus that a transformation may apply to a large class of sequences without being suitable for a reasonable generalization of limit,

If we confine ourselves to K-matrices, $\sum_k |a_{nk}|$ is convergent, so that the radius of convergence ρ_n of the power series $\Sigma a_{nk} z^k$ is at least 1. We shall call the *lower limit* $\rho \geqslant 1$ of the ρ_n *the range* of a_{nk} and define the *lower* and *upper rank*, r and R, of a sequence z_k by putting

$$(11)\qquad r = \varliminf_{k=\infty} |\sqrt[k]{z_k}|,\ R = \varlimsup_{k=\infty} |\sqrt[k]{z_k}|.$$

We say that the sequence z_k is *within the range of* a_{nk} if $R<\rho$ and that z_k is *outside the range of* a_{nk} if $r>\rho$.

V. *A K-transformation applies to every sequence within its range and applies to no sequence outside its range. Every K-transformation applies to every bounded sequence and transforms it into a bounded sequence.*

Proof. It follows from (11) that for every positive $\theta<1$ and $\eta>1$ there is a p such that, for $k>p$,

$$(\theta r)^k<|z_k|<(\eta R)^k. \tag{12}$$

In the same way, for every positive $\theta'<1$ there is an m such that, for $n>m$, $\rho_n>\theta'\rho$. Now if $R<\rho$, there is a $\theta'<1$ sufficiently near 1 so that $R<\theta'\rho$, and an $\eta>1$ sufficiently near 1 so that $\eta R<\theta'\rho<\rho_n$ for $n<m$, m depending on θ'. Therefore $z=\eta R$ is within the circles of convergence of all the power series $\sum_k a_{nk}z^k$, $n>m$, and thus all the power series

$$\sum_k |a_{nk}|(\eta R)^k,\ n>m,$$

are convergent, which, by (12) (ii) proves the first statement.

For any $\eta'>1$ there are infinitely many values n', say, of n for which $\rho_{n'}<\eta'\rho$. Now, if $r>\rho$, there is an η' such that $\eta'\rho<r$, and a positive $\theta<1$ such that $\theta r>\eta'\rho$. Therefore $z=\theta r$ is outside and not on the circle of convergence of all the series $\sum_k a_{n'k}z^k$, and thus there are infinitely many terms in each series whose absolute value is greater than 1. By (12) (i), the same follows for $\sum_k a_{n'k}z_k$, so that all these series are divergent.

Finally, it follows from $|z_k|\leqslant\zeta$ that

$$|z'_n|\leqslant\zeta\sum_k|a_{nk}|\leqslant\zeta M.$$

We notice in addition that there are K-matrices bounded and others not bounded in Hilbert's sense. In fact $1/(n+k)$ is known to be bounded in Hilbert's sense and $\sum_k 1/(n+k)$ is divergent; this matrix is a Hilbert matrix but not a K-matrix.

On the other hand, preceding a K-matrix by the column $1/n^{\alpha}$, $\alpha < 1/2$, we obtain another K-matrix, but the new matrix is not bounded in Hilbert's sense as $\sum_{n} |a_{nk}|^2$ is divergent.

98. *Generalized limits and summations. Problem of consistency.* By definition the A-limit of z_k is the limit of

$$z_n' = \sum_{k} a_{nk} z_k$$

(when n tends to ∞) whenever the latter limit exists. If A is a T-matrix, Toeplitz' theorem shows that the new definition is at least as extensive as the original one, viz. applies to every convergent sequence and leads to the same limit. The same is true of K-matrices with the qualification that the value of the new limit is, in general, not the same as that of the original sequence, but there is a precise relation between the two limits, so that when the transform of a divergent sequence is convergent, we can assign to z_k the value of z calculated from (95. I d) as its generalized limit. However, we shall restrict ourselves to T-matrices and put accordingly

$$\text{(1)} \qquad A\text{-}\lim_{n=\infty} z_n = \lim_{n=\infty} \sum_{k=1}^{\infty} a_{nk} z_k,$$

whenever the limit on the right-hand side exists.

An obvious property of every T-limit, defined by a Toeplitz matrix, is the following:

$$\text{(2)} \qquad A\text{-lim}\,(az_n + bu_n) = a\,A\text{-lim}\,z_n + b\,A\text{-lim}\,u_n$$

whenever the two A-limits on the right-hand side exist separately. The corresponding rule for multiplication is, in general, not true. In fact, if z_n denotes the sequence 1, 0, 1, 0, ... and u_n denotes 0, 1, 0, 1, ..., the arithmetic means of both sequences tend to 1/2, i.e.

$$M\text{-lim}\,z_n = 1/2, \qquad M\text{-lim}\,u_n = 1/2,$$

and $z_n u_n = 0$ for every n, i.e.

$$M\text{-lim}\,(z_n u_n) = 0.$$

An important problem arising from the various generalizations of limit is that of their mutual consistency. In fact, if both the

A-limit and the B-limit of a divergent sequence z_n exist, the values of the two limits may be different, by 95. IV or V. For instance if A is $f_{2k}(a) = 0, f_{2k+1}(a) = a^k/(a+1)^{k+1}$ $(k = 1, 2, \ldots)$, and B is $f_{2k+1}(a) = 0, f_{2k}(a) = a^k/(a+1)^{k+1}$, the A-limit of 1, 0, 1, 0, ... is 1 since

$$\sum f_k'(a) c_k = 1/(a+1) + a/(a+1)^2 + \ldots + a^k/(a+1)^{k+1} + \ldots = 1.$$

On the other hand its B-limit is clearly 0. Finally, if C is $f_k(a) = a^k/(a+1)^{k+1}$, the C-limit of the same sequence is the limit for $a = \infty$ of the sequence

$$\frac{a}{(a+1)^2} + \frac{a^3}{(a+1)^4} + \ldots + \frac{a^{2k+1}}{(a+1)^{2k+2}} + \ldots$$
$$= \frac{a}{(a+1)^2} \sum_{k=0}^{\infty} \left(\frac{a}{a+1}\right)^k = \frac{a}{2a+1} \to \frac{1}{2}.$$

The T-limits are not mutually consistent though applied to any convergent sequence they all lead to the same limit, viz. to the ordinary limit of the sequence.

There is an interesting connexion between *commutability*: $AB = BA$, of matrices and the consistency of the corresponding generalized limits.

I. *If the T-matrices A and B are commutable, i.e. if $AB = BA$, the corresponding T-limits are consistent at least for bounded sequences.*

Proof. If $A(z_n) = z_n' \to z'$ and $B(z_n) = \bar{z}_n \to \bar{z}$, we have, since the sequences z_n' and $\bar{z}_n$ are convergent, $B(z_n') = z_n'' \to z'$ and $A(\bar{z}_n) = \bar{z}_n \to \bar{z}$. But, for bounded sequences

$$\sum_i b_{ni} \sum_k a_{ik} z_k = \sum_k \left(\sum_i b_{ni} a_{ik}\right) z_k$$

and

$$\sum_i a_{ni} \sum_k b_{ik} z_k = \sum_k \left(\sum_i a_{ni} b_{ik}\right) z_k,$$

i. e. $B(z_n') = BA(z_n)$ and $A(\bar{z}_n) = AB(z_n)$. Moreover, by hypothesis, we have $AB = BA$. It follows that $z' = \bar{z}$. Q. e. d.

II. *If the row-finite T-matrices A and B are commutable, the corresponding limits are consistent whenever they exist.*

Proof. By hypothesis, $A(z_k) = z'_n \to z'$, $B(z_k) = \bar{z}_i \to \bar{z}$, and thus also $B(z'_i) \equiv z''_n \to z'$, $A(\bar{z}_i) \equiv \bar{\bar{z}}_n \to \bar{z}$. But

$$z''_n = \sum_{i=1}^{i_n} b_{ni} \sum_{k=1}^{k_i} a_{ik} z_k = \sum_k \Big(\sum_i b_{ni} a_{ik}\Big) z_k = \sum_k \Big(\sum_i a_{ni} b_{ik}\Big) z_k,$$

since $AB = BA$, and thus

$$z''_n = \sum_i a_{ni} \sum_k b_{ik} z_k = \bar{\bar{z}}_n,$$

which proves the proposition.

If the rows are not finite, $A(B)$: B followed by A, may not be identical with the single transformation AB. Moreover, the inversion of the order of the two summations may lead to different results. The above argument is valid however if, for the sequence in question, $B(A) = BA = AB = A(B)$. Hence

III. *If two commutable T-transformations A and B are applied to a sequence z_k for which $B[A(z_k)] = (BA)(z_k)$ and $A[B(z_k)] = (AB)(z_k)$, the A and B limits of z_k are consistent.*

In general, two T-transformations being given, it is difficult to determine the whole class of sequences for which the conditions of III are satisfied. The following result gives the kernel of the class.

We say that z_k is within the range of the two consecutive transformations $B(A)$: A followed by B, if $Z'_i = \sum_k |a_{ik} z_k|$ is within the range of B.

IV. *If z_k is within the range of $A(B)$ and $B(A)$, where A and B are commutable T-matrices, the A and B limit of z_k are consistent whenever they exist.*

Proof. Since z_k is within the range of $B(A)$,

$$\sum_i |b_{ni}| \sum_k |a_{ik} z_k|$$

is convergent and thus

$$B[A(z_k)] \equiv \sum_i b_{ni} \sum_k a_{ik} z_k = \sum_k \Big(\sum_i b_{ni} a_{ik}\Big) z_k = (BA)(z_k).$$

Similarly, since z_k is within the range of $A(B)$,

$$A[B(z_k)] = (AB)(z_k),$$

which proves that the two sequences $z''_n = B[A(z_k)]$ and $\bar{\bar{z}}_n = A[B(z_k)]$ are identical, and thus III establishes IV.

This result shows that, for the problem of consistency, it is important to determine the class of T-matrices commutable with a given T-matrix. This is possible in particular cases only.

V. *All diagonal matrices are commutable among themselves, and a distinct diagonal matrix is commutable with diagonal matrices only.*

In this connexion, *distinct* means that all the diagonal elements are different from one another.

Proof. $DD' = D'D$ follows from $d_n d'_n = d'_n d_n$. Moreover, if A is any matrix, $AD = DA$ means that $a_{nk} d_k = d_n a_{nk}$, i.e. $a_{nk}(d_k - d_n) = 0$. Therefore, since $d_k \neq d_n$ for $k \neq n$, $a_{nk} = 0$ for $n \neq k$.

Now suppose that A is the *Ω-transform* of a distinct diagonal matrix D, i.e. $A = \Omega^{-1} D \Omega$, and take any other matrix B. If $AB = BA$, i.e. $\Omega^{-1} D \Omega . B = B . \Omega^{-1} D \Omega$, multiplying on the left by Ω and on the right by Ω^{-1} we obtain $D . \Omega B \Omega^{-1} = \Omega B \Omega^{-1} . D$. Thus, by V, $\Omega B \Omega^{-1}$ is a diagonal matrix D_1, say. But then $B = \Omega^{-1} D_1 \Omega$, i.e. B is the Ω-transform of a diagonal matrix.

Conversely, if $B = \Omega^{-1} D_1 \Omega$, then $AB = \Omega^{-1} D \Omega . \Omega^{-1} D_1 \Omega$ $= \Omega^{-1} D D_1 \Omega = \Omega^{-1} D_1 D \Omega = \Omega^{-1} D_1 \Omega . \Omega^{-1} D \Omega = BA$.

Thus if A is the Ω-transform of a distinct diagonal matrix, the necessary and sufficient condition that $AB = BA$ appears to be that B should also be the Ω-transform of a diagonal matrix. In our argument, however, we took it for granted that all the products in question exist and that the associative law holds for them.

These conditions are satisfied (a) if A, B, Ω, Ω^{-1} are row-finite, since the product of two row-finite matrices is row-finite, and the double sum $\sum_{ij} a_{ni} b_{ij} c_{jk}$ reduces to a finite sum; (b) if $A, B, \Omega, \Omega^{-1}$ are K_a-matrices and D, D_1 are bounded; (c) if $A, B, \Omega, \Omega^{-1}$ are Hilbert (H) matrices and D, D_1 bounded.

VI. *Suppose that a row-finite (K_a or H) matrix A is the Ω-transform of a distinct and bounded diagonal matrix, where Ω and Ω^{-1} are also row-finite (K_a or H matrices respectively). Then B is commutable with A if and only if B is the Ω-transform of a (bounded) diagonal matrix.*

Proof. The only remark we have to add to the above argument is that if B, Ω and Ω^{-1} are $K_a(H)$ matrices, $D_1 = \Omega B \Omega^{-1}$ is also a $K_a(H)$ matrix and thus it is necessarily bounded.

Another method of obtaining a large class of commutable matrices is to consider power series in commutable matrices, by 97. II.

VII. *If A and B are commutable K_a-matrices with the bounds M and N respectively and if $\Sigma |c_p| M^p = c$ and $\Sigma |e_p| N^p = e$ are convergent, the matrices $C = \Sigma c_p A^p$ and $E = \Sigma e_p B^p$ are commutable.*

Proof. It follows from

$$\sum_k \sum_i |a_{ni}||a_{ik}| = \sum_i |a_{ni}| \sum_k |a_{ik}| \leqslant M \sum_i |a_{ni}| \leqslant M^2 \text{ \&c.}$$

that

$$\sum_k |(A^p)_{nk}| \leqslant M^p, \quad \sum_k |(B^p)_{nk}| \leqslant N^p,$$

and thus

$$\sum_k \sum_p |c_p| \, |(A^p)_{nk}| \leqslant c, \quad \sum_k \sum_p |e_p| \, |(B^p)_{nk}| \leqslant e,$$

so that C and E are K_a-matrices with the bounds c and e respectively.

Moreover,

$$(CE)_{nk} \leqslant \sum_i \sum_p |c_p| \, |(A^p)_{ni}| \sum_q |e_q| \, |(B^q)_{ik}| \leqslant ce,$$

so that we can rearrange the series at will. Collecting terms for which $p+q = m$, we obtain

$$\begin{aligned} CE &= \sum_m (c_0 e_m B^m + c_1 e_{m-1} A B^{m-1} + \ldots + c_{m-1} e_1 A^{m-1} B + c_m e_0 A^m) \\ &= EC \end{aligned}$$

since, by exchanging the coefficients c and e as well as A and B, we do not alter the value of the m-th term.

This result, with due modifications in the conditions, readily extends to series of different commutable matrices.

Combined with III and 97. IV, theorem VII leads to

VIII. *Suppose that* (i) *A and B are two commutable T-matrices with the bounds M and N respectively;* (ii) *the series $\Sigma c_p M^p = c$, $\Sigma e_p N^p = e$ are convergent, and $\Sigma c_p = 1$, $\Sigma e_p = \mathbf{1}$. Then the* *generalized limits corresponding to* $C = \Sigma c_p A^p$ *and* $E = \Sigma e_p B^p$ *are consistent for* z_k, *provided*

$$C[E(z_k)] = (CE)(z_k)$$

and

$$E[C(z_k)] = (EC)(z_k)$$

(certainly satisfied for bounded z_k).

99. *Commutable semi-matrices.* As an application of the general results obtained in the previous article we shall take a semi-matrix A and shall try to determine a distinct diagonal matrix D and a semi-matrix Ω satisfying the conditions (i) a semi-matrix Ω^{-1} exists, (ii) $\Omega A = D\Omega$.

We first notice that if any matrix A has both a left-hand reciprocal A_l^{-1} and a right-hand reciprocal A_r^{-1}, and if A, A_l^{-1}, A_r^{-1} are associative, then $A_l^{-1} = A_r^{-1}$, so that in this case A has a unique, two-sided, reciprocal. In fact, multiplying $A_l^{-1} A = 1$ on the right by A_r^{-1}, we have $A_l^{-1} A \,.\, A_r^{-1} = A_l^{-1} \,.\, AA_r^{-1} = A_l^{-1} = A_r^{-1}$.

Moreover, if A has a unique reciprocal on one side, A_r^{-1}, say, and if $AA_r^{-1} \,.\, A = A \,.\, A_r^{-1} A$, then A_r^{-1} is also a left-hand reciprocal and thus necessarily unique.

Proof. From $AA_r^{-1} = 1$, we have $A \,.\, A_r^{-1} A = A$, i.e. $A_r^{-1} A$ satisfies the equation $AX = A$. An obvious solution of this equation is $X = 1$, and if X_1, X_2 are two different solutions, $A_r^{-1} + X_2 - X_1$ would be another right-hand reciprocal of A.

We remark finally that $AA_r^{-1} \,.\, A = A \,.\, A_r^{-1} A$ is satisfied if A and A_r^{-1} are semi-matrices or row-finite, K_a- or H- matrices.

I. *If* $w_{kk} = 0$ *for some* k, *the semi-matrix* w_{nk} *has no reciprocal. If* $w_{kk} \neq 0$ *for every* k, w_{nk} *has a unique reciprocal which is a semi-matrix whose diagonal elements are* $1/w_{kk}$.

Proof. If we denote by x_{nk} the elements of Ω^{-1}, the condition $\Omega\Omega^{-1} = 1$ means

$$\sum_{i=1}^{n} w_{ni} x_{ik} = \delta_{nk}, \quad \delta_{nk} = 0 \text{ if } n \neq k,\ \delta_{kk} = 1. \tag{1}$$

For $n = 1$ we have $w_{11} x_{11} = 1$, $w_{11} x_{1k} = 0$, $k > 1$. If $w_{11} = 0$, the first equation has no solution in x_{11}, Ω^{-1} does not exist. If $w_{11} \neq 0$, $x_{11} = 1/w_{11}$ and $x_{1k} = 0$ for $k > 1$. For $n = 2$ we have $w_{21} x_{1k} + w_{22} x_{2k} = \delta_{2k}$, i.e. $w_{21} x_{11} + w_{22} x_{21} = 0$, $w_{22} x_{22} = 1$, $w_{22} x_{2k} = 0$ for $k > 2$.

If $w_{22} = 0$, the second equation becomes absurd; if $w_{22} \neq 0$, it gives $x_{22} = 1/w_{22}$. The first equation determines x_{21}, and the last shows that $x_{2k} = 0$ for $k > 2$. Continuing in this way, we establish I.

II. *If in a semi-matrix A all the diagonal elements are distinct, there is a semi-matrix Ω such that $\Omega A = D\Omega$ where $d_k = a_{kk}$ and the diagonal elements w_{kk} are arbitrary.*

Proof. $\Omega A = D\Omega$ means

$$(2) \qquad \sum_{i=k}^{n} w_{ni} a_{ik} = d_n w_{nk}.$$

For $k = n$, $w_{nn} a_{nn} = d_n w_{nn}$ so that $d_n = a_{nn}$ satisfies this equation for arbitrary values of w_{nn}, and if $w_{nn} \neq 0$, a_{nn} is the only possible value for d_n. We shall suppose that $d_n = a_{nn}$ and w_{nn} arbitrarily given. Then (2) gives for $n = 2$, $w_{21} a_{11} + w_{22} a_{21} = d_2 w_{21}$, which determines w_{21} since $a_{11} - d_2 = a_{11} - a_{22} \neq 0$. Similarly the equations

$$w_{31} a_{11} + w_{32} a_{21} + w_{33} a_{31} = d_3 w_{31}, \quad w_{32} a_{22} + w_{33} a_{32} = d_3 w_{32}$$

determine w_{31} and w_{32} since $a_{11} - d_3 \neq 0$. And so forth.

These two results prove by 98. VI the following theorem.

III. *Suppose that A is a semi-matrix with distinct diagonal elements. Then* (i) *there is a semi-matrix Ω such that A is the Ω-transform of its own diagonal elements*; (ii) *a semi-matrix B is commutable with A if and only if B is the Ω-transform of a diagonal matrix*; (iii) *the A and B limits of a sequence z_k, if they exist, are consistent, provided B is the Ω-transform of a diagonal matrix*; (iv) *the two limits corresponding to $B = \Omega^{-1} D_1 \Omega$ and $C = \Omega^{-1} D_2 \Omega$ are consistent if D_1 or D_2 is distinct.*

The last statement is proved by taking B or C for A.

If we take for A the matrix M of the arithmetic means, we can take for Ω the Euler semi-matrix E whose elements are

$$(-1)^{k-1} \frac{(n-1)!}{(n-k)!\,(k-1)!}.$$

It is readily shown that $EE = 1$, so that E is its own reciprocal. Thus we obtain Hurwitz and Silverman's results (1917): *A semi-matrix A is commutable with M if and only if A is the E-trans-*

form of a diagonal matrix; all T semi-matrices commutable with M define mutually consistent limits.

100. *Regular limit processes and summations.* The problem of consistency is intimately connected with the following fundamental problem about generalized limits and summations.

If z_n converges in the ordinary sense to z, every partial sequence of z_n converges to the same limit. In particular, if we suppress or add a finite number of terms, the remaining sequence is convergent and to the same limit. Similarly, if Σc_n converges to s in the ordinary sense, we can suppress or add a finite number of terms, of sum s' say, without destroying convergence, and the sum of the new series is $s \mp s'$. This property does not in general extend to generalized limits and summations, for every term z'_n of the transformed sequence depends on *all the terms* z_n of the original sequence.

We shall say that a T-limit is *regular* if the existence of the T-limit of $z_1, z_2, \ldots$ and of $z_2, z_3, \ldots$ imply one another and lead to the same limit. Similarly the γ-summation is said to be regular if the γ-convergence of $\sum_1^\infty z_k$ and $\sum_2^\infty z_k$ imply one another and $s_2 = s_1 - z_1$, where s_2 is the γ-sum of the latter, and s_1 that of the former series.

Since the various generalized limits of a sequence are not equal, we have in practice to choose one leading to the 'right' value. The usual test for this choice is to take a Taylor series representing a known function and to apply the limit process in question to the partial sums of that Taylor series formed at points outside or on its circle of convergence, and the 'right' value is, by definition, the value, or a specified limiting value, of the function at the point in question.

I. *If a regular summation sums the divergent G.P.,* $\sum_0^\infty z^n$, *its generalized sum will be the 'right' value* $1/(1-z)$.

Proof. By hypothesis,

$$\text{the } \gamma\text{-sum of } \sum_1^\infty z^n = \gamma\text{-sum of } \sum_0^\infty z^n - 1 = \sigma - 1, \text{ say.}$$

But the γ-sum of $z\sum\limits_0^\infty z^n = z$ (γ-sum of $\sum\limits_0^\infty z^n) = z\sigma$. Therefore $\sigma - 1 = z\sigma$, and thus $\sigma = 1/(1-z)$. Q. e. d.

II. *The method of arithmetic means of any real order* $r > -1$ *(Exx.* 1 *and* 2), *Abel's summation, Ex.* 4 *with* $\theta_k = \theta^k$, $\theta < 1$, *Ex.* 7, *and Riesz summation in Ex.* 8 *are regular.*

(Perron, 1920.)

Proof. Putting

$$\sum_{k=1}^{\infty} c_k g_k(a) = s(a), \quad \sum_{k=1}^{\infty} c_k g_{k+1}(a) = \sigma(a),$$

we have to show that if either of the two limits $\lim\limits_{a\to\infty} s(a)$ or $\lim\limits_{a\to\infty} \sigma(a)$ exists, the other also exists and equals the first. But in the case of arithmetic means $\sigma(a) = (a-1)\, s(a-1)/(a+r-1)$, for Abel's sums $\sigma(a) = as(a)/(a+1)$, in Ex. 4, when $\theta_k = \theta^k$, $\sigma(a) = s(\sigma a)$, in Ex. 7 $\sigma(a) = as(a+1)/(a+1)$ and for the Riesz summation $\sigma(a) = \left(\frac{a-1}{a}\right)^r s(a-1)$, which establishes the proposition.

Borel's exponential summation is not regular as is shown by the following example. We determine the coefficients c_k by the equations

$$\sum_{k=0}^{\infty} c_k t^{k+1}/(k+1)! = f'(t) - f(t),$$

where
$$f(t) = 1 + e^t \sin(t^2)/t,$$

which leads to

$$s(a) = \int_0^a e^{-t}[f''(t) - f'(t)]\, dt = e^{-a} f'(a) - 1$$

$$= \frac{\sin(a^2)}{a} - \frac{\sin(a^2)}{a^2} + 2\cos(a^2) - 1,$$

which has no limit when $a \to \infty$, whereas

$$\sigma(a) = \int_0^a e^{-t}[f'(t) - f(t)]dt = e^{-a} f(a) - 1$$

$$= \frac{\sin(a^2)}{a} - e^{-a} - 1 \to -1.$$

For the series $\sum_{1}^{\infty} c_k$, however, the function corresponding to $u(a)$ of $\sum_{0}^{\infty} c_k$ is $u'(a)$, i. e. by the remark following (96. 8) if $\sum_{1}^{\infty} c_k$ is summable by the exponential method to s then also $\sum_{0}^{\infty} c_k$ is summable by the same method to the sum $s+c_0$. Thus adding a term to the series does not destroy its summability though the suppression of a term may destroy it. In such a case we say that the summation is *semi-regular. Borel's exponential summation is semi-regular.* Similar definition for limits:

If the A-convergence of $z_1, z_2, \ldots$ implies that of $z_0, z_1, z_2 \ldots$ to the same limit, we say that the A-limit is a *semi-regular limit process.*

We notice, however, that

III. *Borel's absolute exponential summation is regular.*

Proof. Absolute summability (B) is a particular case of summability (B). Thus, by I, we have only to show that if $\sum_{0}^{\infty} c_n$ is absolutely summable (B), then also $\sum_{1}^{\infty} c_n$ is absolutely summable (B).

The conditions (96. 12) of the absolute summability (B) for $\sum_{0}^{\infty} c_n$ contain also the conditions of the absolute summability (B) for $\sum_{1}^{\infty} c_n$, since in the case of the latter series the function corresponding to $u(a)$ is $u'(a)$. Therefore, denoting by $|B|$ the absolute summability (B), we have to establish that

$$(1) \qquad |B|\text{-sum of } \sum_{0}^{\infty} c_n = c_0 + |B|\text{-sum of } \sum_{1}^{\infty} c_n.$$

The condition for $|B|$-summability contains, in particular, the existence of

$$\int_0^\infty e^{-a}u'(a)da.$$

Therefore, by (96. 8), and by the remark following that formula,

$$\int_0^\infty e^{-a}u(a)\,da,$$

also exists, and

$$\lim_{a\to\infty} e^{-a}u(a) = 0,$$

which proves (1).

101. *General properties of regular limits and summations.* The theory of regular limit processes and summations has not been developed yet, so that we have to restrict ourselves to some more or less obvious consequences of their definitions, followed by some examples.

I. *If A is a regular limit process, then* A-$\lim(z_1, z_2, \ldots) = z$ *implies that* A-$\lim(z_p, z_{p+1}, \ldots) = z$ *and conversely.*

II. *If A is a regular summation and the A-sum of Σc_k is s, then if we insert new terms $c_1', c_2', \ldots, c_p'$ anywhere in the series, the new series is summable by A to the sum*

$$s+c_1'+c_2'+\ldots+c_p'.$$

For the remainder of a series we have the following result:

III. *If T is regular and* T-$\lim\limits_{n=\infty} s_n = s$, *the T-limit of the T-remainder tends to* 0.

Proof. Putting $a_{k+1}+a_{k+2}+\ldots+a_{k+n} = R_{k,n}$, we have $s_{k+n} = s_k+R_{k,n}$. Thus, when T-$\lim s_n = s$ and T is regular, we have T-$\lim\limits_{n=\infty} s_{k+n} = T$-$\lim\limits_{n=\infty}(s_k+R_{k,n}) = s$. But, for any fixed k, T-$\lim\limits_{n=\infty} s_k = s_k$, and thus also the T-remainder: T-$\lim\limits_{n=\infty} R_{k,n} \equiv T$-$R_k$ exists and $= s-s_k$. Since T-$\lim\limits_{k=\infty} s_k = s$, we have

$$\text{(1)} \qquad T\text{-}\lim_{k=\infty} T\text{-}R_k = 0 \qquad \text{Q. e. d.}$$

IV. *If T is regular or only semi-regular and* T-$\lim s_n = z$, *then* T-$\lim c_n = 0$, *where* $s_{n+1} = c_0+c_1+\ldots+c_n$.

Proof. By hypothesis

$$\lim_{n=\infty}\sum_{k=0}^{\infty} s_k a_{nk} = \lim_{n=\infty}\sum_{k=1}^{\infty} s_k a_{n,k-1},$$

whenever the limit on the right-hand side exists. Subtracting the left-hand side from the right-hand side we obtain

$$\lim_{n=\infty}\sum_{k=0}^{\infty} (s_{k+1}-s_k)\, a_{nk} = \lim_{n=\infty}\sum_{k=0}^{\infty} c_k a_{nk} = T\text{-}\lim c_n = 0.$$

Conversely, T-lim $c_n = 0$ means that T-lim $(s_{n+1}-s_n) = 0$, i. e. T-lim $s_{n+1} = T$-lim s_n whenever one of the two limits in question exists. Thus

V. *The necessary and sufficient condition that a T-limit be regular for a given sequence* s_n *is that* T-lim $(s_{n+1}-s_n) = 0$.

The defect of this result is that it only establishes the regularity of a given limit process for a given sequence.

We notice two immediate consequences of V. If the T-limit is regular for s_k, the necessary and sufficient condition that the T'-limit also be regular for s_k is that T' be consistent with T for $s_{k+1}-s_k$. In particular, if $s_{k+1}-s_k = c_k \to 0$, T-lim $c_k = 0$ for every T-limit. Therefore if a T-matrix transforms s_k and s_{k+1} into convergent sequences where $s_{k+1}-s_k = c_k \to 0$, the corresponding T-limit is regular for s_k.

VI. *Suppose that* (i) *A and B are two commutable T-matrices with the bounds M and N respectively* (ii) $\Sigma g_p M^p$, $\Sigma h_p N^p$ *are convergent and* $\Sigma g_p = 1$, $\Sigma h_p = 1$; (iii) *the transformations* $G = \Sigma g_p A^p$ *and* $H = \Sigma h_p B^p$ *transform both sequences* s_k *and* s_{k+1} *into convergent sequences, and the transformation G is regular for* s_k. *Then also H is regular for* s_k, *provided*

$$G[H(C_k)] = (GH)(C_k) \text{ and } H[G(C_k)] = (HG)(C_k).$$

Proof. It follows from 98. VIII that G and H are consistent for c_k. But, the G-limit being regular for s_k, we have G-lim $c_k = 0$ and thus also H-lim $c_k = 0$, which proves the proposition.

Theorem IV restricts the application of a given limit process just as the necessary condition $c_k \to 0$ restricts ordinary convergence. The question of the extension or field of applicability of the various limit processes and summations has not yet been systematically examined. We shall see for instance that arithmetic means of order r are more powerful than those of order $<r$, i. e. the existence of $M^r\text{-}\lim z_k = z$ implies that of $M^{r'}\text{-}\lim z_k = z$ for every $r' > r$. Now, the exponential method applies in many cases where no M^r-limit exists, however large r is, i. e. the exponential method seems to be more powerful than that of the arithmetic means. But Hardy (1910) has shown that the sequence $(s_0 + s_1 + \dots + s_n)/n$ formed from the series $\Sigma(-1)^{n-1} z^{n^3}/n^{3s}$, $-1/3 < s < 0$, at $z = 1$ exists, while that of the corresponding exponential sums does not.

A similar result is the following:

VII. *Every absolutely convergent series is absolutely summable (B) but there are conditionally convergent series which are not absolutely summable (B).*

Proof. If $\Sigma |a_n|$ converges to s, Appell's comparison theorem Ex. III. 13, shows that

$$\lim_{a\to\infty} e^{-a} \sum_0^\infty (|a_0| + |a_1| + \dots + |a_n|)\, a^n/n! = s.$$

Hence, putting $U(a) = \Sigma |a_n| a^n/n!$, we have, by (96. 7),

$$\lim_{a\to\infty} \int_0^a e^{-a}\, U'(a)\, da = s - |a_0|.$$

Similarly it follows from the convergence of $|a_m| + |a_{m+1}| + \dots$ that the integral

$$\int_0^a e^{-a} \frac{d^{m+1} U(a)\, da}{da^{m+1}},$$

tends to a definite limit for $a \to \infty$. We conclude thus, as in Art. 96, that $\lim\limits_{a\to\infty} e^{-a} U(a) = 0$, i. e. that the integral

$$\int_0^\infty e^{-a}\, U(a)\, da$$

exists.

Remarking finally that

$$\int_0^\infty e^{-a} \left| \frac{d^m u(a)}{da^m} \right| da \leqslant \int_0^\infty e^{-a} \frac{d^m U(a)\, da}{da^m},$$

the first part of the statement is proved.

The second part was proved by Hardy (1904), who showed that for the series where $c_n = (-1)^{\sqrt{n}}/\sqrt{n}$ if $\sqrt{n}$ is an integer, and

$c_n = 0$ if $\sqrt{n}$ is not an integer, the integral $\int_0^\infty e^{-a} \mid u(a) \mid da$ does not exist.

102. *The method of arithmetic means.* We are going to give a fairly complete account of the method of arithmetic means and for convenience we reproduce all the formulae already proved in connexion with this subject.

From

$$(1-z)^{-r-1} = \Sigma (r+1)(r+2)\dots(r+n)z^n/n! \equiv \Sigma A_n^r z^n,$$

we have

$$(1) \qquad A_n^r = \frac{\Gamma(r+n+1)}{\Gamma(n+1)\,\Gamma(r+1)}, \quad A_n^0 = 1,$$

$$A_0^r = 1, \quad A_n^1 = n+1,$$

which defines A_n^r for every real or complex value r *except negative integers.*

From $$(1-z)^{-r} \Sigma s_n z^n = \Sigma S_n^r z^n,$$

where $s_n = c_0 + c_1 + \dots + c_n$, we have

$$S_n^r = \sum_{\nu=0}^{n} A_{n-\nu}^{r-1} s_\nu = \sum_{\nu=0}^{n} A_{n-\nu}^{r} c_\nu.$$

Thus $$s_n^{(r)} = \sum_{\nu=0}^{n} A_{n-\nu}^{r-1} s_\nu / A_n^r = S_n^r / A_n^r,$$

and if this tends to a limit, Σc_n is said to be *summable* C^r.

We readily verify that $A_n^r > 0$ for $r > -1$; for a fixed $r > 0$, A_n^r is steadily increasing to $+\infty$ when $n \to \infty$; for $-1 < r < 0$, A_n^r is steadily decreasing to 0. If $r = -s < -1$ and not a negative integer, the sign of A_n^r is alternating up to $n \leqslant [s]$ and has the constant sign $(-1)^{[s]}$ for $n > [s]$.

By Stirling's formula, Ex. IV. 22, we verify that

(2) $A_n^r \sim n^r/\Gamma(r+1)$ for a real fixed r ($\neq$ negative integer).

The identity

$$\frac{1}{(1-z)^{p+1}} \frac{1}{(1-z)^{r+1}} = \frac{1}{(1-z)^{p+r+2}},$$

shows that

$$(3) \qquad \sum_{k=0}^{n} A_{n-k}^{p} A_k^r = A_n^{p+r+1}$$

($p, r, p+r+1$ not negative integers), from which we obtain, putting $p = 0$,

$$(4) \qquad \sum_{k=0}^{n} A_k^r = A_n^{r+1}.$$

A useful limit relation is

$$(5) \qquad \sum_{k=0}^{n} |A_k^{-r} A_{n-k}^{-s}| = O(n^{-r}) + O(n^{-s}) + O(n^{-r-s+1}),$$

(Andersen, 1922)

for any real r and s ($r, s, r+s-1$ not positive integers).

Proof. Putting

$$\rho = \begin{cases} [r] & \text{for } r > 1 \\ 0 & \text{for } r < 1 \end{cases} \qquad \sigma = \begin{cases} [s] & \text{for } s > 1 \\ 0 & \text{for } s < 1 \end{cases},$$

we have

$$|A_p^{-r}| = (-1)^\rho A_p^{-r} \text{ for } p \geqslant \rho, |A_p^{-s}| = (-1)^\sigma A_p^{-s} \text{ for } p \geqslant \sigma.$$

Hence,

$$\sum_{k=0}^{n} |A_k^{-r} A_{n-k}^{-s}| = \sum_{k=0}^{\rho-1} + \sum_{k=\rho}^{n-\sigma} + \sum_{k=n-\sigma+1}^{n}$$

$$= O(n^{-s}) + (-1)^{\rho+\sigma} \sum_{k=\rho}^{n-\sigma} A_k^{-r} A_{n-k}^{-s} + O(n^{-r}),$$

where $\sum_{k=0}^{\rho-1} = 0$ when $\rho = 0$ and $\sum_{k=n-\sigma+1}^{n} = 0$ if $\sigma = 0$. But

$$\sum_{k=\rho}^{n-\sigma} A_k^{-r} A_{n-k}^{-s} = \sum_{k=0}^{n} - \sum_{k=0}^{\rho-1} - \sum_{k=n-\sigma+1}^{n} = A_n^{-r-s+1} + O(n^{-s}) + O(n^{-r}),$$

which proves (5).

An important particular case is

$$(6) \quad \sum_{k=0}^{n} |A_k^{-s}| = O(1) + O(n^{-s}) + O(n^{-s+1}) = O(1) + O(n^{-s+1}).$$

An important result constantly used in the sequel is the following theorem:

I. *If* $a_n/n^r \to a$, $b_n/n^s \to b$, $r > -1$, $s > -1$, *then*

$$(7) \quad \sum_{\nu=0}^{n} a_{n-\nu} b_\nu / n^{r+s+1} \to \Gamma(r+1)\, \Gamma(s+1)\, ab / \Gamma(r+s+2).$$

(Cesàro.)

Proof. By hypothesis, and by (2)

$$a_n = [\Gamma(r+1)a + \epsilon_n]A_n^r, \quad b_n = [\Gamma(s+1)b + \eta_n]A_n^s,$$

ϵ_n, η_n tending to 0 with $1/n$. Hence, by (3),

$$\sum_{\nu=0}^{n} a_{n-\nu} b_\nu = \Gamma(r+1)\Gamma(s+1)\, ab A_n^{r+s+1} + a\Gamma(r+1)\Sigma A_{n-\nu}^r \eta_\nu A_\nu^s$$
$$+ b\Gamma(s+1)\Sigma \epsilon_{n-\nu} A_{n-\nu}^r A_\nu^s + \Sigma \epsilon_{n-\nu} \eta_\nu A_{n-\nu}^r A_\nu^s.$$

By hypothesis there is an M such that $|\epsilon_n| < M, |\eta_n| < M$ for every n and, ϵ being given, there is an N such that for $n > N$,

$$|\epsilon_n| < \epsilon, \quad |\eta_n| < \epsilon.$$

Hence

$$\sum_{\nu=0}^{N} A_{n-\nu}^r |\eta_\nu| A_\nu^s + \sum_{\nu=N+1}^{n} A_{n-\nu}^r |\eta_\nu| A_\nu^s < M \sum_{\nu=0}^{N} A_{n-\nu}^r A_\nu^s + \epsilon A_n^{r+s+1}$$

But, for a fixed ν, $(n-\nu)^r \nu^s \sim n^r \nu^s$, i. e.

$$A_{n-\nu}^r A_\nu^s / A_n^{r+s+1} \sim c/n^{s+1} \to 0.$$

Therefore $\sum_{\nu=0}^{n} A_{n-\nu}^r |\eta_\nu| A_\nu^s / A_n^{r+s+1} \to 0.$

Similarly for the next sum. For the last sum we notice that

$$|\Sigma \epsilon_{n-\nu} \eta_\nu A_{n-\nu}^r A_\nu^s| < M \Sigma |\eta_\nu| A_{n-\nu}^r A_\nu^s,$$

and argue as before. This completes the proof.

II. *If* Σc_n *is summable* C^r, $r > -1$, *then it is also summable* C^{r+s}, $s > 0$, *to the same sum.* (Chapman, 1911.)

Proof. From

$$\frac{\Sigma s_n z^n}{(1-z)^{r+s}} = \frac{\Sigma s_n z^n}{(1-z)^r} \frac{1}{(1-z)^s} = \Sigma S_n^r z^n \Sigma A_n^{s-1} z^n,$$

we obtain

$$S_n^{r+s} = \sum_{\nu=0}^{n} A_{n-\nu}^{s-1} S_\nu^r. \tag{8}$$

By hypothesis, and by (2)

$$\lim_{n=\infty} S_n^r / A_n^r \to \sigma, \text{ i. e. } S_n^r / n^r \to \sigma/\Gamma(r+1).$$

Since, by (2), $\lim_{n=\infty} A_n^{s-1}/n^{s-1} \to 1/\Gamma(s)$, theorem I applies to the right-hand side of (8) and gives

$$S_n^{r+s}/n^{r+s} \to \sigma/\Gamma(r+s+1), \text{ i.e. } S_n^{r+s}/A_n^{r+s} \to \sigma. \quad \text{Q.e.d.}$$

It follows from this theorem that, for any given sequence s_n, there is a least number $r \geqslant -1$, called the *index of summability*, such that $s_n^{(r+\delta)}$ is convergent and $s_n^{(r-\delta)}$ is divergent $(\delta > 0)$ with the restriction that when $r = -1$, only the first condition is retained.

At the same time the result can be interpreted as the consistency theorem for the method of arithmetic means. If for any sequence s_n the arithmetic means of order r and r' are convergent, they converge to the same limit. In fact one of the numbers r and r' is less than the other, $r < r'$, say, and so, by our last result, the arithmetic means converge to the same limit.

III. *If* Σc_n *is summable* C^r, $r > -1$, *then* $s_n^{(r-\delta)}/n^\delta \to 0$, *where* $0 < \delta < r+1$. (Dienes, 1913; Andersen, 1922.)
In particular for $\delta = r$, $s_n/n^r \to 0$ *and thus also* $c_n/n^r \to 0$. (Chapman, 1911.)

Proof. By hypothesis, $S_n^r = (s+\epsilon_n)A_n^r$ and for $n > p$, say, $|\epsilon_n| < \epsilon$, where ϵ is arbitrarily given. If δ is an integer, since $S_n^{k-1} = S_n^k - S_{n-1}^k$, we see, by (2), that $S_n^{r-\delta}/n^r \to 0$. If δ is not an integer, we have

$$S_n^{r-\delta} = \sum_{\nu=0}^{n} A_{n-\nu}^{-\delta-1}(s+\epsilon_\nu)A_\nu^r$$

$$= sA_n^{r-\delta} + \sum_{\nu=0}^{p} A_{n-\nu}^{-\delta-1}\epsilon_\nu A_\nu^r + \sum_{\nu=p+1}^{n} A_{n-\nu}^{-\delta-1}\epsilon_\nu A_\nu^r.$$

The first term and each of the finite number of terms in the first sum when divided by n^r obviously tend to 0. Finally, since $r > -1$,

$$\left|\sum_{\nu=p+1}^{n} A_{n-\nu}^{-\delta-1}\epsilon_\nu A_\nu^r\right| < \epsilon \sum_{\nu=0}^{n} |A_{n-\nu}^{-\delta-1}A_\nu^r| = \epsilon O(n^r), \text{ by (5).}$$

Therefore all the limiting numbers of $S_n^{r-\delta}/n^r$ lie between $-A\epsilon$ and $+A\epsilon$, i.e. ϵ being arbitrarily small and A independent of ϵ, that ratio has the unique limiting number 0. Q.e.d.

This result restricts the field of application of arithmetic means. If c_n/n^r does not tend to 0 for any $r > -1$, the arithmetic means do not apply.

103. *The method of arithmetic means—continued.* Another kind of restriction for the method of arithmetic means is implied in the following result.

I. *If* $|s_n^{(r)}| < M$, $r > -1$, (in which case we say that s_n or Σc_k is oscillating C^r) *and if there is a* $\rho > r$ *such that* s_n *is summable* C^ρ, *then* s_n *is summable* $C^{r+\delta}$ *for every* $\delta > 0$. (Andersen, 1922.)

Proof. We first prove the theorem for $\rho = r+1$ and, for simplicity, we suppose that $\lim_{n=\infty} s_n^{(r+1)} = 0$ and $\delta < 1$. If θ is a fraction, specified later on, and p is the integer satisfying the inequalities $\theta n \leqslant p < \theta n + 1$, we have

$$S_n^{r+\delta} = \sum_{\nu=0}^{n} A_\nu^{-1+\delta} S_{n-\nu}^r = \sum_{\nu=0}^{p-1} + \sum_{\nu=p}^{n} = A_n + B_n,$$

where

$$|A_n| < M \sum_{\nu=0}^{p-1} A_\nu^{-1+\delta} N(n-\nu)^r$$

$$\leqslant \begin{cases} MNn^r A_{p-1}^\delta & < MN_1 n^r (p-1)^\delta \quad \text{if } r \geqslant 0 \\ MN(n-p+1)^r A_{p-1}^\delta & < MN_1 (n-p+1)^r (p-1)^\delta \text{ if } r < 0. \end{cases}$$

i. e.

$$|A_n| < \begin{cases} MN_1 n^r (\theta n)^\delta & = M_1 n^{r+\delta} \theta^\delta \\ MN_1 (n-\theta n)^r (\theta n)^\delta & = M_1 n^{r+\delta} (1-\theta)^r \theta^\delta. \end{cases}$$

Now, if $r \geqslant 0$, take a θ such that $M_1\, \theta^\delta < \epsilon$ and if $r < 0$ take a θ such that $M_1 (1-\theta)^r \theta^\delta < \epsilon$, where ϵ, as usual, is arbitrarily given. If in either case we denote by θ_1 the chosen value of θ, we have

$$\theta_1 n \leqslant p < \theta_1 n + 1, \quad |A_n| < \epsilon n^{r+\delta} \text{ for every } n.$$

Similarly

$$B_n = \sum_{\nu=p}^{n} A_\nu^{-1+\delta} S_{n-\nu}^r = \sum_{\nu=0}^{n-p} S_\nu^r A_{n-\nu}^{-1+\delta}$$

$$= \sum_{\nu=0}^{n-p-1} S_\nu^{r+1} A_{n-\nu}^{-2+\delta} + S_{n-p}^{r+1} A_p^{-1+\delta} = \sum_{\nu=0}^{P} + \sum_{\nu=P+1}^{n-p-1} + S_{n-p}^{r+1} A_p^{-1+\delta}$$

$$= b_1(n) + b_2(n) + b_3(n),$$

where P is determined by the condition that for $n > P$, $|s_n^{(r+1)}| < \eta$, η being arbitrarily given.

Now, putting $|s_n^{(r+1)}| = \epsilon_n$, we have

$$\begin{aligned}|b_3(n)| &= \epsilon_{n-p} A_{n-p}^{r+1} A_p^{-1+\delta} \\ &\leqslant M_2 \epsilon_{n-p} (n-p)^{r+1} p^{-1+\delta} \\ &\leqslant M_2 \epsilon_{n-p} (n-\theta_1 n)^{r+1} (\theta_1 n)^{-1+\delta} \\ &= M_2 (1-\theta_1)^{r+1} \theta_1^{-1+\delta} \epsilon_{n-p} n^{r+\delta} = M_3 \epsilon_{n-p} n^{r+\delta},\end{aligned}$$

where M_3 is independent of n. Hence there is an n_1 such that

$$|b_3(n)| < \epsilon n^{r+\delta} \text{ for } n > n_1.$$

Similarly

$$|b_2(n)| < \eta \sum_{\nu=P+1}^{n-p+1} A_\nu^{r+1} |A_{n-\nu}^{-2+\delta}| < -\eta \sum_{\nu=0}^{n-p+1} A_\nu^{r+1} A_{n-\nu}^{-2+\delta},$$

since $A_{n-\nu}^{-2+\delta} < 0$ for $0 \leqslant \nu \leqslant n-1$. But

$$\sum_{\nu=0}^{n-p+1} A_\nu^{r+1} A_{n-\nu}^{-2+\delta} = \sum_{\nu=0}^{n} - \sum_{\nu=n-p}^{n} = A_n^{r+\delta} - \sum_{\nu=n-p}^{n} A_\nu^{r+1} A_{n-\nu}^{-2+\delta},$$

so that

$$\begin{aligned}|b_2(n)| &< \eta \sum_{\nu=0}^{p} A_\nu^{-2+\delta} A_{n-\nu}^{r+1} - \eta A_n^{r+\delta} \\ &= \eta \left(\sum_{\nu=0}^{p-1} A_\nu^{-1+\delta} A_{n-\nu}^{r} + A_p^{-1+\delta} A_{n-p}^{r+1} \right) - \eta A_n^{r+\delta} \\ &< \eta \left(\sum_{\nu=0}^{n} A_\nu^{-1+\delta} A_{n-\nu}^{r} + A_p^{-1+\delta} A_{n-p}^{r+1} \right) - \eta A_n^{r+\delta} = \eta A_p^{-1+\delta} A_{n-p}^{r+1}.\end{aligned}$$

Hence $$|b_2(n)| < M_4 \eta n^{r+\delta} < \epsilon n^{r+\delta},$$

for every n, if η is sufficiently small.

Finally,

$$\begin{aligned}|b_1(n)| &< M_5 \sum_{\nu=0}^{P} |A_{n-\nu}^{-2+\delta}| < M_5 (P+1) |A_{n-P}^{-2+\delta}| \\ &< M_6 (P+1)(n-P)^{-2+\delta} < M_7 (P+1) n^{-2+\delta} = \frac{M_7(P+1)}{n^{r+2}} n^{r+\delta},\end{aligned}$$

and, as $r+2>1$, there is an n_2 such that $|b_1(n)| < \epsilon n^{r+\delta}$ for $n > n_2$, which proves that $S_n^{r+\delta}/n^{r+\delta} \to 0$, i.e. $s_n^{(r+\delta)} \to 0$. The theorem is thus proved for $\rho = r+1$.

To establish the general case we have only to make the following remarks.

The case $\rho \leqslant r+1$ is included in the result just proved, since, by 102. II, if Σc_n is summable C^ρ it is summable C^{r+1}. If $\rho > r+1$ and $r > -1$, Σc_n is oscillating $C^{\rho-1}$ (since it is oscillating C^r and $\rho-1 > r$); hence, by our result, it is summable $C^{-1+\delta}$ and if $\rho-1 < r+1$, we can take a δ such that $\rho-1+\delta \leqslant r+1$ and thus Σc_n is summable $C^{r+\delta}$. In this way after a finite number of steps we establish the general result with the exception of the case $r=-1$. In the last case, the oscillation C^p, $p>-1$, does not follow from the oscillation C^{-1}.

But, for $s>0$, the identity

$$(n+1)\,S_n^{s-1} = sS_{n-1}^s + \sum_{\nu=0}^{n} c_\nu(\nu+1)\,A_{n-\nu}^{s-1},$$

leads to

$$(n+1)\,|\,S_n^{s-1}\,| < sM_1 A_{n-1}^s + M_2 A_n^s = O(n^s),$$

i.e.

$$|\,S_n^{s-1}\,| < M(n+1)^{s-1}.$$

Hence $|\,s_n^{(s-1)}\,|$ is oscillating.

The theorem shows that:

Corollary. *If there is an r such that $s_n^{(r)}$ is oscillating, either Σc_n is not summable by arithmetic means of any order or it is summable by all the arithmetic means of order $>r$.*

For integral values of r a natural way of forming means of successive orders is to form the arithmetic means of the arithmetic means of the first order and so on:

$$\begin{aligned}
H_n^{(1)} &= (s_0+s_1+\ldots+s_n)/(n+1) = s_n^{(1)},\\
H_n^{(2)} &= (H_0^{(1)}+H_1^{(1)}+\ldots+H_n^{(1)})/(n+1),\\
&\ldots\ldots\ldots\ldots\\
H_n^{(r)} &= (H_0^{(r-1)}+H_1^{(r-1)}+\ldots+H_n^{(r-1)})/(n+1),\\
&\ldots\ldots\ldots\ldots
\end{aligned}$$

called Hölder sums.

II. *If, for a sequence s_n, $H_n^{(r)}(s_k)$ tends to s, then also $s_n^{(r)}(s_k) \to s$ and conversely.* (Knopp, 1907 a; Schnee, 1908.)

Proof. (Andersen, 1928.) We require the following

Lemma. *If $s_n^{(p)}(s_k) \to s$, then $s_n^{(p-1)}(s_k^{(1)}) \to s$ and conversely.*

Proof of the lemma. By Abel's identity,

$$(1)\quad \sum_{\nu=0}^{n} (\nu+p)s_\nu = -\sum_{\nu=0}^{n-1} S_\nu^1 + (n+p)S_n^1$$
$$= -S_n^2 + (n+p+1)\,S_n^1$$

and, by definition, $S_n^1 = (n+1)s_n^{(1)}$. Replacing s_ν by $s_\nu^{(1)}$, we obtain, by (1), for $p = 1$,

$$S_n^2(s_k) = -S_n^2(s_k^{(1)}) + (n+2)S_n^1(s_k^{(1)}).$$

Replacing n by ν and summing for $\nu = 0, 1, \ldots, n$, we have, by (1), for $p = 2$,

$$S_n^3(s_k) = -2S_n^3(s_k^{(1)}) + (n+3)S_n^2(s_k^{(1)}),$$

and, in general,

$$(2)\qquad S_n^p(s_k) = (-p+1)S_n^p(s_k^{(1)}) + (n+p)S_n^{p-1}(s_k^{(1)}).$$

Dividing by $A_n^p = \dfrac{n+p}{p}A_n^{p-1}$, we obtain

$$(3)\qquad s_n^{(p)}(s_k) = (-p+1)s_n^{(p)}(s_k^{(1)}) + ps_n^{(p-1)}(s_k^{(1)}).$$

Now, when $s_n^{(p-1)}(s_k^{(1)}) \to s$, then also, by 102. II, $s_n^{(p)}(s_k^{(1)}) \to s$ and thus, by (3), $s_n^{(p)}(s_k) \to s$ which proves the converse of our statement.

To prove the first part we transform (2) by noticing that

$$S_n^{p-1}(s_k^{(1)}) = S_n^p(s_k^{(1)}) - S_{n-1}^p(s_k^{(1)}),$$

and we obtain

$$S_n^p(s_k) = (n+1)S_n^p(s_k^{(1)}) - (n+p)S_{n-1}^p(s_k^{(1)}),$$

i. e. dividing by $A_n^p = \dfrac{n+p}{n}A_{n-1}^p$, we have

$$(4)\qquad s_n^{(p)}(s_k) = (n+1)s_n^{(p)}(s_k^{(1)}) - ns_{n-1}^{(p)}(s_k^{(1)}).$$

Replacing n by ν and summing from 0 to n, we obtain

$$(5)\qquad \frac{s_0^{(p)}(s_k) + s_1^{(p)}(s_k) + \ldots + s_n^{(p)}(s_k)}{n+1} = s_n^{(p)}(s_k^{(1)}),$$

which shows that when $s_n^{(p)}(s_k) \to s$, then also $s_n^{(p)}(s_k^{(1)}) \to s$ and thus, by (3), $s_n^{(p-1)}(s_k^{(1)}) \to s$. Q. e. d.

Theorem II readily follows from the lemma. In fact, in virtue of our lemma, the equations

$$s_n^{(r)}(s_k) \to s,\ s_n^{r-1}(H_k^{(1)}) \to s,\ \ldots,\ s_n^{(1)}(H^{(r-1)}) \to s,\ H_n^r \to s,$$

hold or do not hold at the same time.

104. *The method of arithmetic means—concluded.*

In this article we are going to establish a set of necessary and sufficient conditions for summability by arithmetic means.

I. *The necessary and sufficient condition that* $\Sigma a_k = A$ *should be summable* C^r *is that the equations*

$$(1) \qquad a_n = (n+1)(b_n - b_{n+1})$$

have a solution $b_0, b_1, \ldots, b_n, \ldots$ *such that* $\Sigma b_k = B$ *is summable* C^{r-1}. (Hardy and Littlewood, 1924.)

We denote by A the sum of the series Σa_k as well as the series itself.

Proof. We notice first that, for any given a_n, (1) has a solution and, if b_n is a solution of (1), then all its solutions are of the form $b_n + c$ where c is a fixed constant. Our next remark is that, putting
$$S_n^r(a_0 + \ldots + a_k) = S_n^r,$$
and similarly
$$S_n^r(b_1 + \ldots + b_k) = S_n'^r,$$
we have

$$(2) \qquad S_n^r = (r+1)S_n'^r - (n+1)S_{n+1}'^{r-1}.$$

In fact, putting $f(z) = \Sigma a_n z^n$, $g(z) = \Sigma b_n z^n$, we have

$$f(z) = [(z-1)g(z)]' = g(z) + (z-1)g'(z).$$

Since, by definition,

$$f(z)/(1-z)^{r+1} = \Sigma S_n^r z^n, \quad g(z)/(1-z)^{r+1} = \Sigma S_n'^r z^n,$$

and

$$[g(z)/(1-z)^r]' = g'(z)/(1-z)^r + rg(z)/(1-z)^{r+1},$$

we obtain

$$f(z)/(1-z)^{r+1} = -[g(z)/(1-z)^r]' + (r+1)g(z)/(1-z)^{r+1},$$

i. e.

$$\begin{aligned}\Sigma S_n^r z^n &\equiv (r+1)\Sigma S_n'^r z^n - (\Sigma S_n'^{r-1} z^n)' \\ &= (r+1)\Sigma S_n'^r z^n - \Sigma (n+1) S_{n+1}'^{r-1} z^n,\end{aligned}$$

which establishes our second remark for every positive r. For $r = 0$ we have

$$(3) \qquad A_n = B_n - (n+1)b_{n+1}.$$

Suppose now that B is summable C^{r-1}. Then B is *a fortiori* summable C^r, i. e. $S_n'^r = A_n^r B + o(n^r)$ and, by (2),

$$S_n^r = [(r+1)A_n^r - (n+1)A_{n+1}^{r-1}]B + o(n^r) = A_n^r B + o(n^r).$$

Thus

II. *If B is summable C^{r-1}, A is summable C^r to B.*

Suppose now that A is summable C^r. We may suppose that its sum is 0. If $r=0$, we have

$$(n+2)B_n-(n+1)B_{n+1} = B_n-(n+1)b_{n+1} = A_n = o(1),$$

i. e.
$$\frac{B_n}{n+1}-\frac{B_{n+1}}{n+2} = \frac{A_n}{(n+2)(n+1)} = o(1/n^2),$$

and thus there is a constant h such that $B_n/(n+1) = h+o(1/n)$, and finally

(4)
$$b_{n+1} = B_{n+1}/(n+1)+o(1/n) = h+o(1/n).$$

For $r>0$ we have similarly

(5)
$$(n+r+2)S_n'^r-(n+1)S_{n+1}'^r = (r+1)S_n'^r-(n+1)S_{n+1}'^{r-1} = S_n^r = o(n^r).$$

Putting $S_n'^r = (n+r+1)\dots(n+1)g_n$ and reducing, we obtain

$$(n+r+2)\dots(n+1)(g_n-g_{n+1}) = S_n^r = o(n^r),$$

i. e.
$$g_n-g_{n+1} = o(1/n^2).$$

Hence, $g_n \to g$ and

$$g_n = g+\sum_{\nu=n}^{\infty}\frac{S_\nu^r}{(\nu+r+2)\dots(\nu+1)} = g+\sum_{\nu=n}^{\infty}o(1/\nu^2) = g+o(1/n),$$

and thus

$$S_n'^r = (n+r+1)\dots(n+1)g+o(n^r).$$

Substituting in (5), we obtain

$$S_{n+1}'^{r-1} = hA_{n+1}^r+o(n^{r-1}), \text{ where } h=(r+1)!\,g.$$

We state this result in the form

III. *If A is summable C^r, then*

(6)
$$S_n'^{r-1} = hA_n^r+AA_n^{r-1}+o(n^{r-1}).$$

This equation readily proves that the condition as stated in theorem I is necessary. In fact, assuming that $A=0$, suppose that b_n is any solution of (1). By our first remark all the other solutions are of the form b_n+c. Taking $c=-h$, we have

$$S_n''^{r-1} = S_n'^{r-1}-hA_n^r = o(n^{r-1}),$$

i. e. b_n-h is summable C^{r-1} to the sum 0.

Finally, if Σa_n is summable C^r, then $\Sigma(a_n+c)$ is certainly not summable. Therefore there is only one solution satisfying the conditions.

If r is an integer, the successive application of I leads to the following general theorem.

IV. *The necessary and sufficient condition that* $A = \Sigma a_n$ *should be summable* C^r *(r an integer) is that there should be a system of numbers* $a_{ns}, s = 0, 1, \ldots, r+1;\ n = 0, 1, 2, \ldots,$ *such that* $a_{n0} = a_n, a_{n,s-1} = (n+1)(a_{ns} - a_{n+1,s}), s > 0$ *and* $A_{r+1} = \Sigma a_{n,r+1}$ *is summable* C^{-1}, i.e. *convergent and* $na_{n,r+1} \to 0$.

(Knopp, 1924; Hardy and Littlewood, 1924.)

Proof. Suppose that A_{r+1} is summable C^{-1}. Applying I repeatedly we see that A_s is summable C^{r-s} for $s = r, r-1, \ldots, 0$, i.e. $A_0 = A$ is summable C^r. Conversely if A is summable C^r, there are numbers a_{n0} such that A_s is summable C^{r-s}, i.e. A_{r+1} is summable C^{-1}.

Theorem I can be slightly transformed by the following considerations. If A is summable C^r, (1) has a solution $\bar{b}_n$ such that $\bar{B}$ is summable C^{r-1}. It follows that $\Sigma(\bar{b}_n - \bar{b}_{n+1})$ is also summable C^{r-1} to $\bar{b}_0$, i.e. $A' = \Sigma a_n/(n+1)$ is summable C^{r-1} to $\bar{b}_0$. If we define b_n by

$$(7) \qquad b_n = C^{r-1}\text{-sum of } \sum_{\nu=n}^{\infty} a_\nu/(\nu+1),$$

b_n satisfies (1) so that $b_n = \bar{b}_n + c$. But by its definition C^{r-1}-lim $b_n = 0$ and, $\bar{B}$ being summable C^{r-1}, then also C^{r-1}-lim $\bar{b}_n = 0$, i.e. $c = 0$, $\bar{b}_n = b_n$, and B is summable C^{r-1}.

Finally, h and thus also g being 0,

$$A' = b_0 = S_0'^r = (r+1)!\,g_0 = (r+1)! \sum_0^{\infty} \frac{A_n^r}{(n+r+2)\ldots(n+1)}.$$

Hence the result

V. *If* A *is summable* C^r, *then* $A' = \Sigma a_n/(n+1)$ *is summable* C^{r-1} *to*

$$(r+1)! \sum_0^{\infty} \frac{S_n^r}{(n+r+2)\ldots(n+1)}$$

(absolutely convergent) and, b_n *being defined by* (7), B *is summable* C^{r-1} *to* A.

This result shows that the particular solution of (1) referred to in I is the b_n defined by (7).

Conversely, if A' and B are summable C^{r-1}, then A is summable C^r, for b_n satisfies (1). Our remarks establish the following statement:

VI. *The necessary and sufficient condition that A should be summable C^r is that b_n can be defined by* (7) *and for the b_n thus defined Σb_n is summable C^{r-1}.*

Some consequences of theorem I are now given.

VII. *If A is summable C^r and $na_n \to 0$, then A is convergent.*

Proof. $$a_{n1} = \sum_n^\infty a_\nu / (\nu+1) = \sum_n^\infty o(1/\nu^2) = o(1/n)$$

and similarly $a_{ns} = o(1/n)$, i. e. A_r is summable C^{-1} and thus A is summable C^{r-1}. Repeating the reasoning r times we see that A is summable C^{-1}, i. e. convergent.

VIII. *If A is summable C^r and $t_n = a_1 + 2a_2 + \ldots + na_n = o(n)$, then A is convergent.*

Proof.

$$\sum_n^N \frac{a_\nu}{\nu+1} = \sum_n^N \frac{t_\nu - t_{\nu-1}}{(\nu+1)\nu}$$

$$= 2\sum_n^{N-1} \frac{t_\nu}{(\nu+2)(\nu+1)\nu} - \frac{t_{n-1}}{(n+1)n} + \frac{t_N}{(N+1)N}.$$

For $N \to \infty$, we obtain

$$a_{n1} = 2\sum_n^\infty \frac{t_\nu}{(\nu+2)(\nu+1)\nu} - \frac{t_{n-1}}{(n+1)n}$$

$$= \sum_n^\infty o(1/\nu^2) + o(1/n) = o(1/n).$$

Hence by VII, A_1 is summable C^{-1} and therefore A is convergent.

The method used in establishing theorem I and its consequences, applies also to Hölder's means. Put

$$\bar{S}_n^0 = S_n, \quad \bar{S}_n^1 = (S_0^0 + \ldots + S_n^0)/(n+1),$$
$$\bar{S}_n^2 = (S_0^1 + \ldots + S_n^1)/(n+1), \ldots .$$

By definition, A is summable H^r if $\bar{S}_n^r \to A$. If we suppose that

(8) $$a_0 = 0, \quad b_0 = 0, \quad a_{n+1} = n(b_n - b_{n+1}),$$

we find without difficulty that

$$\bar{S}_n^0 = \bar{S}'^0_n - nb_n, \quad \bar{S}_n^r = 2\bar{S}'^r_n - \bar{S}'^{r-1}_n, \quad r \geqslant 1,$$

and, following step by step the proof of I, we find

IX. *The necessary and sufficient condition that A should be summable H^r is that there should be a solution b_n of* (8) *such that B is summable H^{r-1}.*

We find also that this solution is given by

$$b_0 = 0, \quad b_n = H^{r-1}\text{-sum of } a_{n+1}/n + a_{n+2}/(n+1) + \dots .$$

The equivalence of Cesàro's and Hölder's methods readily follows from our results. Suppose that the theorem is true for an r. Then

(9) $$H^{r+1}\text{-lim}\,(a_0 + a_1 + \dots + a_n) = A$$

is equivalent to

$$H^{r+1}\text{-lim}\,(0 + 0 + a_2 + a_3 + \dots + a_n) = A - a_0 - a_1,$$

and therefore to

$$H^r\text{-lim}\,(0 + b_1 + \dots + b_n) = A - a_0 - a_1,$$

where

$$b_n = H^r\text{-}\lim_{k=\infty}\,[a_{n+1}/n + \dots + a_{n+k}/(n+k)], \qquad n > 0.$$

Now, in the last two equations, H may be replaced by C, and thus if we write

$$a_n = a'_{n-2}, \quad n > 1, \quad b_n = b'_{n-1}, \quad n > 0,$$

we have

$$b'_n = C^r\text{-}\lim_{k=\infty}\,[a'_n/(n+1) + \dots + a'_{n+k}/(n+k)].$$

Therefore (9) is equivalent to

$$C^r\text{-lim}\,(b'_0 + b'_1 + \dots + b'_n) = A - a_0 - a_1,$$

i. e. to

$$C^{r+1}\text{-lim}\,(a'_0 + \dots + a'_n) = A - a_0 - a_1,$$

i. e.

$$C^{r+1}\text{-lim}\,(a_0 + \dots + a_n) = A,$$

which proves equivalence for $r+1$. The complete equivalence is thus established by induction.

CHAPTER XIII

THE TAYLOR SERIES ON ITS CIRCLE OF CONVERGENCE

Bounded functions.

105. *Elementary properties.* In this chapter we are going to apply the general results of the last chapter to the particular case of the Taylor series on its circle of convergence. When the radius of convergence is r, the transformation $z' = rz$ leads to a Taylor series with the radius of convergence 1. Therefore we shall suppose throughout this chapter that this transformation if necessary has been made, i. e. that the radius of convergence is 1.

Our general object is to establish relations between properties of the series (coefficients, partial sums, &c.) and properties of its sum function at or near the points of the circle $|z| = 1$.

I. *If* $s_n^{(r)}(e^{i\theta}) \to l$, *then* $\lim_{z \to e^i} \Sigma a_n z^n = l$ *provided* z *approaches* $e^{i\theta}$ *inside an angle* $< \pi$, *vertex at* $e^{i\theta}$.

(Abel, 1826; Frobenius, 1880; Hölder, 1882.)

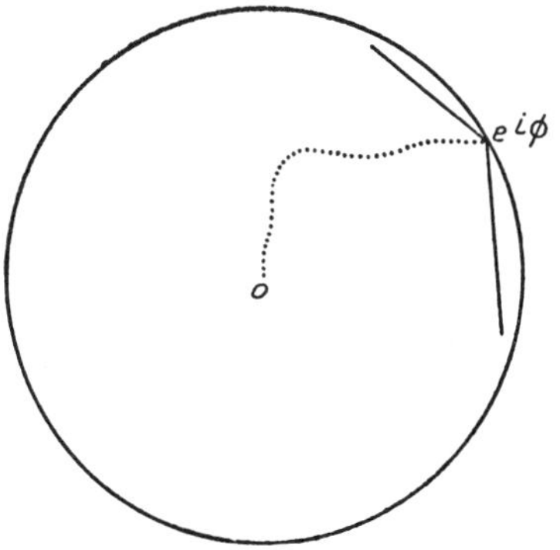

FIG. 56.

Proof. For simplicity, we put $\theta = 0$. By hypothesis, $S_n^{(r)}/A_n^r \to l$, i. e. $S_n^r = lA_n^r + \epsilon_n A_n^r$. Therefore

$$(1) \qquad f(z)/(1-z)^{r+1} = \Sigma S_n^r z^n = l \Sigma A_n^r z^n + \Sigma \epsilon_n A_n^r z^n.$$

But if η_p is the greatest of $|\epsilon_{p+1}|, |\epsilon_{p+2}|, \ldots$, we have

$$|\Sigma \epsilon_n A_n^r z^n| \leqslant \sum_0^p |\epsilon_n| A_n^r |z|^n + \eta_p \sum_0^\infty A_n^r |z|^n,$$

and

$$\sum_0^\infty A_n^r |z|^n = 1/(1-|z|)^{r+1}.$$

Hence, multiplying both sides of (1) by $|1-z|^{r+1}$ we find

$$(2) \quad |f(z)-l| \leqslant |1-z|^{r+1} \sum_{n=0}^p |\epsilon_n| A_n^r |z|^n + \eta_p \left(\frac{|1-z|}{1-|z|}\right)^{r+1}.$$

When $z \to 1$ in any way, the first term tends to 0 for a fixed p. On the other hand, putting $z = 1-\rho e^{i\alpha}$, we have inside an angle $<\pi$, vertex at 1, $\cos\alpha > \delta > 0$. Hence, for $\rho < \delta$,

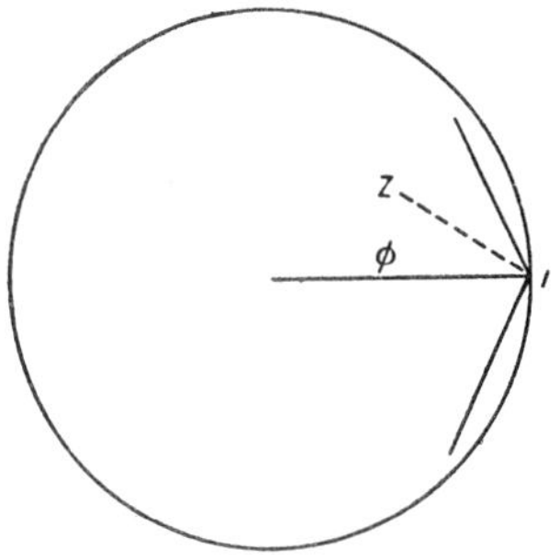

FIG. 56.

$$|z|^2 = 1 - 2\rho\cos\alpha + \rho^2 < 1 - 2\rho\delta + \rho\delta$$
$$= 1 - \rho\delta < 1 - \rho\delta + \rho^2\delta^2/4 = (1-\rho\delta/2)^2,$$

i. e. $|z| < 1 - \rho\delta/2 = 1 - \delta|1-z|/2$, and thus

$$\frac{|1-z|}{1-|z|} < \frac{2}{\delta}.$$

Therefore the second term on the right-hand side of (2) is $< \eta_p (2/\delta)^{r+1} = \epsilon_p$ and thus the limiting numbers of the right-hand side when $z \to 1$ inside the angle in question are all between $-\epsilon_p$ and ϵ_p. Since η_p, and thus also ϵ_p, is arbitrarily small, the theorem is established.

For $r = 0$, i.e. for ordinary convergence, the theorem was first proved by Abel, at least for radial approach. The case $r = 1$ is due to Frobenius and the general result to Hölder.

Another elementary result is the following. When the partial sums

$$s_n(e^{i\theta}) = a_0 + a_1 e^{i\theta} + a_2 e^{2i\theta} + \dots + a_n e^{n i\theta},$$

are bounded, i.e. $|s_n(e^{i\theta})| \leqslant M$, where M is independent of α, then also the sum-function $f(z) = \Sigma a_n z^n$ is bounded in $|z| < 1$, i.e. $|f(z)| \leqslant M$. In fact, from

$$f(re^{i\theta})/(1-r) = \Sigma s_n(e^{i\theta}) r^n$$

we conclude that

$$|f(re^{i\theta})/(1-r)| \leqslant M \Sigma r^n = M/(1-r).$$

The same holds for the arithmetic means of the partial sums.

II. *If* $|s_n^{(k)}(e^{i\theta})| \leqslant M$ *independently of* θ, *then* $|f(z)| \leqslant M$.

Proof. By definition,

$$f(re^{i\theta})/(1-r)^{k+1} = \Sigma S_n^k(e^{i\theta}) r^n,$$

and, by hypothesis,

$$|S_n^k(e^{i\theta})/A_n^k| \leqslant M.$$

Hence,

$$|f(re^{i\theta})|/(1-r)^{k+1} \leqslant M \Sigma A_n^k r^n = M/(1-r)^{k+1}.$$

The main interest of this result lies in the fact that its converse is not true. We shall in fact construct an example where the function is bounded in $|z| < 1$ and the partial sums are not bounded. Thus, when the partial sums are bounded we infer by I that the function also is bounded, but when the partial sums are unbounded, we cannot in general conclude that the function also is unbounded. In view of this fact it is rather surprising that

III. *If* $f(z) = \Sigma a_n z^n$ *is bounded, i.e.* $|f(z)| \leqslant M$ *in* $|z| < 1$, *then the arithmetic means*

$$\sigma_n(e^{i\theta}) = [s_0 + s_1(e^{i\theta}) + \dots + s_n(e^{i\theta})]/(n+1)$$

are bounded, i.e. $|\sigma_n(e^{i\theta})| \leqslant M$. (Landau, 1913–16.)

Proof. We first notice that

$$(3)\quad \int_0^{2\pi} |f(re^{i\theta})|^2\, d\theta = \int_0^{2\pi} \Sigma a_n r^n e^{ni\theta} \Sigma \bar{a}_m r^m e^{-mi\theta} d\theta$$

$$= \sum_{n,m} a_n \bar{a}_m r^{n+m} \int_0^{2\pi} e^{(n-m)\theta i} d\theta = 2\pi \sum_n |a_n|^2 r^{2n},$$

from which it follows that, for every $r<1$,

$$\sum_n |a_n|^2 r^{2n} \leqslant M^2,$$

i. e.

$$(4)\qquad \Sigma |a_n|^2 \leqslant M^2.$$

Hence, $\Sigma |a_n|^2$ for a bounded function is convergent and, in particular, $a_n \to 0$.

Now it follows from

$$f(z)/(1-z)^2 = \Sigma (n+1)\sigma_n(1) z^n$$

that

$$(n+1)\sigma_n(1) = \frac{1}{2\pi i}\int_{|z|=r} \frac{f(z)\,dz}{(1-z)^2 z^{n+1}} \qquad \text{(by 56. 3).}$$

But we can add

$$\frac{f(z)}{(1-z)^2}\,\frac{(1-z^{n+1})^2-1}{z^{n+1}}$$

to the integrand without altering the value of the integral, for this term despite its form is regular at the origin and thus in $|z|<1$. Hence

$$(n+1)\sigma_n(1) = \frac{1}{2\pi i}\int_{|z|=r} \frac{f(z)\,(1-z^{n+1})^2}{(1-z)^2 z^{n+1}}\, dz$$

$$= \frac{1}{2\pi i}\int_{|z|=r} \frac{f(z)}{z^{n+1}} (1+z+z^2+\ldots+z^n)^2\, dz,$$

i. e. if $|f(z)| \leqslant M$,

$$(n+1)|\sigma^n(1)| \leqslant \frac{M}{2\pi r^n}\int_0^{2\pi} |1+z+\ldots+z^n|^2\, d\theta, \quad z = re^{i\theta},$$

therefore, by (3),

$$(n+1)|\sigma_n(1)| \leqslant \frac{M}{2\pi r^n} 2\pi (1^2 + 1^2 r^2 + \ldots + 1^2 r^{2n})$$

$$= \frac{M}{r^n}(1 + r^2 + \ldots + r^{2n}).$$

Since the left-hand side is independent of $r<1$, we have

$$(n+1)\,|\sigma^n(1)| \leqslant \lim_{r\to 1} \frac{M}{r^n}(1+r^2+\ldots+r^{2n}) = (n+1)\,M,$$

which proves that

$$|\sigma_n(1)| \leqslant M.$$

Applying this result to the function $f_1(z) = f(e^{i\theta}z)$, we see that $|\sigma_n(e^{i\theta})| \leqslant M$. Thus if $\sigma_n(e^{i\theta})$ *is unbounded, the function also is unbounded in* $|z|<1$. Q. e. d.

There are, of course, whole classes of Taylor series for which the partial sums are bounded whenever the function is.

IV. *If* $|na_n|<c$ *and* $|f(z)| \leqslant M$ *for* $|z|<1$, *then* $|s_n(e^{i\theta})|<N$, *where* N *is independent of* θ *and* n.

Proof. For $0<r<1$, we have

$$\sum_{k=0}^{n} a_k e^{ki\theta} - f(re^{i\theta}) = \sum_{k=0}^{n} a_k e^{k\theta i}(1-r^k) - \sum_{k=n+1}^{\infty} a_k r^k e^{k\theta i}.$$

But

$$1-r^n = (1-r)(1+r+\ldots+r^{n-1}) \leqslant (1-r)\,n.$$

Thus

$$(5) \qquad \left|\sum_{k=0}^{n} a_k e^{k\theta i} - f(re^{i\theta})\right| \leqslant (1-r)\sum_{k=1}^{n} k\,|a_k| + \sum_{k=n+1}^{\infty} |a_k|\,r^k.$$

Putting $1-r = 1/n$ and remarking that the arithmetic means of the numbers $|a_1|, 2\,|a_2|, \ldots, n\,|a_n|$ cannot exceed c, we see that the first term on the right-hand side is $<c$. On the other hand the second term is less than

$$\frac{c}{n}\sum_{0}^{\infty} r^n = \frac{c}{n(1-r)} = c,$$

for $1-r = 1/n$. Hence

$$\left|\sum_{k=0}^{n} a_k e^{ki\theta}\right| \leqslant M + 2c = N.$$

Q. e. d.

106. *Dominants of partial sums and of the function.* In the general case when, for bounded functions, s_n tends to infinity with n, the order of this infinity is at most logarithmic. More precisely,

I. *If the function $f(z)$ is regular and $|f(z)|<1$ in $|z|<1$, then*

$$(1)\ |s_n(e^{i\theta})| \leqslant 1+\left(\frac{1}{2}\right)^2+\left(\frac{1\,.\,3}{2\,.\,4}\right)^2+\ldots+\left(\frac{1\,.\,3\,.\,5\ldots(2n-1)}{2\,.\,4\ldots 2n}\right)^2 \equiv G_n.$$

(Landau, 1913–16.)

The remarkable fact disclosed by this result is that there is an upper bound, G_n, for the s_n of the *whole class* of functions satisfying the conditions.

Proof. We write $\theta = 0$. By (56. 3),

(2)
$$2\pi i s_n = \int_{|z|=r} f(z)\left[\frac{1}{z}+\frac{1}{z^2}+\ldots+\frac{1}{z^{n+1}}\right]dz$$
$$= \int_{|z|=r} \frac{f(z)}{z^{n+1}}(1+z+z^2+\ldots+z^n)\,dz = \int_{|z|=r}\frac{f(z)}{z^{n+1}}Q(z)\,dz,$$

where $Q(z)$ is any polynomial beginning with the terms $1+z+\ldots+z^n$. For example, since

$$\left[\sum_{\nu=0}^{\infty} C_\nu^{-\frac{1}{2}}(-z)^\nu\right]^2 = [(1-z)^{-1/2}]^2 = 1/(1-z) = \Sigma z^n,$$

if we put

$$(3)\qquad P_n(z) = \sum_{\nu=0}^{n} C_\nu^{-\frac{1}{2}}(-z)^\nu,$$

the polynomial

$$(4)\quad [P_n(z)]^2 = 1+z+\ldots+z^n+b_{n+1}z^{n+1}+\ldots+b_{2n}z^{2n}$$

may be taken for $Q(z)$. Therefore

$$(5)\qquad 2\pi i s_n = \int_{|z|=r}\frac{f(z)}{z^{n+1}}[P_n(z)]^2 dz.$$

From this identity we obtain

$$(6)\qquad 2\pi\,|s_n| \leqslant \int_0^{2\pi}\frac{1}{r^{n+1}}|P_n(z)|^2\, r\,d\alpha$$
$$= \frac{1}{r^n}\int_0^{2\pi}|P_n(z)|^2\,d\alpha = \frac{2\pi}{r^n}\sum_{\nu=0}^{n}[C_\nu^{-\frac{1}{2}}]^2 r^{2\nu},$$

and since the left-hand side is independent of r, we have

$$|s_n| \leqslant \sum_{\nu=0}^{n} [C_\nu^{-\frac{1}{2}}]^2 = \sum_{\nu=0}^{n} \left[\frac{\left(-\frac{1}{2}\right)\left(-\frac{3}{2}\right)\cdots\left(-\frac{2\nu-1}{2}\right)}{\nu!}\right]^2$$

$$= \sum_{\nu=0}^{n} \left[\frac{1.3\ldots(2\nu-1)}{2.4\ldots(2\nu)}\right]^2 \equiv G_n.$$

Q. e. d.

We notice that

$$\frac{1.3\ldots(2n-1)}{2.4\ldots 2n} = \frac{(2n)!}{2^{2n}(n!)^2},$$

i. e. by Stirling's formula, Ex. IV. 22,

$$\log\frac{1.3\ldots(2n-1)}{2.4\ldots(2n)} = 2n\log n + 2n\log 2 - 2n + \tfrac{1}{2}\log n$$
$$+\tfrac{1}{2}\log 2 + \tfrac{1}{2}\log(2\pi) + o(1) - 2n\log 2 - 2n\log n + 2n$$
$$-\log n - \log(2\pi) + o(1) = -\tfrac{1}{2}\log n - \tfrac{1}{2}\log\pi + o(1)$$

i. e.

$$\frac{1.3\ldots(2n-1)}{2.4\ldots(2n)} = e^{-\frac{1}{2}\log n - \frac{1}{2}\log\pi + o(1)} \backsim 1/\sqrt{\pi n},$$

and thus

(7) $$G_n = 1 + \frac{1}{\pi}\sum_{\nu=1}^{n} 1/\nu + \sum_{\nu=1}^{n} o(1/\nu) \backsim \frac{1}{\pi}\log n.$$

Another remark in connexion with Landau's theorem is that *the upper bound G_n cannot be lowered for the whole class.* In fact, for any given n, there is a bounded function for which $s_n = G_n$. For, by Kakeya's theorem, Ex. II. 17, $P_n(z)$ does not vanish for $|z| \leqslant 1$, and thus

(8) $$f_n(z) = z^n P_n(1/z)/P_n(z)$$

$$= \frac{\frac{1.3\ldots(2n-1)}{2.4\ldots(2n)} + \ldots + \frac{1}{2}z^{n-1} + z^n}{1 + \frac{1}{2}z + \ldots + \frac{1.3\ldots(2n-1)}{2.4\ldots(2n)}z^n}$$

is regular *in and on* $|z| = 1$ and, for $|z| = 1$

$$|f_n(z)| = \left|\frac{P_n(1/z)}{P_n(z)}\right| = \frac{|P_n(e^{-\alpha i})|}{|P_n(e^{\alpha i})|} = 1.$$

It follows that

(9) $$|f_n(z)| \leqslant 1 \text{ in and on } |z| = 1.$$

and, by (5), where now the integral can be taken along $|z| = 1$, we have

$$2\pi i s_n = \int \frac{1}{z} P_n(z) P_n(1/z)\, dz$$
$$= i\int_0^{2\pi} P_n(e^{\alpha i}) P_n(e^{-\alpha i})\, d\alpha = i\int_0^{2\pi} | P_n(z) |^2 d\alpha.$$

Thus, by the last equation of (6), $s_n = G_n$, which we wanted to prove.

Finally, by means of the functions (8) we can construct *a bounded function with unbounded* s_n. (Fejér, 1910.)

For this purpose we first remark that if $m \geqslant 0$, $n > 0$, $b_i > 0$, and $c_i > c_{i+1} \geqslant 0$, then *the* s_n *of*

$$R(z) = \frac{b_0 + b_1 z + \ldots + b_m z^m}{c_0 + c_1 z + \ldots + c_n z^n} = \sum_{k=0}^{\infty} g_k z^k$$

are all positive. In fact, by Kakeya's theorem, Ex. II. 17, $R(z)$ is regular in and on $|z| = 1$ and all the coefficients h_k of

$$\frac{1}{(1-z)(c_0 + \ldots + c_n z^n)} = \frac{1}{c_0 - [(c_0 - c_1)z + \ldots + (c_{n-1} - c_n)z^n + c_n z^{n+1}]}$$
$$= \frac{1}{c_0} + \frac{(c_0 - c_1)z + \ldots + c_n z^{n+1}}{c_0^2} + \frac{[(c_0 - c_1)z + \ldots + c_n z^{n+1}]^2}{c_0^3} + \ldots$$
$$= \Sigma h_k z^k$$

are positive. Hence the same is true of the coefficients of $R(z)/(1-z)$.

Consider now the series of functions

$$f(z) = \frac{6}{\pi^2} \sum_{\nu=1}^{\infty} f_{2^{\nu^3}}(z)/\nu^2$$

formed by a sub-sequence of the functions (8). Since, by (9),

$$| f_{2^{\nu^3}}(z)/\nu^2 | \leqslant 1/\nu^2 \quad \text{in and on } |z| = 1,$$

the series converges uniformly and represents a continuous function in and on $|z| = 1$ and

$$| f(z) | \leqslant \frac{6}{\pi^2} \sum_{\nu=1}^{\infty} 1/\nu^2 = 1.$$

Rearranging the series, and noticing that all the partial sums of

$f_{2^{\nu^3}}(z)$ are positive, we see that the partial sums $s_{2^{\nu^3}}$ of the complete series satisfy the inequalities

$$s_{2^{\nu^3}} > \frac{6}{\pi^2 \nu^2} G_{2^{\nu^3}} \sim \frac{6}{\pi^2 \nu^2} \frac{1}{\pi} \log (2^{\nu^3}) = \frac{6 \log 2}{\pi^3} \nu,$$

and are therefore unbounded. Q. e. d.

An obvious dominant for $f(z) = \Sigma a_n z^n$ is $\overline{M}(r) = \Sigma |a_n| r^n$.

II. *If* $f(z)$ *is regular and* $|f(z)| < 1$ *in* $|z| < 1$,

$$\lim_{r \to 1} [\overline{M}(r) \sqrt{1-r}] = 0,$$

(Hardy, 1913.)

i. e. for bounded functions the dominant in question may increase to infinity when $r \to 1$, but the order of this infinity is $\leqslant 1/2$.

Proof. By (105. 4), $\Sigma |a_n|^2$ is convergent, and thus there is an m such that $\sum\limits_{n=m+1}^{\infty} |a_n|^2 \leqslant \epsilon^2$. On the other hand from

$$[\Sigma a_i b_i]^2 \leqslant \Sigma a_i^2 \Sigma b_i^2, \; a_i \geqslant 0, \; b_i \geqslant 0,$$

it follows that

$$\overline{M}(r) = \sum_{n=0}^{m} |a_n| r^n + \sum_{n=m+1}^{\infty} |a_n| r^n \leqslant \sum_{n=0}^{m} |a_n|$$

$$+ \sqrt{\sum_{n=m+1}^{\infty} |a_n|^2 \sum_{n=m+1}^{\infty} r^{2n}} = \sum_{n=0}^{m} |a_n| + \sqrt{\sum_{n=m+1}^{\infty} |a_n|^2} / \sqrt{1-r},$$

i. e. all the limiting numbers of $\overline{M}(r)\sqrt{1-r}$ for $r \to 1$ lie between 0 and ϵ. Since ϵ is arbitrarily small, the theorem is proved.

Another restriction on the increase of $\overline{M}(r)$ is expressed by the following result.

III. *If* $f(z)$ *is regular and* $|f(z)| < 1$ *in* $|z| < 1$, *then* $\overline{M}(1/3) \leqslant 1$ *and for any given* ρ, $1/3 < \rho < 1$, *there is a function of the class considered for which* $\overline{M}(\rho) > 1$. (Bohr, 1916–17.)

Proof. By 105. III, for $n = 1$, we have

$$|\sigma_1(z)| = |s_0 + s_1(z)|/2 = |2a_0 + a_1 z|/2 \leqslant 1$$

for $|z| = 1$. Thus, choosing a $z = e^{i\alpha}$ such that the argument of $a_1 z$ is that of a_0, we have

$$(10) \qquad (2|a_0| + |a_1|)/2 \leqslant 1, \quad \text{i.e.} \quad |a_1| \leqslant 2(1 - |a_0|).$$

Now for $n \geqslant 1$, putting $\eta = e^{2\pi i/n}$, $y = z^n$, the function

$$\frac{f(z)+f(\eta z)+\ldots+f(\eta^{n-1}z)}{n} = \sum_{\nu=0}^{\infty} a_\nu \frac{1^\nu+\eta^\nu+\ldots+\eta^{(n-1)\nu}}{n} z^\nu$$
$$= a_0 + a_n z^n + a_{2n} z^{2n} + \ldots = a_0 + a_n y + a_{2n} y^2 + \ldots$$

of y is regular and <1 in $|y|<1$. Hence, by (10),

$$|a_n| \leqslant 2(1-|a_0|)$$

and thus

$$\overline{M}(1/3) = |a_0| + \sum_{n=1}^{\infty} |a_n|/3^n \leqslant |a_0| + 2(1-|a_0|)\Sigma 1/3^n = 1,$$

which proves the first part of the statement.

Moreover the function

$$f(z) = \frac{\alpha - z}{1-\alpha z}, \quad 0<\alpha<1,$$

maps the unit circle on itself and thus satisfies the conditions of our theorem. But, the expression

$$f(z) = (\alpha - z)(1+\alpha z + \alpha^2 z^2 + \ldots) = \alpha - (1-\alpha^2)z - (\alpha-\alpha^3)z^2 + \ldots$$

valid in $|z| < 1/\alpha \; (>1)$ gives

$$\overline{M}(\rho) = \alpha + (1-\alpha^2)\rho + (\alpha-\alpha^3)\rho^2 + \ldots = \alpha + (1-\alpha^2)\rho/(1-\alpha\rho),$$

and thus $M(\rho) > 1$ when

$$\alpha + (1-\alpha^2)\rho/(1-\alpha\rho) > 1, \quad \text{i.e.} \quad \rho > 1/(1+2\alpha).$$

Hence, when $\rho > 1/3$ is given, there is an α satisfying the conditions, and thus a function such that $M(\rho) > 1$. Q. e. d.

107. *The problem of the coefficients.* When a function $f(z)$ is given by its Taylor expansion $f(z) = \Sigma a_n z^n$, how can we recognize from the coefficients that $f(z)$ is bounded? This is the problem of the coefficients for bounded functions. We shall suppose as before that $|f(z)| \leqslant 1$ in $|z| < 1$.

Since $M(r) \equiv \max_{|z|=r} |f(z)|$ is a non-decreasing function of r and $|f(0)| = |a_0|$, we have $|f(z)| \geqslant |a_0|$ for $0<r<1$, i.e.

$$|a_0| \leqslant 1$$

and equality can only hold if $f(z)$ reduces to a_0. Therefore, when $f(z)$ is not a constant, we have

(1) $$|a_0| < 1.$$

Now consider the function

$$f_1(z) = \frac{f(z)-a_0}{1-\bar{a}_0 f(z)} \cdot \frac{1}{z}.$$

If $|f(z)| \leqslant 1$ and $|\bar{a}_0| < 1$, $f_1(z)$ is regular in $|z| < 1$. Moreover

$$u = \frac{f-a_0}{1-\bar{a}_0 f}$$

maps $|f| < 1$ on itself, i.e. $|u| < 1$ in $|z| < 1$, and Schwarz's lemma, 42. I, shows that the division by z does not increase the maximum modulus in $|z| < 1$. Hence $|f_1(z)| \leqslant 1$ in $|z| < 1$, and thus its first coefficient is $\leqslant 1$. But the limit for $z = 0$ shows that this first coefficient is $a_1/(1-a_0\bar{a}_0)$. Hence a necessary condition for boundedness is

$$\text{(2)} \qquad \left| \frac{a_1}{1-a_0\bar{a}_0} \right| \leqslant 1,$$

where equality can only hold when $f_1(z)$ reduces to the constant $a_1/(1-a_0\bar{a}_0)$, i.e.

$$\text{(3)} \qquad f(z) = g_1(z) = \frac{\dfrac{za_1}{1-a_0\bar{a}_0} + a_0}{1 + \bar{a}_0 \dfrac{za_1}{1-a_0\bar{a}_0}},$$

a linear rational function of z.

We also notice that a_0 and a_1 are only restricted by conditions (1) and (2), i.e. if we take any two numbers for a_0 and a_1 satisfying (1) and (2), there is a function of the class considered (< 1 in $|z| < 1$) whose first two coefficients are a_0 and a_1, viz. the function (3).

We continue this process by putting

$$\text{(4)} \qquad f_n(z) = \frac{f_{n-1}(z) - f_{n-1}(0)}{1 - \bar{f}_{n-1}(0) f_{n-1}(z)} \cdot \frac{1}{z}, \quad f_0(z) = f(z).$$

Therefore, if we suppose that $|f_{n-1}(z)| \leqslant 1$ in $|z| < 1$ and $f_{n-1}(0) < 1$, our previous reasoning shows that

$$\text{(5)} \qquad |f_n(0)| \leqslant 1.$$

If $|f_n(0)| = 1$, the process comes to an end, but then $f_n(z)$ is a constant.

We are going to prove that

I. *The set of inequalities* (5) *form the necessary and sufficient conditions that* $|f(z)| < 1$ *in* $|z| < 1$. (R. Nevanlinna, 1919.)

We have already seen that these conditions are necessary. To prove that they are sufficient, consider the sequence

$$(6) \qquad f_0(0), f_1(0), \dots, f_n(0), \dots, \; |f_n(0)| \leqslant 1,$$

where, if $|f_n(0)| = 1$, $f_n(0)$ is the last number of the sequence. The recurrence relations (4), for $n = 1, 2, \dots, m$, determine the coefficients $a_1, a_2, \dots, a_m$. In fact, putting $f_n(z) = \Sigma \alpha_{ni} z^i$, $|\alpha_{n0}| \leqslant 1$, we have

$$(7) \quad f_n(z) = \frac{f_{n-1}(z) - \alpha_{n-1,0}}{1 - \bar{\alpha}_{n-1,0} f_{n-1}(z)} \cdot \frac{1}{z}, \text{ i. e. } f_{n-1}(z) = \frac{z f_n(z) + \alpha_{n-1,0}}{1 + z f_n(z) \bar{\alpha}_{n-1,0}},$$

from which we see that $\alpha_{n-1,m}$ is a rational function of $\alpha_{n-1,0}$, $\bar{\alpha}_{n-1,0}, \alpha_{n0}, \dots, \alpha_{n,m-1}$. Therefore, if we know $f_0(0), f_1(0), \dots, f_n(0)$, the first two coefficients of $f_{n-1}(z)$ are uniquely determined by $f_n(0)$ and $f_{n-1}(0)$. From the two coefficients thus determined and from $f_{n-2}(0)$ we determine similarly the first three coefficients of $f_{n-2}(z)$, and so finally the first $n+1$ coefficients of $f_0(z) \equiv f(z)$, i. e. $a_0, a_1, \dots, a_n$ are determined by $a_0, f_1(0), \dots, f_n(0)$.

Consider now the function $f(z) = \Sigma a_n z^n$, where the coefficients a_n have been determined from (6) by the above process. We have to prove that $|f(z)| \leqslant 1$ in $|z| < 1$. For this purpose express $f_n(z)$ in terms of $f(z)$ by successive applications of (4) and solve the equation $f_n(z) = f_n(0)$ for $f(z)$. Let the function so obtained be denoted by $g_n(z)$. For example, $g_0(z) \equiv a_0$, $g_1(z)$ is the function (3). By construction, the first $n+1$ coefficients of $g_n(z)$ are $a_0, a_1, \dots a_n$, while, if $|f_n(0)| = 1, g_n(z) = f(z)$. Since $|g_n(z)| \leqslant 1$ in $|z| < 1$, we see that $|a_n| \leqslant 1$, thus $\Sigma a_n z^n$ is convergent in $|z| < 1$. Moreover

$$|f(z) - g_n(z)| \leqslant |z|^{n+1}/(1 - |z|),$$

and thus in every region of $|z| < 1$ we have $g_n(z) \to f(z)$. Finally, since $|g_n(z)| \leqslant 1$, then also $|f(z)| \leqslant 1$ in $|z| < 1$.

Q. e. d.

108. *Fatou's theorem.* Putting $a_n = a_n' + i a_n''$ and $z = re^{i\alpha}$ in $f(z) = \Sigma a_n z^n$ we obtain

$$f(z) = \Sigma r^n (a_n' \cos n\alpha - a_n'' \sin n\alpha) + i \Sigma r^n (a_n' \sin n\alpha + a_n'' \cos n\alpha).$$

In particular for $r = 1$ the Taylor series is the sum of two trigonometrical series

$\Sigma a_n e^{i\alpha n} = \Sigma(a'_n \cos n\alpha - a''_n \sin n\alpha) + i\Sigma(a'_n \sin n\alpha + a''_n \cos n\alpha)$. It is therefore natural that in relations between properties of the function near $|z| = 1$ and properties of the Taylor series the latter is replaced by the two component trigonometrical series. In this way we can make good use of the known results on trigonometrical series. We are going to give a short account of Riemann's method of summation.

By (105. 4), if $\Sigma a_n z^n$ is bounded in $|z| < 1$, $a_n \to 0$. Hence, $\Sigma a_n z^n/n^2$ is absolutely and uniformly convergent in $|z| \leqslant 1$, and thus we can put

$$F(t) = -\sum_{n=1}^{\infty} a_n e^{nit}/n^2. \tag{1}$$

Riemann's method consists in expressing the partial sums $s_n(e^{it})$ of $\Sigma a_n z^n$ in terms of $F(t)$ and its derivatives.

Multiplying (1) by

$$\cos m(\phi - t) = \cos m\phi \cos mt + \sin m\phi \sin mt$$

and integrating, we find

$$\int_0^{\pi} F(t) \cos m(\phi - t)\, dt = -\pi a_m e^{mi\phi}/m^2,$$

and thus

$$\begin{aligned} s_n(e^{i\phi}) &= a_0 + a_1 e^{i\phi} + \dots + a_n e^{in\phi} \\ &= a_0 - \frac{1}{\pi}\int_0^{2\pi} F(t) \sum_{m=1}^{n} m^2 \cos m(\phi - t)\, dt \\ &= a_0 + \frac{1}{\pi}\int_0^{2\pi} F(t) \frac{d^2}{dt^2}\Big[\sum_1^n \cos m(\phi - t)\Big] dt. \end{aligned}$$

Therefore, since

$$\begin{aligned} (2) \quad 1/2 + \sum_1^n \cos m\alpha &= [\sin\frac{\alpha}{2} + \sum_1^n 2\sin\frac{\alpha}{2}\cos m\alpha]\,/2\sin\frac{\alpha}{2} \\ &= \frac{1}{2\sin\frac{\alpha}{2}}[\sin\frac{\alpha}{2} + \sum_1^n (\sin\frac{2m+1}{2}\alpha - \sin\frac{2m-1}{2}\alpha)] \\ &= \frac{\sin\frac{2n+1}{2}\alpha}{2\sin\frac{\alpha}{2}}, \end{aligned}$$

we have

$$(3)\quad s_n(e^{i\phi}) = a_0 + \frac{1}{2\pi}\int_0^{2\pi} F(t)\frac{d^2}{dt^2}\left[\frac{\sin\frac{2n+1}{2}(\phi-t)}{\sin\frac{\phi-t}{2}}\right]dt.$$

Taking the arithmetic means on both sides, we obtain

$$(4)\quad \sigma_n(e^{i\phi}) \equiv \frac{s_0+s_1(e^{i\phi})+\ldots+s_n(e^{i\phi})}{n+1}$$

$$= a_0 + \frac{1}{2\pi(n+1)}\int_0^{2\pi} F(t)\frac{d^2}{dt^2}\left[\frac{\sin\frac{n+1}{2}(\phi-t)}{\sin\frac{\phi-t}{2}}\right]^2 dt.$$

We are going to simplify these formulae by integration by parts. For this purpose, however, we need some results of Lebesgue's theory of integration for bounded functions. See Lebesgue 1928 or Hobson.

Consider a real function $f(t)$ of the real variable t and put

$$D^+ = \overline{\lim_{h\to 0}}\frac{f(t+h)-f(t)}{h},\ h>0, \quad D_+ = \underline{\lim_{h\to 0}}\frac{f(t+h)-f(t)}{h},\ h>0,$$

$$D^- = \overline{\lim_{h\to 0}}\frac{f(t+h)-f(t)}{h},\ h<0, \quad D_- = \underline{\lim_{h\to 0}}\frac{f(t+h)-f(t)}{h},\ h<0.$$

These four numbers are called the four derivates of $f(t)$ at t (right-hand upper and lower, left-hand upper and lower derivates respectively). We say that $f(t)$ has bounded derivates at t if none of these four numbers is $\pm\infty$. If the four finite numbers coincide, $f(t)$ has a differential coefficient $f'(t)$ at t in the ordinary sense. Lebesgue proved that if $f(t)$ has bounded derivates at every point of an interval (a, b), it has an ordinary differential coefficient 'almost everywhere' (= everywhere except maybe for a set of values of t of measure zero).

(A) The Lebesgue integral $F(t)$ of a bounded function $f(t)$ (if this integral exists) is a continuous function of the upper limit of integration, has bounded derivates, and also $F'(t) = f(t)$ almost everywhere.

(B) If $F'(t)$ be completed by any bounded set of values for the values of t at which $F'(t)$ does not exist, the indefinite Lebesgue integral of $F'(t)$ so completed is $F(t)$.

(C) For almost every value of t_0 the differential coefficient at $t = t_0$ of $\int_{t_0}^{t} |f(t)-a|\,dt$ is $|f(t_0)-a|$ for all values of a—in particular, for $a = f(t_0)$.

(D) The method of integration by parts applies to bounded functions integrable (L).

(E) If the integrable functions $f_n(t)$ are collectively bounded in (a, b) and if, almost everywhere in (a, b), $f_n(t) \to f(t)$, also integrable, then

$$\lim_{n=\infty} \int_a^b f_n(t)\,dt = \int_a^b f(t)\,dt.$$

(F) If, in (a, b), the lower or upper (L) integral of $f(x)$ is finite where $f(x)$ is not necessarily bounded in (a, b), then $f(x)$ is integrable (L) in (a, b).

If $f(z) = \Sigma a_n z^n$ is bounded in $|z|<1$, $[f(z)-a_0]/z$ is also bounded, and thus the integral

$$f_1(z) = \int_0^z \frac{f(z)-a_0}{z}\,dz,$$

taken along any rectifiable curve between 0 and z in $|z| \leqslant 1$, exists and is uniform, and $[f_1(e^{i(t+h)})-f_1(e^{it})]/h$ is bounded. Therefore, from $F(t) = -\int_0^{e^{it}} f_1(z)\,dz/z$, we see that $F'(t)$ exists and has bounded derivates, i. e. $F''(t)$ also exists almost everywhere. At the points t where $F''(t)$ does not exist, we complete it by taking for $F''(t)$ the right upper derivate of $F'(t)$, say.

The function in the brackets on the right-hand side of (3) is a periodic function of the period 2π, and the same is true of its first two derivatives, which are bounded functions in spite of the apparent infinity due to the vanishing of the denominator for $t = \phi$.

Consequently we can integrate by parts, and the completely integrated parts cancel one another, so that we obtain for bounded functions

$$(5) \qquad s_n(e^{i\phi}) = a_0 + \frac{1}{2\pi}\int_0^{2\pi} F''(t)\,\frac{\sin\dfrac{2n+1}{2}(\phi-t)}{\sin\dfrac{\phi-t}{2}}\,dt.$$

$$(6) \quad \sigma_n(e^{i\phi}) = a_0 + \frac{1}{2\pi(n+1)}\int_0^{2\pi} F''(t)\left[\frac{\sin\dfrac{n+1}{2}(\phi-t)}{\sin\dfrac{\phi-t}{2}}\right]^2 dt.$$

Therefore, to establish convergence or C^1-convergence we have to prove that integral (5), called Fourier's integral, or integral (6), called Fejér's integral, tends to a definite limit as $n \to \infty$. The second integral is considerably simpler than the first, for the factor multiplying $F''(t)$ is positive throughout the interval of integration.

Since the integrand has the period 2π, we may replace the limits of integrations by $c, c+2\pi$ with an arbitrary fixed c. We simplify both integrals by putting $t = \phi + 2\tau$ which replaces the limits of integration c, $c+2\pi$ by b, $b+\pi$ and, by choosing $b = -\pi/2$, we have

$$(7) \quad s_n(e^{i\phi}) = a_0 + \frac{1}{\pi}\int_{-\pi/2}^{\pi/2} F''(\phi+2\tau)\frac{\sin(2n+1)\tau}{\sin\tau}\,d\tau,$$

and similarly

$$(8) \quad \sigma_n(e^{i\phi}) = a_0 + \frac{1}{\pi(n+1)}\int_{-\pi/2}^{\pi/2} F''(\phi+2\tau)\left[\frac{\sin(n+1)\tau}{\sin\tau}\right]^2 d\tau.$$

The integrals (7) and (8) are simpler than (5) and (6) inasmuch as the parameter of integration does not figure in the brackets and the denominator vanishes only once in the interval of integration. Consider now an integral of the type (8)

$$(9) \qquad J_n = \frac{1}{n\pi}\int_0^{\pi/2} g(t)\left(\frac{\sin nt}{\sin t}\right) dt,$$

and put

$$(10) \qquad \int_0^t |g(t)|\,dt = G(t).$$

Suppose that (a) $g(t)$ is integrable (L) in $(0, \pi/2)$, (b) $g(0) = 0$, (c) $G(t)$ is differentiable at $t = 0$ and $G'(0) = 0$. We are going to prove that *under these conditions* $J_n \to 0$ *when* $n \to \infty$.

From

$$(11) \qquad 1 > \frac{\sin t}{t} > \frac{2}{\pi}, \text{ for } 0 < t < \frac{\pi}{2},$$

we have

$$|J_n| \leqslant \frac{\pi}{4n}\int_0^{\pi/2} |g(t)|\frac{\sin^2 nt}{t^2}\,dt.$$

We now divide $(0, \pi/2)$ into three intervals $(0, 1/n)$, $(1/n, c)$, $(c, \pi/2)$. Then

$$(12) \qquad \frac{1}{n}\int_c^{\pi/2} |g(t)|\frac{\sin^2 nt}{t^2}\,dt \leqslant \frac{1}{nc^2}\int_c^{\pi/2} |g(t)|\,dt \to 0,$$

and, by (11) (i) and (c),

$$\frac{1}{n}\int_0^{1/n} |g(t)| \frac{\sin^2 nt}{t^2} dt \leqslant n \int_0^{1/n} |g(t)|\, dt = nG(1/n) \to 0.$$

Finally,

$$\frac{1}{n}\int_{1/n}^{c} |g(t)| \frac{\sin^2 nt}{t^2} \leqslant \frac{1}{n}\int_{1/n}^{c} |g(t)| \frac{dt}{t^2}$$

$$= \frac{1}{n} \cdot \frac{G(c)}{c^2} - \frac{1}{n} \cdot n^2 G(1/n) + \frac{2}{n}\int_{1/n}^{c} G(t) \frac{dt}{t^3},$$

and the first two terms on the right-hand side $\to 0$, while, if we choose c such that $|G(t)/t| < \epsilon$, for $0 < t < c$, we have

$$\frac{2}{n}\int_{1/n}^{c} \frac{G(t)}{t} \cdot \frac{dt}{t^2} < \frac{2\epsilon}{n}\int_{1/n}^{c} \frac{dt}{t^2} < 2\epsilon.$$

Thus all the limiting numbers of $|J_n|$ are $< \frac{1}{2}\pi\epsilon$, i. e. $J_n \to 0$.

If $g(0)$ is not zero, we apply the reasoning to $g(t) - g(0)$ with $G(t) = \int_0^t |g(t) - g(0)|\, dt$. Noticing that, by (2),

$$\frac{2}{n\pi}\int_0^{\pi/2} \left(\frac{\sin nt}{\sin t}\right)^2 dt = 1,$$

we obtain the result

$$J_n \to g(0)/2 \quad \text{when } n \to \infty.$$

Similarly,

$$\frac{1}{n\pi}\int_{-\pi/2}^{0} g(t) \left(\frac{\sin nt}{\sin t}\right)^2 dt \to g(0)/2.$$

Thus we have

I. *If* $g(t)$ *is integrable* (L) *in* $(-\pi/2, \pi/2)$ *and* $G'(0) = 0$, *where*

$$G(t) = \int_{-t}^{t} |g(t) - g(0)|\, dt,$$

then

$$\frac{1}{n\pi}\int_{-\pi/2}^{\pi/2} g(t) \left(\frac{\sin nt}{\sin t}\right)^2 dt \to g(0) \tag{13}$$

when $n \to \infty$. *We have also, by* (12),

$$\frac{1}{n\pi}\int_{-\epsilon}^{+\eta} g(t) \left(\frac{\sin nt}{\sin t}\right)^2 dt \to g(0), \quad 0 < \eta < \pi/2, \quad 0 < \epsilon < \pi/2. \tag{14}$$

(Lebesgue, 1905.)

This result applies to (8) for every ϕ for which the differential coefficient of

$$\int_{-\tau}^{\tau} | F'''(\phi+2\tau) - F'''(\phi) | \, d\tau$$

with respect to τ vanishes at $\tau = 0$. Putting, for fixed ϕ, $\phi + 2\tau = t$, we have

$$\int_{0}^{\tau} | F'''(\phi+2\tau) - F'''(\phi) | \, d\tau = \tfrac{1}{2} \int_{\phi}^{t} | F'''(t) - F'''(\phi) | \, dt,$$

and thus by Lebesgue's theorem (C), at $t = \phi$ the differential coefficient, with respect to t, of the integral considered is $| F'''(\phi) - F'''(\phi) | = 0$ *for almost every* ϕ. Hence the corresponding result for the left-hand side, i.e. for almost every ϕ, the differential coefficient at $\tau = 0$, with respect to τ, of the left-hand side is 0. Similarly for $\int_{-\tau}^{0}$. Thus I applies for almost every value of ϕ and proves that, for almost every value of ϕ, $\sigma_n(e^{i\phi})$ tends to a limit when $n \to \infty$. Therefore by 105. I (Frobenius), $\lim_{r \to 1} f(re^{i\phi})$ also exists for the same values of ϕ.

II. *If* $f(z) = \Sigma a_n z^n$ *is bounded in* $|z| < 1$, *the limit* $\lim_{r \to 1} f(re^{i\phi})$ *exists for almost every value of* ϕ. (Fatou, 1906.)

109. *Limiting values of bounded functions.* In connexion with his result Fatou raised the question whether a function $f(z)$ regular and bounded in $|z| < 1$ can tend to 0 along every radius. F. and M. Riesz answered this question in a satisfactory way. The proof here given is due to F. Riesz (1921). If, for a fixed value of θ, the limit $\lim_{r \to 1} f(re^{i\theta})$ exists, we denote this limit by $f(e^{i\theta})$ and we call the integral

$$\mu_\delta(r) = \frac{1}{2\pi} \int_0^{2\pi} |f(re^{i\theta})|^\delta \, d\theta$$

the δ-mean of $f(z)$ on $|z| = r$.

I. *If* $f(z)$ *is regular and bounded in* $|z| < 1$, *or if at least* $\mu_\delta(r)$ *is bounded when* $r \to 1$, *the set of values* θ *for which* $f(e^{i\theta}) = 0$ *form a set of zero measure.* (F. and M. Riesz, 1916.)

Proof. We establish first an important inequality due to Szegö (1921 b).

Let us suppose for a moment that $f(z) \neq 0$ in $|z| \leqslant r < 1$. Then every branch of $\log |f(z)|$ is regular and thus, by Poisson's formula (54. 5),

$$2\pi \log |f(z_0)| = \int_0^{2\pi} P \log |f(re^{i\theta})| \, d\theta,$$

where
$$P = \frac{r^2 - r_0^2}{r^2 + r_0^2 - 2rr_0 \cos(\theta - \theta_0)}$$

and $z_0 = r_0 e^{i\theta_0}$, $r_0 < r$. Decompose the interval $(0, 2\pi)$ into two sets of points: (a) for which $|f(re^{i\theta})| > 1$, (b) for which $|f(re^{i\theta})| \leqslant 1$. Then

$$2\pi \log |f(z_0)| = \int_{(a)} P \log |f(re^{i\theta})| \, d\theta + \int_{(b)} P \log |f(re^{i\theta})| \, d\theta,$$

and

$$\int_{(b)} P \log |f(re^{i\theta})| \, d\theta$$
$$= \int_{(a)} P \log |f(re^{i\theta})| \, d\theta - \int_0^{2\pi} P \left| \log |f(re^{i\theta})| \right| d\theta.$$

Hence

$$2\pi \log |f(z_0)| = 2 \int_{(a)} P \log |f(re^{i\theta})| \, d\theta - \int_0^{2} P \left| \log |f(re^{i\theta})| \right| d\theta.$$

Replacing P by its maximum and minimum respectively, we obtain Szegö's important inequality

$$(1) \quad 2\pi \log |f(z_0)|$$
$$\leqslant 2 \frac{r + r_0}{r - r_0} \int_{(a)} \log |f(re^{i\theta})| \, d\theta - \frac{r - r_0}{r + r_0} \int_0^{2\pi} \left| \log |f(re^{i\theta})| \right| d\theta.$$

The formula is also valid when $f(z)$ vanishes in $|z| \leqslant r$. In fact, since $f(z)$ is regular, it has only a finite number of zeros in $|z| \leqslant r$. If a_i $(i = 1, 2, \ldots, k)$ are the zeros, we form the rational function

$$h(z) = r^k \prod_{i=1}^{k} \frac{z - a_i}{r^2 - \bar{a}_i z}.$$

By 44. I, $|h(re^{i\theta})| = 1$ and its poles are outside $|z| = r$. Thus the result applies to $g(z) = f(z)/h(z)$. If we notice moreover that $|h(z_0)| < 1$, i. e. $|f(z_0)| < |g(z_0)|$, the remark is proved.

Noticing that, for $x > 0$, $\log x < x$ or, more generally,

$$\log x = \frac{1}{\delta} \log(x^\delta) \leqslant \frac{1}{\delta} x^\delta, \quad \delta > 0,$$

we see that, if $|f(z)| < M$, the first integral in (1) is $< 2\pi M/\delta$ and, more generally, when $\mu_\delta(r) \leqslant M$, the first integral is $\leqslant 2\pi M/\delta$.

Taking a value z_0 for which $f(z_0) \neq 0$, and taking a measurable part E of (b), we have from (1)

$$\int_E \left| \log |f(re^{i\theta})| \right| d\theta \leqslant \frac{4\pi M}{\delta}\left(\frac{r+r_0}{r-r_0}\right)^2 - 2\pi \frac{r+r_0}{r-r_0} \log |f(z_0)|.$$

But the right-hand side is bounded for r between $r_1 > r_0$ and 1, and tends to a limit B as $r \to 1$. Thus, if r_1 is sufficiently near 1, the bound is as near to B as we like. It follows that the upper (L) integral of the limit of the integrand exists and is $\leqslant B$, and thus, by 108. F, this limit function is integrable (L) in E and we have Szegö's inequality

$$(2) \quad \int_E \left| \log |f(e^{i\theta})| \right| d\theta \leqslant \frac{4\pi M}{\delta}\left(\frac{1+|z_0|}{1-|z_0|}\right)^2 - 2\pi \frac{1+|z_0|}{1-|z_0|} \log|f(z_0)|.$$

Now, if $f(e^{i\theta}) = 0$ for a set of positive (>0) measure, its logarithm is not integrable, which contradicts the fact just established and proves the theorem.

It also follows that, if for two bounded functions f_1 and f_2 the limits $f_1(e^{i\theta})$ and $f_2(e^{i\theta})$ are the same for a set of non-zero measure, they are identical. We have only to apply I to $f_1 - f_2$.

The same is true when $\mu_\delta(r)$ is bounded for both functions.

Another important consequence of I is the following.

II. *If the functions $f_n(z)$ are regular and collectively bounded in $|z|<1$ and if $f_n(e^{i\theta}) \to 0$ for a set E of θ of measure $m>0$, then $f_n(z) \to 0$ at every point of $|z<1$.* (F. Riesz, 1923 b.)

Proof. Under the conditions of the theorem the left-hand side and thus also the right-hand side of (2), where f is replaced by f_n, tends to ∞ with n, i. e. we must have $\log f_n(z) \to -\infty$, i. e. $f_n(z) \to 0$, for every inner point of $|z|<1$ and uniformly in $|z| \leqslant r < 1$. Q. e. d.

Theorem II can also be formulated as follows:

III. *If the functions $f_n(z)$ are regular and collectively bounded in $|z|<1$ and $f_n(e^{i\theta})$ converges for a set E of θ of measure $m>0$, then the sequence $f_n(z)$ converges at every point of $|z|<1$.*

(Ostrowski, 1922.)

Proof. Apply II to $f_m(z) - f_n(z)$, m and n increasing independently to ∞.

110. *Limiting values along different lines leading to the same point.* Another problem of great interest in connexion with

bounded functions is that of the limiting values obtained along different paths ending at the same point of the circle of convergence. In this connexion we shall discuss some important results due to Montel and Lindelöf.

I. *Suppose* $f(z)$ *is bounded in a sector* A_0OB_0 *limited by an arc* A_0B_0, *centre at* O. *If* $f(z) \to \alpha$ *as* z *tends to* 0 *along a radius vector* LO *inside the sector,* $f(z)$ *tends uniformly to* α *as* $z \to 0$ *in any sector inside* A_0OB_0. (Montel, 1912.)

Proof. We shall suppose that $OA_0 = OB_0 = 1$. Consider the circles $|z| = 1/2^n$ $(n = 0, 1, \ldots)$ cutting OA, OB, OA', OB' and

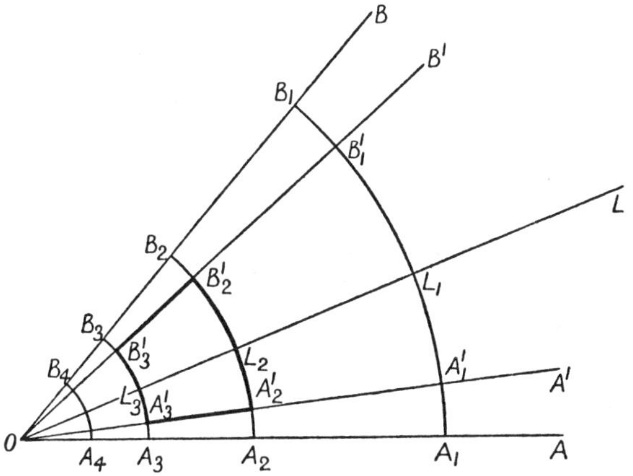

Fig. 58.

OL at $A_0, A_1, \ldots$; $B_0, B_1, \ldots$; $A_0', A_1', \ldots$; $B_0', B_1' \ldots$; $L_0, L_1, \ldots$. Let Δ_n denote the domain limited by the two segments $A'_{n+1}A'_{n+2}$, $B'_{n+1}B'_{n+2}$ and by the two arcs $A'_{n+1}B'_{n+1}$, $A'_{n+2}B'_{n+2}$, and put $f_n(z) = f(z/2^{n-1})$.

When z is in Δ_1, $z/2^n$ is in Δ_n, so that the functions $f_n(z)$ are collectively bounded in Δ_1. Moreover, $f_n(z)$ on L_2L_3 is equal to $f(z)$ on $L_{n+1}L_{n+2}$ so that, at every point on L_2L_3, $f_n(z)$ tends to α. Therefore, by Vitali's thorem, 42. IV, $f_n(z)$ tends uniformly to the constant function α in the whole domain Δ_1, and thus

$$|f_n(z) - \alpha| < \epsilon \text{ in } \Delta_1' \text{ for } n \geqslant p, \text{ say,}$$

i. e.

$$|f(z/2^{n-1}) - \alpha| < \epsilon \text{ in } \Delta_1' \text{ for } n \geqslant p.$$

But, in Δ_1', $|z| < 1/2$, and thus $|z/2^{n-1}| < \delta = 1/2^p$, if $n \geqslant p$. Hence $|f(z) - \alpha| < \epsilon$ if $|z| < \delta$ in the sector $A'OB'$. Q. e. d.

We notice that it does not follow from our hypothesis that the function also tends to definite limiting values along AO and BO, even if $f(z)$ is regular at the points on AO and BO, O excepted. In fact, putting $z = r\,e^{i\theta}$, we have

$$|\,e^{-1/z}\,| = e^{-\frac{1}{r}\cos\theta} \leqslant 1 \text{ if } \cos\theta \geqslant 0,$$

and thus $e^{-1/z}$ is bounded in the semicircle $-\pi/2 \leqslant \theta \leqslant \pi/2$, $|\,z\,| \leqslant 1$, say. But, for $\theta = \pm\pi/2$, $e^{-1/z}$ reduces to $\cos(1/r) \pm i\sin(1/r)$, which tends to no definite limit as $r \to 0$.

The corresponding problem for the boundary has been investigated by Lindelöf. His beautiful general results are established by the correspondence between boundaries in biuniform mapping. Two of his simpler results, however, are based on a fairly straightforward generalization of Phragmen-Lindelöf's principle of the maximum 41. VI.

II. *Suppose* $f(z)$ *is regular and that* (a) $|\,f(z)\,| \leqslant M$ *in the finite domain* D *limited by a simple Jordan curve* C, (b) *when* z *in* D *is sufficiently near to certain arcs* (γ) *of* C, $|\,f(z)\,| < \sigma < M$, (c) *the arcs* (γ) *satisfy the following condition: that there are* $n-1$ *biuniform mappings*

$$(1) \qquad \zeta = g_\nu(z), \quad z = h_\nu(\zeta)$$

of D *on* $D_1, \ldots, D_{n-1}$ *leaving invariant a certain inner point* z_0 *and being such that the common part* D_0 *of* $D, D_1, \ldots, D_{n-1}$ *contains* z_0 *and is limited exclusively by sections of the arcs* (γ) *and of their pictures by* (1). *Then*

$$(2) \qquad |\,f(z_0)\,|^n < M^{n-1}\sigma.$$

(Lindelöf, 1915.)

Proof. $f_\nu(\zeta) = f[h_\nu(\zeta)]$ is regular and $|\,f_\nu(\zeta)\,| < M$ in D_ν and in particular $|\,f_\nu(\zeta)\,| < \sigma$ sufficiently near to the parts of its boundary corresponding to arcs (γ) of C. By hypothesis $h_\nu(z_0) = z_0$ and $f_\nu(z_0) = f(z_0)$. Hence, $F(z) = f(z)f_1(z)\ldots f_{n-1}(z)$ is regular in the common part D_0 of D, $D_1, \ldots, D_{n-1}$ and $|\,F(z)\,| < M^{n-1}\sigma$ at points of D_0 sufficiently near to its boundary. Hence, by the fundamental principle of the maximum, the same inequality holds at every inner point, in particular, at z_0. Hence the result.

We are going to apply this result to the particular case when D is a part of a circle, centre at z_0, containing z_0. If AB is the greatest arc cut off by the arcs (γ), we take n so large that the nth part of the circumference is less than AB, and we choose for mappings (1) the $n-1$ rotations about z_0:

(3) $\zeta - z_0 = e^{\nu\frac{2\pi i}{n}}(z-z_0),$
$\nu = 1, 2, \dots, n-1.$

Then every part of the circumference is outside one of

$$D, D_1, \dots, D_{n-1},$$

i.e. their common part which contains z_0 is limited only by the arcs (γ) and their transforms by the rotations considered.

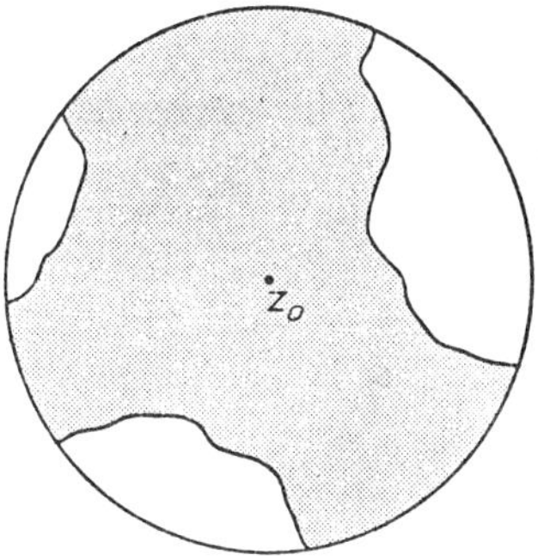

FIG. 59.

III. *Suppose $f(z)$ is regular in the sector D*

(4) $\phi_1 < \phi < \phi_2, \quad 0 < r < R, \quad z = a + re^{i\phi}$

and continuous also on its contour except perhaps at $z = a$. If

$$\lim_{r\to 0} f(a+re^{i\phi_1}) = \lim_{r\to 0} f(a+re^{i\phi_2}) \equiv \omega,$$

and if $f(z)$ is bounded in D, then $f(z)$ is also continuous at $z = a$. If the two limits exist and are different, $f(z)$ is not bounded in D. (Lindelöf 1915.)

Proof. If this result is proved for $\phi_2 - \phi_1$, the substitution $\zeta - a = (z-a)^\mu$ establishes it for any other angle. Thus we shall suppose that $\phi_2 - \phi_1 < \pi/2$.

A. The two limits are equal. Then, for every $\epsilon > 0$, there is a sector D' in D with $0 \leqslant r \leqslant R_\epsilon$ such that $|f(z) - \omega| < \epsilon$ is verified on the two radii up to R_ϵ. Take a point z_0 in $|z-a| < R_\epsilon/2$ and consider the circle C about z_0 passing through a.

The sum of the angles $az_0\alpha$ and $az_0\beta$ is $2\pi - 2(\phi_2 - \phi_1)$, i.e. one of the angles is $> \pi/2$. Hence, if we turn D' three times about z_0 by the angle $\pi/2$, the common part D_0' of the domains

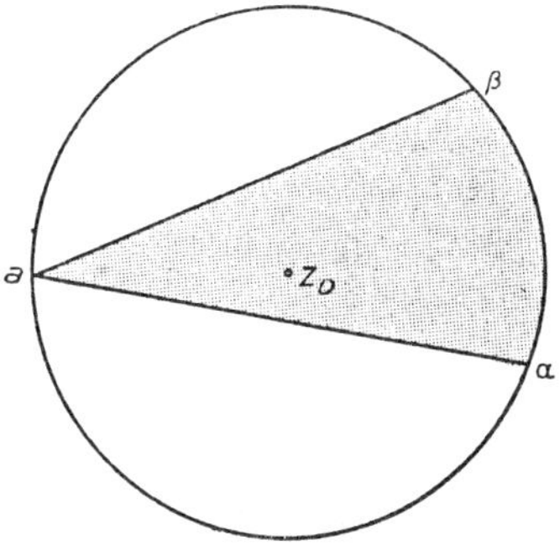

FIG. 60.

D_1', D_2', D_3', thus obtained is entirely within C and is limited exclusively by portions of $a\alpha$, $a\beta$ and their transforms by the rotations. By hypothesis, $|f(z)-\omega|<M$ in D'. On the other hand, $|f(z)-\omega|<\epsilon$ along $a\alpha$ and $a\beta$ except possibly at the point a. But a and its transforms are outside D_0'. Thus, by II,

$$|f(z_0)-\omega|^4<M^3\epsilon, \quad |f(z)-\omega|<M^{3/4}\epsilon^{1/4}$$

for every z_0 in $|z-a|<R_2/2$ and M, ϵ, ω being independent of z_0, $f(z)\to\omega$ when $r\to 0$ in $\phi_1\leqslant\phi\leqslant\phi_2$.

B. The two limits are different, i.e.

$$\lim_{r\to 0} f(a+re^{i\phi_1})\equiv\omega_1\neq\lim_{r\to 0} f(a+re^{i\phi_2})\equiv\omega_2.$$

The function $F(z)=\left[f(z)-\frac{\omega_1+\omega_2}{2}\right]^2$ is regular in D and continuous on its contour except at a, and it tends to $\left(\frac{\omega_1-\omega_2}{2}\right)^2$ along both of the limiting radii. Thus if $f(z)$ is bounded in D, so is $F(z)$, and by the first part of the theorem just established, $F(z)$ tends uniformly to $\left(\frac{\omega_1-\omega_2}{2}\right)^2$ when $r\to 0$ in $\phi_1\leqslant\phi\leqslant\phi_2$. Since $\frac{\omega_1-\omega_2}{2}\neq 0$ R_ϵ can be chosen so that $F(z)\neq 0$ for $0<r<R_\epsilon$, $\phi_1\leqslant\phi\leqslant\phi_2$. Hence in this sector we can choose a uniform branch of $\sqrt{F(z)}$, $f(z)-\frac{\omega_1-\omega_2}{2}$, say, which tends uniformly either to $\frac{\omega_1-\omega_2}{2}$ or $\frac{\omega_2-\omega_1}{2}$. It follows that $f(z)$ tends to ω_1 or to ω_2 which is contrary to our hypothesis. Therefore $f(z)$ cannot be bounded in D.

IV. *Suppose $f(z)$ is regular in D, enclosed by a simple Jordan curve C, and is continuous on its contour, except perhaps at $z=a$. Denote by C_1 and C_2 the arcs of C determined by a and any other point P of C. If $f(z)$ tends to the same limit ω when z tends to a along C_1 or along C_2, and if $f(z)$ is bounded in D, then $f(z)$ is also continuous at $z=a$. If the two limits are different, $f(z)$ is not bounded in D.* (Lindelöf, 1915.)

Proof. It is sufficient to prove the first part (the last part follows as before). The circle C_r of radius r about the point a splits D into a finite or infinite number of distinct portions, but only one of them, D_r, say, has the point a on its boundary. We denote by A_1 and A_2 the first point of C_r along aC_1, aC_2 respectively.

The arcs aA_1 and aA_2 divide the circle $|z-a|<r$ into two distinct domains, one of which, $\bar{D}_r$, say, contains D_r. We suppose

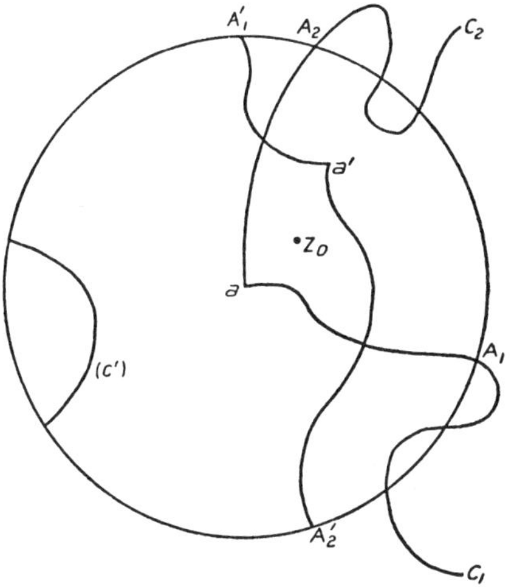

FIG. 61.

that the arc of C_r forming part of the boundary of $\bar{D}_r$ is $<2\pi r/3$ (the transformation $\zeta-a=(z-a)^{1/3}$ leads to this, if necessary).

Now take a point z_0 in D_r and apply the transformation

$$(5) \qquad (\zeta-z_0)/(\zeta-Z_0) = -(z-z_0)/(z-Z_0),$$

where
$$Z_0 = \frac{1}{\bar{a}-\bar{z}_0},$$

transforming C_r into itself and leaving z_0 and Z_0 invariant. When z_0 tends to a, Z_0 tends to ∞ and, in the limit, (5) reduces to a rotation of angle π about $z=a$. It follows that when $|z_0-a|/r<\mu$ (conveniently chosen), then the arc A_1A_2 of C_r ($<2\pi r/3$, by hypothesis) is transformed by (5) into $A_1'A_2'$ of C having no common point with A_1A_2.

D_r is limited by portions of A_1A_2 and parts (c) of C inside $|z-a|<r$. The transform D_r' of D_r by (5) is thus limited by portions of $A_1'A_2'$ and by the transforms (c') of (c). Since A_1A_2 and $A_1'A_2'$ are distinct, the common part D_0 of D_r and D_r', which

contains z_0, is entirely inside $|z-a|<r$ and its contour consists exclusively of parts of (c) and (c').

Now consider $F(z) = [f(z)-\omega][f_1(z)-\omega]$, where $f_1(z)$ is defined by $f_1(\zeta) = f(z)$. By hypothesis, $|f(z)-\omega| < M$ in D and thus also in D_r. Therefore $|f_1(z)-\omega| < M$ in D'_r. On the other hand, for every given ϵ, there is an R_ϵ such that $|f(z)-\omega|<\epsilon$ is verified on the arcs (c), except perhaps at a, whenever r is $<R_\epsilon$. Hence, for such values of r, $|f_1(z)-\omega|<\epsilon$ on (c') except at a', corresponding to a by (5). Thus $F(z)$ is regular and bounded in D_0 and is continuous; moreover $|F(z)|<M\epsilon$ on its boundary except at a and a'. Hence, by II, this inequality is valid inside D_0 and in particular at z_0 where it reduces to

$$|f(z_0)-\omega| < \sqrt{M\epsilon}$$

established for every z_0 of D inside $|z-a|<\mu R_\epsilon$. This proves the theorem.

Convergence on the circle of convergence.

111. *Examples.* A Taylor series may converge at every point of its circle of convergence $|z|=1$, e.g. when $|n^{1+\epsilon}a_n|<A$, $\epsilon>0$, or it may diverge at every point of $|z|=1$, e.g. when a_n does not tend to 0, or finally it may converge at some points and diverge at other points of $|z|=1$, e.g. $\Sigma z^n/n$ which diverges for $z=1$ but converges for every other point of $|z|=1$. In the latter case, as we shall see, the convergence or divergence at a given point is in close connexion with the analytic character of the sum function $f(z) = \Sigma a_n z^n$.

Appell's comparison theorem, Ex. III. 13, applied to

$$f(z) = \Sigma a_n z^n$$

and $1/(1-r) = \Sigma r^n$ shows that when $a_n \to 0$, then

$$\lim_{r\to 1} \frac{\Sigma |a_n| r}{\Sigma r} = \lim_{n=\infty} \frac{a_n}{1} = 0,$$

i.e. $(1-r)\Sigma a_n r^n$ tends to 0 when $r \to 1$. Hence, if $\Sigma a_n z^n$ has a pole on $|z|=1$ or an algebraic singularity of order higher than 1, e.g. $(1-z)^\alpha$, $\alpha<-1$, then a_n does not tend to 0 (since $(1-r)\Sigma a_n r^n$ does not tend to 0) and thus the series diverges at every point of $|z|=1$.

But even when $a_n \to 0$, i.e. when the series $\Sigma a_n e^{ni\phi}$ could converge, *the series may diverge for every value of* ϕ, as is shown by Lusin's example. (Lusin, 1911.)

Putting

$$g_m(z) = \frac{1-z^m}{1-z},$$

we have

$$|g_m(e^{i\phi})| = \left| \frac{e^{-\frac{m}{2}\phi i} - e^{\frac{m}{2}\phi i}}{e^{-\frac{1}{2}\phi i} - e^{\frac{1}{2}\phi i}} \right| = \left| \frac{\sin\frac{m\phi}{2}}{\sin\frac{\phi}{2}} \right|, \quad \phi \neq 0.$$

Thus on the arc $-\pi/m \leqslant \phi \leqslant \pi/m$, $\phi = 0$ excluded,

$$(1) \qquad |g_m(e^{i\phi})| \geqslant \frac{\frac{2}{\pi}\left|\frac{m\phi}{2}\right|}{\left|\frac{\phi}{2}\right|} = \frac{2m}{\pi},$$

and (1) is valid also for $\phi = 0$. If $e^{\phi i}$ be denoted by ξ, there is a positive integer $k < m$ for every ξ, such that

$$|g_m(e^{-\frac{2\pi k i}{m}}\xi)| \geqslant \frac{2m}{\pi},$$

and so

$$(2) \qquad \max_{0 \leqslant k < m} |g_m(e^{-\frac{2\pi k i}{m}}\xi)| \geqslant \frac{2m}{\pi}.$$

Now consider the polynomial

$$h_m(z) = g_m(z) + z^m g_m(e^{-\frac{2\pi i}{m}}z) + \dots$$
$$+ z^{mk} g_m(e^{-\frac{2\pi k i}{m}}z) + \dots + z^{m(m-1)} g_m(e^{-\frac{2\pi(m-1)i}{m}}z).$$

In each term all the indices are higher than in the preceding term (the degree of $h_m(z)$ is therefore $(m-1)(m+1)$) and the modulus of every coefficient is 1. Now form the series

$$(3) \qquad \sum_{m=1}^{\infty} \frac{1}{\sqrt{m}} z^{1^2+2^2+\dots+(m-1)^2} h_m(z) = \sum_{n=0}^{\infty} b_n z^n.$$

Since

$$1^2+2^2+\dots+(m-1)^2+(m-1)(m+1)$$
$$< 1^2+2^2+\dots+(m-1)^2+m^2,$$

we see that the indices of each term on the left-hand side are all greater than the indices of the preceding terms. Thus we also see that $a_n = |b_n|$ steadily decreases to 0.

If the series (3) were convergent at a point of $|z| = 1$, we would have

$$\lim_{m=\infty} \frac{1}{\sqrt{m}} |\xi^{1^2+2^2+\ldots+(m-1)^2}| \max_{0\leqslant k<m} |\xi^{mk} g_m(e^{-\frac{2\pi k}{m}}\xi)| = 0,$$

which is impossible, since, by (2), the expression in question is

$$\geqslant \frac{1}{\sqrt{m}} \cdot \frac{2m}{\pi} = \frac{2\sqrt{m}}{\pi}.$$

Again, *a series may converge at just one point of the circle of convergence.* The series

$$(4) \qquad a_0 - a_0 z + a_1 z^2 - a_1 z^3 + a_2 z^4 - a_2 z^5 + \ldots,$$

where a_n is taken from (3), is convergent for $z = 1$, because $a_n \to 0$. On the other hand, if it were convergent for

$$\xi = e^{i\phi} \neq 1,$$

then
$$a_0(1-\xi) + a_1\xi^2(1-\xi) + a_2\xi^4(1-\xi) + \ldots,$$

and thus also $\Sigma a_n \xi^{2n}$ would be convergent, which is impossible since $|\xi^2| = 1$. (Sierpiński, 1916.)

Hardy (1913–14) showed that *a Taylor series may converge uniformly on* $|z| = 1$ *without converging absolutely.*

Consider for this purpose the function

$$(5) \qquad g(z) = (1-z)^i = \sum_{n=0}^{\infty} (-1)^n C_n^{-i} z^n = \sum_0^{\infty} b_n z^n.$$

This function is regular and bounded in $|z| < 1$, for

$$g(z) = e^{-i\log(1-z)} \text{ and } -\pi/2 < \operatorname{Im}[\log(1-z)] < \pi/2.$$

But
$$|nb_n| = n\left|\frac{i(i+1)\ldots(i+n-1)}{1.2\ldots(n-1)} \frac{1}{n}\right|$$

$$= \sqrt{\left(1+\frac{1}{1^2}\right)\left(1+\frac{1}{2^2}\right)\cdots\left(1+\frac{1}{(n+1)^2}\right)},$$

i.e.
$$|nb_n| \to \sqrt{\prod_{\nu=1}^{\infty}(1+1/\nu^2)},$$

and thus

$$(6) \qquad b_n = O(1/n) \text{ and } \sum_{n=2}^{\infty} |b_n|/\log n = \infty .$$

On the other hand, putting

$$B_m(\phi) = \sum_{n=2}^{\infty} b_n e^{n\phi i},$$

we have from (6), since $|g(z)|<M$, by 105. IV, $|B_m(\phi)|<N$ independently of m and ϕ.

Now putting $a_n = b_n/\log n$, the series $\sum_{n=2}^{\infty} |a_n|$ is divergent and, as we are going to prove, $\sum_{n=2}^{\infty} a_n e^{n\phi i}$ is uniformly convergent. The last statement is proved by noticing that, for $v \geqslant u \geqslant 3$,

$$\left|\sum_{n=u}^{v} a_n e^{n\phi i}\right| = \left|\sum_{n=u}^{v} \frac{B_n(\phi)-B_{n-1}(\phi)}{\log n}\right|$$

$$= \left|\sum_{n=u}^{v} B_n(\phi)\left(\frac{1}{\log n} - \frac{1}{\log (n+1)}\right) - \frac{B_{u-1}(\phi)}{\log u} + \frac{B_v(\phi)}{\log (v+1)}\right|$$

$$< N\sum_{n=u}^{v}\left(\frac{1}{\log n} - \frac{1}{\log (n+1)}\right) + \frac{N}{\log u} + \frac{N}{\log (v+1)} = \frac{2N}{\log u},$$

i. e. the remainder

$$\left|\sum_{n=p}^{\infty} a_n e^{n\phi i}\right| < 2N/\log p$$

independently of ϕ.

The case when $na_n \to 0$ displays a remarkable regularity.

I. *If* $na_n \to 0$ *and* $\lim_{r\to 1} f(r) = A$, *then also* $s_n \to A$.

(Tauber, 1897.)

Proof. Replacing a_0 by $a_0 - A$, we may suppose that $A = 0$.

From $$s_m - f(r) = \sum_{n=1}^{m} a_n(1-r^n) - \sum_{n=m+1}^{\infty} a_n r^n$$

and $1-r^n = (1-r)(1+r+\ldots+r^{n-1}) \leqslant (1-r)n$ we obtain, for $0<r<1$,

$$|s_m - f(r)| \leqslant (1-r)\sum_{n=1}^{m} n\,|a_n| + \sum_{n=m+1}^{\infty} |a_n|\,r^n.$$

Moreover, denoting by η_m the greatest of $(m+1)\,|a_{m+1}|$, $(m+2)\,|a_{m+2}|, \ldots$ we have

$$\sum_{n=m+1}^{\infty} |a_n|\,r^n = \sum_{n=m+1}^{\infty} n\,|a_n|\,\frac{1}{n}\,r^n \leqslant \frac{\eta_m}{m}\sum_{0}^{\infty} r^n = \frac{\eta_m}{m(1-r)}.$$

Now since the $n\,|a_n|$ tend to zero their arithmetic means also tend to zero, i.e.

$$\frac{1}{m}\sum_{n=1}^{m} n\,|a_n| \to 0, \text{ when } m \to \infty.$$

Putting $r = 1-1/m$, we have

$$|s_m - f(1-1/m)| \leqslant \frac{1}{m}\sum_{n=1}^{m} n\,|a_n| + \eta_m \to 0,$$

when $m \to \infty$.

Since, by hypothesis, $f(1-1/m) \to 0$, the theorem is proved.

A more general theorem on the same lines is the following:

II. *If* $w_m = \sum_{1}^{m} n a_n = o(m)$, *and* $\lim_{r\to 1} f(r) = A$, *then* $s_n \to A$.

(Tauber, 1897.)

Proof. We suppose that $a_0 = 0$, $A = 0$ (for if $f(z) \to A$ then $f(z) - a_0 + (a_0 - A)z \to 0$ for $z \to 1$). Thus, for $|z|<1$,

$$f(z) = \sum_{1}^{\infty} \frac{w_n - w_{n-1}}{n} z^n = \sum_{1}^{\infty} w_n\left(\frac{z^n}{n} - \frac{z^{n+1}}{n+1}\right)$$

$$= \sum_{1}^{\infty} w_n\left(\frac{z^n - z^{n+1}}{n+1} + \frac{z^n}{n(n+1)}\right)$$

$$= (1-z)\sum_{1}^{\infty} \frac{w_n}{n+1} z^n + \sum_{1}^{\infty} \frac{w_n}{n(n+1)} z^n.$$

From $w_n = o(n)$, we have $(1-z)\sum_{1}^{\infty} \frac{w_n}{n+1} z^n \to 0$ and thus, since

$f(z) \to 0$, it follows that $\sum_1^\infty \frac{w_n}{n(n+1)} z^n \to 0$. Applying I to $\sum_1^\infty \frac{w_n}{n(n+1)} z^n$, since $\frac{w_n}{n(n+1)} = o(1/n)$, we have

$$0 = \sum_{n=1}^\infty \frac{w_n}{n(n+1)} = \lim_{m=\infty} \sum_{n=1}^m \frac{w_n}{n(n+1)} = \lim_{m=\infty} \sum_{n=1}^m w_n\left(\frac{1}{n} - \frac{1}{n+1}\right)$$

$$= \lim_{m=\infty}\left[\sum_1^m \frac{w_n - w_{n-1}}{n} - \frac{w_m}{m+1}\right] = \lim_{m=\infty} \sum_1^m \frac{w_n - w_{n-1}}{n} = \lim_{m=\infty} \sum_{n=1}^m a_n.$$

This proves the theorem.

112. *Convergence at regular points.* We are going to investigate the influence of regularity of the function $f(z) = \Sigma a_n z^n$ at a point $e^{i\phi}$ on the convergence of $\Sigma a_n e^{in\phi}$. For ordinary convergence $a_n \to 0$ and for the convergence of $s_n^{(r)}(e^{i\phi})$ the condition $a_n/n^r \to 0$ is, as we have seen, 102. III, necessary but not sufficient.

I. *If* $a_n \to 0, f(z) = \Sigma a_n z^n$ *converges at every regular point of* $|z| = 1$ *and uniformly on arcs of regularity.* (Fatou, 1906.)

Hadamard, 1892, proved this result for the case $n^\epsilon a_n \to 0$,

Proof. (Riesz, 1916.)

If $f(z)$ is regular on (x_1, x_2), it is regular in and on the boundary of a sector $0z_1z_2 0$. Put

$$g_n(z) = \frac{f(z) - a_0 - a_1 z - \dots - a_n z^n}{z^{n+1}} (z - y_1)(z - y_2),\ n = 1, 2, \dots.$$

We are going to prove that, on $(0z_1z_2 0), g_n(z)$ *converges uniformly to* **0**. Since $|g_n(z)|$ assumes its maximum M on the contour, it will follow that $g_n(z) \to 0$ *uniformly* on (x_1, x_2), and on this arc

$$|f(z) - (a_0 + a_1 z + \dots + a_n z^n)| \leqslant |g_n(z)|/L^2,$$

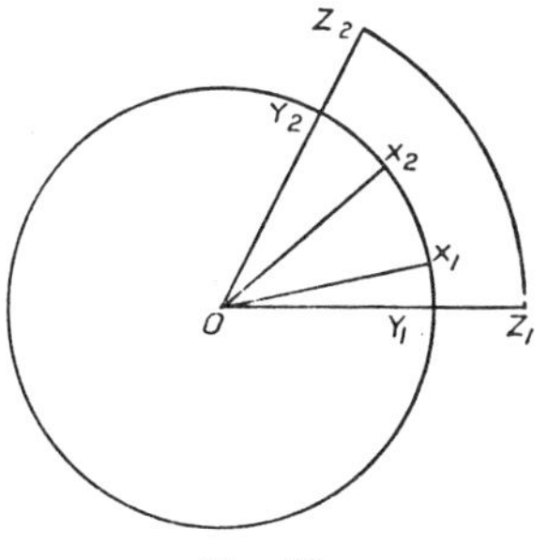

Fig. 62.

where L is the least distance of the arc (x_1, x_2) from the contour. This will prove the theorem in question.

(a) At $z=0$, $\qquad g_n(z) = a_{n+1}y_1y_2 \to 0.$

Also $\qquad g_n(y_1) = 0,\ g_n(y_2) = 0.$

Consider the section $(0, y_1)$, extremities excluded.

$$|f(z)-(a_0+\ldots+a_nz^n)| = |a_{n+1}z^{n+1}+\ldots|$$
$$\leqslant \epsilon_n(|z|^{n+1}+\ldots) = \frac{\epsilon_n|z|^{n+1}}{1-|z|},$$

where ϵ_n is the upper bound of $|a_{n+1}|, |a_{n+2}|, \ldots$. Putting $|z| = r$, we have $z = ry_1$, and thus $|z-y_1| = 1-r$, $|z-y_2| < 2$, i. e.

$$|g_n(z)| \leqslant \frac{\epsilon_n r^{n+1}}{1-r}\frac{1}{r^{n+1}}(1-r)2 = 2\epsilon_n,$$

which establishes the result for $(0, y_1)$.

(b) Along (y_1, z_1), extremities excluded, $z = ry_1$. Let $|z_1| = R$ and put $M+|a_0|+\ldots+|a_m|R^m = A_m$, where M is the maximum modulus of $f(z)$ for the sector. For $n>m$,

$$|f(z)-(a_0+\ldots+a_nz^n)| \leqslant A_m+\epsilon_m(r^{m+1}+\ldots+r^n)$$
$$< A_m+\epsilon_m\frac{r^{n+1}-1}{r-1} \leqslant A_m+\epsilon_m\frac{r^{n+1}}{r-1}.$$

On the other hand $|z-y_1| = r-1$, $|z-y_2| < 2R$. Hence

$$|g_n(z)| \leqslant \left(A_m+\epsilon_m\frac{r^{n+1}}{r-1}\right)\frac{1}{r^{n+1}}(r-1)2R = A_m\frac{r-1}{r^{n+1}}2R+\epsilon_m 2R.$$

But

$$\frac{r-1}{r^{n+1}} < \frac{r-1}{r^{n+1}-1} = \frac{1}{r^n+\ldots+1} < \frac{1}{n},$$

i.e. $$|g_n(z)| \leqslant \frac{2A_mR}{n}+2R\epsilon_m.$$

For every δ we can determine an m such that $2R\epsilon_m < \delta/2$. Then, for every point of the section in question, $|g_n(z)| < \delta/2+\delta/2$, if $n>m$ and also $n>4A_mR/\delta$.

(c) Along (z_1, z_2), extremities included. If $n>m$,

$$|f(z)-(a_0+\ldots+a_nz^n) < A_m+(R^{m+1}+\ldots+R^n)$$
$$< A_m+\epsilon_m R^{n+1}/(R-1).$$

Moreover $|z-y_1| < 2R$, $|z-y_2| < 2R$. Hence

$$|g_n(z)| < \left(A_m+\epsilon_m\frac{R^{n+1}}{R-1}\right)\frac{1}{R^{n+1}}4R^2 = A_m\frac{4}{R^{n-1}}+\epsilon_m\frac{4R^2}{R-1}.$$

Again for every δ there is an m such that $\epsilon_m 4R^2/(R-1) < \delta/2$

and an N such that, for $n > N$, $A_m 4/R^{n-1} < \delta/2$, i.e. for every point of the section $| g_n(z) | < \delta/2 + \delta/2$.

Similarly for (z_2, y_2) and $(y_2, 0)$. This proves the theorem.

M. Riesz generalized it for arithmetic means.

II. *If* $a_n/n^r \to 0$, *the arithmetic means* $s_n^{(r)}(e^{i\phi})$ *converge at every regular point of* $|z| = 1$. (M. Riesz, 1909 and 1911.)

Hadamard (1892) proved the convergence of $s_n^{(r)}(e^{i\phi})$ at regular points for $a_n/n^{r-\epsilon} \to 0$. We only give the proof for $r = 1$.

Let $g(z) = a_0 + \Sigma a_n z^n/n = a_0 + \int_0^z \frac{f(z) - a_0}{z} dz$. Then $g(z)$ is regular at 1 and thus, by I, $a_0 + \Sigma a_n/n$ is convergent, i.e. $\sigma_n \equiv a_0 + a_1/1 + \ldots + a_n/n \to g(1)$. But

$$(\sigma_1 + \ldots + \sigma_n)/n = a_0 + a_1/1 + \ldots + a_n/n - (a_1 + a_2 + \ldots + a_n)/n.$$

Since σ_n tends to a limit, the arithmetic mean tends to the same limit. Hence $s_n/n \to 0$. On the other hand

$$| s_n^{(1)} - s_{n-1}^{(1)} | = \left| -\frac{s_0 + \ldots + s_{n-1}}{n(n+1)} + \frac{s_n}{n+1} \right|$$
$$< \frac{|s_0| + \frac{|s_1|}{1} + \ldots + \frac{|s_{n-1}|}{n-1}}{n} + \frac{|s_n|}{n+1}.$$

Since $|s_n|/n$ tends to 0, the arithmetic mean also tends to 0, and thus $s_n^{(1)} - s_{n-1}^{(1)} \to 0$.

Suppose now that $f(1) = 0, f'(1) = 0$. Then theorem I, applied to

$$\sum_{n=1}^{\infty} (s_n^{(1)} - s_{n-1}^{(1)}) z^n = \frac{1-z}{z} \int_0^z \frac{f(z)dz}{(1-z)^2},$$

proves the theorem, since the partial sums on the left-hand side for $z = 1$ are just $s_n^{(1)}$. The addition of $a + bz$ to $f(z)$ leads to $\bar{s}_n = s_n + a + b$ and $\bar{s}_n^{(1)} = s_n^{(1)} + a + b$ and thus it does not modify the theorem.

The generalization to integers $r > 1$ is immediate.

To show the limitations of the method of arithmetic means we construct an example. (Fejér, 1910.)

The functions

$$f_m(z) = \frac{1}{(1+z)^{m+1}} = \sum_{n=0}^{\infty} (-1)^n C_m^{n+m} z^n$$

are collectively and uniformly bounded between 0 and 1, since $|f_m(z)| < 1$. Moreover $\lim_{z \to 1} f(z) = 1/2^{m+1}$.

The double series

$$f(z) = \sum_{m=0}^{\infty} \frac{f_m(z)}{m!} = \sum_{m=0}^{\infty} \frac{1}{m!} \sum_{n=0}^{\infty} (-1)^n C_m^{n+m} z^n = \frac{1}{1+z} e^{1/(1+z)}$$

is absolutely convergent for $|z| < 1$, for a dominant function of $f_m(z)$ is

$$\sum C_m^{n+m} |z|^m = f_m(-|z|) = \frac{1}{(1-|z|)^{m+1}}.$$

Consequently, putting

$$(-1)^n a_n = \sum_{m=0}^{\infty} \frac{1}{m!} C_m^{n+m},$$

we have

(1) $$f(z) = \Sigma(-1)^n a_n z^n \text{ where } \lim_{z \to 1} f(z) = \tfrac{1}{2} e^{\frac{1}{2}}.$$

On the other hand if Σa_n were summable by arithmetic means of any finite order (k say), we would have

$$\frac{|a_n|}{n^k} < M.$$

But

$$(-1)^n a_n > \frac{1}{(k+1)!} C_{k+1}^{n+k+1} = \frac{(n+k+1)\ldots(n+1)}{[(k+1)!]^2} > \frac{n^{k+1}}{[(k+1)!]^2},$$

which proves that the series (1) is not summable at $z = 1$ by the method of arithmetic means of any order, though its sum function is regular at this point. The reason of it is that the essential point at $z = -1$ makes the increase of $f(z)$ very rapid when $z \to -1$, and thus the coefficients must be very large.

113. *Convergence at singular points.* We have seen that a single pole on the circle of convergence makes convergence impossible on the circle. Our last example shows that an essential point on the circle of convergence may make impossible the convergence of arithmetic means. Since the same Taylor series represents the function in the whole circle $|z| < 1$, the construction of the coefficients reflects the character of the

function all along $|z| = 1$. Therefore it is relatively easy to obtain *direct theorems*, i. e. conclusions concerning the function drawn from hypotheses on the coefficients or, what amounts to the same thing, on the behaviour of the series, as in the case of Abel's theorem 105. I. Moreover, when we suppose that the series converges at $e^{i\phi}$, the condition $a_n \to 0$ is tacitly implied in our supposition.

The *converse* theorems are of two distinct types. On the one hand we may start as in 105. III with a *general* supposition about the function in the whole circle $|z| < 1$ and deduce from it a corresponding character of the series. These are the most obvious and also the easiest inversions of direct theorems. On the other hand, we may start as in 112. I and 112. II with a *local* supposition about the function in the neighbourhood of a single point of $|z| = 1$ and try to draw conclusions as to the behaviour of the series at the same point. In this case to counteract the possibly disturbing influences of the other points of $|z| = 1$, we have to make explicitly some supposition about the function all along $|z| = 1$ or else about the coefficients. The less we suppose the better the result, of course, but at the same time we are forced to make use of new, more penetrating, weapons for the proofs.

For example, having in view to establish convergence, we have to suppose that $a_n \to 0$. We have seen in 112. I that, with this general hypothesis, the local condition that the sum function $f(z)$ be regular at $e^{i\phi}$ assures the convergence. The problem is to find less stringent local conditions implying convergence. Fejér (1910) constructed an example showing that continuity along a small arc about $e^{i\phi}$ does not necessarily imply convergence.

I. *If* $a_n \to 0$ *and* $f(z)$ *is of bounded variation on an arc containing* ϕ, $\Sigma a_n e^{in\phi}$ *converges.*

(Dienes, 1911, 1913.)

Proof. For our actual purpose we want the generalization of (108. 3) expressing $s_n(e^{i\phi})$ by an integral extending only along a small arc containing ϕ. It was true also in Art. 108 that the part of the integral extending from c to $\pi/2$ tended to 0, but only in virtue of the hypothesis that $f(z)$ was bounded in the whole circle $|z| < 1$.

Lemma 1. *Putting*

$$a_n \cos n\theta + b_n \sin n\theta = A_n,$$

$$F(t) = -\sum_1^\infty (a_n \cos nt + b_n \sin nt)/n^2,$$

and supposing that $a_n \to 0$, $b_n \to 0$ (*where* a_n *and* b_n *are real*), *the difference*

$$(1) \qquad \sum_{i=1}^{n} A_n - \frac{1}{2\pi}\int_b^c F(t)\rho(t)\frac{d^2}{dt^2}\left(\frac{\sin\frac{2n+1}{2}(\theta-t)}{\sin\frac{\theta-t}{2}}\right)dt \to 0$$

when $n \to \infty$, *where* (b, c) *is an arbitrarily small interval containing* $t = \theta$, *and* $\rho(t)$ *and its first five derivatives, continuous in* (b, c), *satisfy the conditions*

$$(2) \qquad \rho(b) = \rho(c) = \rho'(b) = \rho'(c) = 0, \quad \rho(\theta) = 1,$$
$$\rho'(\theta) = \rho''(\theta) = \rho'''(\theta) = \rho''''(\theta) = 0,$$

and $\rho''(t)$ *has only a finite number of extrema in* (b, c).

(Riemann, 1854.)

More accessible proofs in Lebesgue (1928), Hobson (1921–6), Dienes (1913).

To prove I, we notice that if $f(e^{i\theta})$ is of bounded variation in (α, β), i. e. if this is true of its real and imaginary parts, the same is true of

$$f_1(z) = \int_0^z \frac{f(z)-a_0}{z}\,dz = \int_0^{e^{i\alpha}} \frac{f(z)-a_0}{z}\,dz + i\int_\alpha^\theta [f(e^{i\theta})-a_0]\,d\theta$$

and of

$$f_2(z) = \int_0^z \frac{f_1(z)}{z}\,dz = \int_0^{e^{i\alpha}} \frac{f_1(z)}{z}\,dz + i\int_\alpha^\theta f_1(e^{i\theta})\,d\theta$$

as functions of θ, where $z = e^{i\theta}$. The functions $f_1(z)$ and $f_2(z)$ of z are represented in $|z| < 1$ by $\sum_1^\infty a_n z^n/n$ and $\sum_1^\infty a_n z^n/n^2$ respectively, the latter converging, and thus also representing $f_2(z)$, on $|z| = 1$. It follows that $F(t)$, $F'(t)$, and $F''(t)$ are of bounded variation in (α, β) and since, by hypothesis, the same is true of $\rho(t)$, $\rho'(t)$, and $\rho''(t)$, it follows that $[F(t)\,\rho(t)]''$ is of bounded variation in (α, β). Making use of (1) for both the real and imaginary parts of $F(t)$, and integrating twice by parts (the integrated parts vanish by (2)), we obtain

$$(3)\quad s_n(e^{i\theta}) - a_0 - \frac{1}{2\pi}\int_\alpha^\beta [F(t)\rho(t)]'' \frac{\sin\frac{2n+1}{2}(\theta-t)}{\sin\frac{\theta-t}{2}}\,dt \to 0$$

when $n \to \infty$.

This formula reduces the problem of convergence of the series to that of the Fourier integral in the above expression. By Dirichlet's theorem (see Hobson ii, p. 506), this integral tends to zero if the function $[F(t)\rho(t)]''$ is of bounded variation. Theorem I is thus proved.

The condition imposed upon $f(z)$ of being of bounded variation on an arc containing ϕ implies, like regularity, that the same condition is satisfied in a small but definite neighbourhood of the point in question. Continuity is a condition which may be fulfilled at a point without being fulfilled at points approaching it. We know, however, by Fejér's example that convergence does not necessarily follow from continuity even when the function is continuous all along $|z| = 1$. Hence the interest of the following result, theorem III, based on two lemmas.

Lemma 2. *Under the conditions of lemma* 1

$$(4)\quad \frac{s_1+s_2+\dots+s_n}{n} - a_0 - \frac{1}{2\pi n}\int_b^c F(t)\rho(t)\frac{d^2}{dt^2}\left[\frac{\sin(n+1)\frac{\theta-t}{2}}{\sin\frac{\theta-t}{2}}\right]^2 dt = \eta_n \to 0,$$

where $s_n = A_0 + A_1 + \dots + A_n$.

Proof. Take the arithmetic means of both sides of (1).

An immediate consequence of lemma 2 is the generalization of Fatou's theorem on bounded functions, 108. II. In fact, applying (108. 14) to (4) we obtain

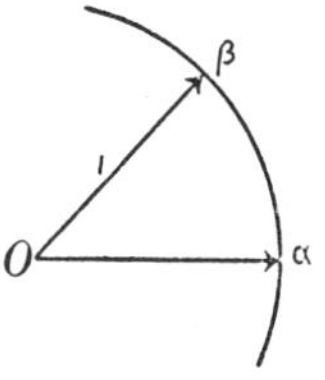

FIG. 63.

II. *If* $a_n \to 0$ *and* $f(z)$ *is bounded in the sector* $(O;\ \alpha, \beta)$, *the limit* $\lim\limits_{r\to 1} f(re^{i\phi})$ *exists for almost every value of* ϕ *pertaining to the arc* (α, β).

We remark that the condition $a_n \to 0$, though not explicitly stated in 108. II, is implied by the hypotheses. It has, however, been shown by Priwaloff (1924 b) that no restriction on a_n is necessary. This would follow from lemma 1 of Art. 120 if the latter were proved independently.

The second lemma refers to the special condition in our result in view.

Lemma 3. *If along every path inside* $|z|=1$ *leading to* $e^{i\phi}$

$$\lim_{z\to e^{i\phi}} |f(z)| \leqslant M, \tag{5}$$

then to any given $\eta > 0$, *there is an arc* (α, β) *containing* ϕ, *such that, when* z *tends, inside* $|z| = 1$, *to any point* θ *of* (α, β), *we have*

$$\text{(a)} \qquad \overline{\lim_{z\to e^{i\theta}}} |f(z)| \leqslant M+\eta,$$

$$\text{(b)} \qquad f_1(z) = \int_0^{re^{i\theta}} \frac{f(z)-a_0}{z}\,dz$$

tends to a limit when $r \to 1$ *and the limit function* $h(\theta)$ *thus defined is continuous and has bounded derivates, and almost everywhere*

$$h'(\theta) = \lim_{r\to 1} \frac{f(re^{i\theta})-a_0}{e^{i\theta}}. \tag{6}$$

Proof. Suppose that, for a given η and for every arc (α, β), however small, containing ϕ, there are on (α, β) points $z_\nu \to e^{i\phi}$ such that $\overline{\lim}_{z\to z_\nu} |f(z)| > M+\eta$. Then there are, inside $|z|=1$, points $z'_\nu \to e^{i\phi}$ arbitrarily near z_ν for which $|f(z_\nu)| > M+\eta$, which contradicts (5).

To prove (b) we notice that, by II,

$$\lim_{r\to 1} \frac{f(re^{i\theta})-a_0}{re^{i\theta}} = g(\theta) \tag{7}$$

exists for almost every value of θ in (α, β). For the other values of θ we put $g(\theta) = A$, any constant. By Lebesgue's theorem (108. E),

$$\lim_{r\to 1} \int_\alpha^\theta \frac{f(re^{i\theta})-a_0}{re^{i\theta}}\,d\theta = \int_\alpha^\theta g(\theta)\,d\theta. \tag{8}$$

But $f_1(e^{i\theta})$ is given by integrating $[f(z)-a_0]/z$ along $OAB\theta$, say. And since the parts of this integral along $A\alpha$ and $B\theta$ tend to 0 when the arc AB tends to (α, θ), we have, by (8),

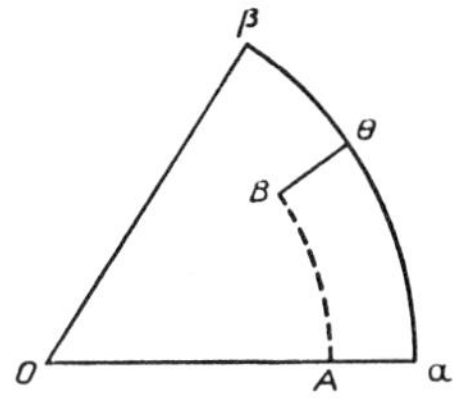

FIG. 64.

$$(9)\quad f_1(e^{i\theta}) \equiv h(\theta) = c + \int_\alpha^\theta g(\theta)\,d\theta$$

where

$$c = \int_0^{e^{i\alpha}} \frac{f(z)-a_0}{z}\,dz.$$

Therefore, by Lebesgue's theorem, (108. A), $h(\theta)$ is a continuous function, has bounded derivates, and $h'(\theta) = g(\theta)$ almost everywhere. Q. e. d.

We remark that lemma 3 implies no restriction on the coefficients.

III. *If* $a_n \to 0$ *and along every path, inside* $|z| = 1$, *leading to* $e^{i\phi}$

$$\lim_{z \to e^{i\phi}} f(z) = A,$$

then also

$$s_n^{(1)}(e^{i\phi}) \to A.$$

(Dienes, 1911, 1913.)

Proof. We have to prove that under the conditions of the theorem the integral in (4) tends to a limit. It follows from

$$\sum_1^\infty \frac{a_n}{n^2} z^n = \int_0^z \frac{f_1(z)}{z}\,dz$$

and from the continuity of $f_1(z)$ in the sector $(O\,;\,\alpha, \beta)$ that

$$F(t) \equiv -\Sigma \frac{a_n}{n^2} e^{int} = -\int_0^{e^{i\alpha}} \frac{f_1(z)}{z}\,dz - \int_{e^{i\alpha}}^{e^{it}} \frac{f_1(z)}{z}\,dz,$$

i. e. $F'(t) = -if_1(e^{it}) = -ih(t)$, which proves that $F'(t)$ is continuous and has bounded derivates, like $h(t)$. By (6),

$$F''(t) = -ih'(t)$$

exists almost everywhere along (α, β), viz. for every value of t for which $\lim_{r \to 1} f(re^{it})$ exists. By hypothesis this is the case for $t = \phi$.

These remarks justify two successive integrations by parts,

in (4), applied in reality separately to the real and imaginary parts of $F(t)$. Thus we obtain

$$(10)\quad \frac{s_1(e^{i\theta})+s_2(e^{i\theta})+\ \dots\ +s_n(e^{i\theta})}{n}-a_0$$

$$-\frac{1}{2\pi n}\int_b^c [F(t)\,\rho(t)]''\left[\frac{\sin\,(n+1)\,\dfrac{\theta-t}{2}}{\sin\,\dfrac{\theta-t}{2}}\right]^2 dt=\eta_n\rightarrow 0$$

where, for values of t at which $F''(t)$ does not exist, we put $F''(t)=A-a_0$.

In order to apply (108. 14) to the integral in (10), we have only to remark that, by (6), $h'(t)$ and thus also $F''(t)$ are continuous at $t=\phi$. In fact, denoting by $E(\theta)$ the set of limiting numbers of $[f(re^{i\theta})-a_0]/e^{i\theta}$ when $r\rightarrow 1$, the condition that $f(z)\rightarrow A$ whenever $z\rightarrow e^{i\theta}$ inside $|z|=1$ requires that the diameter of $E(\theta)$ dwindles to nothing when θ approaches ϕ. Thus the oscillation of $h'(\theta)$ at ϕ is 0 and (108. 14) applies; therefore the integral in (10) tends to $A-a_0$ and so the arithmetic means tend to A. Q. e. d.

CHAPTER XIV

DIVERGENCE AND SINGULARITIES

Degree of infinity and order of singularity.

114. *The nature of the problem.* In the preceding chapters we made good use of divergent series by 'summing' them, i.e. by assigning values as their sums. We might as well say that we transformed the divergent series or the sequences of the partial sums into convergent ones. From the point of view of regular points this way of proceeding was quite satisfactory because at a regular point an analytic function, or more precisely, a definite branch of an analytic function, has a unique value.

Investigations on singularities require, however, a different method. The function is not defined at a singular point, and it may tend to various limiting values when z approaches the singular point z_0 in question; in particular it may tend to infinity. And again, the way the function tends to infinity in the neighbourhood of z_0 is highly characteristic of the singularity of the function $f(z)$. Consequently, to detect the behaviour of the function in the neighbourhood of a singular point z_0 by means of the Taylor series or by its various transforms, we have to make use of their divergence at z_0 by establishing relations between the kind of irregularity of the function and the kind of divergence of the series and its transforms. This is the leading idea of this chapter (see Dienes, 1913, preface).

Consider a function $f(z) = \Sigma a_n z^n$ with real coefficients. By 95. V, if $s_n(1) \to +\infty$ (i.e. no finite limiting numbers) and if the elements of the matrix belonging to a Toeplitz transformation are positive, as in almost every practical case, the transformed sequence also tends to $+\infty$. *Direct divergence to $+\infty$ or to $-\infty$ is not destroyed by a real positive Toeplitz transformation.*

This is an important fact for our actual purpose since we do not want to transform a divergent series into a convergent one, but into another divergent series whose kind of divergence is in close connexion with the singular behaviour of the function at the point in question.

For example the partial sums of $\Sigma A_n^r z^n = 1/(1-z)^{r+1}$ at $z=1$ are $s_n(1) = A_n^{r+1}$ and thus $s_n(1)/n^{r+1} \to 1/\Gamma(r+2)$, i.e. the degree of infinity of $s_n(1)$ is the same as the order of infinity of the function at $z=1$. Now, when $f(z)$ has a pole of order r at $z=1$, and no other singularity on $|z|=1$, we have $f(z) = f_1(z) + \sum_{i=1}^{r} A_i/(1-z)^i$, where $f_1(z)$ is regular in a circle of radius $\rho > 1$. Hence the partial sums of $f_1(z) = \Sigma b_n z^n$ at $z=1$ converge to $f_1(1)$, and therefore $s_n(1)/n^r \to A_r/\Gamma(r+1)$. This detects the order of the pole as well as the value of the coefficient A_r. If we subtract $A_r/(1-z)^r$, the same method detects A_{r-1}, &c.

When there are several poles or algebraic singularities on $|z|=1$ of the kind just considered, the influence of the pole or algebraic singularity of the highest degree upon the partial sums is dominating as before. If there are several poles of the same highest degree r: $f(z) = A/(1-z)^r + B/(1-e^{-\alpha i}z)^r$, say, we have again

$$s_n(1) = A A_n^r + B \sum_{k=0}^{n} e^{-ki\alpha} A_k^{r-1}.$$

The partial sums of $1/(1-e^{-i\alpha}z) = \Sigma e^{-in\alpha} z^n$, at $z=1$, are

$$(1) \qquad 1 + e^{-i\alpha} + e^{-i2\alpha} + \ldots + e^{-in\alpha} = \frac{1-e^{-i(n+1)\alpha}}{1-e^{-i\alpha}},$$

i.e. they are bounded when $n \to \infty$ so that, divided by any positive power of n, they tend to 0. Multiplying $1/(1-e^{-i\alpha}z)$ by itself we see that the partial sums of $1/(1-e^{-i\alpha}z)^2$ at $z=1$ are

$$e^{i\alpha} \sum_{k=1}^{n} k e^{-ik\alpha}.$$

Differentiating (1) with respect to α we find that the degree of infinity of the partial sums is 1, i.e. dividing by n we obtain a bounded sequence, and so on. Thus we see that the partial sums of $1/(1-z)^r$ formed at $z=1$ have the degree of infinity r, while those of $1/(1-e^{-i\alpha}z)^r$ formed also at $z=1$ have the degree of infinity $r-1$. Thus the poles of equal, highest, order do not disturb one another. Hence we obtain the theorem

I. *If $f(z) = \Sigma a_n z^n$ is meromorphic on its circle of convergence $|z| = 1$ and if $e^{i\phi}$ is a pole of the highest order r, then*

$$\frac{s_n(e^{i\phi})}{n^r} \to \frac{B_r}{\Gamma(r+1)} \tag{2}$$

where B_r is the coefficient of $(1-e^{-i\phi}z)^{-r}$ in the Laurent expansion of $f(z)$ about $z = e^{i\phi}$. (Dienes, 1908.)

Thus, for functions meromorphic on the circle of convergence, the mode of divergence of the partial sums formed for the affix of a pole is in close connexion with the particular features of the singularity at the pole.

We notice also, that, at a regular point of $|z| = 1$, ordinary convergence is stopped by the presence of poles on the circle of convergence. To obtain the value of $f(z)$ at a regular point $e^{i\phi}$ we have to make use of arithmetic means of order $r' > r$ in order that the condition $a_n/n^{r'} \to 0$ should be satisfied, where $r+1$ is the order of the pole of highest order. Thus the singularities (poles) are detected by the behaviour of the original partial sums, whereas the values at regular points require more complicated methods. The reason for this is that the contribution of a pole to the formation of the Taylor coefficients dominates over that of the regular points. In fact, adding to $f(z)$ a pole of degree r, we add to its coefficients numbers comparable with n^{r-1}, whereas adding to $f(z)$ a function whose first singularity is outside $|z| = 1$, we add to its coefficients numbers comparable with R^{-n}, $R > 1$, i.e. the contribution is negligible as compared with that of a pole.

The same fact may be illustrated by Cauchy's formula

$$a_n = \frac{1}{2\pi i}\int_{|z|=r} \frac{f(z)dz}{z^{n+1}},$$

where we can take for r any value < 1. If we choose an r very nearly 1 we practically integrate along the inner side of the circle $|z| = 1$. But the integral is the sum of m integrals along m arcs making up $|z| = r$. If we take m very large, i.e. the arcs very small, a_n appears as a sum of contributions from the neighbourhoods of all the points of the circle of convergence. Now, in the neighbourhood of a pole, $|f(z)|$ is very large, so that it seems natural that the neighbouring contributions should prevail and display themselves in the partial sums.

We notice that, *for every* $z \neq 1/\alpha$,

$$s^{(1)}_{\alpha, n}(z) \equiv 1+\alpha z+ \dots +\alpha^n z^n = \frac{\alpha^{n+1} z^{n+1}}{\alpha z-1} - \frac{1}{\alpha z-1},$$

so that, if $|\alpha z| > 1$,

$$\lim_{n=\infty} \frac{s^{(1)}_{\alpha\, n}(z)}{\alpha^n z^n} = \frac{\alpha z}{\alpha z-1}.$$

More generally, if $s^{(r)}_{\alpha, n}$ denotes the partial sums of

$$\frac{1}{(1-\alpha z)^r} = \Sigma A_n^{r-1} \alpha^n z^n,$$

then since

$$\frac{1}{(1-\alpha z)^r} = \frac{1}{\Gamma(r)\alpha^{r-1}} \left[\frac{1}{1-\alpha z}\right]^{(r-1)},$$

we have

$$s^{(r)}_{\alpha, n}(z) = \frac{1}{\Gamma(r)\alpha^{r-1}} [s^{(1)}_{\alpha, n+r-1}(z)]^{(r-1)}.$$

It readily follows that

$$\text{(3)} \qquad \lim_{n=\infty} \frac{s^{(r)}_{\ ,n}(z)}{n^{r-1}\alpha^n z^n} = \frac{\alpha z}{\Gamma(r)(\alpha z-1)}.$$

If then, on the circle of convergence of $f(z) = \Sigma a_n z^n$, $z = 1/\alpha$ is the only pole of the highest order r, and if $f(z)$ is meromorphic in $|z| \leqslant R$, we have, for every z in the ring $1/|\alpha| < z < R$,

$$\text{(4)} \qquad \lim_{n=\infty} \frac{s_n(z)}{n^{r-1}\alpha^n z^n} = \frac{B_r}{\Gamma(r)} \frac{\alpha z}{\alpha z-1},$$

where B_r is the coefficient of $(1-\alpha z)^{-r}$ in the Laurent expansion of $f(z)$ about $z = 1/\alpha$.

To prove this statement if z is not the affix of a pole, we only have to remark that, besides the contribution from a series $\Sigma b_n z^n$ convergent in and on $|z| = R$, the finite number of poles will contribute to the partial sum terms like $s^{(r)}_{\beta, n}(z)$ and, by hypothesis, $|\beta z| < |\alpha z|$.

If $z = 1/\beta$ is the affix of a pole in $|z| < R$ outside $|z| = 1/|\alpha|$, there will only be a finite number of poles in $|z| \leqslant 1/|\beta|$. Moreover

$$s^{(p)}_{\beta, n}(1/\beta) = A_n^p \backsim \frac{n^p}{\Gamma(r+1)}$$

and, from (3)

$$s^{(r)}_{\alpha, n}(1/\beta) \backsim \frac{n^{r-1}}{\Gamma(r)} \frac{\alpha^{n+1}}{\beta^{n+1}} \frac{1}{(\alpha/\beta)-1}.$$

Thus the largest contribution comes from $s^{(r)}_{\alpha, n}(1/\beta)$, and so

$$(5) \qquad \lim_{n=\infty} \frac{s_n(1/\beta)}{n^{r-1}(\alpha/\beta)^n} = \frac{B_r}{\Gamma(r)} \frac{\alpha}{\alpha-\beta}.$$

The Taylor series certainly diverges at every regular or singular point outside its circle of convergence. Formulae (4) and (5) show, however, that the character of its divergence at such a regular or singular point may be fully determined by the nature of the most powerful singularity nearest to the centre of its circle of convergence.

R. Wilson (1927–9) obtained similar results for the rational fractions of Padé's table (Padé, 1892), where the successive rows represent the function in circles ultimately extending to its circle of meromorphy about the origin.

Thus the character of the divergence at points on or outside the circle of convergence may detect singularities. For this purpose however we need converse theorems, rather difficult to establish.

Suppose for example we do not know whether $f(z) = \Sigma a_n z^n$ is meromorphic or not on its circle of convergence $|z| = 1$, but we see that $s_n(1) \to +\infty$ (coefficients real, positive) or more precisely that $s_n(1)/n^r \to A$, $r > 0$. It follows, by Appell's comparison theorem, Ex. III. 13, that $(1-z)^r f(z)$ tends to A when z tends to 1 along the radius. We say that $f(z)$ when z tends to 1, is comparable with $A/(1-z)^r$.

To establish a converse to this simple result we have to prove that a certain kind of divergence at $z = 1$ *necessarily* follows from such a behaviour of the function at $z = 1$. The chief difficulty, as we have seen several times, lies in the disturbing effects of singularities at other points of the circle of convergence.

115. *Two converse theorems by Hardy and Littlewood.* Two very important converse theorems have been proved by Hardy and Littlewood. The proof of both theorems is based on the following three lemmas.

Lemma 1. *Suppose* $g(x)$ *real and differentiable between* 0 *and* 1, $g'(x)$ *monotone increasing and, for* $x \to 1$, $g(x) \sim (1-x)^{-\alpha}$, $\alpha > 0$. *Then* $g'(x) \sim \alpha(1-x)^{-\alpha-1}$ *for* $x \to 1$.

Proof. Denote by θ a fixed real number between 0 and 1. By the mean value theorem and from the fact that $g'(x)$ is increasing we obtain, for $0<x<1$,

$$g'(x) \leqslant \frac{g[x+\theta(1-x)]-g(x)}{\theta(1-x)} \leqslant g'[x+\theta(1-x)],$$

and, by hypothesis, for $x \to 1$,

$$g[x+\theta(1-x)] \backsim [1-\{x+\theta(1-x)\}]^{-\alpha} = (1-\theta)^{-\alpha}(1-x)^{-\alpha},$$

i. e.

$$(1) \qquad \overline{\lim_{x\to 1}}\,(1-x)^{\alpha+1}g'(x) \leqslant \frac{(1-\theta)^{-\alpha}-1}{\theta} \leqslant \underline{\lim_{x\to 1}}\,(1-x)^{\alpha+1}g'[x+\theta(1-x)].$$

The first of the two inequalities (1) shows that

$$\overline{\lim_{x\to 1}}\,(1-x)^{\alpha+1}g'(x) \leqslant \alpha.$$

In fact, the right-hand side tends to α and the left-hand side is independent of θ. The second inequality, when multiplied by $(1-\theta)^{\alpha+1}$, gives

$$\underline{\lim_{x\to 1}}[1-\{x+\theta(1-x)\}]^{\alpha+1}g'[x+\theta(1-x)] \geqslant (1-\theta)^{\alpha+1}\frac{(1-\theta)^{-\alpha}-1}{\theta}$$

and, since $\lim\limits_{x\to 1}[x+\theta(1-x)] = 1$, the left-hand side is independent of θ. Therefore

$$\underline{\lim_{x\to 1}}\,(1-x)^{\alpha+1}g'(x) \geqslant \lim_{\theta\to 0}(1-\theta)^{\alpha+1}\frac{(1-\theta)^{-\alpha}-1}{\theta} = \alpha,$$

which proves that $\lim\limits_{x\to 1}(1-x)^{\alpha+1}g'(x) = \alpha$.

Lemma 2. *Suppose* $b_n \geqslant 0$, $\Sigma b_n x^n = h(x)$ *is convergent in* $(0, 1)$ *and, for* $x \to 1$, $h(x) \backsim (1-x)^{-\beta}$, $\beta > 0$. *Then, for any integer* ν,

$$\Sigma b_n n^\nu x^n \backsim \beta(\beta+1)\dots(\beta+\nu-1)(1-x)^{-\beta-\nu},$$

for $x \to 1$.

Proof. $h(x)$ satisfies the conditions of lemma 1, α being replaced by β, i. e.

$$xh'(x) = \Sigma b_n n x^n \backsim \beta(1-x)^{-\beta-1},$$

and if the theorem is assumed for $\nu-1$, i. e.

$$\Sigma \frac{b_n n^{\nu-1}x^n}{\beta\dots(\beta+\nu-2)} \backsim (1-x)^{-\beta-\nu+1}$$

this function satisfies the conditions of lemma 1 with

$$\alpha = \beta + \nu - 1,$$

which proves lemma 2.

Lemma 3. *Let*

$$\Sigma_1 = \sum_{n \leqslant (\nu - \nu^{\frac{2}{3}})t^{-1}} n^\nu e^{-nt}, \qquad \Sigma_2 = \sum_{n > (\nu + \nu^{\frac{2}{3}} - 2)t^{-1}} n^\nu e^{-nt}$$

where, in Σ_1, $n \geqslant 0$. *Then* $t^{\nu+1}\Sigma_1/\nu!$ *and* $t^{\nu+1}\Sigma_2/\nu!$ *tend to* 0 *with* $1/\nu$ *uniformly in the interval* (0, 1) *of* t.

Proof. Since $(u^\nu e^{-ut})'_u = \nu u^{\nu-1} e^{-ut} - u^\nu t e^{-ut}$, the maximum of $u^\nu e^{-ut}$ for fixed ν and t is assumed at $u = \nu t^{-1}$, and thus the terms of Σ_1 are increasing and the terms of Σ_2 are decreasing, at least for $\nu \geqslant 3$, when ν is between $\nu - \nu^{\frac{2}{3}}$ and $\nu + \nu^{\frac{2}{3}} - 2$. The number of terms in Σ_1 is

$$\leqslant (\nu - \nu^{2/3})\, t^{-1} + 1 \leqslant (\nu - \nu^{2/3})\, t^{-1} + t^{-1} < \nu t^{-1},$$

i. e.

$$t^{\nu+1}\Sigma_1 < t^{\nu+1} \nu t^{-1} (\nu - \nu^{2/3})^\nu t^{-\nu} e^{-\nu + \nu^{2/3}} = e^{\log \nu + \nu \log (\nu - \nu^{2/3}) - \nu + \nu^{2/3}},$$

independently of t. But, when $\nu \to \infty$,

$$\begin{aligned} &\log \nu + \nu \{\log \nu + \log (1 - \nu^{-1/3})\} - \nu + \nu^{2/3} \\ &\quad = O(\log \nu) + \nu \{\log \nu - \nu^{-1/3} - \tfrac{1}{2}\nu^{-2/3} + o(\nu^{-2/3})\} - \nu + \nu^{2/3} \\ &\quad = \nu \log \nu - \nu - \tfrac{1}{2}\nu^{1/3} + o(\nu^{1/3}). \end{aligned}$$

Since, by Stirling's formula Ex. IV. 22,

$$\log (\nu!) = \nu \log \nu - \nu + O(\log \nu) = \nu \log \nu - \nu + o(\nu^{1/3}),$$

we have

$$t^{\nu+1}\Sigma_1 < e^{\log (\nu!) - \frac{1}{2}\nu^{1/3} + o(\nu^{1/3})} = O(\nu!).$$

On the other hand, the ratio of two consecutive terms in Σ_2 is

$$\begin{aligned} (1 + 1/n)^\nu e^{-t} &< \{1 + t/(\nu + \nu^{2/3} - 2)\}^\nu e^{-t} \\ &< e^{-t} \exp \frac{t\nu}{\nu + \nu^{2/3} - 2} = \exp \frac{-t(\nu^{2/3} - 2)}{\nu + \nu^{2/3} - 2} = e^{-q}, \end{aligned}$$

where q is a number between 0 and 1 and is *independent of* n. Now

$$\frac{1}{1 - e^{-q}} = \frac{e^q}{e^q - 1} < \frac{e}{e^q - 1} < \frac{e}{q} = \frac{e(\nu + \nu^{2/3} - 2)}{t(\nu^{2/3} - 2)} < \frac{e(\nu + \nu^{2/3})}{t(\nu^{2/3} - 2)},$$

and the first term in Σ_2 is $< (\nu + \nu^{2/3} - 2)^\nu t^{-\nu} e^{-\nu - \nu^{2/3} + 2} \equiv Q$, say.

Therefore

$$t^{\nu+1}\Sigma_2 < t^{\nu+1}(Q + Qe^{-q} + Qe^{-2q} + \dots)$$
$$= t^{\nu+1}Q/(1-e^{-q}) < \frac{e(\nu+\nu^{2/3})^{\nu+1}}{\nu^{2/3}-2}\, e^{-\nu-\nu^{2/3}+2}$$

independently of t.

For $\nu \to \infty$, the logarithm of the last expression is equivalent to

$$1 + (\nu+1)\log(\nu+\nu^{2/3}) - \log(\nu^{2/3}-2) - \nu - \nu^{2/3} + 2$$
$$= O(\log\nu) + \nu\,\{\log\nu + \log(1+\nu^{-1/3})\} - \nu - \nu^{2/3}$$
$$= O(\log\nu) + \nu\,\{\log\nu + \nu^{-1/3} - \tfrac{1}{2}\nu^{-2/3} + o(\nu^{-2/3})\} - \nu - \nu^{2/3}$$
$$= \nu\log\nu - \nu - \tfrac{1}{2}\nu^{1/3} + o(\nu^{1/3}),$$

i.e. $t^{\nu+1}\Sigma_2 < o(\nu!)$, which proves the proposition.

Corollary. Replacing ν by $\nu+1$ and noticing that for sufficiently large ν, $\nu+1-(\nu+1)^{2/3} > \nu - \nu^{2/3}$ and that

$$\nu+1+(\nu+1)^{2/3} - 2 > \nu + \nu^{2/3},$$

we have, for sufficiently large ν, and t in $(0, 1)$,

$$\frac{t^{\nu+2}\Sigma_3}{(\nu+1)!} \equiv \frac{t^{\nu+2}}{(\nu+1)!}\sum_{n\leqslant(\nu-\nu^{2/3})t^{-1}} n^{\nu+1}e^{-nt} \to 0$$

uniformly when t is in $(0, 1)$, and

$$\frac{t^{\nu+2}\Sigma_4}{(\nu+1)!} \equiv \frac{t^{\nu+2}}{(\nu+1)!}\sum_{n>(\nu+\nu^{2/3})t^{-1}} n^{\nu+1}e^{-nt} \to 0,$$

uniformly when t is in $(0, 1)$.

I. *If* $f(z) = \Sigma a_n z^n$, $a_n \geqslant 0$, *has unit radius of convergence and*

$$\lim_{x\to 1}(1-x)f(x) = 1,$$

then $s_n/n \to 1$. (Hardy and Littlewood, 1913.)

Proof.

$$s_n = \sum_{m=0}^{n} a_m \leqslant \sum_{m=0}^{n} a_m e^{\frac{n-m}{n}} < e\sum_{m=0}^{\infty} a_m e^{-\frac{m}{n}} = ef(e^{-1/n}) = O(n),$$

i.e. there is a c such that $s_n/n < c$. Since

$$\sum_0^{\infty} s_n x^n = f(x)/(1-x) \sim (1-x)^2 \text{ for } x \to 1,$$

we have, by lemma 2, for every positive ν,

$$\sum_{n=0}^{\infty} s_n n^{\nu} x^n \sim (\nu+1)!\,(1-x)^{-\nu-2}.$$

Thus for $t \to 0$

$$\sum_{n=0}^{\infty} s_n n^{\nu} e^{-nt} \sim (\nu+1)!(1-e^{-t})^{-\nu-2} \sim (\nu+1)!\,t^{-\nu-2}.$$

But (from the case $f(x) = x+x^2 \ldots, s_n = n$ and with $\nu-1$ for ν)

$$\sum_{n=0}^{\infty} n^{\nu} e^{-nt} \sim \nu!\,t^{-\nu-1}.$$

Denoting by j the suffixes n between $(\nu-\nu^{2/3})t^{-1}$ and $(\nu+\nu^{2/3})t^{-1}$ we have, by the corollary of lemma 3, for an arbitrarily given δ,

$$\left|\sum_{n=0}^{\infty} n^{\nu} e^{-nt} - \sum_{j} n^{\nu} e^{-nt}\right| < 2\delta(\nu!)t^{-\nu-1},$$

for sufficiently large ν, and so

$$\left|\Sigma s_n n^{\nu} e^{-nt} - \sum_{j} s_n n^{\nu} e^{-nt}\right| < 2c\delta(\nu+1)!t^{-\nu-2}.$$

Thus to every $\nu > \nu_1(\delta)$ there corresponds a $\tau = \tau(\delta,\nu)$ such that, for t in $(0,\tau)$,

$$(1-3\delta)(\nu!)t^{-\nu-1} < \sum_{j} n^{\nu} e^{-nt} < (1+3\delta)(\nu!)t^{-\nu-1}$$

$$(1-3c\delta)(\nu+1)!\,t^{-\nu-2} < \sum_{j} s_n n^{\nu} e^{-nt} < (1+3c\delta)(\nu+1)!\,t^{-\nu-2}.$$

On the other hand, putting

$$q_1 = [(\nu-\nu^{2/3})t^{-1}],\ q_2 = [(\nu+\nu^{2/3})t^{-1}],$$

we have

$$s_{q_1}\sum_{j} n^{\nu} e^{-nt} \leqslant \sum_{j} s_n n^{\nu} e^{-nt} \leqslant s_{q_2}\sum_{j} n^{\nu} e^{-nt};$$

i.e., if $\delta < 1/3$,

$$s_{q_1} < \frac{1+3c\delta}{1-3\delta}\cdot\frac{\nu+1}{t},\quad s_{q_2} > \frac{1-3c\delta}{1+3\delta}\cdot\frac{\nu+1}{t}.$$

Now when $t < \tau$ decreases to 0, $(\nu-\nu^{2/3})t^{-1}$ passes through all sufficiently large integers, and we have, if $\delta < \frac{1}{3}$,

$$s_n < \frac{1+3c\delta}{1-3\delta}\,\frac{\nu+1}{\nu-\nu^{2/3}}\,n \text{ for } n > n_0(\delta,\nu)$$

$$s_n > \frac{1-3c\delta}{1+3\delta}\,\frac{\nu+1}{\nu+\nu^{2/3}}\,n \text{ for } n > n_1(\delta,\nu),$$

i. e. for $n > n_2(\delta, \nu)$

$$\frac{1-3c\delta}{1+3\delta}\,\frac{\nu+1}{\nu+\nu^{2/3}} < \frac{s_n}{n} < \frac{1+3c\delta}{1-3\delta}\,\frac{\nu+1}{\nu-\nu^{2/3}}.$$

When ϵ is given we choose $\delta < 1/3$ such that

$$1-\epsilon < \frac{1-3c\delta}{1+3\delta}, \quad 1+\epsilon > \frac{1+3c\delta}{1-3\delta}.$$

Then we choose a $\nu = \nu(\delta, \epsilon) = \nu(\epsilon) \geqslant \nu_1(\delta)$ such that

$$1-\epsilon < \frac{1-3c\delta}{1+3\delta}\,\frac{\nu+1}{\nu+\nu^{2/3}}, \quad \frac{1+3c\delta}{1-3\delta}\,\frac{\nu+1}{\nu-\nu^{2/3}} < 1+\epsilon,$$

and thus, for $n > n_2$, $1-\epsilon < s_n/n < 1+\epsilon$.
This proves the theorem.

II. *If* $na_n < c$ *and* $\lim_{r\to 1} \Sigma a_n r^n = A$, *then* $s_n \to A$.

(Hardy and Littlewood, 1913.)

Proof. We suppose, as usual, that $A = 0$ and establish a lemma.

Lemma 4. *Suppose* $g(x)$ *real and twice differentiable in* $(0, 1)$ *and* $\lim_{x\to 1} g(x) = 0$. *If moreover* $(1-x)^2 g''(x) < c$ *in* $(0,1)$, *then* $\lim_{x\to 1} (1-x) g'(x) = 0$.

Proof. We may suppose $c > 0$; let θ be fixed and such that $0 < \theta < 1$, and let ξ_1 and ξ_2 denote numbers between x and $x_1 = x + \theta(1-x)$. Then, by Taylor's theorem,

$$g(x_1) - g(x) = \theta(1-x) g'(x) + \frac{\theta^2}{2}(1-x)^2 g''(\xi_1),$$

$$\begin{aligned}(1-x) g'(x) &= \frac{1}{\theta}[g(x_1) - g(x)] - \frac{\theta}{2}(1-x)^2 g''(\xi_1) \\ &> \frac{1}{\theta}[g(x_1) - g(x)] - \frac{\theta}{2}(1-x)^2 \frac{c}{(1-x_1)^2} \\ &= \frac{1}{\theta}[g(x_1) - g(x)] - \frac{\theta c}{2(1-\theta)^2},\end{aligned}$$

since
$$\frac{1-x}{1-x_1} = \frac{1}{1-\theta}.$$

Therefore, if $x \to 1$ and thus, by hypothesis, $g(x)$ tends to 0, we have

$$\varliminf_{x\to 1} (1-x) g'(x) \geqslant -\frac{\theta c}{2(1-\theta)^2},$$

and, as the left-hand side is independent of θ, we have

$$\underline{\lim}_{x\to 1} (1-x) g(x) \geqslant 0.$$

On the other hand,

$$g(x_1) - g(x) = \theta(1-x) g'(x_1) - \frac{\theta^2}{2}(1-x)^2 g''(\xi_2),$$

$$\begin{aligned}(1-x_1)g'(x_1) &= \frac{1-\theta}{\theta}[g(x_1)-g(x)] + \frac{(1-\theta)\theta}{2}(1-x)^2 g''(\xi_2)\\ &< \frac{1-\theta}{\theta}[g(x_1)-g(x)] + \frac{(1-\theta)\theta}{2}(1-x)^2 \frac{c}{(1-x_1)^2}\\ &= \frac{1-\theta}{\theta}[g(x_1)-g(x)] + \frac{\theta c}{2(1-\theta)},\end{aligned}$$

i. e.

$$\overline{\lim}_{x_1\to 1} (1-x_1) g'(x_1) \leqslant \frac{\theta c}{2(1-\theta)},$$

$$\overline{\lim}_{x\to 1} (1-x) g'(x) \leqslant \lim_{\theta\to 0} \frac{\theta c}{2(1-\theta)} = 0,$$

which proves lemma 4.

To prove II we suppose $c > 0$. We have then

$$f''(x) = \sum_2^\infty n(n-1) a_n x^{n-2} < c \sum_2^\infty (n-1) x^{n-2} = c/(1-x)^2.$$

Since $f(r) \to 0$ we have by lemma 4, $(1-x) f'(x) \to 0$, i. e.

$$\sum_1^\infty \frac{n a_n x^n}{c} = x f'(x)/c = o[1/(1-x)], \quad \sum_1^\infty \left(1 - \frac{n a_n}{c}\right) x^n \backsim 1/(1-x).$$

By I, since $\left(1 - \frac{n a_n}{c}\right) > 0$, we have $\sum_1^m \left(1 - \frac{n a_n}{c}\right) \backsim m$,

$$m - \frac{1}{c} \sum_1^m n a_n = m + o(m), \text{ i. e. } \sum_1^m n a_n = o(m),$$

and thus by 111. II, the statement is proved.

116. *Order of a singular point.* One of the most delicate problems in the field of analytic functions is that of assigning a number as a measure of singularity, i. e. to give a precise meaning to the vague phrase 'more singular than'. The example $1/(1-z)^r$, $r > 0$, shows that integration, leading to $A/(1-z)^{r-1}$, may decrease, and similarly that differentiation may increase, the degree of infinity, so that, if k is the integral part of r, after

$k+1$ successive integrations we obtain a function finite and continuous at 1. On the other hand, the case $r<0$ e.g. $\sqrt{1-z}$, shows that continuity may be destroyed by differentiation.

We notice, however, that at a regular point both differentiation and integration lead to functions also regular at that point. Thus the behaviour of a function in the neighbourhood of a singular point after differentiation or integration may form a test for the singularity. The grade of the singularity may then be measured by its resistance to integration. Hadamard developed this idea by means of Riemann's differentiation and integration of any real order.

There is, however, a general requirement for any operation used for the purpose, viz. that the operation should not introduce new singularities. Hence the importance of the following result.

I. *If* $\int_0^1 |v(t)|\,dt = A$ *exists, the vertices of the star-domain, with respect to the origin, of*

$$g(z) = \int_0^1 v(t) f(zt)\,dt \tag{1}$$

are all vertices of the star-domain of $f(z) = \Sigma a_n z^n$.

(Hadamard, 1892.)

Proof. When t varies from 0 to 1 and z is in the star-domain D of $f(z)$, zt describes the segment $(0, z)$, along which $f(z)$ is regular and thus $|f(z)|<M$, i.e. the integral (1) exists for every point of D. For a sufficiently small h, the triangle $(0, z, z+h)$ is entirely in D and thus

$$g(z+h)-g(z) = \int_0^1 v(t)[f(zt+ht)-f(zt)]\,dt,$$

and $\quad f(zt+ht)-f(zt) = ht[f'(zt)+\theta\epsilon]$, where $0<\theta<1$

and ϵ tends to 0 with h independently of t. Hence

$$\frac{g(z+h)-g(z)}{h} = \int_0^1 v(t)tf'(zt)\,dt + \epsilon\int_0^1 \theta t v(t)\,dt,$$

and the modulus of the second integral is $<A$. Therefore $g(z)$ is differentiable at every point of D, which proves the theorem.

Putting

(2) $$c_n = \int_0^1 v(t) t^n dt,$$

we have

(3) $$g(z) = \Sigma c_n a_n z^n.$$

By replacing a_n by $c_n a_n$ we do not introduce new singularities. As the only condition imposed on $v(t)$ is that its modulus should be integrable in $(0, 1)$ we have determined a large class of *regular factors* i. e. not introducing new singularities.

For example, if

(4) $$v(t) = \frac{1}{\Gamma(\alpha)} \frac{1}{(1-t)^{1-\alpha}}, \quad \alpha > 0,$$

we have

(5) $$c_n = \frac{1}{\Gamma(\alpha)} \int_0^1 \frac{t^n dt}{(1-t)^{1-\alpha}} = \frac{\Gamma(n+1)}{\Gamma(n+1+\alpha)},$$

by (Ex. IV. 23 (1)). The corresponding operation is Riemann's integral of the real index α, which gives a generalization of successive integrations:

(6) $$R^\alpha f(z) = \frac{1}{\Gamma(\alpha)} \int_0^1 \frac{f(tz)}{(1-t)^{1-\alpha}} dt = \Sigma \frac{\Gamma(n+1)}{\Gamma(n+1+\alpha)} a_n z^n.$$

When α is an integer,

$$c_n = \frac{1}{(n+1)(n+2)\dots(n+\alpha)},$$

and thus

$$z^\alpha R^\alpha f(z) = D^{-\alpha} f(z),$$

where $D^{-\alpha}$ denotes ordinary integration repeated α times. Integration of the real negative order α is defined by

(7) $$z^\alpha R^\alpha f(z) = z^{k+\alpha} \frac{d^k R^{k+\alpha} f(z)}{dz^k}, \quad R^0 f(z) = f(z),$$

where k is an integer such that $k + \alpha \geqslant 0$.

Hadamard modified the Riemann operator in order to simplify the regular factors belonging to it. We suppose that $a_0 = 0$ (a_0 may be added after the operation) and put

(8) $$v(t) = \frac{1}{\Gamma(\alpha)} \frac{1}{t} \left[\log \frac{1}{t}\right]^{\alpha-1}, \quad \alpha > 0.$$

By the known formula in the theory of Gamma functions

$$\int_0^1 t^{x-1}\left(\log\frac{1}{t}\right)^{y-1} dt = x^{-y}\Gamma(y),$$

and thus

$$(9) \qquad c_n = \frac{1}{\Gamma(\alpha)}\int_0^1 \left(\log\frac{1}{t}\right)^{\alpha-1} t^{n-1}dt = 1/n^\alpha.$$

We put

$$(10) \qquad H^\alpha f(z) = \frac{1}{\Gamma(\alpha)}\int_0^1 \frac{1}{t}\left[\log\frac{1}{t}\right]^{\alpha-1} f(zt)\,dt$$
$$= \Sigma\frac{a_n z^n}{n^\alpha}, \quad \alpha > 0.$$

When α is an integer, H^α reduces to alternating integrations and divisions by z. For $\alpha < 0$, we calculate first, by (10), $H^{\alpha+k}f(z)$, $(\alpha+k>0)$, and then we alternately differentiate $H^{\alpha+k}f(z)$ and multiply it by z, (k times).

The two operations R^α and H^α are very similar. In particular

$$\frac{\Gamma(n+1)}{\Gamma(n+1+\alpha)} = n^{-\alpha}(1+\epsilon_n).$$

We notice also that the two operations do not completely destroy singularities, i.e. the star-domains of $f(z) = \Sigma a_n z^n$, $R^\alpha f(z)$ and $H^\alpha f(z)$ are identical. In fact, by I, the vertices of $H^\alpha f$ all belong to f, while the vertices of $H^k f = H^{k-\alpha}(H^\alpha f)$, $\kappa-\alpha \geqslant 0$, all belong to $H^\alpha f$. Moreover the operation $x\,d/dx$ creates no singularities, and so the vertices of $H^{-\alpha}(H^\alpha f)$ all belong to $H^\alpha f$. Similarly for $R^\alpha f$.

In order to be able to use H^α as an instrument for measuring the order of the singularity at a point, we have yet to fix a zero point of our scale. For this purpose Hadamard introduced the notion of *finite span* (écart fini): a continuous, real or complex, function $f(\theta)$ of the real variable θ is said to have a finite span in (a, b) if the integrals

$$(11) \qquad n\int \cos n\theta f(\theta)\,d\theta, \quad n\int \sin n\theta f(\theta)\,d\theta, \quad n = 1, 2, \ldots,$$

taken for any interval (a', b') in (a, b) are collectively bounded, and their collective bound is called the *span* of $f(\theta)$ in (a, b).

A function of bounded variation has a finite span but the converse is not necessarily true. If $g(\theta)$ is monotone and

$|g| \leqslant M$ in (a, b) and the span of $f(\theta)$ in (a, b) is σ, then the span of $g(\theta) f(\theta$ in (a, b) is $\leqslant 2 M\sigma$. When $g(\theta)$ has a finite number of extrema, we replace 2 by their number.

In a sub-interval of (a, b) the span is $\leqslant \sigma$, i.e. if the intervals dwindle to a point θ, the corresponding spans form a never increasing sequence of positive numbers and thus tend to a limit called *the span at* θ.

Consider now an arc (a, b) of $|z| = 1$, the circle of convergence of $f(z) = \Sigma a_n z^n$. We say that α is the *order* of $f(z)$ on (a, b) if $H^{\alpha+\epsilon} f(z)$ is continuous and of finite span on (a, b) for arbitrarily small $\epsilon > 0$, but one of the two properties fails for $H^{\alpha-\epsilon} f(z)$. If there is no finite number satisfying the conditions the order is $+\infty$, while if the first condition is satisfied for every α the order is $-\infty$. The *order at a point* θ is the limit of orders on arcs dwindling to θ.

117. *Properties of order.* We have still to prove that there is only one number α satisfying the definition of order. This will result from the following two theorems.

I. *If* $a_n n \log n = O(1)$ *and* $\Sigma |a_n| = A$ *is convergent, then* $f(z) = \Sigma a_n z^n$ *is continuous and has a finite span on* $|z| = 1$.

(Hadamard, 1892.)

Proof. It readily follows from the second condition that $f(z)$ is continuous in and on $|z| = 1$ (by uniform convergence).

Moreover we can replace the integrals (116. 11) by the integrals

$$(1) \qquad n \int e^{ni\theta} f(e^{i\theta})\, d\theta, \quad n \int e^{-ni\theta} f(e^{i\theta})\, d\theta,$$

whose sum and difference reproduce (116. 11) multiplied by a constant factor.

The convergence of $\Sigma a_m e^{im\theta}$ being uniform, we can integrate the series term by term:

$$n \int_a^b e^{ni\theta} f(e^{i\theta})\, d\theta = \sum_{m=0}^{\infty} \frac{n}{m+n} a_m \left[e^{(m+n)ib} - e^{(m+n)ia}\right],$$

i. e.

$$\left| n \int_a^b e^{ni\theta} f(e^{i\theta})\, d\theta \right| \leqslant 2 \Sigma |a_n| = 2A.$$

On the other hand

$$n \int_a^b e^{-ni\theta} f(e^{i\theta})\, d\theta = \sum_{m=0}^{\infty} \frac{n}{m-n} a_m \left[e^{(m-n)ib} - e^{(m-n)ia}\right]$$

where the term for which $m = n$ is $na_n(b-a)$. To evaluate this sum we split it into three parts. Take two numbers $k<1$, $K>1$. Let the first group contain the suffixes $<kn$. Then $|n/(m-n)| < 1/(1-k)$ in this group and thus its sum is $< 2A/(1-k)$. Similarly if the third group contains all the suffixes $>Kn$, this group has a sum $<2A/(K-1)$. The middle group contains all the intermediate terms, whose number is $N = [(K-k)n]$, i.e. the integral part of $(K-k)n$. If $|a_r|$ is the greatest coefficient in this middle group, the sum of the moduli of its terms is

$$< |a-b|\,n\,|a_n| + 4n\,|a_r|\,[1 + 1/2 + 1/3 + \ldots + 1/N]$$

$$\leqslant |a-b|\,n\,|a_n| + \frac{4|a_r|\,r}{k}\,(1 + 1/2 + 1/3 + \ldots + 1/[\rho r]),$$

where $\rho = (K-k)/K < 1$, and n has been eliminated by the inequalities $kn \leqslant r \leqslant Kn$. Now

$$1 + 1/2 + \ldots + 1/[\rho r] < 1 + 1/2 + \ldots + 1/r = \log r + c_r,$$

where $\lim_{r=\infty} c_r = c$ (Euler's constant, Ex. III. 1). Also $r \to \infty$ with n and, by hypothesis, $|a_r|\,r \log r$ is bounded. Hence the middle term is also bounded, which proves the theorem.

An upper bound for the span σ on $|z| = 1$ is $c_1 A + c_2 \mu$, where μ is the greatest value of $n \log n\,|a_n|$, $A = \Sigma\,|a_r|$ and c_1 and c_2 are two positive constants.

II. *If* $f(z) = \Sigma a_n z^n$ *is continuous and of finite span on* $|z| = 1$, *then* $n\,|a_n| = O(1)$; *in particular,* $\Sigma\,|a_n|/n^\epsilon$ *is convergent and* $a_n n^{1-\epsilon} \log n \to 0$ *for every positive* ϵ.

(Hadamard, 1892.)

Proof. By Cauchy's formula,

$$(2) \qquad a_n = \frac{1}{2\pi i}\int_{|z|=1} \frac{f(z)\,dz}{z^{n+1}} = \frac{1}{2\pi}\int_0^{2\pi} f(e^{i\theta})\,e^{-in\theta}\,d\theta,$$

where we can take $|z| = 1$ as path of integration, since $f(z)$ is continuous in and on $|z| = 1$. Therefore, as $f(z)$ has a finite span on $|z| = 1$, $n\,|a_n|$ is bounded, which proves the theorem.

It follows from I and II that the double property of $f(z)$, that it is continuous and of finite span on $|z| = 1$, depends only on the magnitude of the coefficients $|a_n|$, i.e. if this double condition be fulfilled for H^α or R^α, it is also fulfilled when we replace α by a greater number. It follows that there is a unique number α separating the numbers for which $H^\alpha f(z)$ does not satisfy the double condition from those for which it does satisfy it.

It is easy to show that the order of $f(z)$ on $|z|=1$ defined by this number is given by the formula

$$(3) \qquad \Omega = 1 + \overline{\lim_{n=\infty}} \frac{\log|a_n|}{\log n}.$$

In fact, if Ω is determined by this condition, for sufficiently large n,

$$(4) \qquad |a_n| < n^{\Omega+\epsilon/2-1}$$

for an arbitrary positive ϵ. Hence the coefficients of $H^{\Omega+\epsilon} f(z)$ satisfy the conditions of I, i.e. $H^{\Omega+\epsilon} f(z)$ is continuous and of finite span on $|z|=1$. On the other hand, for an infinity of suffixes

$$|a_n| > n^{\Omega-\epsilon/2-1},$$

i.e. the coefficients d_n of $H^{\Omega-\epsilon} f(z)$ do not satisfy the condition that $\Sigma |d_n|/n^\eta$ is convergent for every positive η. It is sufficient to take $\eta < \epsilon/2$. Hence, by II, $H^{\Omega-\epsilon} f(z)$ cannot be continuous and of finite span on $|z|=1$, which proves Hadamard's important formula (3).

To prove that there is only one number α satisfying the definition of the order on an arc (a, b) or at a point, we require a lemma on the separation of singularities.

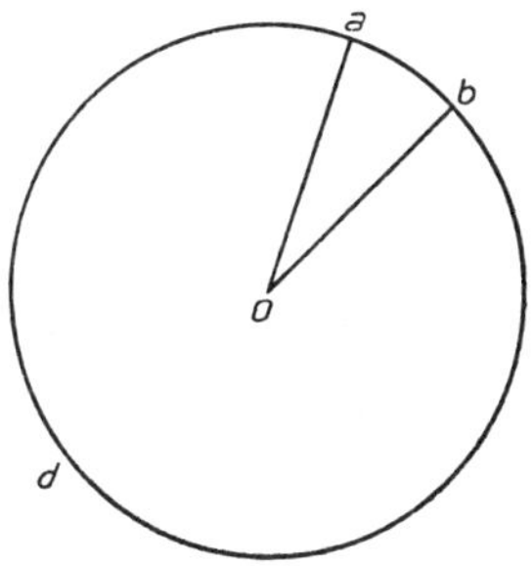

Fig. 65.

Lemma 1. *If $f(z)$ is continuous and of finite span on the arc (a, b) of $|z|=1$, then $f(z)$ is the sum of two functions $f_1(z)$ and $f_2(z)$ such that $H^\epsilon f_1(z)$, $\epsilon > 0$, is continuous and of finite span on the whole circle $|z|=1$ (and regular inside) and $f_2(z)$ is regular on the open arc (a, b).* (Hadamard, 1892.)

Proof. The function $f(z)$ being continuous on (a, b), we have

$$f(z) = \frac{1}{2\pi i}\int_{ba} \frac{f(x)\,dx}{x-z} + \frac{1}{2\pi i}\int_{adb} \frac{f(x)\,dx}{x-z} = f_1(z) + f_2(z).$$

Moreover,

$$\frac{[f_1^{(n)}(z)]_{z=0}}{n!} = \frac{1}{2\pi i}\int_{ba} \frac{f(z)\,dz}{z^{n+1}} \equiv b_n, \text{ say,}$$

and, as $f(z)$ has a finite span on (a, b),

(5) $$|b_n| < M/n,$$

i. e. the radius of convergence of $\Sigma b_n z^n$ is $\geqslant 1$. The function $\Sigma c_n z^n = f_2(z)$, as a difference of two Taylor series convergent in $|z| < 1$, is itself convergent in $|z| < 1$ and its integral form shows that it is regular at the inner points of (a, b).

It follows from (5) that b_n/n^ϵ satisfies the conditions of I and thus $H^\epsilon f_1$ is continuous and of finite span on $|z| = 1$. Q. e. d.

Suppose now that $H^\alpha f(z)$ is continuous and of finite span on (a, b). We have, by lemma 1, $H^\alpha f(z) = F_1(z) + F_2(z)$, where $F_2(z)$ is regular on (a, b) and thus $H^\epsilon F_2(z) = H^{\alpha+\epsilon} f_2(z)$ is also regular. On the other hand, $F_1(z)$ may be chosen such that

$$H^\epsilon F_1(z) = H^{\alpha+\epsilon} f_1(z)$$

is continuous and of finite span on $|z| = 1$. Thus

$$H^{\alpha+\epsilon} f(z) = H^{\alpha+\epsilon} f_1(z) + H^{\alpha+\epsilon} f_2(z)$$

is continuous and of finite span on (a, b) whenever $H^\alpha f(z)$ possesses the same properties. Since $\epsilon > 0$ is arbitrary, this proves that there is only one number satisfying the definition of order on (a, b). The same follows readily for the limit of orders belonging to arcs dwindling to a point.

III. *The order of a regular point is* $-\infty$.

(Hadamard, 1892.)

Proof. Since $f(z)$ is, by hypothesis, regular on a closed arc (a, b), containing the regular point z_0, $|f'(z)| \leqslant M$ for all points of (a, b), and thus from

$$\int_a^b n \cos n\theta\, f(\theta)\,d\theta = [f(\theta) \sin n\theta]_a^b - \int_a^b f'(\theta) \sin n\theta\, d\theta$$

we have

$$\sigma \leqslant |f(b)| + |f(a)| + M\,|b-a|,$$

i. e. $f(z)$ has a finite span on (a, b). This property is preserved in the operation $H^{-\alpha}$ since $H^{-\alpha}f(z)$ is regular on (a, b). Thus the operation $H^{-\alpha}$ or $R^{-\alpha}$ cannot destroy continuity and the finiteness of the span on a regular arc. This is the exact meaning of the statement that the order is $-\infty$. Thus, when the order is finite or $+\infty$, it is the order of a singularity.

IV. *The order on an arc is the greatest order at the points of the arc.* (Hadamard, 1892.)

Proof. By the definition of order on an arc, the orders at its various points are $\leqslant$ the order on the arc. Conversely, if α is the order on the arc (a, b), we see by dividing (a, b) into small arcs that there are always arcs on which the order is α, and thus also points at which the order is α, which proves the theorem.

It readily follows from (3) that $\Sigma|a_n|$ is convergent when $\Omega < 0$: thus we have

V. *If the order of* $f(z) = \Sigma a_n z^n$ *is negative on* $|z| = 1$, $\Sigma a_n z^n$ *is absolutely convergent and, in particular, converges at every point of* $|z| = 1$ *and* $f(z)$ *is continuous in and on* $|z| = 1$.

118. *Degree of infinity and order.* In order to determine the order of singularity in simple cases, we have to establish its connexion with the simpler notion of degree of infinity.

I. *If on the arc* (a, b) *of* $|z| = 1$, *the order of* $f(z)$ *is* $\alpha > 0$ *we have, uniformly for the arguments between a and b,*

$$\lim_{r \to 1} (1-r)^{\alpha'} f(re^{i\theta}) = 0, \quad \alpha' > \alpha, \tag{1}$$

$$\lim_{r \to 1} (1-r)^{\alpha'} \sigma(r) = 0, \tag{2}$$

where $\sigma(r)$ *is the span of* $f(re^{i\theta})$ *on* (a', b') *of radius* r. (Hadamard, 1892.)

Proof. Both equations (1) and (2) are obviously satisfied for functions regular on the closed arc (a, b). But, by lemma 1 of Art. 117, $f(z) = f_1(z) + f_2(z)$, where $f_2(z)$ is regular on (a, b) and the order β of $f_1(z)$ is $< \alpha + \epsilon < \alpha'$. Thus we have only to establish the theorem for functions whose order on $|z| = 1$ is $\beta < \alpha'$.

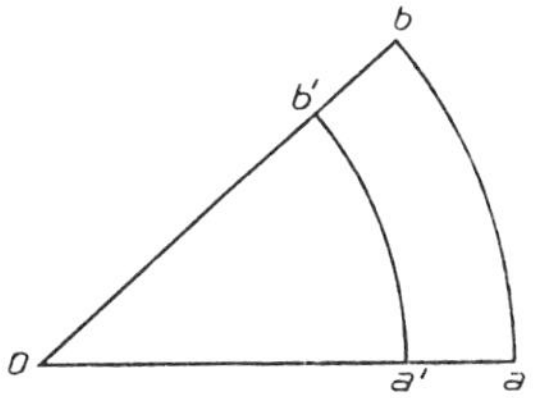

FIG. 66.

For such a function, by (117. 3) we have $|a_n| < n^{\beta-1+\epsilon}$ and,

ϵ being arbitrarily small, we may suppose that $\beta-1-\epsilon<\alpha'-1$. Now, by Appell's comparison theorem Ex. III. 13,

$$\lim_{r\to 1}(1-r)^{\alpha'}\,|\,\Sigma a_n r^n e^{in\theta}\,|\leqslant \lim_{r\to 1}\frac{\Sigma\,|\,a^n\,|\,r^n}{\Sigma A_n^{(\alpha'-1)}r^n}=\lim_{n=\infty}\frac{|\,a_n\,|}{A_n^{\alpha'-1}}=0,$$

which proves (1).

To prove (2) we notice that, as we have seen in the previous article,

$$\sigma(r)\leqslant c_1\Sigma\,|\,a_n\,|\,r^n+c_2\max(|\,a_n\,|\,r^n n\log n).$$

We have just seen that $\lim_{r\to 1}(1-r)^{\alpha'}\Sigma\,|\,a_n\,|\,r^n=0$. Moreover, in the second term we might neglect the terms for which $|\,a_n\,|>n^{\beta-1}/\log n$ (their number is finite). Therefore, replacing r by $1-\eta$ we have to determine the maximum of $(1-\eta)^n n^\beta \eta^{\alpha'}$ for a fixed η and calculate the limit of this maximum when $\eta\to 0$.

Now $(1-\eta)^n n^\beta\eta^\alpha\leqslant(1-\eta)^{n+1}(n+1)^\beta\eta^\alpha$ provided only

$$n\leqslant\frac{1}{(1-\eta)^{-1/\beta}-1}=\frac{k\beta}{\eta},\quad\text{where }\lim_{\eta\to 0}k=1.$$

Moreover we have

$$\lim_{\eta\to 0}(1-\eta)^{k\beta/\eta}=e^{-\beta},$$

and

$$\lim_{\eta\to 0}\left(\frac{k\beta}{\eta}\right)^\beta\eta^{\alpha'}=\beta^\beta\lim_{\eta\to 0}k^\beta\lim_{\eta\to 0}\eta^{\alpha'-\beta}=0,$$

which establishes (2).

II. *If, for every θ between a and b,*

$$\overline{\lim_{r\to 1}}\,|\,(1-r)^\alpha f(re^{i\theta})\,|<A, \tag{3}$$

$$\overline{\lim_{r\to 1}}\,(1-r)^\alpha\sigma(r)<A, \tag{4}$$

the order of $f(z)$ on (a,b) is $\leqslant\alpha$.

(Hadamard, 1892.)

Proof. In this case the operation R^α is preferable to H^α (in the definition of order). Take $\alpha'>\alpha$ and consider the integral

$$R^{\alpha'}f(e^{i\theta})=\frac{1}{\Gamma(\alpha')}\int_0^1(1-t)^{\alpha'-1}f(te^{i\theta})\,dt. \tag{5}$$

To prove that the integral (5) exists, we notice that, for $n > n_0$,

$$\left|\int_{\frac{n}{n+1}}^{1} (1-t)^{\alpha'-1} f(te^{i\theta})\, dt\right| < A\int_{\frac{n}{n+1}}^{1} \frac{(1-t)^{\alpha'-1}}{(1-t)^{\alpha}}\, dt = \frac{A}{\alpha'-\alpha}\left(\frac{1}{n+1}\right)^{\alpha'-\alpha},$$

independently of θ, and thus the series

$$(6) \qquad \int_0^{1/2} (1-t)^{\alpha'-1} f(te^{i\theta})\, dt + \int_{1/2}^{2/3} + \int_{2/3}^{3/4} + \dots$$

is uniformly convergent. It follows that $R^{\alpha} f(e^{i\theta})$ is continuous on (a, b).

For its span we have to consider the integrals

$$(7) \qquad \frac{n}{\Gamma(\alpha')}\int_a^b e^{\pm ni\theta}\, d\theta \int_0^1 (1-t)^{\alpha'-1} f(te^{i\theta})\, dt,$$

where, by our remark on the uniform convergence of (6), the order of the two integrations can be inverted. But the upper bound of the modulus of the second integral in

$$(8) \qquad \frac{1}{\Gamma(\alpha')}\int_0^1 (1-t)^{\alpha' -1} dt \int_a^b n e^{\pm in\theta} f(te^{i\theta})\, d\theta$$

is not greater than the span of $f(z)$ on the arc of radius t, and is thus, by hypothesis, $< A/(1-t)^{\alpha}$. Hence the modulus of (8) is $< \dfrac{A}{\Gamma(\alpha')(\alpha'-\alpha)}$. Thus $R^{\alpha'} f(z)$ is continuous and of finite span on (a, b) for every $\alpha' > \alpha$, and so the order is $\leqslant \alpha$.

III. *If on (a, b) the function $g(z)$ is regular and the order of $f(z)$ is α, that of $g(z)f(z)$ is $\leqslant \alpha$; in particular if $g(z) \neq 0$ on (a, b), the order of $g(z)f(z)$ on (a, b) is α.*

(Hadamard, 1892.)

Proof. For positive α, the product $(1-r)^{\alpha+\epsilon} f(re^{i\theta}) g(re^{i\theta})$ is bounded when $r \to 1$, and an upper bound for the span of the product fg is the span of $f(z)$ multiplied by τ times the maximum modulus of $g(z)$, where τ is the total number of extrema in (a, b) for the real and imaginary parts of $g(z)$ and this is finite since $g(z)$ is regular, by 41. II. Therefore (4) is also satisfied by fg and thus, by II, its order is $\leqslant \alpha$. Thus the multiplication by a regular function does not increase a positive order.

For negative α the same reasoning shows that the order of the product cannot be positive. More precisely, if the order of $f(z)$ on (a, b) is $-k$ and s is the integral part of $k+1$ or $s = k$, if k is an integer itself, the s-th derivative of $f(z)\,g(z)$ is composed of terms like $cD^{s-r}f\,D^r g$, $r = 0, 1, 2, \dots, s$. But $D^r g(z)$ is regular on (a, b) and the order of $D^{s-r} f$ is by definition that of $f(z)$ increased by $s-r$. Now, if $r \neq 0$, we have $-k+s-r<0$ and thus, by our first remark on negative α, the order of the corresponding term is negative. Finally $cg(z)D^s f$ is a product of a function of the positive order $-k+s$ and of a regular function. Hence its order is $\leqslant -k+s$. Thus the order of $D^s(fg)$ is $\leqslant -k+s$ and therefore that of fg is $\leqslant -k+s-s = -k$. This proves the first part.

When $g(z) \neq 0$ on (a, b), suppose that the order of fg is less than the order of $f(z)$. As $1/g$ is regular on (a, b), the order of $fg\dfrac{1}{g} = f$ is, by the first part of III just established, $\leqslant \alpha' < \alpha$, which is manifestly absurd. This completes the proof.

We now apply these results for the determination of the order of $1/(1-z)^r$ at $z = 1$. From

$$\frac{1}{(1-z)^r} = \Sigma A_n^{r-1} z^n, \text{ and } \frac{A_n^{r-1}}{n^{r-1}} \to \frac{1}{\Gamma(r)},$$

i. e. $A_n^{r-1} = n^{r-1}(1+\epsilon_n)/\Gamma(r)$ and by (117. 3), the order of our function on $|z| = 1$ is

$$\Omega = 1 + \lim_{n=\infty} \frac{(r-1)\log n - \log \Gamma(r) + \log(1+\epsilon_n)}{\log n} = r,$$

and at every point of $|z| = 1$, except $z = 1$, the function is regular, i. e. its order is $-\infty$. Hence, by 117. IV, the order at 1 is r. Thus in this case *degree of infinity* and *order* coincide.

Consider now $f(z) = P[\log(1-z)]/(1-z)^r$, where $P(z)$ is a polynomial of degree q in z. The order of $f(z)$ at $z = 1$ is again r as proved by I and II. In fact if $r > 0$ and $\sigma(\rho)$ refers to $(1-z)^{-r}$, the multiplication of $1/(1-z)^r$ by $\log^q(1-z)$ multiplies $(1-\rho)^\alpha f(\rho e^{i\theta})$ and $(1-\rho)^\alpha \sigma(\rho)$ by $\log^q(1-\rho)$, whose product into $(1-\rho)^\epsilon$ tends to 0 for every positive ϵ. Hence I and II apply and show that the order of $f(z)$ at 1 is r.

When r is negative (and not an integer, in which case the order is $-\infty$), we reason as before by taking the least integer $s > r$ and calculating the s-th derivative of the function. The result is the same.

Also in this last example degree of infinity and order of singularity are the same provided we define, as usual, the degree of infinity r at $e^{i\theta}$ by the condition that r is the least number for which $\lim_{\rho\to 1}(1-\rho)^{r+\epsilon}f(\rho e^{i\theta}) = 0$ for an arbitrary positive ϵ. We remark that this definition of degree of infinity is not perfect, in the sense that, when $z \to e^{i\theta}$ along any other path than the radius $(0, e^{i\theta})$, the function may increase more rapidly than $1/(z-e^{i\theta})^r$. If, for instance, $\lim_{\rho\to 1} f(\rho e^{i\theta}) = \infty$ for an infinity of θ_k and θ is a limiting point of θ_k, there is a point z_k on $(0, e^{i\theta_k})$ sufficiently near $e^{i\theta_k}$ at which $|f(z_k)| > A_k/|e^{i\theta}-z_k|^s$, with arbitrarily given s and $A_k \to \infty$. Therefore the degree of infinity of $f(z)$ along the polygonal path

$$(0, z_1)\,(z_1, z_2)\,\ldots\,(z_k, z_{k+1})\,\ldots$$

leading to $e^{i\theta}$ is $\geqslant s$. We may, however, exclude the effect of neighbouring infinities by excluding paths tangential to $|z| = 1$ as in theorem 105. I.

But even if we restrict ourselves to radial approach, the degree of infinity and the order of singularity may differ. Consider the function (Dienes, 1909 c)

$$(9) \qquad g(z) = \sum_0^\infty (-1)^{[\sqrt{n}]} z^n = \Sigma \alpha_n z^n,$$

where $[m]$ denotes the integral part of m. Since $|\alpha_n| = 1$, *the order on* $|z| = 1$ *is* 1. On the other hand it is readily verified that

$$\overline{\lim_{n=\infty}} \left| \frac{s_n(1)}{\sqrt{n}} \right| = 1,$$

and we are going to prove that

$$(10) \qquad \overline{\lim_{n=\infty}} \left| \frac{s_n(e^{i\theta})}{\sqrt{n}} \right| = A(\theta),$$

finite for every θ. This will prove, by Appell's comparison theorem Ex. III. 13, that the degree of infinity of $g(z)$, along the radii is $\leqslant 1/2$ for every θ. Therefore the order exceeds the degree of infinity by $1/2$.

To prove (10) we notice that, putting $\sigma_n = \sum_{=1}^{n} p_k$, we have

$$\sum_{1}^{n} p_k q_k = \sum_{1}^{n-1} \sigma_k (q_k - q_{k+1}) + \sigma_n q_n.$$

In our case $q_k = \alpha_n$, $p_k = e^{ik\theta}$, i. e.

$$s_n(e^{i\theta}) = \sum_{k=1}^{n} \alpha_k e^{ik\theta} = \sum_{1}^{n-1} (e^{i\theta} + e^{2i\theta} + \ldots + e^{ki\theta})(\alpha_k - \alpha_{k+1})$$
$$+ (e^{i\theta} + e^{2i\theta} + \ldots + e^{ni\theta})\alpha_n$$
$$= \frac{e^{i\theta}}{1 - e^{i\theta}} \left[\sum_{1}^{n-1} (1 - e^{ik\theta})(\alpha_k - \alpha_{k+1}) + (1 - e^{ni\theta})\alpha_n \right].$$

But $\lim_{n=\infty} (1 - e^{ni\theta})\alpha_n/\sqrt{n} = 0$ and, for the suffixes $k \neq r^2 - 1$, we have $\alpha_k - \alpha_{k+1} = 0$, while for $k = r^2 - 1$, we have $|\alpha_k - \alpha_{k+1}| = 2$. Thus the number of surviving terms in $\sum_{1}^{n-1} (1 - e^{ki\theta})(\alpha_k - \alpha_{k+1})$ is $\sqrt{n}$, which proves (10).

Arithmetic Means and Singularities.

119. *The case* $a_n \to 0$.

In this case, by 113. III, when $f(z)$ is continuous at $e^{i\theta}$ from inside, i. e. $f(z)$ tends to the same limit A along any inner path leading to $e^{i\theta}$, the arithmetic means of $s_n(e^{i\theta})$ also converge to A, while, by 105. I, if they converge $f(z)$ is continuous, anyway in an angle. Moreover, when $f(z)$ is bounded at $e^{i\theta}$ from inside, the reasoning of 113. II applies and thus also (113. 10) holds. Therefore, since

$$\frac{1}{2\pi(n+1)} \int_0^{2\pi} \left[\frac{\sin (n+1) \frac{\phi - t}{2}}{\sin \frac{\phi - t}{2}} \right]^2 dt = 1,$$

we see that the arithmetic means $s_n^{(1)}(e^{i\phi})$ are also bounded at every point of an arc containing θ and, in particular at $\phi = \theta$ Thus $s_n^{(1)}(e^{i\theta})$ cannot be unbounded unless $f(z)$ is also unbounded near $e^{i\theta}$. To sum up:

I. $a_n \to 0$. *When* $s_n^{(1)}(e^{i\theta}) \to A$, *then also* $\lim_{z\to e^{i\theta}} f(z) = A$ *provided* z *approaches* $e^{i\theta}$ *in an angle* $\gamma < \pi$ *of* $|z| < 1$, *vertex at* $e^{i\theta}$. *When* $s_n^{(1)}(e^{i\theta})$ *is bounded without tending to a limit, then* $f(z)$ *is bounded in* γ *and does not tend to the same limit along every inner path leading to* $e^{i\theta}$. *When* $s_n^{(1)}(e^{i\theta})$ *is unbounded, then also* $f(z)$ *is unbounded in the complete inner neighbourhood of* $e^{i\theta}$.

The last case, viz. when $s_n^{(1)}(e^{i\theta})$ is unbounded, needs further investigation, due to the fact that the infinity of $f(z)$ near $e^{i\theta}$, as well as that of $s_n^{(1)}(e^{i\theta})$, may be of various kinds. One of the interesting features of this case is that in many cases the original partial sums can be used instead of their arithmetic means.

II. *If* $a_n \to 0$ *and, in the neighbourhood of* $e^{i\theta}$,

$$(1) \qquad f(z) = \frac{P\left(\log \dfrac{1}{1-e^{-i\theta}z}\right)}{(1-e^{-i\theta}z)^r} + f_1(z),$$

where $P(z) = A_q z^q + \ldots + A_0$ *and the order* r' *of* $f_1(z)$ *at* $e^{i\theta}$ *is* $< r$ $(0 < r < 1)$, *then*

$$(2) \qquad \lim_{n=\infty} \frac{s_n(e^{i\theta})}{n^r \log^q n} = \frac{A_q}{\Gamma(r+1)}. \quad \text{(Dienes, 1911 b.)}$$

Proof. Based on two lemmas.

Lemma 1. *Putting*

$$\frac{\log \dfrac{1}{1-z}}{(1-z)^r} = \Sigma \alpha_n^{r,q} z^n \quad \textit{and} \quad s_n^{r,q} = \alpha_0^{r,q} + \alpha_1^{r,q} + \ldots + \alpha_n^{r,q},$$

we have

$$(3) \qquad \frac{s_n^{r,q}}{n^r \log^q n} \to \frac{1}{\Gamma(r+1)}.$$

From

$$\left[\log \frac{1}{1-z}\right]^q = \left(z + \frac{z^2}{2} + \ldots + \frac{z^n}{n}\right)^q$$
$$+ q\left(z + \frac{z^2}{2} + \ldots + \frac{z^n}{n}\right)^{q-1} R_n(z) + \ldots + [R_n(z)]^q,$$

where $R_n(z) = z^{n+1}/(n+1) + \ldots$, we have

$$s_n^{0,q} \leqslant \left(1 + \frac{1}{2} + \ldots + \frac{1}{n}\right)^q,$$

since all the terms involving $z^k, k \leqslant n$, are in the first bracket. Similarly

$$s_n^{0,q} \geqslant \left(1+\frac{1}{2}+\ldots+\frac{1}{[n/q]}\right)^q$$

and thus, by Euler's formula, Ex. III. 1,

$$(4) \qquad (\log n - \log q + c')^q \leqslant s_n^{0,q} \leqslant (\log n + c'')^q,$$

where c' and c'' tend to a limit c (= Euler's constant), which proves (3) for $r = 0$.

In the general case

$$\log^q \frac{1}{1-z} \cdot \frac{1}{(1-z)^r}$$
$$= [\alpha_0^{0,q} + \alpha_1^{0,q} z + \ldots \alpha_n^{0,q} z^n + R_n][A_0^{r-1} + A_1^{r-1} z + \ldots A_n^{r-1} z^n + R_n'],$$

and thus, by (102. 4) and (102. 2),

$$(5) \qquad \overline{\lim_{n=\infty}} \frac{s_n^{r,q}}{(\log n)^q n^r} \leqslant \frac{1}{\Gamma(r+1)}.$$

To find the lower limit we choose a $k > 1$ and put $\left[\frac{k-1}{k} n\right] = u$, $[n/k] = v$ and we prove that

$$(6) \qquad s_n^{r,q} \geqslant s_u^{0,q} s_v^{r,0}.$$

In fact, writing

$$\log^q \frac{1}{1-z} \cdot \frac{1}{(1-z)^r}$$
$$= [\alpha_0^{0,q} + \alpha_1^{0,q} z + \ldots \alpha_u^{0,q} z^u + R_u][A_0^{r-1} + A_1^{r-1} z + \ldots A_v^{r-1} z^v + R_v'],$$

we see that the largest index of z in [ ][ ] is

$$u + v \leqslant (k-1)n/k + n/k = n,$$

which proves (6).

To eliminate u and v, we put $u = \epsilon_n n(k-1)/k$, $v = n/k + \eta_n$, where $\epsilon_n \to 1$ when $n \to \infty$ and $|\eta_n| < 1$. Thus

$$\lim_{n=\infty} \frac{\log u}{\log n} = 1, \quad \lim_{n=\infty} \frac{v}{n} = \frac{1}{k}.$$

Hence the formulae

$$\lim_{u=\infty} \frac{s_u^{0,q}}{(\log u)^q} = 1, \text{ and } \lim_{v=\infty} \frac{s_v^{r,0}}{v^r} = \frac{1}{\Gamma(r+1)},$$

are transformed into

$$\lim_{n=\infty} \frac{s_u^{,q}}{(\log n)^q} = 1 \text{ and } \lim_{n=\infty} \frac{s_v^{r,0}}{n^r} = \frac{1}{k^r \Gamma(r+1)},$$

i. e. by (6),

$$(7) \qquad \varlimsup_{n=\infty} \frac{s_n^{r,q}}{(\log n)^q n^r} \geqslant \frac{1}{k^r \Gamma(r+1)},$$

and hence, as k is as near to 1 as we like,

$$\varlimsup_{n=\infty} \frac{s_n^{r,q}}{(\log n)^p n^r} \geqslant \frac{1}{\Gamma(r+1)},$$

and this, together with (5), proves (3).

Lemma 2. *If* $a_n \to 0$ *and the order of singularity at* $e^{i\theta}$ *is* $<r$ $(0<r<1)$, *then* $n^{-r}s_n(e^{i\theta}) \to 0$.

This lemma restricts the order of infinity of $s_n(e^{i\theta})$.

Proof. By lemma 1 of Art. 117 we put

$$f(z) = \Sigma \alpha_n z^n + \Sigma \beta_n z^n = f_1(z) + f_2(z)$$

where $f_2(z)$ is regular at $z = e^{i\theta}$, and thus, by Fatou's theorem, 112. I, since the coefficients tend to 0,

$$(8) \qquad \lim_{n=\infty} (\beta_0 + \beta_1 e^{i\theta} + \ldots + \beta_n e^{ni\theta}) = f_2(e^{i\theta}),$$

and so $n^{-r}(\beta_0 + \beta_1 e^{i\theta} + \ldots + \beta_n e^{ni\theta})$ tends to 0.

On the other hand we can suppose that the order r' of $f_1(z)$ on $|z| = 1$ is $<r$. Hence, by (117. 3), for sufficiently large n, $|\alpha_n| < n^{r'-1+\epsilon}$ for any positive ϵ, i. e. $|\alpha_n| = \epsilon_n n^{r-1}$, where $\epsilon_n \to 0$. Now suppose, for a given positive ϵ, that $\epsilon_n < \epsilon$ for $n > m$. Then

$$\sum_{k=1}^{n} \epsilon_k k^{r-1} < \sum_{k=1}^{m} \epsilon_k k^{r-1} + \epsilon \sum_{k=m+1}^{n} k^{r-1} < c_1 m^r + c_2 n^r \epsilon,$$

where c_1 and c_2 are independent of ϵ. Since the first term on the right-hand side is independent of n and ϵ is arbitrary, it follows that

$$n^{-r} \sum_{k=0}^{n} |\alpha_k| \to 0,$$

which establishes the lemma.

To prove II we observe that, since $a_n \to 0$ and $r<1$, the coefficients of $f_1(z)$ tend to zero. Thus, applying lemma 1 to the terms in (1) coming from the polynomial and lemma 2 to $f_1(z)$, we see that all the contributions to $s_n(e^{i\theta})$ divided by $(\log n)^q n^r$ tend to zero, which proves the theorem.

Thus when $a_n \to 0$, the algebraico-logarithmic singularities are detected by the way in which the partial sums formed at the affix of the singularity diverge. Theorem II establishes a close relation between divergence and singularity of the type considered.

The generalization to more general types of singularities, e. g. to those containing $\log\log(1-z)$, is immediate. We notice also that the theorem does not require that the singularity should be isolated. The effect of neighbouring singularities is excluded by the hypothesis that the order of $f_1(z)$ is $< r$.

120. $a_n/n^r \to 0$, $r > 0$. *Convergence.* The series cannot converge on $|z| = 1$, but by 112. II, the arithmetic means of order r converge at every regular point of $|z| = 1$. We extend this result by proving the following theorem.

I. *If* $n^{-r} a_n \to 0$, $r > 0$, *the arithmetic means of the order* r *converge on* $|z| = 1$ *at every point of negative order.*

(Dienes, 1911 a.)

Proof. If the order at $z_0 = e^{i\theta_0}$ is $\sigma < 0$, there is an arc (a, b) enclosing z_0 on which $H^{\sigma+\epsilon} f(z)$ is continuous and of finite span. Applying lemma 1 of Art. 117 to this function we see that

$$f(z) = \Sigma a_n z^n = \Sigma b_n z^n + \Sigma c_n z^n = f_1(z) + f_2(z),$$

where $f_2(z)$ is regular at the point z_0 and the order of $f_1(z)$ on $|z| = 1$ is negative. Thus $\Sigma b_n z^n$ is absolutely convergent all along $|z| = 1$. On the other hand $c_n = a_n - b_n$, $b_n \to 0$, $n^{-r} a_n \to 0$, i. e. $n^{-r} c_n \to 0$. Therefore 112. II applies to $\Sigma c_n z^n$, and thus we have only to remark that from the convergence of $\Sigma b_n e^{ni\theta}$ follows also the convergence of the arithmetic means of any positive order.

The generalization of 113. III needs that of lemma 1 in Art. 117 on the separation of singularities.

Lemma 1. *If* $f(z) = \Sigma a_n z^n$ *is bounded in a sector* $(O; a, b)$, *then* $f(z) = \Sigma b_n z^n + \Sigma c_n z^n = f_1(z) + f_2(z)$, *where* $f_2(z)$, *is regular on the open arc* (a, b) *of* $|z| = 1$ *and* $b_n \to 0$.

(Dienes, 1913.)

Proof. By our remark after 113. II, the limit $\lim\limits_{r\to 1} f(re^{i\theta}) = h(\theta)$ exists for almost every value of θ between a and b. Thus, by Lebesgue's theorem (108. E),

$$\lim_{r\to 1} \int_a^b f(re^{i\theta})\, d\theta = \int_a^b h(\theta)\, d\theta.$$

It follows that

$$f(z)=\frac{1}{2\pi i}\int_{a'b'}\frac{f(x)dx}{x-z}+\frac{1}{2\pi i}\int_{b'deca'}\frac{f(x)dx}{x-z},$$

whose value is not altered when we replace (a', b') by a similar arc nearer to (a, b), we can put $r=1$, i.e.

$$f(z)=\frac{1}{2\pi}\int_a^b\frac{h(\theta)e^{i\theta}d\theta}{e^{i\theta}-z}+\frac{1}{2\pi i}\int_{deca}\frac{f(x)dx}{x-z}$$
$$\equiv f_1(z)+f_2(z).$$

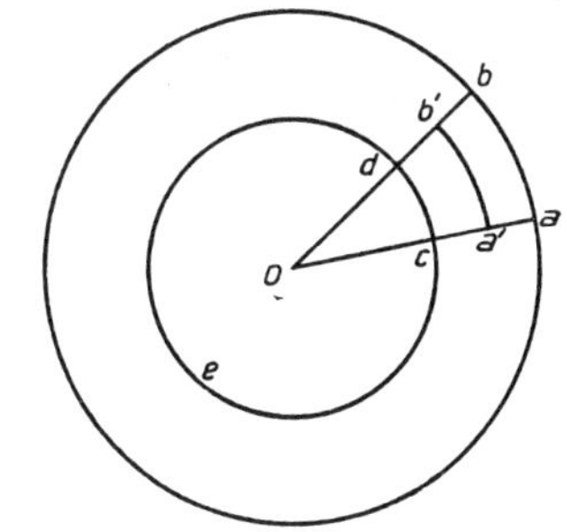

FIG. 67.

The integral form of $f_2(z)$ shows that it is regular on the open arc (a, b) as stated in the lemma. The coefficients b_n are given by

$$b_n=\frac{1}{2\pi i}\int_{ab}\frac{f(z)dz}{z^{n+1}}=\frac{1}{2\pi}\int_a^b h(\theta)e^{-ni\theta}d\theta,$$

and Lebesgue's theorem (1906, p. 61) applied separately to the real and imaginary parts shows that $b_n \to 0$. This theorem requires only that $h(\theta)$ should be integrable (L) on (a, b).

II. *If* $n^{-r}a_n \to 0$, $r \geqslant 1$, *and along every inner path leading to* $e^{i\theta}$

(1) $$\lim_{z\to e^{i\theta}} f(z) = A,$$

then also

(2) $$s_n^{(r)}(e^{i\theta}) \to A.$$

(Dienes, 1911, 1913.)

Proof. By (a) of lemma 3 in Art. 113, $f(z)$ is bounded in a sector $(O; a, b)$, the arc (a, b) containing θ, and thus by lemma 1 we decompose $f(z)$ into the sum $f_1(z)+f_2(z)$. Since $f_2(z)$ is regular on the open arc (a, b) and $b_n \to 0$, i. e. $n^{-r}c_n \to 0$, 112. II applies and thus the arithmetic means of order r of the partial sums of $f_2(z)$ at $e^{i\theta}$ converge to $f_2(e^{i\theta})$. On the other hand, by 113. III, the first arithmetic means of the partial sums of $f_1(z)$ at $e^{i\theta}$ converge and thus also the arithmetic means of order $r>1$. The two remarks put together prove the theorem. By the Abel-Hölder theorem 105. I, the functional limit and the limit of the arithmetic means are necessarily the same.

The particular case $r = 1$ of II is more general than the original theorem 113. III, since, without altering the conclusion, the condition $a_n \to 0$ has been replaced by the more general condition $a_n/n \to 0$

When we replace, as at the beginning of this section, condition (1) by the condition that $\overline{\lim}_{z \to e^{i\theta}} |f(z)| \leqslant M$, the above reasoning together with I shows that

III. *If* $n^{-r} a_n \to 0$, $r \geqslant 1$, *and along every inner path leading to* $e^{i\theta}$

$$\text{(3)} \qquad \overline{\lim}_{z = e^{i\theta}} |f(z)| \leqslant M,$$

then also

$$\text{(4)} \qquad \overline{\lim}_{n = \infty} |s_n^{(r)}(e^{i\theta})| \leqslant M.$$

(Dienes, 1911 a.)

The only remark we have to add is that when $|s_n^{(r)}|$ is bounded, then also $s_n^{(r+\delta)}$, $\delta > 0$, is bounded. In fact, by (102. 8),

$$|S_n^{(r+\delta)}| \leqslant M \sum_{\nu=0}^{n} A_{n-\nu}^{\delta-1} A_\nu^r = M A_n^{r+\delta}.$$

To sum up

IV. $n^{-r} a_n \to 0, r \geqslant 1$. *When* $s_n^{(r)}(e^{i\theta}) \to A$, *then also* $\lim_{z \to e^{i\theta}} f(z) = A$ *provided* z *approaches* $e^{i\theta}$ *in an angle* $\gamma < \pi$ *of* $|z| < 1$ *vertex at* $e^{i\theta}$. *When* $s_n^{(r)}(e^{i\theta})$ *is bounded without tending to a limit, then also* $f(z)$ *is bounded in* γ *and does not tend to the same limit along every inner path leading to* $e^{i\theta}$. *When* $s_n^{(r)}(e^{i\theta})$ *is unbounded, then also* $f(z)$ *is unbounded in the complete inner neighbourhood of* $e^{i\theta}$.

Hardy and Littlewood have completed these results by giving a set of necessary and sufficient conditions that $\Sigma a_n e^{in\theta}$ should be summable by the method of arithmetic means. When Σa_n is summable by Cesàro's means of any order, the order not being specified, we say that Σa_n is *summable C*. If A is the sum thus obtained we say that $\Sigma a_n = A$ *by* (*C*). Similarly if there is an r such that $a_n/n^r \to 0$, but we do not want to specify r, we say that a_n is of *finite increase.*

V. *The necessary and sufficient conditions that* $\Sigma a_n = A$ *by* (*C*) *are:*

(a) a_n *is of finite increase,*

(b) *successive sequences of numbers* a_{ns} *can be determined by the equations:*

$$a_{n0} = a_n;$$

$$a_{01} = \sum_0^\infty a_\nu/(\nu+1) \text{ by } (C),$$

$$a_{n1} = a_{01} - \left(a_0 + \frac{a_1}{2} + \ldots + \frac{a_{n-1}}{n}\right);$$

$$\cdot \quad \cdot \quad \cdot \quad \cdot \quad \cdot \quad \cdot \quad \cdot$$

$$a_{0,s+1} = \sum_0^\infty a_{\nu s}/(\nu+1) \text{ by } (C),$$

$$a_{n,s+1} = a_{0,s+1} - \left(a_{0s} + \frac{a_{1s}}{2} + \ldots + \frac{a_{n-1,s}}{n}\right);$$

$$\cdot \quad \cdot \quad \cdot \quad \cdot \quad \cdot \quad \cdot \quad \cdot \quad \cdot$$

and there is an integer k *such that* $\lim_{z\to 1} \Sigma a_{nk} z^n = A$ *when* $z \to 1$ *in any manner from within the circle.*

(Hardy and Littlewood, 1924.)

The proof is based on the following lemma.

Lemma 2. *If* $\Sigma a_n = A$ *is convergent and* $na_n \to 0$, *then* $F(z) = \dfrac{1}{1-z} \Sigma \dfrac{a_n}{n+1}(1-z^{n+1}) \to A$ *when* $z \to 1$ *in any manner from within the circle.*

Proof of lemma 2.

$$F(z) = \frac{1}{1-z}\sum_{n\leqslant N} + \frac{1}{1-z}\sum_{n>N} = F_1 + F_2, \text{ where } N = \left[\frac{1}{|1-z|}\right].$$

But, for a fixed n,

$$1 - \frac{1-z^{n+1}}{(n+1)(1-z)} \sim \frac{n}{2}(1-z).$$

In fact, putting $1-z = d$, we have

$$1 - \frac{1-(1-d)^{n+1}}{(n+1)d} = 1 - \frac{(n+1)d - C_2^{n+1}d^2 + \ldots}{(n+1)d} = \frac{n}{2}d + \epsilon(d).$$

Thus

$$(5) \quad |F_1(z) - \sum_{n\leqslant N} a_n| < \frac{|1-z|}{2} \sum_{n\leqslant N} |a_n| n + \epsilon(d) \left|\sum_{n\leqslant N} a_n\right|$$

Since $|a_n| n \to 0$, the same holds for the arithmetic means, i.e.

$(a_1+2a_2+\ldots+Na_N)/N=\epsilon_N$, and, Σa_n being convergent, $|s_n|$ has a finite maximum M, i.e.

(6) $$|F_1(z)-\sum_{n\leqslant N} a_n|<|1-z|\,N\epsilon_N/2+M\epsilon(d).$$

On the other hand,

$$|F_2(z)|<\frac{1}{|1-z|}\sum_{n>N}\frac{a_n}{n+1},$$

and, putting $(n+1)|a_n|=\epsilon_n$ and denoting by η_N the largest term of the sequence $(N+1)\,|a_N|$, $(N+2)\,|a_{N+1}|$, ..., we have

$$F_2(z)\,|<\frac{1}{|1-z}\,\eta_N\sum_{n>N}\frac{1}{(n+1)^2}.$$

Noticing that $\sum_{n>N} 1/(n+1)^2<\int_N^\infty dx/x^2=1/N$,

we see that

(7) $$|F_2(z)|<\frac{1}{|1-z|}\,\frac{\eta_N}{N}.$$

But, by our choice of N, $|1-z|\,N=dN\to 1$ with z, and $d\to 0$, i.e., by (6) and (7),

$$\lim_{z\to 1}F_1(z)=\sum_{n=0}^{\infty}a_n=A \text{ and } \lim_{z\to 1}F_2(z)=0,$$

i.e. $$\lim_{z\to 1}F(z)=A.$$

We notice that no restriction has been made on the manner in which z approaches 1 from within the circle.

Remark. Since in lemma 2 $\Sigma a_n/(n+1)=B$ is absolutely convergent, $\lim\limits_{\xi\to 1}\Sigma a_n\xi^n/(n+1)=B$ and thus

$$F(z)=\frac{1}{1-z}\lim_{\xi\to 1}\int_z^{\xi}\Sigma a_n z_1^n\,dz_1=\frac{1}{1-z}\int_z^1 f(z_1)dz_1.$$

To prove that conditions (a) and (b) are necessary. By 102. III, if Σa_n is summable C^r, (a) is satisfied and, by 104. IV, the numbers a_{ns} exist and satisfy the equations

$$a_{n,s-1}=(n+1)\,(a_{ns}-a_{n+1,s}).$$

By 104. V, Σa_{n1} is summable C^{r-1} and so on, $\Sigma a_{n,r+1}$ is summable C^{-1}, i.e. by lemma 2,

(8) $$\frac{1}{1-z}\,\Sigma\,\frac{a_{n,r+1}}{n+1}(1-z^{n+1})\to A,$$

when $z\to 1$ in any manner from within the circle.

But for $|z|<1$,

$$(1-z)\,\Sigma a_{n,\,r+2}z^n = a_{0,\,r+2} - \sum_0^\infty (a_{n,\,r+2}-a_{n+1,\,r+2})\,z^{n+1}$$

$$= \sum_0^\infty \frac{a_{n,\,r+1}}{n+1} - \sum_0^\infty \frac{a_{n,\,r+1}}{n+1} z^{n+1},$$

i.e.
$$\frac{1}{1-z}\,\Sigma\,\frac{a_{n,\,r+1}}{n+1}(1-z^{n+1}) = \Sigma a_{n,\,r+2}z^n,$$

which, by (8), proves the necessity of our conditions.

To prove that conditions (a) and (b) are sufficient. By (b),

$$|a_{n1}| \leqslant |a_{01}| + |a_0| + \frac{|a_1|}{2} + \ldots + \frac{|a_{n-1}|}{n},$$

i.e. if $|a_n| < K(n+1)^r$,

$$|a_{n1}| < L[1+2^{r-1}+\ldots+(n+1)^{r-1}] = O(n^r),$$

and thus step by step,

$$|a_{nk}| = O(n^r).$$

Therefore, by lemma 2 and 120. II, Σa_{nk} is summable $C^{r'}$ to A, for $r'>r$ and $r'\geqslant 1$, and thus, by 104. II, $\Sigma a_{n,\,k-1}$ is summable $C^{r'+1}$ to A and so on, $\Sigma a_{n0} \equiv \Sigma a_n$ is summable $C^{r'+k+1}$ to A.

Q. e. d.

121. $a_n/n^r \to 0$. *Divergence.* When $s_n^{(r)}(e^{i\theta})$, and thus also $f(z)$ at $e^{i\theta}$, is unbounded, we can establish further connexions between divergence and singularities.

I. *If* $n^{-r}a_n \to 0$, $r \geqslant 1$, *and*

$$f(z) = P\left(\log\frac{1}{1-e^{-i\theta}z}\right)\Big/(1-e^{-i\theta}z)^\rho + f_1(z),$$

where $P(z) = A_q z^q + \ldots + A_0$ *and the order of* $f_1(z)$ *at* $z=e^{i\theta}$ *is* $\rho'<\rho$ $(0<\rho<r+1)$, *then*

$$\frac{s_n^{r-\rho}}{n^\rho \log^q n} \to \frac{\Gamma(r-\rho+1)}{\Gamma(r+1)} A_q.$$

(Dienes, 1913.)

Proof. Denoting by $s_n'(e^{i\theta})$ the partial sum of

$$P\left(\log\frac{1}{1-e^{-i\theta}}\right)\Big/(1-e^{-i\theta}z)^\rho \text{ at } z = e^{i\theta}$$

we have, by (119. 3),

$$(1) \qquad \frac{s_n'(e^{i\theta})}{n^\rho \log^q n} \to \frac{A_q}{\Gamma(\rho+1)}.$$

On the other hand, writing as usual

$$f_1(z) = \Sigma b_n z^n + \Sigma c_n z^n = f_2(z) + f_3(z),$$

where $f_3(z)$ is regular at $e^{i\theta}$ and $f_2(z)$ is of order $\rho'+\epsilon < \rho$ on $|z| = 1$ and denoting the corresponding partial sums and arithmetic means by $s_n(b_k; e^{i\theta})$, $s_n(c_k; e^{i\theta})$, &c., we have, for an arbitrary $\eta > \epsilon$ and sufficiently large n, $|b_n| < n^{\rho'+\eta-1}$ and thus $b_n/n^{\rho-1} \to 0$, so that

$$s_n(b_k; e^{i\theta})/n^\rho \to 0.$$

Moreover, by (102. 8),

$$S_n^{r-\rho} = \sum_{\nu=0}^{n} A_{n-\nu}^{r-\rho-1} s_\nu,$$

and thus, by 102. I, $S_n^{r-\rho}(b_k; e^{i\theta})/n^r \to 0$. Therefore,

$$(2) \qquad s_n^{r-\rho}(b_k; e^{i\theta})/n^\rho \to 0.$$

Finally, by 112. II, since $f_3(z)$ is regular at $e^{i\theta}$ and $n^{-r}c_n \to 0$,

$$s_n^{(r)}(c_k; e^{i\theta}) \to f_3(e^{i\theta}),$$

and thus, by 102. III,

$$(3) \qquad s_n^{r-\rho}(c_k; e^{i\theta})/n^\rho \to 0.$$

Equations (2) and (3) show that the contribution of $f_1(z)$ to the $s_n^{r-\rho}$ of $f(z)$, divided by n^ρ, tends to 0. Finally we observe that $S_n'^{(\alpha)}$ is the partial sum of $\log^q \frac{1}{1-z} / (1-z)^{\rho+\alpha}$. Thus, putting $\alpha = r-\rho$, we obtain

$$\frac{S'^{r-\rho}_n}{n^r \log^q n} \to \frac{A_q}{\Gamma(r+1)},$$

i. e. since $A_n^{r-\rho} \sim n^{r-\rho}/\Gamma(r-\rho+1)$, we obtain (1). Q. e. d.

This theorem establishes a precise relation between arithmetic means and singularities. The remarkable feature of it is that the character of the divergence of the arithmetic means of a certain order formed at a singular point is closely related by this result to the character of the singularity at the same point. The disturbing effect of the other singularities, if any, on the arithmetic means at the given point is removed by the assumptions (a) $n^{-r}a_n \to 0$ which excludes infinities beyond a certain degree, (b) $f_1(z)$ is of order $\rho' < \rho$, which says that in the neighbourhood of the point $e^{i\theta}$ in question the order of $f(z)$ at $e^{i\theta}$ is dominating.

We also notice that we are making use of *divergence* in the detection and characterization of singularities *without transforming the divergent series into a convergent one.* When $a_n \to 0$, the character of divergence of $s_n(e^{i\theta})$ is directly used. When $n^{-r}a_n \to 0$, we have to refer to the arithmetic means, i. e. we have to transform the divergent sequence of s_n, but we transform it into another divergent sequence and make direct use of its more regular divergence.

This fact is a first step into the *theory of divergence,* as distinguished from that of summation of divergent sequences or series, which means transformation into a convergent one. After a descriptive classification of divergences the new problem has two aspects. (A) How does the transformation of a divergent sequence affect the divergence of the sequence? This problem corresponds to the arithmetic theory of summation. Applied to Taylor series or to similar sequences of functions the second question is: (B) what are the connexions between the original or transformed divergence and the analytic character of the function at the point of divergence? This aspect of the problem corresponds to the testing of a summation by applying it to a divergent Taylor series. In the following articles we are going to illustrate both aspects of the problem of divergence.

General Means and Singularities.

122. *Convergence.* In Art. 79 we established Mittag-Leffler's representation of $f(z) = \Sigma a_n z^n$ in the star-domain by the formula

$$(1) \qquad f(z) = \lim_{\alpha \to \infty} \frac{\Sigma s_n(z) c_{n+1} \alpha^{n+1}}{\Sigma c_n \alpha^n},$$

where $E(z) = \Sigma c_n z^n$ is an integral function satisfying the conditions of 79. I. At the end of Art. 87 we proved that Lindelöf's integral function

$$(2) \qquad L_\beta(z) = \sum_{n=0}^{\infty} \frac{z^n}{[\log(n+\beta)]^n}, \; \beta > 1,$$

satisfies those conditions and thus $L_\beta(z)$ is a suitable summatory function for the whole star-domain. Borel's results, established in Art. 78, may be summed up by saying that the exponential function e^a is a summatory function for Borel's polygon of summability. The simplicity and elegance of Borel's exponential means make their use preferable to more general means inside their restricted field of application.

For example when the coefficients a_n do not satisfy the condition $n^{-r}a_n \to 0$, for any positive r however large, the arithmetic means are of no use for the detection or characterization of singularities on the circle of convergence $|z| = 1$. They cannot even converge at regular points of $|z| = 1$. But we have seen that the exponential means $e^{-a}\Sigma s_n(e^{i\theta})\, a^n/n!$ do converge at every regular point of $|z| = 1$.

Similarly, when $f(z)$ is not regular at $e^{i\theta}$, but is of bounded variation on an arc (a, b) containing θ, we put, by lemma 1 of Art. 120, $f(z) = f_1(z) + f_2(z) = \Sigma b_n z^n + \Sigma c_n z^n$, where $f_2(z)$ is of bounded variation (in fact regular) on every arc (a', b') contained in the open arc (a, b), and thus also $f_1(z)$ is of bounded variation. Since $b_n \to 0$, theorem 113. I applies to $f_1(z)$, i. e. $s_n(b_n; e^{i\theta})$ tends to a limit, and consequently its exponential means also tend to the same limit. Since $f_2(z)$ is regular at $e^{i\theta}$, we have $\Sigma s_n(c_k; e^{i\theta})\, a^n/n! \to f_2(e^{i\theta})$ which proves that

I. *If $f(z) = \Sigma a_n z^n$ is of bounded variation on an arc of the circle of convergence, the exponential means of the partial sums converge at the inner points of that arc.* (Dienes, 1911 a.)

The same result extends to points on the polygon of summability, and more generally, for general Mittag-Leffler means, to vertices z_0 of the star-domain. In fact lemma 1 of Art. 120 extends to arcs (a, b) of $|z| = |z_0|$, provided $f(z)$ is regular and bounded in the sector $(O; a, b)$. Hence the result formulated for Mittag-Leffler means:

II. *Suppose the point z_0 is a vertex of the star-domain and $f(z) = \Sigma a_n z^n$ is regular inside the sector $(O; a, b)$, where (a, b), an arc of the circle $|z| = |z_0|$, contains z_0. If $f(z)$ is of bounded variation on (a, b), the Mittag-Leffler means $M[s_n(z_0), a]$ of $s_n(z_0)$ converge to the limit value of $f(z)$ for $z \to z_0$.*

Theorem 120. III extends in the same way to the vertices of the star-domain.

III. *Suppose the point* z_0 *is a vertex of the star-domain and*

$$f(z) = \Sigma a_n z^n$$

is regular inside the sector $(O; a, b)$. *If* $f(z)$ *tends to* A *along every path leading to* z_0 *inside the sector* $(O; a, b)$, *then*

$$\lim M[s_n(z_0); a] = A. \tag{3}$$

(Dienes, 1910.)

Similarly for functions bounded in a sufficiently small sector $(O; a, b)$ and regular inside it.

The definition of order extends to the vertices z_0 of the star-domain provided $f(z)$ is regular inside a sector $(O; a, b)$, where (a, b) is an arc of the circle $|z| = |z_0|$ containing z_0. It readily follows that the Mittag-Leffler means of $s_n(z_0)$ converge at every vertex of negative order. We can sum up these results in the following statement.

IV. *Suppose the point* z_0 *is a vertex of the star-domain of* $f(z) = \Sigma a_n z^n$ *regular in a sufficiently small sector* $(O; a, b)$, *where* (a, b), *an arc of the circle* $|z| = |z_0|$, *contains* z_0. $M[s_n(z_0); a]$ *converges if the order of* $f(z)$ *at* z_0 *is negative or if there is a small arc* (a, b) *along which* $f(|z_0| e^{i\phi})$ *is of bounded variation.* $M[s_n^{(1)}(z_0); a]$ *converges to* A *if* $f(z)$ *tends to* A *along every path leading to* z_0 *inside the sector* $(O; a, b)$. $M[s_n^{(1)}(z); a]$ *is bounded for* $a \to \infty$ *if* $f(z)$ *is bounded in a sector* $(O; a, b)$.

We see that the general character of $f(z)$ at z_0 is revealed with remarkable precision by the behaviour of Mittag-Leffler means at the same point. The same holds when we pass to poles or more general singularities characterized precisely by the way in which $f(z)$ tends to ∞ in the neighbourhood of the singular point in question.

123. *Divergence.* In the case of algebraico-logarithmic singularities, including poles, we have to consider, by (119. 3), partial sums of the type $n^r \log^q n$. Therefore, we have to determine the transform of such a type of divergence, i.e. we have to determine the type of infinity of

$$\Sigma n^r \log^q n \,.\, c_{n+1} a^{n+1} / \Sigma c_n a^n \quad \text{when } a \to \infty. \tag{1}$$

For the detailed calculation in the case of the exponential

function, i. e. $c_n = 1/n!$ and in the case of Lindelöf's integral function where $c_n = 1/[\log(n+\beta)]^n$ see Dienes, 1913, p. 119. Valiron (1914) extended these two results to a whole class of integral functions.

The leading idea of these researches is the extension and precision of a remark by Borel. When $a>0$ is very large, the greatest term of $\Sigma a^n/n!$ is nearly as large as the complete sum, i. e. e^a. In fact the indices of the two greatest terms of $\Sigma a^n/n!$ are a and $a-1$, or the index between these two numbers if there is only one greatest term, since, for a fixed a, the terms are increasing for $n = 1, 2, 3, \ldots, [a-1]$ and decreasing after $[a]$. Therefore the greatest term is comparable with $a^a/a! \backsim e^a/\sqrt{2\pi a}$ (by Stirling's formula Ex. IV. 22).

Since we need a precise evaluation, we consider a range of terms about the maximum term such that the neglected terms on both sides, divided by the complete function, should tend to 0. In order to satisfy the latter condition, the length of the surviving middle range of terms has, in most cases, to be increased indefinitely when $a \to \infty$. Still, comparing the first and last surviving terms, we obtain in many cases a precise evaluation of the type of infinity involved.

Consider the integral function $f(x) = \Sigma c_n x^n$, $0 < c_n = e^{-G(n)}$, x real and >0, and suppose that G', G'' exist, $G''(x) > 0$ for $x > n_0$. Putting $g(t) = e^{-G(t)}x^t$, for a fixed x, we have

$$g'(t) = g(t)\,[-G'(t) + \log x],$$
$$g''(t) = g(t)\,[-G'(t) + \log x]^2 - g(t)\,G''(t),$$

i. e. the suffix $n = [\xi]$ of the maximum term, for a sufficiently large fixed x, is given by the root ξ of the equation

$$G'(t) = \log x. \tag{2}$$

We want to establish an asymptotic relation

$$f(x) \backsim \sum_{n=N_1(x)}^{N_2(x)} c_n x^n, \qquad \text{for } x \to \infty, \tag{3}$$

where the suffix ξ of the maximum term is between N_1 and N_2.

Valiron proposes to impose conditions on $G(n)$ in order to get precision in the determination of the effective range (N_1, N_2).

Let us consider a function $\epsilon(x)$ satisfying the conditions $\lim_{x\to\infty}\epsilon(x) = 0$ and $\lim_{x\to\infty} x\epsilon(x) = +\infty$ and put

$$(N)\qquad \begin{aligned} N_1(x) &= \text{integral part of } \xi[1-\epsilon(\xi)],\\ N_2(x) &= \text{integral part of } \xi[1+\epsilon(\xi)],\\ n_0 &= \text{integral part of } \xi,\\ N &= \text{integral part of } \xi\,.\,\epsilon(\xi)/2. \end{aligned}$$

We group the terms $n > n_0$ as follows:

$$\sum_{n_0+1}^{\infty} c_n x^n = \sum_{i=0}^{\infty} S_i(x),\quad S_i(x) = \sum_{n_i+1}^{n_{i+1}} c_n x^n,$$

where $n_{i+1} = n_i + N$. We have

$$(4)\qquad c_{n_{i+1}+q}x^{n_{i+1}+q}/c_{n_i+q}x^{n_i+q} = x^N e^{-G(n_{i+1}+q)+G(n_i+q)}.$$

By hypothesis, for $i \geqslant 1$,

$$\begin{aligned} G(n_{i+1}+q)-G(n_i+q) &= NG'(n_i+q)+N^2G''(n_i+q+\theta N)/2\\ &> NG'(n_i+q) > NG'(n_1), \end{aligned}$$

i.e. the log of $(4) \leqslant N[\log x - G'(n_1)$ or, replacing $\log x$ by $G'(\xi)$ and this again by $G'(n_0+1) > G'(\xi)$,

$$\log \text{ of } (4) \leqslant \alpha(x) = -N(N-1)\,G''(N_1),\ N_1 = n_0+1+\theta\,(N-1).$$

Hence $$S_{i+1}(x) < e^{\alpha(x)} S_i(x),$$

i.e. $$\sum_{n_0+1}^{\infty} c_n x^n < S_0(x) + S_1(x)/[1-e^{\alpha(x)}]$$

$$< [S_0(x)+S_1(x)]/[1-e^{\alpha(x)}] \leqslant \sum_{n_0+1}^{N_2(x)} c_n x^n/[1-e^{\alpha(x)}].$$

Thus, to establish our asymptotic formula, we must suppose that $\lim_{x\to\infty}\alpha(x) = -\infty$, i.e.

$$\text{(a)}\ \lim_{x\to\infty}\epsilon(x)x\sqrt{G''(x)} = +\infty,\ \text{and so (b)}\ \lim_{x\to\infty} x^2G''(x) = \infty.$$

This condition is a condition of regularity of increase not restricting the order of increase. If $\epsilon(x)$ satisfies (a), the sum of all the terms $n > n_0$, divided by the sum of the terms $n_0 < n \leqslant N_2(x)$, tends to 1, and any term outside this block divided by the maximum term is $< e^{\alpha(x)}$.

In the same way we deal with terms for which $n < n_0$, neglecting those terms, h, say, for which $G''(n) < 0$. [The ratio of the sum of these h terms to the whole block $< n_0$ tends to zero since $h/n_0 \to 0$.]

I. *If* $G(x)$ *satisfies the condition* (b) *and* $\epsilon(x)$ *satisfies the conditions*

$$0 < \epsilon(x) \to 0,\ x\epsilon(x) \to \infty,\ \lim_{x\to\infty} \epsilon(x) x \sqrt{G''(x)} \to \infty,$$

then we have $f(x) \sim \sum_{N_1(x)}^{N_2(x)} c_n x^n$; N_1 *and* N_2 *are are determined by* $\epsilon(x)$ *and the suffix of the maximum term is in* (N_1, N_2). *Furthermore,*

$$1 < f(x) \Big/ \sum_{N_1(x)}^{N_2(x)} c_n x^n < \frac{1}{1 - e^{\alpha_1(x)}},\ \alpha_1(x) = -\frac{[\xi \cdot \epsilon(\xi) - 2]^2}{4} G''(\xi_1),$$

where $G''(\xi_1)$ *denotes the minimum of* $G''(x)$ *when* x *varies from* $N_1(x)$ *to* $N_2(x)$. (Valiron, 1914.)

If $G''(x)$ is bounded, (a) requires that $x\epsilon(x)$ should not be bounded, and thus the group of effective terms does not remain finite. But if $\lim_{x\to\infty} G''(x) = \infty$, we can restrict the effective range to a bounded one.

The result remains true if we replace c_n by $(1+\eta_n)c_n$ with $\eta_n \to 0$. In fact the ratio $S_{i+1}(x)/S_i(x)$ is multiplied by an expression of the form $1+\epsilon$ and in the first n_0 terms we have to neglect the first $\epsilon(\xi) n_0$ terms.

Consider now

$$\text{(5)} \qquad F(x) = \sum_0^\infty (1+\eta_n') c_n g(n) x^n, \quad \eta_n' \to 0,$$

where $g(x)$ is supposed to be continuous and twice differentiable. For the applications the following particular case is of importance.

$$\text{(6)} \quad h(x) \equiv \log g(x) = p \log x + A_1 (\log_2 x)^{\alpha_1} + \ldots + A_i (\log_{i+1} x)^{\alpha_i},$$

$\alpha_i \geq 0$, p and A_i real numbers.

We have in this case

$$\lim_{x\to\infty} x^2 h''(x) = p,\ \lim_{x\to\infty} \frac{g[x(1+\alpha)]}{g(x)} = (1+\alpha)^p.$$

The first shows that $F(x)$, like $f(x)$, satisfies (b), i.e. the same $\epsilon(x)$ can be taken for both. The second equation shows that the index of the maximum term is again between $N_1(x)$ and $N_2(x)$. Thus we have

$$F(x) \backsim \sum_{N_1'(x)}^{N'(x)} c_n g(n)(1+\eta_n')x^n \backsim g(\xi)\sum_{N_1(x)}^{N_2(x)} (1+\eta_n)c_n x^n \backsim g(\xi)f(x),$$

which leads to the theorem

II. *If* $g(x)$ *satisfies* (6) *and* $f(x)$ *satisfies* (b), *we have*

(7) $$F(x) \backsim g(\xi)f(x) \quad \textit{where} \quad G'(\xi) = \log x.$$

(Valiron, 1914.)

This result can be interpreted in terms of transformation of divergent sequences. Consider, for instance, the case of Lindelöf's integral function

$$L_\beta(z) = \Sigma z^n/\log^n(n+\beta), \; \beta > 3.$$

In this case

$$G(x) = x \log\log(x+\beta), \; G'(x) = \log\log(x+\beta) + \frac{x}{\log(x+\beta)} \frac{1}{x+\beta},$$

$$G''(x) = \frac{2}{\log(x+\beta)} \frac{1}{x+\beta} - \frac{x}{(x+\beta)^2 \log(x+\beta)} \left[1 + \frac{1}{\log(x+\beta)}\right]$$

which shows that $G''(x) > 0$ for sufficiently large x and

$$x^2 G''(x) \to \infty.$$

Moreover, from $G'(\xi) = \log x$, we obtain, for $x \to \infty$,

$$\xi \backsim e^{x-1}.$$

Therefore, for $g(n) = n^r \log^q n$ the condition (6) is satisfied and we obtain the limit relation

(8) $$\lim_{a\to\infty} \frac{\Sigma n^r \log^q n\, a^n/\log^n(n+\beta)}{e^{ra} a^q \Sigma a^n/\log^n(n+\beta)} = \frac{1}{e^r}.$$

Thus, denoting by $L(z_n, a)$ the Lindelöf transform of z_n, if the divergence of the sequence z_n is such that

$$\frac{z_n}{n^r \log^q n} \to \frac{A}{\Gamma(r+1)},$$

then $$\lim_{a\to\infty} \frac{L(z_n, a)}{e^{ra} a^q} = \frac{A}{e^r \Gamma(r+1)}.$$

Ordinary infinity of the degree r, i. e. n^r, is replaced by an exponential infinity $(e^a)^r$ of the degree r. Logarithmic infinity, i. e. $\log^q n$, is replaced by an ordinary infinity a^q. If with Borel (1910) we denote the increase of n^r by (r), that of $\log^q n$ by $q \cdot \frac{1}{\omega}$ and the exponential increase by ω, we might say that *the Lindelöf transformation multiplies the increase by* ω, viz., the increase $q \cdot \frac{1}{\omega} + r$ is replaced by $(q \cdot \frac{1}{\omega} + r)\omega = q + r\omega$.

It is readily seen that the exponential transformation

$$e^{-a} \Sigma z_n a^n / n!$$

reproduces the character of infinity, since the suffix of the maximum term is $\xi = x$. Borel's generalized exponential transformation, where e^a is replaced by e^{a^p}, multiplies the increase by p.

A straightforward application of (8) leads to the generalization of theorem 121. I.

III. *If* (a, b) *is an arc of* $|z| = |z_0|$ *containing* z_0 *and*

$$f(z) = P\left(\log \frac{1}{1-z/z_0}\right) / (1-z/z_0)^r + f_1(z),$$

where $P(z) = A_q z^q + \ldots + A_0$ *and* $f_1(z)$ *is regular inside the sector* $(O;\ a,\ b)$ *and is of the order* $r' < r\ (r > 0)$ *on* (a, b), *then*

$$\lim_{a \to \infty} \frac{L[s_n(z_0);\ a]}{e^{ra} a^q} = e^r \frac{A_q}{\Gamma(r+1)}.$$

(Dienes, 1913.)

Proof. If $s_n'(z_0)$ denotes the partial sums of $P\left(\log \frac{1}{1-z/z_0}\right)$ at $z = z_0$, we have by (8) and by (119. 3),

$$\lim_{a \to \infty} \frac{L[s_n'(z_0);\ a]}{e^{ra} a^q} = e^r \frac{A_q}{\Gamma(r+1)},$$

so that we only have to prove that the Lindelöf transform of the partial sums of $f_1(z)$ at z_0 divided by $e^{ra} a^q$ tends to 0.

For this purpose we decompose $f_1(z)$ as usual by putting $f_1(z) = f_2(z) + f_3(z)$, where $f_3(z)$ is regular in and on the sector $(O;\ a',\ b')$ the arc (a', b') being an arc of the open arc (a, b) and the order of $f_2(z)$ on $|z| = |z_0|$ is $r'' = r' + \epsilon < r$. As z_0 is an inner point of the star-domain belonging to $f_3(z)$ the corresponding Mittag-Leffler sum formed by $L_\beta(a)$ tends to $f_3(z)$, i.e. when divided by $e^{ra}a^q$ it tends to 0.

As for the partial sums $s''_n(z_0)$ of $f_2(z) = \Sigma b_n z^n$, whose circle of convergence is $|z| = |z_0|$, we know that $s''_n(z_0)/n^r \to 0$ and thus also

$$\lim_{a\to\infty} \frac{L[s''_n(z_0);\, a]}{e^{ra}} = 0,$$

which proves that the contribution of $f_1(z)$ is negligible. Thus the theorem is established.

In view of the generality of Valiron's result II, the extension of III to more general cases is immediate.

Our last result shows that an appropriate transform of a divergent sequence of partial sums may be in much closer relation to the singularities than the original sequence. Thus the two aspects of the theory of divergence as distinct from that of summation, viz. the change in the character of divergence caused by the transformation and the use of divergence in the detection and characterization of singularities, are closely interconnected.

We notice that, in the examples dealt with, only the arithmetic and exponential means reproduced the character of divergence unchanged. The generalized exponential means multiplied the increase by a positive number p and the Lindelöf means exponentialized the increase (multiplied it by ω). The question arises whether there are transforms sufficiently general to represent the function in its star-domain and at the same time sufficiently simple to reproduce the type of increase at the singularities.

Painlevé's representation of an analytic function in a general curvilinear star-domain constructed by means of conformal mapping (see Arts. 80 and 81) furnishes us with an elegant solution of this problem. It is a representation by series of polynomials, instead of integral functions, and the correspondence between the divergence of this series at a singular point and the singularity at the same point is nearly as simple as in the case of arithmetic or exponential means. But the instrument used is fairly complicated, and thus we refer the reader to the fifth chapter of Dienes, 1913. However, a coherent theory of divergence is yet to be developed.

BIBLIOGRAPHY

LIST OF ABBREVIATIONS

I.

A. = Annals, Annalen, &c.
Ac. = Acta.
Am. = American.
Ber. = Sitzungsberichte einer Akademie.
Bull. = Bulletin(s).
C. R. = Comptes Rendus.
J. = Journal.
ahr. Ber. = Jahresbericht.
M. = Mathematics (-tical), &c.
Nach. = Nachrichten.
Pr. = Proceedings.
Qu. = Quarterly.
S. = Society, société, &c.
Sc. = Science(s), &c.
Tr. = Transactions.
Ver. = Vereinigung.
Z. = Zeitschrift.

II.

A. Fenn. = A. Academiae Sc. Fennicae. Helsingfors.
Ac. S. Fenn. = Ac. S. Sc. Fennicae. Helsingfors.
Ac. Szeged = Ac. Litt. ac Sc. Regiae Universitatis Hungaricae Francisco-Josephinae. Szeged.
A. E. N. = A. Sc. de l'Ecole Normale.
Atti Lincei = Atti della Reale Accademia dei Lincei. Roma.
Atti Torino = Atti della Reale Accademia delle Sc. di Torino.
Atti Veneto = Atti del Reale Instituto Veneto di Sc., Lett. ed Arti. Venezia.
C. R. = C. R. de l'Académie des Sciences de Paris.
Crelle = J. für reine und angewandte M.
Hamburg M. Abh. = Abhandlungen aus dem M. Seminar der Hamburgischen Universität.
Palermo Rend. = Rendiconti del Circolo M. di Palermo.
Rend. Lincei = Rendiconti della Reale Accademia dei Lincei. Roma.

N. H. Abel

1826 Untersuchungen über die Reihe

$$1+\frac{m}{1}x+\frac{m(m-1)}{1\,.\,2}x^2+\ldots$$

Crelle 1: 311–39.

C. A. dell' Agnola

1899 Estensione di un teorema di Hadamard. Atti Veneto 58: 525–39 and 669–77.

J. W. Alexander

1919 A proof of Jordan's theorem. A. of M. 21: 180–4.

G. von Alexits

1928a Über die Annäherung einer stetigen Funktion durch die Cesàroschen Mittel ihrer Fourierreihe. M. A. 100 : 264–77.

1928b Zwei Sätze über Fourier Koeffizienten. M. Z. 27 : 65–8.

L. D. Ames

1905 An arithmetic treatment of some problems in Analysis Situs. Am. J. M. 27 : 343–80.

A. F. Andersen

1919 *H. Bohr*, and *I. J. Mollerup*, Cesàro's Summabilitetsmetode. København.

1922 Studier over Cesàro's Summabilitetsmetode. København.

1928 Bemerkung zum Beweis des Herrn Knopp für die Äquivalenz der Cesàro- und Hölder- Summabilität. M. Z. 28 : 356–9.

P. Appell

1878 Sur certaines séries ordonnées par rapport aux puissances d'une variable. C. R. 87 : 689–92.

1879 Sur les séries divergentes à termes positifs. Archiv d. Math. u. Physik, 64 : 387–92.

E. W. Barnes

1902 A memoir on integral functions. Phil. Tr. R. Soc. London A, 199 : 411–500.

Jean Bernoulli

1694 Additamentum effectionis omnium quadraturarum et rectificationum curvarum per seriem quandam generalissimam. Acta Eruditorum Leipzig, anno 1694.

A. S. Besicovitch

1928 On Kakeya's problem and a similar one. M. Z. 27 : 312–21.

L. Bianchi

1901 Lezione sulla teoria delle funzioni di variabile complessa e delle funzioni ellittiche. Pisa.

L. Bieberbach

1915 Einführung in die konforme Abbildung. Berlin.

1916 Über die Koeffizienten derjenigen Potenzreihen, welche eine schlichte Abbildung des Einheitskreises vermitteln. Berlin Ber. 38 : 940–55.

1918 Zwei Sätze über das Verhalten analytischer Funktionen in der Umgebung wesentlich singulärer Stellen. M. Z. 2 : 158–70.

1919 Aufstellung und Beweis des Drehungsatzes für schlichte, konforme Abbildungen. M. Z. 4 : 295–305.

1921 Neuere Untersuchungen über Funktionen von komplexen Variablen. Encykl. der Math. Wiss. Bd. II, t. 3 A: 379–532.

1921–7 Lehrbuch der Funktionentheorie: vols. i–ii.

1927 Eine hinreichende Bedingung für schlichte Abbildungen des Einheitskreises. Crelle 157 : 189–92.

W. Blaschke

1915 Eine Erweiterung des Satzes von Vitali über Folgen analytischer Funktionen. Leipzig. Ber. 67: 194–200.

A. Bloch

1925 Les théorèmes de M. Valiron sur les fonctions entières et la théorie de l'uniformisation. A. Toulouse (3) 17: 1–224.

1926 Les fonctions holomorphes et méromorphes dans le cercle unité. Mémorial Sc. M. fasc. xx. Paris.

O. Blumenthal

1910 Principes de la théorie des fonctions entières d'ordre infini. Paris.

H. Bohr

1914 A theorem concerning Power Series. Pr. London M. S. (2) 13: 1–5.

1916–17 Über die Koeffizientensumme einer beschränkten Potenzreihe. Göttingen Nach. 1916: 276–91 and 1917: 119–28.

B. Bolzano

1851 Paradoxien des Unendlichen.

E. Borel

1894 Sur une application d'un théorème de M. Hadamard. Bull. Sc. M. (2) 18: 22–5.

1895 Sur quelques points de la théorie des fonctions. A. E. N. (3) 12: 9–55.

1896a Fondements de la théorie des séries divergentes sommables. J. de M. (5) 2: 103–22.

1896b Démonstration élémentaire d'un théorème de M. Picard sur les fonctions entières. C. R. 122: 1045–8.

1896c Sur les séries de Taylor. C. R. 123: 1051–2.

1896d Sur les séries de Taylor admettant leur cercle de convergence comme coupure. J. de M. (5) 2: 441–51.

1897 Sur les séries de Taylor. Ac. M. 21: 243–8.

1898a Sur les singularités des séries de Taylor. Bull. S. M. France 26: 238–48.

1898b Sur la recherche des singularités d'une fonction définie par un développement de Taylor. C. R. 127: 1001–3.

1899 Mémoire sur les séries divergentes. A. E. N. (3) 16: 9–136.

1901 Sur les séries de polynomes et de fractions rationnelles. Ac. M. 24: 309–87.

1902 Leçons sur les séries à termes positifs. Paris.

1903a Leçons sur les fonctions méromorphes. Paris.

1903b Sur la détermination de classes singulières de série de Taylor. C. R. 137: 695–7.

1905 Leçons sur les fonctions de variables réelles et les développements en séries de polynomes. Paris.

1910 Leçons sur la théorie de la croissance. Paris.

1912 Les fonctions monogènes non analytiques. Bull. S. M. France 40: 205–19.

1917 Leçons sur les fonctions monogènes uniformes. Paris.

1921 Leçons sur les fonctions entières. 2nd ed. Paris.

1922 Méthodes et problèmes de la théorie des fonctions. Paris.

1928a Leçons sur les séries divergentes. 2nd ed. Paris.

1928b Leçons sur la théorie des fonctions. 3rd ed. Paris.

S. Borgen

1927 Über (C, 1) Summierbarkeit von Reihen orthogonalen Funktionen. M. A. 98: 125–50.

H. E. Bray

1929 Functions of Écart Fini. Am. J. M. 51: 149–64.

T. J. I'A. Bromwich

1926 An introduction to the theory of infinite series. 2nd ed. London.

A. Buhl

1912 Sur la représentation des fonctions méromorphes. Ac. M. 35: 73–95.

1925 Séries analytiques. Sommabilité. Mémorial Sc. M. fasc. vii. Paris.

1926 Formules Stokiennes. Mémorial Sc. M. fasc. xvi. Paris.

H. Burkhardt

1908 Einführung in die Theorie der analytischen Funktionen einer komplexen Veränderlichen. 3rd ed. Leipzig. Translated into English, 1913. London.

G. Cantor

1873 Über eine Eigenschaft des Inbegriffes aller reellen algebraischen Zahlen. Crelle 77 : 258–62.

1875 Ein Beitrag zur Mannigfaltigkeitslehre. Crelle 84 : 242–58.

1883 Grundlagen einer allgemeinen Mannigfaltigkeitslehre. Leipzig.

1879–83 Über unendliche, lineare Punktmannigfaltigkeiten. M. A. 15 : 1–7 ; 17 : 355–8 ; 20 : 113–21 ; 21 : 51–8 and 545–86.

1895–7 Beiträge zur Begründung der transfiniten Mengenlehre. M. A. 46 : 481–512 and 49 : 207–46.

C. Carathéodory

1912 Untersuchungen über die konformen Abbildungen von festen und veränderlichen Gebieten. M. A. 72 : 107–44.

1913 Über die gegenseitige Beziehung der Ränder beider konformen Abbildungen des Inneren einer Jordanschen Kurve auf einen Kreis. M. A. 73 : 305–20.

T. Carleman

1926a Extension d'un théorème de Liouville. Ac. M. 48 : 363–6.

1926b Les fonctions quasi analytiques. Paris.

F. Carlson

1921 Über Potenzreihen mit ganzzahligen Koeffizienten. M. Z. 9 : 1–13.

1921a and *E. Landau*, Neuer Beweis und Verallgemeinerungen des Fabryschen Lückensatzes. Göttingen Nach. 1921 : 184–8.

1924 Sur quelques suites de polynomes. C. R. 178 : 1677–80.

R. D. Carmichael

1918 General aspects of the theory of summable series. Bull. Am. M. S. 25 : 97–131.

H. S. Carslaw

1930 Introduction to the theory of Fourier's series and integrals. 3rd ed. London.

A. L. Cauchy

1821 Analyse algébrique. Paris.

1827 Mémoire sur les intégrales définies (presented to the Paris Academy in 1814). Œuvres (1) 1 : 339–506.

1831a Mémoire sur la mécanique céleste et sur un noveau calcul appelé Calcul des limites. Bull. de Férussac 15 : 260–9.

1831b Mémoire sur les rapports qui existent entre le calcul des résidus et le calcul des limites. Bull. de Férussac 16: 116–28.

1843a and *Liouville*, Rapport sur un mémoire de M. Laurent. C. R. 17: 938-9.

1843b Note sur le développement des fonctions en séries convergentes ordonnées suivant les puissances entières des variables. C. R. 17: 193–198.

1844 Mémoire sur quelques propositions fondamentales du calcul des résidus et sur la théorie des intégrales singulières. C. R. 19 : 1337 and Œuvres (1) 8 : 366–75.

1846 Sur les intégrales qui s'étendent à tous les points d'une courbe fermée. C. R. 23 : 251–5 and Œuvres (1) 10 : 70–4.

Cellerier

1890 Sur les principes fondamentaux de l'Analyse. Bull. Sc. M. (2) 14: 145–99.

E. Cesàro

1890 Sur la multiplication des séries. Bull. Sc. M. (2) 14 : 114–20.

1893 Démonstration d'un théorème de M. Appell. Mathesis (2) 3 : 241–3.

S. Chapman

1911 On non-integral orders of summability of series and integrals. Pr. London M. S. (2) 9: 369–409.

1912 On the general theory of summability, with applications to Fourier's and other series. Qu. J. M. 43: 1–52.

1913 Some theorems on the multiplication of series which are infinite in both directions. Qu. J. M. 44 : 219–33.

J. le Rond d'Alembert

1768 Opuscules.

J. G. Darboux

1878 Mémoire sur l'approximation des fonctions de très grands nombres et sur une classe étendue de développements en série. J. de M. (3) 4 : 5–56 and 377–416.

L. Desaint

1902 Théorèmes généraux sur les points singuliers des fonctions données par une série de Taylor. J. de M. (5) 8 : 433–51.

1904 Les séries de Taylor et la représentation exponentielle. A. E. N. (3) 21: 415–48.

P. Dienes

1905 La série de Taylor sur le cercle de convergence. C. R. 140: 489–91.

1908 Sur les singularités des fonctions analytiques. C. R. 147: 1388-90.

1909a Sur les singularités des fonctions analytiques en dehors du cercle de convergence. C. R. 148: 694-8.

1909b and *V. Dienes*, Sur les singularités algébrico-logarithmiques. C. R. 149: 972-4.

1909c Essai sur les singularités des fonctions analytiques. Thèses-Paris and J. de M. (6) 5: 327-413.

1910 Sur un problème d'Abel. C. R. 151: 294-6.

1911a Sur la sommabilité de la série de Taylor. C. R. 153: 802-5.

1911b and *V. Dienes*, Recherches nouvelles sur les singularités des fonctions analytiques. A. E. N. (3) 28: 389-457.

1913 Leçons sur les singularités des fonctions analytiques. Paris.

1923 Sur les suites transfinies de nombres réels. C. R. 176: 67-9.

1924 Sur la structure mathématique du calcul tensoriel. J. de M. (9) 3: 79-106.

1930 The exponential function in linear algebras. Qu. J. M. (Oxford series) 1: 300-9.

V. Dienes

1909 Sur les points critiques logarithmiques. C. R. 148: 1087-90.

L. E. Dixon

1923 Algebras and their arithmetics. Chicago.

G. Doetsch

1921 Über die Summabilität von Potenzreihen auf dem Rande des Borelschen Summabilitätspolygons. M. A. 84: 245-51.

E. Egerváry

1928 Über gewisse Extremumprobleme der Funktionentheorie. M. A. 99: 542-61.

F. G. M. Eisenstein

1852 Über eine allgemeine Eigenschaft der Reihen-Entwicklungen aller algebraischen Funktionen. Berlin Ber. 1852: 441-3.

G. Faber

1903 Über die Fortsetzbarkeit gewisser Taylorschen Reihen. M. A. 57: 369-88.

1903-7 Über polynomische Entwickelungen. M. A. 57: 389-408 and 64: 116-35.

1904 Über die Nicht-fortsetzbarkeit gewisser Potenzreihen. München Ber. 34: 63-74.

1905 Über analytischen Funktionen mit vorgeschriebenen Singularitäten. M. A. 60 : 379–97.

1906 Über Potenzreihen mit unendlich vielen verschiedenen Koeffizienten. München. Ber. 36 : 581–3.

1907a Über das Anwachsen analytischer Funktionen. M. A. 63 : 549–51.

1907b Bemerkungen zu einem funktionentheoretischen Satze des Herrn Hadamard. Jahr.-ber. Deutsch. M. Ver. 16 : 285–98.

1917 Über das Verhalten analytischer Funktionen an Verzweigungsstellen. München. Ber. 1917 : 263–84.

1920a Über Tschebischeffsche Polynome. Crelle 150 : 79–106.

1920b Über Potentialtheorie und konforme Abbildung. München Ber. 1920 : 49–64.

1922 Über den Hauptsatz aus der Theorie der konformen Abbildung. München Ber. 1922 : 91–100.

E. Fabry

1896 Sur les points singuliers d'une fonction donnée par son développement en série et sur l'impossibilité du prolongement analytique dans les cas très généraux. A. E. N. (3) 13 : 107–14.

1898 Sur les points singuliers d'une série de Taylor. J. de M. (5) 4 : 317–58.

1899 Sur les séries de Taylor qui ont une infinité de points singuliers. Ac. M. 22 : 65–88.

1912 Ordre des points singuliers de la série de Taylor. Ac. M. 36 : 69–104.

P. Fatou

1906 Série trigonométrique et série de Taylor. Ac. M. 30 : 335–400.

1913 Sur les lignes singulières des fonctions analytiques. Bull. S. M. France 41 : 113–19.

1921 Sur l'évanouissement d'une branche de fonction uniforme aux points d'une ligne singulière. Bull. Sc. M. (2) 45 : 65–81.

1923 Sur les fonctions holomorphes et bornées à l'intérieur d'un cercle. Bull. S. M. France 51 : 191–202.

M. Fekete

1926 Über Potenzreihen, deren Koeffizienten fast alle ganzzahlig sind. M. A. 96 : 410–17.

L. Fejér

1903 Untersuchungen über Fouriersche Reihen. M. A. 58 : 51–69.

1908 Über die Laplacesche Reihe. M. A. 67 : 76–109.

1910 Über gewisse Potenzreihen an der Konvergenzgrenze. München Ber. 3 : 17.

1913 La convergence sur son cercle de convergence d'une série de puissances effectuant une représentation conforme du cercle sur le plan simple. C. R. 156 : 46–9.

1917 Fourierreihe und Potenzreihe. Monatshefte f. Math. u. Phys. 28 : 64–76.

1925–6 Über die Summabilität der Laplaceschen Reihe durch arithmetische Mittel. M. Z. 24 : 267–84.

1926 Über gewisse Minimumprobleme der Funktionentheorie. M. A. 97 : 104–23.

Z. Ferenczi

1928 Essai sur le procédé de la moyenne arithmétique des séries trigonométriques quelconques. Palermo Rend. 52 : 254–9

T. S. Fiske

1906 Functions of a complex variable. New York.

W. B. Ford

1917 Studies on divergent series and summability. Univ. of Michigan, Sc. series, ii. New York.

A. R. Forsyth

1914 Lectures introductory to the theory of functions of two complex variables. Cambridge.

1918 Theory of functions of a complex variable. 3rd ed. Cambridge.

T. Fort

1930 Infinite Series. Oxford.

G. Frobenius

1880 Über die Leibnitzsche Reihe. Crelle 89 : 262–4.

E. J. B. Goursat

1884 Démonstration du théorème de Cauchy. Ac. M. 4 : 197–200.

1900 Sur la définition générale des fonctions analytiques, d'après Cauchy. Tr. Am. M. S. 1 : 14–16.

1916 A course in mathematical analysis. I, II, pt. 1–2.

A. Haar

1914 Über analytische Funktionen mit singulärer Linie. Göttingen Nach. 1914 : 115–23.

J. Hadamard

1888 Sur le rayon de convergence des séries ordonnées suivant les puissances d'une variable. C. R. 106: 259–62.

1889 Sur la recherche des discontinuités polaires. C. R. 108: 722–4.

1892 Essai sur l'étude des fonctions données par leurs développements de Taylor. J. de M. (4) 8: 101–86.

1893 Sur les propriétés des fonctions entières et en particulier une fonction étudiée par Riemann. J. de M. (4) 9: 171–215.

1896 Sur les fonctions entières. Bull. S. M. France 24: 186–7.

1897 Théorème sur les séries entières. C. R. 124: 492–3.

1898 Théorème sur les séries entières. Ac. M. 22: 55–64.

1903 Deux théorèmes d'Abel sur la convergence des séries. Ac. M. 27 (1903): 177–83.

1914 Sur le module maximum d'une fonction et de ses dérivées. Bull. S. M. France.

1926 and *S. Mandelbrojt.* La série de Taylor et son prolongement analytique. 2nd ed. Paris.

L. Hanni

1905 Über den Beziehungen zwischen der Darstellung eines eindeutigen Zweiges einer monogenen Funktion durch Herrn Mittag-Leffler, der Metode der Mittelwerte des Herrn Borel, und der Transformation des Herrn Lidelöf. Ac. M. 29: 25–58.

G. H. Hardy

1903a On differentiation and integration of divergent series. Trans. Cambridge Phil. S. 19: 297–321.

1903b Researches in the theory of divergent series and divergent integrals. Qu. J. M. 35: 22–66.

1906 Some theorems connected with Abel's theorem on the continuity of power series. Pr. London M. S. (2) 4: 247–65.

1907a Some theorems on infinite series. M. A. 64: 77–94.

1907b On certain oscillating series. Qu. J. M. 38: 269–88.

1907c Generalization of a theorem in the theory of divergent series. Pr. London M. S. (2) 6: 255–64.

1908 Further researches in the theory of divergent series and integrals. Tr. Cambridge Phil. S. 21: 1–48.

1909 Theorems relating to the summability and convergence of slowly oscillating series. Pr. London M. S. (2) 8: 301–20.

1910 Theorems connected with Maclaurin's test for the convergence of series. Pr. London M. S. (2) 9: 126–44.

1911a The uniform convergence of Borel's integral. Messenger of M. 40 : 161–5.

1911b and *S. Chapman*, A general view of the theory of summable series. Qu. J. M. 42 : 181–215.

1911c and *J. E. Littlewood*, The relations between Borel's and Cesàro's methods of summation. Pr. London M. S. (2) 11 : 1–16.

1913 and *J. E. Littlewood*, Contributions to the arithmetic theory of series. Pr. London M. S. (2) 11 : 411–78.

1914 and *J. E. Littlewood*, Tauberian theorems concerning power series and Dirichlet's series whose coefficients are positive. Pr. London M. S. (2) 13 : 174–91.

1913–14 A theorem concerning Taylor's series. Qu. J. M. 44: 147–60 and 45 : 77–84.

1915a The second theorem of consistency for summable series. Pr. London M. S. (2) 15 : 72–88.

1915b The mean value of the modulus of an analytic function. Pr. London M. S. (2) 14 : 269–77.

1916 and *J. E. Littlewood*, Theorems concerning the summability of series by Borel's exponential method. Palermo Rend. 41 : 36–53.

1917 and *J. E. Littlewood*, Sur la convergence des séries de Fourier et des séries de Taylor. C. R. 165 : 1047–9.

1918 and *J. E. Littlewood*, Abel's theorem and its converse, I. Pr. London M. S. (2) 18 : 205–35.

1920 A theorem concerning summable series. Pr. Cambridge Phil. S. 20 : 304–7.

1923 and *J. E. Littlewood*, Abel's theorem and its converse, II. Pr. London M. S. (2) 22 : 254–69.

1924 and *J. E. Littlewood*, Solution of the Cesàro summability problem for power series and for Fourier series. M. Z. 19 : 67–96.

1926 and *J. E. Littlewood*, A further note on the converse of Abel's theorem. Pr. London M. S. (2) 25 : 219–36.

1928 and *J. E. Littlewood*, Some properties of fractional integrals. M. Z. 27 : 565–607.

J. Harkness

1898 and *F. Morley*, Introduction to the theory of analytic functions. London.

F. Hartogs

1925 Beweis des Jordanschen Kurvensatzes. M. Z. 22 : 66–74.

1927 Über die Grenzfunktionen beschränkter Folgen von analytischen Funktionen. M. A. 98 : 164–78.

1928 and *A. Rosenthal*, Über Folgen analytischer Funktionen. M. A. 100: 212–63.

F. Hausdorf

1919 Zur Verteilung der fortsetzbaren Potenzreihen. M. Z. 4: 98–103.

1921 Summationsmethoden und Momentfolgen, I–II. M. Z. 9: 74–109, 280–99.

1927 Mengenlehre. 2nd ed. Berlin.

E. Heine

1853 Der Eisensteinsche Satz über Reihen-Entwickelung algebraischer Funktionen. Crelle 45: 285–302.

1854 Théorèmes d'Eisenstein sur les séries qui sont les développements de fonctions algébriques. Nouvelles A. M. 13: 245–53.

E. Hellinger

1910 and *O. Toeplitz*, Grundlagen für eine Theorie des unendlichen Matrizen. M. A. 69: 289–330.

E. W. Hobson

1921–6 The theory of functions of a real variable and the theory of Fourier's series. 2nd ed. I–II. Cambridge.

O. Hölder

1882 Grenzwerte von Reihen an der Convergenzgrenze. M. A. 20: 535–49.

A. Hurwitz

1889 Über die Nullstellen der Bessel'schen Funktion. M. A. 33: 246–66.

1899 Sur un théorème de M. Hadamard. C. R. 128: 350–3.

1916 and *G. Pólya*, Zwei Beweise eines von Herrn Fatou vermuteten Satzes. Ac. M. 40: 179–83.

1922 and *R. Courant*, Funktionentheorie. Berlin.

W. A. Hurwitz

1917 and *L. L. Silverman*, On the consistency and equivalence of certain definitions of summability. Tr. Am. M. S. 18: 1–20.

1926 A trivial Tauberian theorem. Bull. Am. M. S. 32: 77–82.

A. E. Ingham

1924 Note on the converse of Abel's continuity theorem. Pr. London M. S. (2) 23: 326–36.

E. Jakobsthal

1920 Mittelwertbildung und Reihentransformationen. M. Z. 6: 100–17.

G. James

1919 On the theory of summability. A. of M. 21: 120–7.

V. Jarnik

1926 Über bedingt konvergente Reihen. M. Z. 24: 715–32.

J. L. W. V. Jensen

1899 Sur un nouvel et important théorème de la théorie des fonctions. Ac. M. 22: 359–64.

1906 Sur les fonctions convexes et les inégalités entre les valeurs moyennes. Ac. M. 30: 175–93.

R. Jentzsch

1917a Untersuchungen zur theorie der Folgen analytischer Funktionen. Ac. M. 41: 219–51.

1917b Fortgesetzte Untersuchungen über die Abschnitte von Potenzreihen. Ac. M. 41: 253–70.

1917c Über Potenzreihen mit endlich vielen verschiedenen Koeffizienten. M. A. 78: 276–85.

C. Jordan

1893–6 Cours d'Analyse, I–III. 2nd ed. Paris.

G. Julia

1919–21 Sur quelques propriétés nouvelles des fonctions entières ou méromorphes. A. E. N. (3) 36: 93–125; 37: 165–218; 38: 165–81.

1924 Leçons sur les fonctions uniformes à point singulier isolé. Paris.

1925 Sur les familles de fonctions analytiques de plusieurs variables. Ac. M. 47: 53–115.

S. Kakeya

1912 On the limits of the roots of an algebraic equation with positive coefficients. Tohoku M. J. 140–2.

B. Kerékjártó

1919 Beweis des Jordanschen Kurvensatzes. Budapest Ber. 38: 194–8.

1923 Vorlesungen über Topologie, I. Berlin.

A. Kienast

1918 Extensions of Abel's theorem and its converse. Pr. Cambridge Phil. S. 19 : 129–47.

K. Knopp

1907a Grenzwerte von Reihen bei der Annäherung an die Konvergenzgrenze. Inaug.-Diss., Berlin.

1907b Multiplication divergenter Reihen. Sitz. Ber. Berlin M. Ges. 7 : 1–12.

1908 Eine notwendige und hinreichende Konvergenz-bedingung. Palermo Rend. 25 : 237–52.

1917 Über die Oszillationen einfach unbestimmter Reihen. Sitz. Ber. Berlin M. Ges. 16 : 45–50.

1918–20 Funktionentheorie, I–II, Sammlung Göschen. 2nd ed. Leipzig.

1922–3 Über das Eulersche Summierungsverfahren. M. Z. 15 : 226–53 and 18 : 125–56.

1923 Aufgabensammlung zur Funktionentheorie, I, Sammlung Göschen. Leipzig.

1924 Zur Theorie der Cesàroschen und Hölderschen Summierbarkeit. M. Z. 19 : 97–113.

1925a Mehrfach monotone Zahlenfolgen. M. Z. 22 : 75–85.

1925b Über eine paradoxe Eigenschaft gewisser bedingt konvergenter unendlichen Reihen. M. Z. 23 : 254–62.

1928 Theory and application of infinite series. Translated from the 2nd German ed. London.

H. von Koch

1902 Sur le prolongement analytique d'une série de Taylor. Ac. M. 27 : 79–104.

P. Koebe

1907 Über die Uniformisierung beliebiger analytischen Kurven. Göttingen Nach. 1907 : 191–210.

E. Kogbetliantz

1925 Sur la sommation des séries divergentes par les moyennes simples et doubles. A. E. N. (3) 42 : 193–216.

T. Kojima

1917 On generalized Toeplitz's theorems on limit and their applications. Tohoku M. J. 12 : 291–326.

1922 On the theory of double sequences. Tohoku M. J. 21 : 3–14.

J. König

1884 Über eine Eigenschaft der Potenzreihen. M. A. 23 : 447–50.

L. Kronecker

1881 Zur Theorie der Elimination einer Variablen aus zwei algebraische Gleichungen. Berlin Ber. 1881 : 535–600.

J. L. Lagrange

1797 Théorie des fonctions analytiques. Paris. 2nd ed. 1813.

E. Landau

1904 Über eine Verallgemeinerung des Picardschen Satzes. Berlin Ber. 1904 : 1118–33.

1907 Über die Konvergenz einiger Klassen von unendlichen Reihen am Rande des Konvergenzgebietes. Monat. für M. 18 : 8–28.

1913–16 Abschätzung der Koeffizientensumme einer Potenzreihe. Arch. für M. (3) 21 : 42–50 and 250–5 ; 24 : 250–60.

1926a Einige Bemerkungen über schlichte Abbildung. Jahr.-ber. Deutsch. M. Ver. 34 : 239–43.

1926b Der Picard-Schottkysche Satz und die Blochsche Konstante. Berlin Ber. 1926 : 467–74.

1929 Darstellung und Begründung einiger neuerer Ergebnisse der Funktionentheorie. 2nd ed. Berlin.

P. A. Laurent

1843 Extension du théorème de M. Cauchy relatif à la convergence du développement d'une fonction suivant les puissances ascendentes de la variable. (See *Cauchy* 1843a). C. R. 17 : 348–9.

L. Leau

1899 Recherches sur les singularités d'une fonction définie par un développement de Taylor. J. de M. (5) 5 : 365–425.

H. Lebesgue

1905 Recherches sur la convergence des séries de Fourier. M. A. 61 : 251–80.

1906 Leçons sur les séries trigonométriques. Paris.

1928 Leçons sur l'intégration et la recherche des fonctions primitives, 2nd ed. Paris.

E. Le Roy

1900a Sur les séries divergentes et les fonctions définies par un développement de Taylor. A. Toulouse (2) 2 : 317–430.

1900b Sur les séries divergentes. C. R. 130 : 1293–6 and 1535–6.

P. Lévy

1905 Sur les séries semi-convergentes. Nouv. A. M. (4) 5 : 506–11.

E. Lindelöf

1898 Remarques sur un principe général de la théorie des fonctions analytiques. Ac. S. Fenn. (24) 7 : 1–39.
1902 Quelques applications d'une formule sommatoire générale. Ac. S. Fenn. 31 : 3.
1903 Sur une formule sommatoire générale. Ac. M. 27 : 305–11.
1905 Le calcul des résidus et ses applications à la théorie des fonctions. Paris.
1915 Sur un principe général de l'analyse et ses applications à la théorie de la représentation conforme. Ac. S. Fenn. (46) 4 : 1–35.

J. E. Littlewood

1910 The converse of Abel's theorem on power series. Pr. London M. S. (2) 9 : 434–48

(See also *G. H. Hardy*)

F. Lukács

1915 Eine Eigenschaft des Konvergenzkreises der Potenzreihen. Arch. der M. (3) 23 : 34–5.
1922 Über die Laplacesche Reihe. M. Z. 14 : 250–62.

N. Lusin

1911 Über eine Potenzreihe. Palermo Rend. 32 : 386–90.
1925 and *J. Priwaloff*, Sur l'unicité et multiplicité des fonctions analytiques. A. E. N. (3) 42 : 143–91.

C. Maclaurin

1742 Treatise on fluxions. Edinbourgh.

T. M. Macrobert

1917 Functions of a complex variable. London.

S. Mandelbrojt

1923 Sur les séries de Taylor qui présentent des lacunes. A. E. N. (3) 40 : 413–62.
1924 Sur la définition des fonctions analytiques. Ac. M. 45 : 129–43.
1926a Sur les séries de Taylor qui ont des lacunes généralisées. Bull. S. M. France 53 : 235–45.
1926b La recherche des points singuliers d'une fonction analytique représentée par une série entière. J. de M. (9) 5 : 197–210.

1927a Sur les points singuliers d'une série de Taylor situés sur le cercle de convergence. J. de M. (9) 6 : 435–9.

1927b Modern researches on the singularities of functions defined by Taylor's series. The Rice Institute Pamphlet. 14. Houston.

(See also *Hadamard*)

R. Mehmke

1928 Zum Rechnen mit Potenzreihen. M. A. 99 : 616–24.

F. Mertens

1875 Über die Multiplicationsregel für zwei unendliche Reihen. Crelle 79 : 182–4.

G. Mittag-Leffler

1884 Sur la représentation analytique des fonctions monogènes uniformes d'une variable indépendante. Ac. M. 4 : 1–79.

1890 Sur une transcendante remarquable découverte par M. Fredholm. C. R. 110 : 627–9.

1900–5 Sur la représentation d'une branche uniforme d'une fonction monogène, I–V. Ac. M. 23 : 43–62 ; 24 : 183–204 and 205–44 ; 26 : 353–91 ; 29 : 101–81.

1902 Sur l'intégral de Laplace-Abel. C. R. 135 : 937–9.

1903 Une généralisation de l'intégral de Laplace-Abel. C. R. 136 : 537–9.

1915 Über die analytische Darstellung eines eindeutigen Zweiges einer monogenen Funktion. München Ber. 1915 : 109–64.

A. de Moivre

1706–7 Aequationum quarundam Potestatis tertiae, quintae, septimae, nonae, etc. Phil. Tr. London 25 : 2368–71.

1730 Miscellanea analytica.

P. Montel

1907 Sur les suites infinies de fonctions. A. E. N. (3) 24 : 233–334.

1910 Leçons sur les séries de polynomes à une variable complexe. Paris.

1917 Sur la représentation conforme. J. de M. (7) 3 : 1–54.

1922 Sur les familles quasi-normales de fonctions holomorphes. Mémoires de l'académie de Belgique (2) 6 : 15.

1927 Leçons sur les familles normales de fonctions analytiques et leurs applications. Paris.

C. N. Moore

1907 On the introduction of convergence factors into summable series and integrals. Tr. Am. M. S. 8 : 299–330.

1913 On convergence factors in double series and the double Fourier's series. Tr. Am. M. S. 14 : 73–104.

1922 Generalized limits in general analysis, I. Trans. Am. Math. S. 24 : 79–88.

G. Morera

1902 Sulla definizione di funzione di una variabile complessa. Atti di Torino 37 : 99–102.

F. Morley

(See *Harkness*)

L. Neder

1921 Zur theorie der trigonometrischen Reihen. M. A. 84 : 117–36.

R. Nevanlinna

1919 Über beschränkte Funktionen, die in gegebenen Punkten vorgeschriebene Werte annehmen. A. Fenn. (A) 13 : 1–71.

1922a and *F. Nevanlinna*, Über die Eigenschaften analytischer Funktionen in der Umgebung einer analytischen Stelle oder Linie. Ac. S. Fenn. 50 : 1–46.

1922b Kriterien über die Randwerte beschränkter Funktionen. Math. Z. 13 : 1–9.

1923 Über die Anwendung des Poisson'schen Integral zur Untersuchung der Singularitäten analytischer Funktionen. 5th congress of Scandinavian mathematicians, Helsingfors.

1924 Untersuchungen über den Picardschen Satz. Ac. Fenn. 50 : no. 6.

1925 Zur Theorie der meromorphen Funktionen, Ac. M. 46 : 1–99.

1926 Einige Eindeutigkeitsätze in der Theorie der meromorphen Funktionen. Ac. M. 48 : 367–91.

N. Obrechkoff

1926 Sur la sommation des séries divergentes et le prolongement analytique. C. R. 182 : 307–9.

1927 Sur les points singuliers des fonctions analytiques. C. R. 184 : 271–3.

Y. Okada

1925–7 Über die Annäherung analytischer Funktionen. M. Z. 23 : 62–71 and 27 : 212–17.

L. Olivier

1827 Remarques sur les séries infinies et leur convergence. Crelle 2 : 31–44.

W. F. Osgood

1914 Topics in the theory of functions of several variables. The Madison Colloquium. New York.

1923–4 Lehrbuch der Funktionentheorie, I, 4th ed. (1923), II, 1st ed. (1924).

A. Ostrowski

1921 Über eine Eigenschaft gewisser Potenzreihen mit unendlich vielen verschiedenen Koeffizienten. Berlin Ber. 34 : 557–65.

1922a Über vollständige Gebiete gleichmässiger Konvergenz von Folgen analytischer Funktionen. Hamburg Math. Abh. 1 : 326–50.

1922b Auszug aus einem Brief von A. Ostrowski an L. Bieberbach. Jahr.-ber. Deutsch. M. Ver. 31 : 82–5.

1923a Über Potenzreihen die überkonvergente Abschnittsfolgen besitzen. Berlin Ber. 1922 : 185–92.

1923b Über die Bedeutung der Jensenschen Formel für einige Fragen der komplexen Funktionentheorie. Ac. Szeged 1 : 80–7.

1925a Über die Nullstellen gewisser in Einheitskreis regulärer Funktionen und einige Sätze zur Konvergenz unendlicher Reihen. Jahr.-ber. Deutsch. M. Ver. 34 : 161–71.

1925b Über Folgen analytischer Funktionen und einige Verschärfungen des Picardschen Satzes. M. Z. 24 : 215–58.

1926a On Hadamard's test for singular points. J. London M. S. 1 : 236–9.

1926b On representation of analytic functions by power series. J. London M. S. 1 : 251–63.

1926c Über einen Satz von Herrn Hadamard. Jahr.-ber. Deutsch. M. Ver. 35 : 179–82.

1926d Über Singularitäten gewisser mit Lücken behafteten Potenzreihen. Jahr.-ber. Deutsch. M. Ver. 35 : 269–80.

H. Padé

1892 Sur la représentation approchée d'une fonction par des fractions rationnelles. A. E. N. (3) 9 : 1–93 (supplement).

1894 Sur les séries entières convergentes ou divergentes et les fractions continues rationnelles. Ac. M. 18 : 97–111.

P. Painlevé

1888 Sur les lignes singulières des fonctions analytiques. A. Toulouse 2 : 1–130.

1905 Sur le développement des fonctions analytiques. Note I in Borel 1905 : 101–48.

G. Peano

1890a Sur une courbe, qui remplit toute une aire plane. M. A. 36 : 157–60.

1890b Sulla definizione dell'area d'una superficie. Rend. Lincei. (4) 6 : 54–7.

O. Perron

1920 Zur Theorie der divergenten Reihen. M. Z. 6 : 158–60 and 286–310.

E. Phragmèn

1904 Sur une extension d'un théorème classique de la théorie des fonctions. Ac. M. 28 : 351–68.

1908 and *E. Lindelöf*, Sur une extension d'un principe classique de l'analyse et sur quelques propriétés des fonctions monogènes dans le voisinage d'un point singulier. Ac. M. 31 : 381–406.

E. Picard

1879a Sur une propriété des fonctions entières. C. R. 88 : 1024–7.

1879b Sur les fonctions analytiques uniformes dans le voisinage d'un point singulier essentiel. C. R. 89 : 745–7.

Traité d'analyse, I (3rd ed. 1922), II.

M. Plancherel

1911 Sur la sommation des séries de Laplace et de Legendre. Palermo Rend. 33 : 41–66.

H. Poincaré

1883a Sur un théorème de la théorie générale des fonctions. Bull. S. M. France 11 : 112–25.

1883b Sur les fonctions entières. Bull. Soc. Math. France 11 : 136–44.

1884 Sur les groupes des équations linéaires. Ac. M. 4 : 201–312.

1888 Sur une propriété des fonctions analytiques. Palermo Rend. 2 : 197–200.

G. Pólya

1916a Über den Zusammenhang zwischen dem Maximalbetrag einer analytischen Funktion und dem grössten Gliede der zugehörigen Taylorschen Reihe. Ac. M. 40 : 311–19.

1916b Über Potenzreihen mit ganzzahligen Koeffizienten. M. A. 77 : 497–513.

1918 Über die Potenzreihen, deren Konvergenzkreis natürliche Grenze ist. Ac. M. 41 : 99–118.

1922 Sur les séries entières à coefficientes entiers. Pr. London M. S. (2) 21 : 22–38.

1925 and *G. Szegö*, Aufgaben und Lehrsätze aus der Analysis, I–II. Berlin.

1927a Eine Verallgemeinerung des Fabryschen Lückensatzes. Göttingen Nach. 1927 : 187–95.

1927b Sur un théorème de M. Hadamard relatif à la multiplication des singularités. C. R. 184 : 579–81.

1927c Sur les fonctions entières à série lacunaire. C. R. 184 : 1526–7.

1927d Sur les coefficients de la série de Taylor. C. R. 185 : 1107–8.

1928 Über gewisse notwendige Determinantenkriterien für die Fortsetzbarkeit einer Potenzreihe. M. A. 99 : 687–706.

1929 Untersuchungen über Lücken und Singularitäten von Potenzreihen. M. Z. 29 : 549–640.

M. B. Porter

1904–5 Concerning series of analytic functions. A. of M. (2) 6 : 190–2.

1906–7 On the polynomial convergents of a power series. A. of M. (2) 8 : 189–92.

A. Pringsheim

1885 Über das Verhalten gewisser Potenzreihen auf dem Konvergenzkreis. M. A. 25 : 419–27.

1894 Über Funktionen, welche in gewissen Punkten endliche Differentialquotienten jeder endlichen Ordnung, aber keine Taylor'sche Reihenentwickelung besitzen. M. A. 44 : 41–56.

1912 Über einige funktionentheoretische Anwendungen der Eulerschen Reihen-Transformation. München Ber. 1912 : 11–92.

J. Priwaloff

1924a Eine Erweiterung des Satzes von Vitali über Folgen analytischer Funktionen. M. A. 93 : 149–52.

1924b Sur certaines propriétés métriques des fonctions analytiques. J. E. Polytech. (2) 24 : 77–112.

J. L. Raabe

1832 Untersuchungen über die Convergenz und Divergenz der Reihen. Zeitschr. f. Phys. u. Math. 10 : 41–74.

H. Rademacher

1919a Über streckentreue und winkeltreue Abbildung. M. Z. 4 : 131–8.

1919b Bemerkungen zu den Riemannschen Differentialgleichungen und zum Moreraschen Satz. M. Z. 4 : 177–85.

T. Radó

1922–3a Zur Theorie der mehrdeutigen konformen Abbildungen. Ac. Szeged 1 : 55–64.

1922–3b Sur la représentation conforme des domaines variables. Ac. Szeged 1 : 180–6.

B. Riemann

1851 Grundlagen für eine allgemeine theorie der Funktionen einer veränderlichen complexen Grösse. Inaugural dissertation Göttingen. Werke 1876 : 1–47.

1854 Über die Darstellbarkeit einer Funktion durch eine trigonometrische Reihe. Hab.-Schrift, Göttingen. Werke, 2nd ed.

F. Riesz

1916 and *M. Riesz*, Über die Randwerte einer analytischen Funktion. C. R. du 4e congrès des math. scand. Stockholm : 27–47.

1923a Über die Randwerte einer analytischen Funktion. M. Z. 18 : 87–95.

1923b Sur les suites des fonctions analytiques. Ac. Szeged, 1 : 88–97.

M. Riesz

1909 Sur les séries de Dirichlet et les séries entières. C. R. 149 : 909–12.

1910 Sur un problème d'Abel. Palermo Rend. 30 : 339–45.

1911 Über einen Satz des Herrn Fatou. Crelle 140 : 89–99.

1916a Neuer Beweis des Fatouschen Satzes. Göttingen Nach. 1916 : 62–5.

1916b Satze über Potenzreihen. Arkiv für M. 11 : 12.

1924 Sur l'équivalence de certaines méthodes de sommation. Pr. London M. S. (2) 22 : 412–19.

1928 Sur les fonctions conjuguées. M. Z. 27 : 218–44.

W. Rogosinski

1923 Über Bildschranken von Potenzreihen und ihren Abschnitten. M. Z. 17 : 260–76.

1928 and *G. Szegö*, Über die Abschnitte von Potenzreihen, die in einem Kreise beschränkt bleiben. M. Z. 28 : 73–94.

E. Rouché

1862 Mémoire sur la série de Lagrange. J. École Polyt. 22: 193–224.

C. Runge

1885 Zur Theorie der eindeutigen analytischen Funktionen. Ac. M. 6: 229–44.

G. Sannia

1917 Nuovo metodo di sommazione delle serie: estensione del metodo di Borel. Palermo Rend. 42: 303–22.

1921 Serie assolutamente sommabili col metodo di Borel generalizzato. Atti di Torino 56: 34–40.

W. Saxer

1923 Über die Picardschen Ausnahmewerte sukzessiver Derivierten. M. Z. 17: 206–27.

1928a Über quasinormalen Funktionsscharen und eine Verscharfung des Picardschen Satzes. M. A. 99: 707–37.

1928b Über die Verteilung von Nullstellen und Pole von rationalen Funktionen konvergenten Folgen. M. Z. 27: 518–32.

E. Schmidt

1923 Über den Jordanschen Kurvensatz. Berlin Ber. 1923: 318–29.

R. Schmidt

1925 Über divergente Folgen und lineare Mittelbildungen. M. Z. 22: 89–152.

W. Schnee

1908 Die Identitat des Cesàroschen und Hölderschen Grenzwertes. M. A. 67: 110–25.

A. Schoenflies

1924 Über das eindeutige und stetige Abbild eines Kreises. Jahr.-ber. Deutsch. M. Ver. 33: 147–57.

F. Schottky

1904 Über den Picardschen Satz und die Borelschen Ungleichungen. Berlin Ber. 1904: 1244–63.

I. Schur

1919 Über das Maximum des absoluten Betrages eines Polynoms in einem gegebenen Interval. M. Z. 4: 271–84.

1920 Über lineare Trasformationen in der Theorie der unendlichen Reihen. Crelle 151: 79–111.

1922 Zur Arithmetik der Potenzreihe mit ganzzahligen Koeffizienten. M. Z. 12 : 95–113.
1925 and *G. Szegö*, Über die Abschnitte einer im Einheitkreise beschränkten Potenzreihe. Berlin Ber. 1925 : 545–60.

T. Shimizu

1929 On the theory of meromorphic functions. Japanese J. M. 6 : 119–71.

M. Servant

1899 Essai sur les séries divergentes. A. Toulouse (2) 1 : 117–75.

W. Sierpiński

1916 Sur une série potentielle qui, étant convergente en tout point de son cercle de convergence, représente sur ce cercle une fonction discontinue. Palermo Rend. 41 : 187–90.
1928 Leçons sur les nombres transfinis. Paris.

L. L. Silverman

1913 On the definition of the sum of a divergent series. Univ. of Missouri Studies, Math. Ser. 1 : 1–96.
1916 On the notion of summability for the limit of a function of a continuous variable. Tr. Am. M. S. 17 : 284–94.
1919 On the consistency and equivalence of certain generalized definitions of the limit of a function of a continuous variable. A. of M. 21 : 128–40.
1924 The equivalence of certain regular transformations. Tr. Am. M. S. 26 : 101–12.
1928 and *J. D. Tamarkin*, On the generalization of Abel's theorem for certain definitions of summability. M. Z. 29 : 161–70.
(See *W. A. Hurwitz*)

J. Sire

1913 Sur la puissance de l'ensemble des points singuliers transcendants des fonctions inverses des fonctions entières. Bull. S. M. France 41 : 148–60.

L. L. Smail

1918 A general method of summation of divergent series. A. of M. (2) 20 : 149–54.
1920 Summability of double series. A. of M. (2) 21 : 221–3.
1923 Elements of the theory of infinite processes. New York.
1925 History and synopsis of the theory of summable infinite processes. Univ. of Oregon Publ. 2 : No. 8.

J. Soula

1921 Sur la recherche des points singuliers de certaines fonctions définies par leur développement de Taylor. J. de M. (8) 4 : 97–153.

1922 Sur la 'séparation' des points singuliers d'une fonction analytique. J. de M. (9) 1 : 85–93.

E. Steinitz

1913–15 Bedingt konvergente Reihen und konvexe Systeme. Crelle 143 : 128–75 ; 144 : 1–40 ; 146 : 1–52.

H. Steinhaus

1911 Remarks on the generalization of the idea of limit. (In Polish.) Prace mat.-fiz. 22 : 121–34.

T. J. Stieltjes

1894–5. Recherches sur les fractions continues. A. Toulouse 8 : 1–122 and 9 : 5–47.

J. F. Steffensen

1914 Über Potenzreihen, im besonderen solche, deren Koeffizienten zahlentheoretische Funktionen sind. Palermo Rend. 38 : 376–86.

O. Stolz

1893 Grundzüge der Differential- und Integralrechnung. I.

1904 and *J. A. Gmeiner*. Einleitung in die Funktionentheorie. Leipzig.

M. H. Stone

1924 On the order of an analytic function at a singular point. A. of M. (2) 26 : 145–54.

E. Study

1913 Konforme Abbildung einfach zusammenhangenden Bereiche. Leipzig.

O. Szász

1918 Ungleichungen für die Koeffizienten einer Potenzreihe. M. Z. 1 : 163–83.

1919 Über Potenzreihen und Bilinearformen. M. Z. 4 : 163–76.

1920 Über Potenzreihen, die im Einheitskreise beschränkte Funktionen darstellen. M. Z. 8 : 222–36.

1922 Über Singularitäten von Potenzreihen und Dirichletschen Reihen am Rande des Konvergenzbereiches. M. A. 85 : 99–110.

1928 Über die Partialsummen der Binomialreihe. M. Z. 28 : 147–9.

G. Szegö

1919 Über Orthogonalsysteme von Polynomen. M. Z. 4 : 139–51.

1920–4 Über Potenzreihen, deren Koeffizienten zahlentheoretische Funktionen sind. M. Z. 8 : 36–51 and 21 : 203–8.

1921a Über orthogonale Polynome, die zu einer gegebenen Kurve der komplexen Ebene gehören. M. Z. 9 : 218–70.

1921b Über die Randwerte einer analytischen Funktion. M. A. 84 : 232–44.

1922a Über Potenzreihen mit endlich vielen verschiedenen Koeffizienten. Berlin Ber. 1922 : 88–91.

1922b Tschebyscheffsche Polynome und nichtvorsetzbare Potenzreihen. M. A. 87 : 90–111.

1928 Über Funktionen mit positivem Realteil. M. A. 99 : 142–9.

(See *G. Pólya*)

A. Tauber

1897 Ein Satz aus der Theorie der unendlichen Reihen. Monatshefte für Math. und Physik 8 : 273–7.

B. Taylor

1715 Methodus incrementorum directa et inversa. London.

W. Threlfall

1925 Bedingt konvergente Reihen. M. Z. 24 : 212–14.

E. C. Titchmarsh.

1930 The Zeta-function of Riemann. Cambridge Tracts.

O. Toeplitz

1911 Über allgemeine lineare Mittelbildungen. Prace Mat.-Fiz. 22 : 113–19.

1922 Über das Wachstum der Potenzreihen in ihrem Konvergenzkreise, I. M. Z. 12 : 189–200.

(See also *Hellinger*)

N. Tschebotareff

1928 Über die Realitat von Nullstellen ganzer transzendenter Funktionen. M. A. 99 : 660–86.

G. Valiron

1913 Sur les fonctions entières d'ordre fini et d'ordre nul. A. Toulouse (3) 5 : 117–257.

1914 Sur le calcul approché de certaines fonctions entières. Bull. S. M. France 42 : 252–64.

1916 Sur la croissance du module maximum des séries entières. Bull. S. M. France 44 : 45–64.

1917 Remarques sur la sommation des séries divergentes par les méthodes de M. Borel. Palermo Rend. 42 : 267–84.

1920 Les théorèmes généraux de M. Borel dans la théorie des fonctions entières. A. E. N. (3) 37 : 219–53.

1921–2 Recherches sur le théorème de M. Picard. A. E. N. (3) 38 : 389–437 ; 39 : 317–41.

1923 Lectures on the general theory of integral functions. Toulouse.

1925 Fonctions entières et fonctions méromorphes d'une variable. Mémorial Sc. M. fasc. 2.

Ch. de la Vallée-Poussin

1911 Sur les polynomes d'approximation à une variable complexe. Bull. Acad. Belgique, Classe de Sc. 1911 : 199–211.

G. Vitali

1903 Sopra le serie di funzioni analitiche. Rend. R. Inst. Lombardo (2) 36 : 772–4.

1904 A. di M. (3) 10 : 65–82.

E. B. van Vleck

1900 On linear criteria for the determination of the radius of convergence of a power series. Tr. Am. M. S. 1 : 293–309.

1905 Selected topics in the theory of divergent series and of continued fractions. Boston Colloquium, 1903 : 75–187. New York.

G. Vivanti

1893 Sulle serie di potenze. Rivista di M. 3 : 111–14.

1901 Teoria delle funzioni analitiche. Milano. German translation by Gutzmer in 1906, Leipzig.

V. Volterra

1888 Sulle funzioni analitiche polidrome. Atti Lincei (4) 4 : 355–61.

J. L. Walsh

1926 Über die Entwicklung einer analytischen Funktion nach Polynomen. M. A. 96 : 430–50.

G. N. Watson

1914 Complex integration and Cauchy's theorem. Cambridge Tracts.

(See also *Whittaker*)

K. Weierstrass

1886 Abhandlungen aus der Funktionenlehre. Berlin.

H. Weyl

1913 Die Idee der Riemannschen Fläche. Leipzig.

E. T. Whittaker

1920 and *G. N. Watson*. A course on modern analysis. Cambridge.

S. Wigert

1900 Sur les fonctions entières. Ofversigt af Svenska Vetenskaps-Akad. Forhandl. 57 : 1001–11.

R. Wilson

1927–9 Divergent continued fractions and polar singularities. Pr. London M. S. (2) 26: 159–68; 27: 497–512; 28: 128–44; 30: 38–57.

A. Wiman

1905a Über den Fundamentalsatz in der Theorie der Funktionen $E(x)$. Ac. M. 29 : 191–201.

1905b Über die Nullstellen der Funktionen $E(x)$. Ac. M. 29: 217–23.

J. Wolff

1927 Une généralisation d'un théorème de H. Jentzsch. C. R. 184 : 795–8.

L. Zoretti

1905 Sur les fonctions analytiques uniformes qui possèdent un ensemble parfait discontinu de points singuliers. J. de M. (6) 1 : 1–51.

1911 Leçons sur le prolongement analytique. Paris.

A. Zygmund

1926a Sur la théorie riemannienne des séries trigonométriques. M. Z. 24 : 47–104.

1926b Sur un théorème de la théorie de la sommabilité. M. Z. 25 : 291–6.

INDEX

(Numbers refer to pages.)

CATALOG OF DOVER BOOKS

MATHEMATICS, INTERMEDIATE TO ADVANCED

Geometry

THE FOUNDATIONS OF EUCLIDEAN GEOMETRY, H. G. Forder. The first rigorous account of Euclidean geometry, establishing propositions without recourse to empiricism, and without multiplying hypotheses. Corrects many traditional weaknesses of Euclidean proofs, and investigates the problems imposed on the axiom system by the discoveries of Bolya and Lobatchefsky. Some topics discussed are Classes and Relations; Axioms for Magnitudes; Congruence and Similarity; Algebra of Points; Hessenberg's Theorem; Continuity; Existence of Parallels; Reflections; Rotations; Isometries; etc. Invaluable for the light it throws on foundations of math. Lists: Axioms employed, Symbols, Constructions. 295pp. 5⅜ x 8.
S481 Paperbound **$2.00**

ADVANCED EUCLIDEAN GEOMETRY, R. A. Johnson. For years the standard textbook on advanced Euclidean geometry, requires only high school geometry and trigonometry. Explores in unusual detail and gives proofs of hundreds of relatively recent theorems and corollaries, many formerly available only in widely scattered journals. Covers tangent circles, the theorem of Miquel, symmedian point, pedal triangles and circles, the Brocard configuration, and much more. Formerly "Modern Geometry." Index. 107 diagrams. xiii + 319pp. 5⅜ x 8.
S669 Paperbound **$1.65**

Calculus and function theory, Fourier theory, real and complex functions, determinants

A COLLECTION OF MODERN MATHEMATICAL CLASSICS, edited by R. Bellman. 13 classic papers, complete in their original languages, by Hermite, Hardy and Littlewood, Tchebychef, Fejér, Fredholm, Fuchs, Hurwitz, Weyl, van der Pol, Birkhoff, Kellogg, von Neumann, and Hilbert. Each of these papers, collected here for the first time, triggered a burst of mathematical activity, providing useful new generalizations or stimulating fresh investigations. Topics discussed include classical analysis, periodic and almost periodic functions, analysis and number theory, integral equations, theory of approximation, non-linear differential equations, and functional analysis. Brief introductions and bibliographies to each paper. xii + 292pp. 6 x 9.
S730 Paperbound **$2.00**

MATHEMATICS OF MODERN ENGINEERING, E. G. Keller and R. E. Doherty. Written for the Advanced Course in Engineering of the General Electric Corporation, deals with the engineering use of determinants, tensors, the Heaviside operational calculus, dyadics, the calculus of variations, etc. Presents underlying principles fully, but purpose is to teach engineers to deal with modern engineering problems, and emphasis is on the perennial engineering attack of set-up and solve. Indexes. Over 185 figures and tables. Hundreds of exercises, problems, and worked-out examples. References. Two volume set. Total of xxxiii + 623pp. 5⅜ x 8.
S734 Vol I Paperbound **$1.65**
S735 Vol II Paperbound **$1.65**
The set **$3.30**

MATHEMATICAL METHODS FOR SCIENTISTS AND ENGINEERS, L. P. Smith. For scientists and engineers, as well as advanced math students. Full investigation of methods and practical description of conditions under which each should be used. Elements of real functions, differential and integral calculus, space geometry, theory of residues, vector and tensor analysis, series of Bessel functions, etc. Each method illustrated by completely-worked-out examples, mostly from scientific literature. 368 graded unsolved problems. 100 diagrams. x + 453pp. 5⅝ x 8⅜.
S220 Paperbound **$2.00**

THEORY OF FUNCTIONS AS APPLIED TO ENGINEERING PROBLEMS, edited by R. Rothe, F. Ollendorff, and K. Pohlhausen. A series of lectures given at the Berlin Institute of Technology that shows the specific applications of function theory in electrical and allied fields of engineering. Six lectures provide the elements of function theory in a simple and practical form, covering complex quantities and variables, integration in the complex plane, residue theorems, etc. Then 5 lectures show the exact uses of this powerful mathematical tool, with full discussions of problem methods. Index. Bibliography. 108 figures. x + 189pp. 5⅜ x 8.
S733 Paperbound **$1.35**

ADVANCED CALCULUS, E. B. Wilson. An unabridged reprinting of the work which continues to be recognized as one of the most comprehensive and useful texts in the field. It contains an immense amount of well-presented, fundamental material, including chapters on vector functions, ordinary differential equations, special functions, calculus of variations, etc., which are excellent introductions to these areas. For students with only one year of calculus, more than 1300 exercises cover both pure math and applications to engineering and physical problems. For engineers, physicists, etc., this work, with its 54 page introductory review, is the ideal reference and refresher. Index. ix + 566pp. 5⅜ x 8.
S504 Paperbound **$2.45**

CALCULUS OF VARIATIONS, A. R. Forsyth. Methods, solutions, rather than determination of weakest valid hypotheses. Over 150 examples completely worked-out show use of Euler, Legendre, Jacoby, Weierstrass tests for maxima, minima. Integrals with one original dependent variable; with derivatives of 2nd order; two dependent variables, one independent variable; double integrals involving 1 dependent variable, 2 first derivatives; double integrals involving partial derivatives of 2nd order; triple integrals; much more. 50 diagrams. 678pp. 5⅝ x 8⅜. S622 Paperbound **$2.95**

LECTURES ON THE CALCULUS OF VARIATIONS, O. Bolza. Analyzes in detail the fundamental concepts of the calculus of variations, as developed from Euler to Hilbert, with sharp formulations of the problems and rigorous demonstrations of their solutions. More than a score of solved examples; systematic references for each theorem. Covers the necessary and sufficient conditions; the contributions made by Euler, Du Bois Reymond, Hilbert, Weierstrass, Legendre, Jacobi, Erdmann, Kneser, and Gauss; and much more. Index. Bibliography. xi + 271pp. 5⅜ x 8. S218 Paperbound **$**

A TREATISE ON THE CALCULUS OF FINITE DIFFERENCES, G. Boole. A classic in the literature of the calculus. Thorough, clear discussion of basic principles, theorems, methods. Covers MacLaurin's and Herschel's theorems, mechanical quadrature, factorials, periodical constants, Bernoulli's numbers, difference-equations (linear, mixed, and partial), etc. Stresses analogies with differential calculus. 236 problems, answers to the numerical ones. viii + 336pp. 5⅜ x 8. S695 Paperbound **$1.85**

THE ANALYTICAL THEORY OF HEAT, Joseph Fourier. This book, which revolutionized mathematical physics, is listed in the Great Books program, and many other listings of great books. It has been used with profit by generations of mathematicians and physicists who are interested in either heat or in the application of the Fourier integral. Covers cause and reflection of rays of heat, radiant heating, heating of closed spaces, use of trigonometric series in the theory of heat, Fourier integral, etc. Translated by Alexander Freeman. 20 figures. xxii + 466pp. 5⅜ x 8. S93 Paperbound **$2.00**

AN INTRODUCTION TO FOURIER METHODS AND THE LAPLACE TRANSFORMATION, Philip Franklin. Concentrates upon essentials, enabling the reader with only a working knowledge of calculus to gain an understanding of Fourier methods in a broad sense, suitable for most applications. This work covers complex qualities with methods of computing elementary functions for complex values of the argument and finding approximations by the use of charts; Fourier series and integrals with half-range and complex Fourier series; harmonic analysis; Fourier and Laplace transformations, etc.; partial differential equations with applications to transmission of electricity; etc. The methods developed are related to physical problems of heat flow, vibrations, electrical transmission, electromagnetic radiation, etc. 828 problems with answers. Formerly entitled "Fourier Methods." Bibliography. Index. x + 289pp. 5⅜ x 8. S452 Paperbound **$1.75**

THE FOURIER INTEGRAL AND CERTAIN OF ITS APPLICATIONS, Norbert Wiener. The only book-length study of the Fourier integral as link between pure and applied math. An expansion of lectures given at Cambridge. Partial contents: Plancherel's theorem, general Tauberian theorem, special Tauberian theorems, generalized harmonic analysis. Bibliography. viii + 201pp. 5⅜ x 8. S272 Paperbound **$1.50**

INTRODUCTION TO THE THEORY OF FOURIER'S SERIES AND INTEGRALS, H. S. Carslaw. 3rd revised edition. This excellent introduction is an outgrowth of the author's courses at Cambridge. Historical introduction, rational and irrational numbers, infinite sequences and series, functions of a single variable, definite integral, Fourier series, Fourier integrals, and similar topics. Appendixes discuss practical harmonic analysis, periodogram analysis. Lebesgues theory. Indexes. 84 examples, bibliography. xiii + 368pp. 5⅜ x 8. S48 Paperbound **$2.00**

FOURIER'S SERIES AND SPHERICAL HARMONICS, W. E. Byerly. Continues to be recognized as one of most practical, useful expositions. Functions, series, and their differential equations are concretely explained in great detail; theory is applied constantly to practical problems, which are fully and lucidly worked out. Appendix includes 6 tables of surface zonal harmonics, hyperbolic functions, Bessel's functions. Bibliography. 190 problems, approximately half with answers. ix + 287pp. 5⅜ x 8. S536 Paperbound **$1.75**

ASYMPTOTIC EXPANSIONS, A. Erdélyi. The only modern work available in English, this is an unabridged reproduction of a monograph prepared for the Office of Naval Research. It discusses various procedures for asymptotic evaluation of integrals containing a large parameter and solutions of ordinary linear differential equations. Bibliography of 71 items. vi + 108pp. 5⅜ x 8. S318 Paperbound **$1.35**

LINEAR INTEGRAL EQUATIONS, W. V. Lovitt. Systematic survey of general theory, with some application to differential equations, calculus of variations, problems of math, physics. Partial contents: integral equation of 2nd kind by successive substitutions; Fredholm's equation as ratio of 2 integral series in lambda, applications of the Fredholm theory, Hilbert-Schmidt theory of symmetric kernels, application, etc. Neumann, Dirichlet, vibratory problems. Index. ix + 253pp. 5⅜ x 8. S175 Clothbound **$3.50**
S176 Paperbound **$1.60**

ELLIPTIC INTEGRALS, H. Hancock. Invaluable in work involving differential equations containing cubics or quartics under the root sign, where elementary calculus methods are inadequate. Practical solutions to problems that occur in mathematics, engineering, physics: differential equations requiring integration of Lamé's, Briot's, or Bouquet's equations; determination of arc of ellipse, hyperbola, lemiscate; solutions of problems in elastica; motion of a projectile under resistance varying as the cube of the velocity; pendulums; many others. Exposition is in accordance with Legendre-Jacobi theory and includes rigorous discussion of Legendre transformations. 20 figures. 5 place table. Index. 104pp. 5⅛ x 8.
S484 Paperbound **$1.25**

FIVE VOLUME "THEORY OF FUNCTIONS' SET BY KONRAD KNOPP

This five-volume set, prepared by Konrad Knopp, provides a complete and readily followed account of theory of functions. Proofs are given concisely, yet without sacrifice of completeness or rigor. These volumes are used as texts by such universities as M.I.T., University of Chicago, N. Y. City College, and many others. "Excellent introduction . . . remarkably readable, concise, clear, rigorous," JOURNAL OF THE AMERICAN STATISTICAL ASSOCIATION.

ELEMENTS OF THE THEORY OF FUNCTIONS, Konrad Knopp. This book provides the student with background for further volumes in this set, or texts on a similar level. Partial contents: foundations, system of complex numbers and the Gaussian plane of numbers, Riemann sphere of numbers, mapping by linear functions, normal forms, the logarithm, the cyclometric functions and binomial series. "Not only for the young student, but also for the student who knows all about what is in it," MATHEMATICAL JOURNAL. Bibliography. Index. 140pp. 5⅜ x 8.
S154 Paperbound **$1.35**

THEORY OF FUNCTIONS, PART I, Konrad Knopp. With volume II, this book provides coverage of basic concepts and theorems. Partial contents: numbers and points, functions of a complex variable, integral of a continuous function, Cauchy's integral theorem, Cauchy's integral formulae, series with variable terms, expansion of analytic functions in power series, analytic continuation and complete definition of analytic functions, entire transcendental functions, Laurent expansion, types of singularities. Bibliography. Index. vii + 146pp. 5⅜ x 8.
S156 Paperbound **$1.35**

THEORY OF FUNCTIONS, PART II, Konrad Knopp. Application and further development of general theory, special topics. Single valued functions, entire, Weierstrass, Meromorphic functions. Riemann surfaces. Algebraic functions. Analytical configuration, Riemann surface. Bibliography. Index. x + 150pp. 5⅜ x 8.
S157 Paperbound **$1.35**

PROBLEM BOOK IN THE THEORY OF FUNCTIONS, VOLUME 1, Konrad Knopp. Problems in elementary theory, for use with Knopp's THEORY OF FUNCTIONS, or any other text, arranged according to increasing difficulty. Fundamental concepts, sequences of numbers and infinite series, complex variable, integral theorems, development in series, conformal mapping. 182 problems. Answers. viii + 126pp. 5⅜ x 8.
S158 Paperbound **$1.35**

PROBLEM BOOK IN THE THEORY OF FUNCTIONS, VOLUME 2, Konrad Knopp. Advanced theory of functions, to be used either with Knopp's THEORY OF FUNCTIONS, or any other comparable text. Singularities, entire & meromorphic functions, periodic, analytic, continuation, multiple-valued functions, Riemann surfaces, conformal mapping. Includes a section of additional elementary problems. "The difficult task of selecting from the immense material of the modern theory of functions the problems just within the reach of the beginner is here masterfully accomplished," AM. MATH. SOC. Answers. 138pp. 5⅜ x 8.
S159 Paperbound **$1.35**

* * *

LECTURES ON THE THEORY OF ELLIPTIC FUNCTIONS, H. Hancock. Reissue of the only book in English with so extensive a coverage, especially of Abel, Jacobi, Legendre, Weierstrasse, Hermite, Liouville, and Riemann. Unusual fullness of treatment, plus applications as well as theory, in discussing elliptic function (the universe of elliptic integrals originating in works of Abel and Jacobi), their existence, and ultimate meaning. Use is made of Riemann to provide the most general theory. 40 page table of formulas. 76 figures. xxiii + 498pp.
S483 Paperbound **$2.55**

THE THEORY AND FUNCTIONS OF A REAL VARIABLE AND THE THEORY OF FOURIER'S SERIES, E. W. Hobson. One of the best introductions to set theory and various aspects of functions and Fourier's series. Requires only a good background in calculus. Provides an exhaustive coverage of: metric and descriptive properties of sets of points; transfinite numbers and order types; functions of a real variable; the Riemann and Lebesgue integrals; sequences and series of numbers; power-series; functions representable by series sequences of continuous functions; trigonometrical series; representation of functions by Fourier's series; complete exposition (200pp.) on set theory; and much more. "The best possible guide," Nature. Vol. I: 88 detailed examples, 10 figures. Index. xv + 736pp. Vol. II: 117 detailed examples, 13 figures. Index. x + 780pp. 6⅛ x 9¼.
Vol. I: S387 Paperbound **$3.00**
Vol. II: S388 Paperbound **$3.00**

ALMOST PERIODIC FUNCTIONS, A. S. Besicovitch. This unique and important summary by a well-known mathematician covers in detail the two stages of development in Bohr's theory of almost periodic functions: (1) as a generalization of pure periodicity, with results and proofs; (2) the work done by Stepanoff, Wiener, Weyl, and Bohr in generalizing the theory. Bibliography. xi + 180pp. 5⅜ x 8.
S18 Paperbound **$1.75**